# PHYSICAL CHEMISTRY

# CHEMISTRY

## *for*

# ENGINEERS

Bassim Hamadeh, CEO and Publisher
Kristina Stolte, Senior Acquisitions Editor
Sean Adams, Project Editor
Jess Estrella, Senior Graphic Designer
Natalie Piccotti, Director of Marketing
Kassie Graves, Vice President of Editorial
Jamie Giganti, Director of Academic Publishing

ISBN: 978-1-5165-0959-1 (pbk) / 978-1-5165-0960-7 (br)

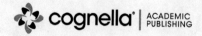

cognella | ACADEMIC PUBLISHING

FIRST EDITION

# Physical Chemistry

## *for*

# Engineers

## JAMES PATTERSON

*Brigham Young University*

cognella® | ACADEMIC PUBLISHING

# ACKNOWLEDGMENTS

I first want to thank all of my students in my physical chemistry courses over the years. This book would not have been written without their positive feedback for my supplemental materials and the encouragement to someday write my own book. That is a big reason why this book was written with the student in mind.

I also want to thank my wife, Emily, for her support and encouragement in this undertaking. It was a long road, but we did it.

# CONTENTS

CHAPTER 12

# Approximate Methods for Solving Real Problems, Electronic Structure of Molecules, and Electronic Spectroscopy — 219

## SECTION 4 Return to Statistical Mechanics— Predicting Bulk Properties — 245

CHAPTER 13

# The Molecular Partition Function and Connections to Thermodynamics — 247

## CHAPTER 14
# The Canonical Ensemble and Molecular Interactions    268

## SECTION 5 Chemical Thermodynamics— Why Things Happen    289

## CHAPTER 15
# State Variables and Equations of State Revisited    291

## CHAPTER 16

# First Law of Thermodynamics    307

## CHAPTER 17

# Second and Third Laws of Thermodynamics    333

## CHAPTER 20

# Activity and Chemical Equilibrium

# PREFACE

Welcome to the exciting world of physical chemistry! The central ideas and concepts of physical chemistry are not confined to the chemical sciences, but have broad reach and applicability. A healthy understanding of the molecular model of matter is essential both to appreciate current materials and technologies and to develop new capabilities in the future. Therefore, the overarching goal of this book is to help students develop an understanding of and familiarity with the modern, molecular view of the physical world. An appreciation for molecular models, including how they are developed, how we use them, and what their limitations might be, is at the heart of this understanding.

This textbook is designed to support the instruction of physical chemistry for students in engineering, materials science, and other applied physical sciences. Single or double-semester courses could be supported by this text. What follows is some discussion of the background and history of the development of this text, as well as some suggestions to both instructors and students on how to use it.

## Background of This Text and the Order of Topics

The main core of this text grew out of the author's development and instruction of a single-semester course in physical chemistry for chemical engineering students at Brigham Young University. Because the needs of these students are somewhat different from the needs of chemistry majors, and because chemical engineers go on to take other specialized courses in thermodynamics and reaction kinetics, a different approach was in order. Most physical chemistry texts follow one of two orders. The traditional ordering of topics places thermodynamics first, since it was the first to be developed historically. A more modern treatment places quantum mechanics at the beginning, and then builds from the microscopic to the macroscopic. This book starts very differently, and the order of topics was deliberately chosen to quickly establish the idea of a molecular model with the simplest possible system, the ideal gas.

Molecular models are at the heart of physical chemistry, so putting one in place became the first goal of the course. In order to accomplish this goal, it was also necessary to develop the foundation of statistical mechanics. Once the ideal gas is developed at a molecular level, and the kinetic theory of gasses explored, it is not a big conceptual leap to allow the colliding molecules to react with each other. Chemical kinetics thus comes much earlier in this book than is typically seen. This was also a conscious choice for two reasons. First, the central concepts of chemical kinetics are much more accessible than those of quantum mechanics or thermodynamics, so placing kinetics early in the course should give students confidence in working in the subject of physical chemistry. Second, the required mathematics are also simpler than what will be required in quantum mechanics and thermodynamics, so students who are still completing their math courses may have time to catch up. Third, since this is a chemistry course, it is good to encounter some chemistry early on.

Following the development of chemical kinetics and some applications of those ideas, the text quickly moves into the development of a detailed molecular model of matter, which involves an exploration of quantum mechanics. Following this, statistical mechanics is revisited to provide a bridge from the microscopic realm to the macroscopic world, and then thermodynamics is developed. By placing thermodynamics last, after the molecular models are well established, we can "peak under the hood" to see how bulk phenomena are governed by molecular interactions and how bulk measurements can inform us about those interactions. The final technical topic to be presented is transition state theory, which ties together all the major areas of physical chemistry. The book ends with a discussion of some of the philosophical implications of the scientific ideas and how those ideas have influenced society and history.

One other thing that should be noted about the text is the numbering of equations. Most equations have been numbered to make them easier to refer to. Some expressions, however, are midpoints in a derivation and not of much use on their own; such equations may not have a designated number. Equations that are particularly important and represent critical concepts are designated by a box around the expression. While the equations of physical chemistry are necessary, it is even more important to have an understanding of the physical models they represent and what the limitations and range of applicability of those models may be. This is the reason that the derivations of central relations are shown in such detail. The other reason for this level of detail is to illustrate for students how we can develop new mathematical relations by making appropriate assumptions and building on previous results. Some of the end-of-chapter problems may require the students to develop new relations, not just "crank and grind" with equations from the chapter.

## To the Instructor

The first thing you probably noticed when glancing through the Table of Contents is that the order of topics is somewhat unconventional. The ordering of topics was deliberate, as discussed above. The second thing you may have noticed is that some topics are not covered as completely as others. In particular, the chapters on chemical kinetics and applications of thermodynamics are not as exhaustive as in other physical chemistry texts. This is also by design. The goal of this text is to establish a strong foundation in physical chemistry for an engineering or materials science student on which subsequent courses can build, as required by the respective programs. Chemical engineers are likely to take more advanced courses in reaction kinetics, thermodynamics, and separations, thus some of the more advanced topics in those areas have been omitted from this text. For example, binary phase diagrams, azeotropes, and other more advanced topics relating to mixtures are not presented. Students in other disciplines probably don't require as much depth in those areas, so again they are not needed here. In the author's experience, coverage of quantum mechanics and models of chemical bonding are not likely to be seen in other courses in engineering programs, so the depth of coverage in this text is greater on those topics. For students who want or need training in more advanced topics, this course should provide them with a foundation upon which to build such understandings.

The third response you may have in looking at the Table of Contents is a concern about covering this much material in a single-semester course. There is likely more material here than can fully be covered in a single semester. (In the author's own course, for example, the material in Chapter 21 on ionic solutions and electrochemistry is not covered.) One reason the chapters are shorter than they might otherwise be is to give the instructor greater flexibility in designing a course to fit the needs of the students. Certain topics are foundational and later chapters would suffer if they were neglected, but other chapters could be skipped if that is what is appropriate for the course. For example, if it is felt that the kinetics of reactions on surfaces are not relevant for a given course, Chapter 6 could be omitted. Similar choices could be made with the latter chapters of Sections 3 and 5. As mentioned above, the author has not tried to present an exhaustive coverage of all of physical chemistry. All of the fundamentals and many applications are here for an instructor to design a course that is well suited to the needs of the students and their overall program.

Students learn physical chemistry by doing physical chemistry. Most chapters contain multiple Sample Problems with fully worked solutions, and students will benefit from following through those examples. End-of-chapter problems are provided with a range of difficulty and applications. A mixture of numerical and theoretical problems is provided, in addition to some conceptual questions that require written answers. You will note, however, that there are very few exercise-type problems that basically involve plugging numbers into particular equations. Because the students taking this course are most likely at the junior or senior level, it was felt that they should have matured academically to the point where such low-level problems are probably not needed. It is hoped that by the time they complete this course, students should be prepared to tackle real-world problems that require more than a "canned" solution. After all, by the time they complete this course, they are likely a year or two away from entering the work force where they will be faced with such problems on a regular basis.

## To the Student

The main goal of this course is for you to develop a molecular understanding of the physical world and how you can use that understanding to solve real-world problems. Pursuit of this goal will require you to enhance your analytical reasoning in ways that may be uncomfortable at times. Just as working out in a gym can be painful, developing these mental muscles will also cause discomfort. The end goal, however, is worth the work. Great effort has been made to ensure that this textbook will be an effective guide on your journey through physical chemistry. The writing style is deliberately conversational to help you see the connections between ideas. Most chapters include Sample Problems that provide fully worked solutions to relevant problems. End-of-chapter problems, with a range of difficulty, give you a chance to put what you have learned into practice.

Some of what follows is discussed further in Chapter 1, but there are some things you need to keep in mind to be successful in physical chemistry. First, math is at the heart of physical chemistry. That being said, mathematics are used to represent the physical world, not for their own sake. Facility and comfort with the mathematical representation of an idea does not mean you have a good conceptual understanding of that idea. Make sure you think about the relevant physical model when working a problem; don't just look for "the right equation". As you strengthen these conceptual ideas, you will find ways to connect them to other fields and disciplines.

In order to be successful in this course, you should have good proficiency in algebra and calculus, both differential and integral. Ideally, you should have completed work in multivariate calculus. Some understanding of the main concepts of differential equations will also be of use to you. In addition to knowing *how* to do math, you need to have a sense of *when* to do math, meaning you need to know when a given mathematical operation should be used. Real-world problem solving is more than just plugging numbers into equations that you looked up somewhere; it involves constructing a physical model, representing that model mathematically, and then applying mathematical reasoning to arrive at a physically meaningful solution. If you can become adept at these skills, you will be well prepared for success in whatever field you ultimately pursue.

# FROM THE MICRO
## TO THE
# MACRO

Introduction to
Statistical Mechanics

# Introduction to Physical Chemistry

The Ideal Gas Law

## 1.1 What Is Physical Chemistry?

If you tell someone you are enrolled in a physical chemistry class, the first question you are likely to hear in response is "What is physical chemistry?" (You may have asked this question yourself when enrolling in this course.) Renowned physical chemist Henry Eyring was known to respond to this question with the answer, "Physical chemistry is the study of all that is interesting." While this is clearly a broad statement, it doesn't give us many specifics to discuss, unlike the other subdisciplines of chemistry. Biochemistry is quite obviously the study of the chemistry of life and life processes. Organic chemistry covers organic (carbon-based) compounds, and inorganic chemistry basically encompasses everything else. Analytical chemistry has to do with the analysis of a chemical system to determine its composition. But what is physical chemistry?

We can make some headway in understanding what physical chemistry is all about by looking at the two words individually. The word *physical* implies to many people the separate field of physics, and this a correct inference. If we were to condense all of physics into a single word, most university students would probably settle on something like *forces*. While this is mostly correct, a better word choice for our purposes is *interactions*. Interactions between objects, mediated by forces such as gravity and electromagnetism, lead to changes in the motion of those objects. If we were to likewise condense all of chemistry into a single word, that word could be *molecules*. Thus, physical chemistry can be thought of as the study of interactions within and between molecules. With this description, we can see the basis for Eyring's statement; virtually everything in the physical world involves molecules and their interactions.

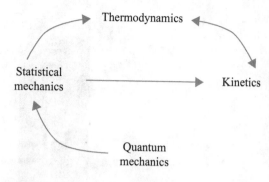

**FIGURE 1.1.** Interrelationships between the four main areas of physical chemistry.

Physical chemistry started out as an attempt to understand physical processes and chemical reactions in a detailed, quantitative fashion. This was done through the application of fundamental physical laws, such as Newton's laws of motion and the relevant mathematics, to chemical problems. Physical chemistry is generally subdivided into four main areas: thermodynamics, quantum mechanics/spectroscopy, kinetics, and statistical mechanics. Each of these areas influences and is influenced by the others, as shown schematically in Figure 1.1. Because we will explore all of these areas of physical chemistry, it is worthwhile to spend a little time introducing each of them.

*Thermodynamics*: The part of physical chemistry that was developed first and contains many ideas that are foundational to all of chemistry is **thermodynamics**. The word *thermodynamics* basically defines itself; it involves ideas of heat, and by extension energy and motion, or change. Classical thermodynamics was developed based on empirical observations of the interchange between heat and work and the rules for these conversions. New ideas such as entropy were introduced to provide a framework for describing why some processes were observed to happen spontaneously—meaning without an outside driving force—and other processes weren't.

Like Newtonian mechanics, which is based on his three laws of motion, thermodynamics is based on four simple postulates, or ideas, known as the laws of thermodynamics. These laws have successfully been applied to a very impressive array of phenomena, including—but by no means limited to—phase transitions, heat engines, chemical reactions, planetary science, cellular biology, and many, many more. Albert Einstein once said the following about thermodynamics:

> A theory is the more impressive the greater the simplicity of its premises, the more different are the kinds of things it relates, and the more extended is its range of applicability. Therefore, the deep impression which classical thermodynamics made upon me. It is the only physical theory of universal content which, I am convinced, that within the framework of applicability of its basic concepts, will never be overthrown. (*Autobiographical Notes*, 1946; quoted in Holton & Elkana, *Albert Einstein: Historical and Cultural Perspectives*, 1997)

If thermodynamics impressed Albert Einstein, it seems like something we should take seriously.

Even though thermodynamics was the first area of physical chemistry to be developed, reaching maturity in the late 19th century, we will actually present it last in this book. The reason for this is that thermodynamics actually makes no assumptions about the underlying structure of matter. This is both a strength and a weakness of thermodynamics. In one sense, it is nice to not have to worry about what all the molecules are doing; we just have to keep track of macroscopic variables like temperature, pressure, and volume. However, our understanding of the molecular basis of macroscopic phenomena enriches our understanding of them. Therefore, we will defer our discussion of thermodynamics until we have more fully explored the molecular realm. This will allow us to "look under the hood," so to speak, when we talk about macroscopic phenomena toward the end of the book.

*Quantum Mechanics and Spectroscopy*: Thermodynamics was one of the crowning scientific achievements of the 19th century. In fact, many physicists of that era firmly believed that all the major problems had been solved and that the great challenge of the

20th century would be extending the precision of their results. Little did they know that a new field of physics would emerge in the early 20th century that would fundamentally challenge our view of the world. This field would come to be known as **quantum mechanics**. Quantum mechanics is the science of the very small, in particular the atom and subatomic particles. As you learned in general chemistry, chemical bonds involve the sharing of electrons between atoms. Thus, any complete discussion of chemical bonding—in fact of matter itself—requires that we deal with the quantum mechanical behavior of these very small particles.

Because quantum mechanical objects are so small, we cannot observe them with macroscopic tools. Fortunately, we can tell what is happening at the molecular scale because of the way light interacts with matter. The use of light to understand the molecular structure and behavior of matter is called **spectroscopy**. Many spectroscopic techniques have been developed over the past century that enable us to determine the structure of molecules and how those molecules interact with each other. Spectroscopy is also the basis of many analytical chemistry techniques, as well as many quality and process-control methods. Thus a basic understanding of spectroscopy and its uses is essential to any scientist or engineer in the modern area.

*Kinetics*: Chemical reactions don't happen all at once, rather they take place over some period of time. The study of how quickly chemical reactions occur, and the detailed molecular mechanisms of these reactions, is the area of **kinetics**. Like thermodynamics, chemical kinetics has its roots in macroscopic observations of chemical reactions. Empirical laws were developed based on the observed phenomena, but our understanding of how reactions occur is greatly strengthened by taking a molecular approach. We will approach the study of kinetics early in this text because it provides a very good example of the two approaches we can take to understand physical phenomena—a top-down empirical approach based on observations, and a bottom-up molecular approach based on theoretical models. Another reason we will cover kinetics early is so that we actually encounter some chemistry early on in our study of physical chemistry.

*Statistical Mechanics*: Because molecules are so small, even a sample of only 100 grams contains trillions of trillions ($\sim 10^{24}$) of molecules. These very large numbers mean that we can reliably apply the statistics of large numbers to molecular systems. Quantum mechanics tells us about the possible states of individual molecules. Applying statistics to large collections of molecules is the area known as **statistical mechanics**. Statistical mechanics, or stat mech as it is often called, allows us to bridge from the microscopic, molecular realm to the macroscopic realm with great confidence in our results.

# 1.2 Your Trip Through Physical Chemistry

## 1.2.1 Physical Chemistry Is an Active Endeavor

By taking this course, you are embarking on an exciting journey of discovery in an active realm of science that will significantly affect your view of the world around you. The purpose of this section is to give you a rough sense of what that trip will look like. Many courses in physical chemistry begin with thermodynamics, since that was historically the first area to be developed. Other courses adopt a "quantum-first" approach that begins at the molecular level with quantum mechanics and builds up to the macroscopic level and ends with thermodynamics. Because the four areas of physical chemistry all tie into each other, either order works—but there are strengths and weaknesses to both of these approaches.

We will be taking something of a hybrid approach that will reinforce some of the important ideas about developing and applying physical models to real world problems. After a brief review of the development of the ideal gas law, we will start developing the statistical mechanical tools we need to build a molecular model of ideal gases. This will involve a discussion of how molecules collide with each other, which leads naturally into a discussion of chemical reactions and kinetics. (Again, we want to see some actual chemistry early in the course!) We will then return to our molecular model and attempt to describe the macroscopic property of heat capacity, but we will find significant deficiencies in our simple model. This will lead us into the development of quantum mechanics and a better understanding of the fundamental structure of matter and the allowed energy states atoms and molecules can have. We will then revisit the statistical mechanical approach and move into developing thermodynamics while maintaining a healthy molecular perspective. The last topic we will explore is transition state theory, which brings everything together to describe the most fundamental aspects of chemical reactions.

As we go through this journey, we will also explore applications of the key ideas of physical chemistry to a variety of real-world situations. We will also work to develop skills in problem solving and critical thinking that will serve you well in your chosen field.

## 1.2.2 Use of Mathematics

Now is also a good time to talk about the use of mathematics in physical chemistry. One of the first things people notice upon opening a physical chemistry textbook is the large number of equations, and this can be intimidating. But those equations serve a very useful purpose. In addition to conceptual descriptions of the phenomena, the ideas of physical chemistry are often best presented and discussed in terms of mathematical expressions. In fact, many discoveries in physical chemistry arose directly from predictions based on mathematical reasoning. It is often said that mathematics is the language of physical chemistry, and you will gain an appreciation for that idea as we move along.

You will need to be proficient with calculus—both differential and integral, of single and multiple variables—and be familiar with the important ideas of linear algebra and differential equations. It is important to remember, however, that proficiency with mathematics does not necessarily guarantee an understanding of the underlying physical phenomena. You need to develop a familiarity both with the mathematical formalism of physical chemistry and the qualitative, conceptual understanding of what is going on. In a sense, you need to be bilingual to be successful in physical chemistry; you need to be proficient in both the descriptive, conceptual approach and the quantitative, mathematical approach.

Many students are tempted to try solving a problem by finding an equation that has the relevant variables and start throwing numbers at it. This approach is fraught with danger and pitfalls, especially if you are not careful in your choice of equations, because each equation is based on certain assumptions or approximations. If you attempt to use an equation in a situation that violates any of these assumptions, you will get results that don't make physical sense. A better approach to solving a problem in physical chemistry is to first describe the relevant phenomena qualitatively. Then, we review our mathematical models and "translate" the physical description into a mathematical expression. We can then use our mathematical tools to solve the problem. It is important to note, however, that we're not done until the answer has been interpreted in a physical context. An example of this approach to problem solving is provided below.

Because mathematics is so important in the formal development of physical chemistry, you will see several long derivations in this text. These derivations are important because they reflect the progression of the ideas and, perhaps most importantly, describe the assumptions that go into developing the various mathematical expressions. Any assumptions we make in the course of a derivation will limit the applicability of that equation to situations where those assumptions hold true. Thus it is not good practice to simply memorize equations without knowing the models upon which they are based and the assumptions that were used in deriving them. A more powerful approach is to learn the key concepts and their relevant mathematical expressions, and then train yourself to apply those ideas logically, making appropriate assumptions along the way—in effect re-deriving the ultimate result. Not only will this approach make you more adept at solving new problems that are different from ones you've seen before, but it will also reduce the amount of material you need to learn. As you will see when we reach the formal development of thermodynamics, as long as you know a few fundamental relations, you can readily derive a broad range of expressions for a wide variety of physical situations.

## 1.2.3 An Approach to Problem Solving

As we have just discussed, physical chemistry is a very mathematical field. Basically, every problem you will be asked to solve will be a story problem. It is up to you to take that (sometimes complicated) physical situation and "translate" it into a mathematical problem so that you can apply the mathematical tools you have learned to use over the last several years. It is this translation process where students often run into difficulty. If we tell you to "take a derivative" or "evaluate an integral," most science and engineering students at this level are comfortable doing that. However, if we give you a real-world problem and ask you to solve it, many students don't know where to start. In this section, we are going to outline a general approach to solving problems that you can apply to virtually any situation—in physical chemistry and in other fields of study.

The first step is to make sure you clearly understand what you are being asked to determine; if you don't know where you're trying to go, it's very hard to find a way to get there. It is often very helpful to draw a picture or make some sort of diagram to represent what is physically happening. Maybe sketch the initial and final situations as part of this to make sure you understand what is taking place. Next, you want to collect the information you have been given. At this point, you may also want to write down basic mathematical definitions of some of the physical properties you are given in the problem statement. This will help to "translate" the story problem into a mathematical exercise. Then, start to put the mathematical relations together into a symbolic solution to the problem. I personally like to work symbolically as long as possible and only put numbers into the relation at the very end. This does two things; it lets me see the general mathematical relations all the way through, and it reduces the chance of making computational errors. Lastly, once you have a solution, you need to evaluate that answer and make sure it makes sense. You need to develop an intuition for the range of possible values you expect to see, so you can recognize when something has gone wrong in your solution.

Let's see this approach in action with a fairly complicated sample problem. Most of the ideas in this problem should be familiar to you, although you may not be fully versed in all the details. Don't be alarmed if you feel you couldn't come up with this solution on your own; we are at the beginning of the journey. By the end of the course, however, you should be able to readily tackle this type of problem.

### Sample Problem 1.1

Consider a 100.0 L sealed, insulated reaction vessel that is initially at 25.0°C. A reaction begins at time $t = 0$. The reaction is of the form

$$A \rightarrow P$$

The rate of formation of product is described by the relation

$$\frac{d[P]}{dt} = k[A]_0 e^{-kt}$$

where [P] is the concentration of the product, $[A]_0 = 0.050$ mol L$^{-1}$ is the initial concentration of reactant, $t$ is time, and $k$ is the rate constant, which has a value of $5.3 \times 10^{-4}$ s$^{-1}$. The reaction is exothermic with a heat of reaction $\Delta rH° = -4.50$ kJ mol$^{-1}$. The heat capacity of the entire reaction vessel, including everything inside, is 500.0 J K$^{-1}$. Assume that the reacting system is well mixed and the temperature is uniform throughout the container. You can also assume that the rate constant, heat of reaction, and heat capacity are constant with respect to temperature.

a. How long will it take for the temperature to rise by 20.0°C?
b. What fraction of the possible amount of product has been formed at this time?
c. If the reaction is allowed to run to completion, what is the final temperature of the reaction vessel?

Solution

a. We are asked to determine the time at which the temperature will have increased by 20.0°C, so we need a relation that tells us the temperature as a function of time. What we have been given is an expression for the rate of the chemical reaction. Let's build some relations that will lead us to temperature.

First, let's look at mathematical formulations of some of the parameters we have been given. The heat of reaction tells us how much heat is evolved per amount of reactant produced.

Mathematically, we can write

$$\Delta_r H° = \frac{dq}{dn_P}$$

where $q$ symbolizes heat and $n_P$ is the number of moles of product.
Heat capacity is the ratio of heat to temperature change

$$C = \frac{dq}{dT}$$

We can relate change in concentration to change in amount by

$$d[P] = \frac{dn_P}{V}$$

since the volume is fixed.
Putting all this together, we can write our rate expression in a different form:

$$\frac{d[P]}{dt} = \frac{dn_P}{Vdt} = \frac{dq}{V\Delta_r H° dt} = \frac{CdT}{V\Delta_r H° dt} = k[A]_0 e^{-kt}$$

Now, we separate variables and integrate. We assume that none of the parameters are temperature or time dependent.

We write the integral as

$$\frac{C}{V\Delta_r H^\circ} \int_0^{\Delta T} dT = k[A]_0 \int_0^t e^{-kt} dt$$

$$\frac{C\Delta T}{V\Delta_r H^\circ} = k[A]_0\left(\frac{-1}{k}\right)(e^{-kt} - 1) = [A]_0(1 - e^{-kt})$$

We can solve this expression for $t$ to determine that it takes $\underline{1.09 \times 10^3 \text{ s or}}$ $\underline{18.2 \text{ min}}$ for the temperature to rise by 20.0°C.

b. We can go back to our initial expression and determine the concentration of product as a function of time by integrating the rate expression for formation of product.

$$[P] = [A]_0(1 - e^{-kt})$$

At time $1.09 \times 10^3$ s, $[P]/[A]_0 = 0.44$, or $\underline{44\%}$ conversion of reactant to product.

c. Assuming none of the heat can leave, we just need to know what the temperature is at a very long time. At infinite time, the exponential in our temperature expression in part a) will go to zero, so the total increase in temperature is simply

$$\Delta T = \frac{V\Delta_r H^\circ[A]_0}{C} = 45.0 \text{ K} = 45.0°C$$

So the final temperature will be $\underline{70.0°C}$.

There is another way to do this last calculation. We know we have 100.0 L of solution, and the initial reactant concentration is 0.050 mol L$^{-1}$. Therefore, we have 5.0 mol of reactant. Using the given heat of reaction, this will produce a total of 2.25 kJ of heat. For a heat capacity of 500.0 J K$^{-1}$, this will lead to a temperature rise of 45.0 K, which is the same thing we just determined. It is important to note that our quick calculation here gives the same answer as our more complicated expression in the infinite time limit, which increases our confidence in our answer to part a).

---

One of the skills you will need to develop to be successful in your eventual career is the ability to take a complex physical situation and break it down into manageable pieces so that you can apply appropriate mathematical tools. Another skill to develop is the ability to determine whether your answer makes physical sense. You will need to use both of these skills throughout your career, so now is as good a time as any to develop them if you haven't already.

## 1.2.4 The Scientific Method

At some point in your elementary education, you learned about the scientific method, which forms the basis for how we approach scientific inquiry in the modern age. The steps of the scientific method are usually described as:

**Observation:** We observe something and want to understand it better.
**Hypothesis:** We form a hypothesis, or model, of what is causing our observations.

**Prediction:** We make a prediction based on our hypothesis.
**Experiment:** We design an experiment to test our prediction.
**Refinement:** We modify or extend the hypothesis as needed based on the experimental results.

This process then continues until a hypothesis is sufficiently refined and expanded that it can be described as a **theory**, meaning it provides an explanation for a wide range of phenomena and has not been contradicted by experimental evidence. It is important to note that a hypothesis or a theory can never be proven correct; it can only be disproven. Experiments can validate a hypothesis by not contradicting it, but they cannot prove that it is correct.

Science is an active endeavor, in which we continually revise our hypotheses, or models, and design and carry out new experiments to test those models. Unfortunately, too often science is treated as merely a collection of facts to be learned, and therefore it feels like a passive, encyclopedic activity. Hopefully you will view this course as an opportunity to be engaged in physical chemistry; you are not here to learn *about* physical chemistry, but to learn *how to do* physical chemistry. Taking an active role will not only help you to better master the subject but will make it more interesting and engaging—and maybe even enjoyable. Think of yourself as an explorer discovering these things for the first time; if it's your first time learning something, then it is a new discovery as far as you are concerned.

As with any active endeavor, the only way to improve is to get involved. One does not become a concert pianist or professional athlete by merely attending concerts or sporting events. While it is certainly valuable to observe professionals in action, you will only improve your own abilities by actively practicing and improving your skills. Physical chemistry is in many ways like a contact sport. You have to meaningfully engage with the material in order to gain mastery. You will likely feel challenged, but that is a sign that you are developing new mental muscle and will come out stronger and more capable.

There is one final thought on the scientific method in the context of physical chemistry to share here. In highly mathematical fields such as physics and physical chemistry, hypotheses often take the form of mathematical expressions. We then use mathematical reasoning to develop new relations, which can then either be compared to prior observations or form the basis for new experiments. Thus, an entire cycle of the scientific method can be carried out with pencil and paper. In fact, this is how theoretical physicists and physical chemists often operate.

# 1.3 Historical Development of the Ideal Gas Law

Now that we have introduced many important ideas that will help us in our study of physical chemistry, let's go through what is arguably the first triumph of this field—the development of the ideal gas law. Even though it represents an idealized system that is at best a crude approximation of reality, the ideal gas law is one of the most successful attempts to describe physical phenomena with a simple mathematical relationship. To begin this development, we first need to introduce the mathematical variables that we need to describe the properties of a gas.

## 1.3.1 State Variables

In order to mathematically describe the properties of a sample of gas, we must first define a set of mathematical variables that correspond to the physical properties of the system. Because they describe the physical state of the system, we refer to them as **state variables**. Fortunately, we only need four variables to completely describe the system: temperature ($T$), pressure ($P$), volume ($V$), and amount ($n$). These variables are either **extensive**—which means they depend on the size of the system ($V$ and $n$)—or **intensive**, which means they don't depend on the size of the system ($T$ and $P$). Note that the ratio of two extensive variables is intensive; density is one such example.

*Temperature* ($T$): At first glance, the concept of temperature is quite basic and involves how hot or cold something is. Observations tell us that when two bodies of different temperature are placed in contact with each other, the temperature of the two will eventually become the same, with the warm body getting colder and the cold body getting warmer. This concept is stated in the Zeroth Law of thermodynamics:

> If A is in **thermal equilibrium** with B, and B is in thermal equilibrium with C, then C is also in thermal equilibrium with A.

This idea forms the basis of thermometry. Temperature is actually more complex than this, and we will refine our notion of temperature in this course and come up with a more exact definition. The unit of temperature we will use the most is Kelvin. We will also use the Celsius, or centigrade, scale.

*Pressure* ($P$): The concept of pressure is basic to physics and is defined as force applied over a given area. This also allows us to define the concept of **mechanical equilibrium**. If we have two samples of gas separated by a movable barrier and the pressure on the two sides is different, the barrier will move until the pressures become the same. Two units of pressure we will use are the atmosphere (atm) and the bar (1 bar = $10^5$ Pa).

*Volume* ($V$): Volume is simply a measure of the space taken up by something, in this case a sample of gas. In fact, one definition of gas as a state of matter is that it will fill the available space. Volume is typically given in liters. To make volume an intensive property, we often divide by the number of moles to define a molar volume, symbolically expressed as $V_m$. (In older notation, $\overline{V}$ signifies molar volume.)

*Amount* ($n$): This is simply how much of something we have, or the number of moles of the substance. Another way to represent the amount of something is with the mass. Chemists generally prefer the mole; therefore molar quantities, such as molar mass and molar volume, will typically be used in this text.

## 1.3.2 Development of the Ideal Gas Law

The ideal gas law was the result of multiple experimental observations by scientists over a period of ~150 years. We will now summarize the principal experiments that led to the final mathematical relationship.

*Boyle's law*: Robert Boyle (1662) took samples of a fixed amount of gas (constant $n$) in a closed container and held the temperature constant. He then measured the dependence of pressure on the volume of the container. He obtained a series of curves, one for each temperature. Each of these curves is called an **isotherm**, plotted in Figure 1.2. Note that isotherms never cross each other.

Looking at the plotted data, we can clearly see that pressure and volume are inversely proportional; as the volume increases, the pressure decreases. However, with the data plotted this way, it is difficult to be more precise in our description of this behavior.

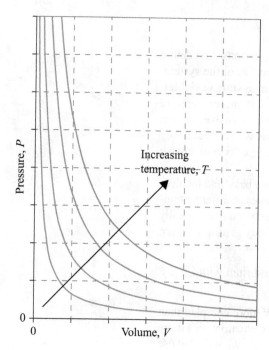

**FIGURE 1.2.** Plots of isotherms of an ideal gas.

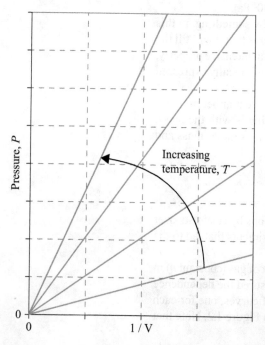

**FIGURE 1.3.** Isotherms plotted as $P$ vs. $1/V$.

Boyle then plotted his data not as $P$ vs. $V$, but as $P$ vs. $1/V$, as shown in Figure 1.3. This gave a series of straight lines, with the slope increasing with the temperature. (It is often desirable to treat data in such a way that they can be plotted linearly, as it makes the relevant mathematical relations easier to identify.) This functional form allows us to develop a mathematical expression to describe the observed behavior. The standard equation for a straight line is

$$y = mx + b \qquad (1.1)$$

where $m$ is the slope and $b$ is the intercept. In this case, we write

$$P = m(n,T)\frac{1}{V} + b$$

where we are using $P$ as our $y$ variable and $1/V$ as our $x$ variable. By writing $m(n, T)$, we are saying that $m$ depends on $n$ and $T$, which are fixed in each experiment. Looking more closely at our plotted data, we can see that all the lines extrapolate to the same intercept, which is zero. In other words, as $1/V$ decreases—or as $V$ increases—the pressure drops to zero. Taken another way, this means that in order to decrease the pressure toward zero, we need to increase the volume toward infinity. This lets us set the $b$ term in our equation to zero and move the $V$ to the left side of the equation. Now we can write a mathematical expression of Boyle's law:

$$PV = C(n,T) \qquad (1.2)$$

The constant is fixed for a given amount and temperature of gas. This relation is termed a *law* because it is based on a series of experimental results that all follow the same pattern.

In words, for a given amount of gas at a particular temperature, the product of the pressure and volume is a constant. Expressed differently, if we know this constant for a given amount and temperature, then we can freely vary the pressure or the volume, but not both; the value of the other state variable is fixed by this equation. For example, doubling the volume at fixed amount and temperature causes the pressure to drop by one half.

*Charles's law*: Jacques Charles (1780s) was also interested in the behavior of gases, but he did a different set of experiments. Instead of keeping the temperature constant, he fixed the pressure and then determined the relationship between temperature and volume. Interestingly, he also observed straight-line behavior, shown in Figure 1.4. Each of these lines is known as an **isobar** (meaning same pressure). For a given pressure, the volume increases linearly with the temperature. The slope of this line increases as the pressure decreases, meaning the volume increases faster with temperature at low pressure than at high pressure. These experiments were also among the first to suggest that there might be an absolute zero of temperature—that is, the temperature at which the volume goes to zero. This absolute zero of temperature also appeared to be the same for all pressures and for all gases; the extrapolation is shown as the dashed lines. We write this mathematically as

$$V = C'(n, P)T \qquad (1.3)$$

We are using $C'$ in Eq. 1.3 instead of $C$ because this constant depends on $n$ and $P$, not $n$ and $T$. Note also that $T$ must be in terms of the absolute Kelvin scale.

Charles did another set of experiments in which he kept the volume constant instead of the pressure. Again, he observed straight-line behavior. Each of these lines is called an **isochore**, shown in Figure 1.5. For these experiments, we have

$$P = C''(n, V)T \qquad (1.4)$$

We should note that all three of these laws are limiting laws, meaning they only hold true in a certain limit. That limit is zero (or very low) pressure. As the pressure increases, deviations from these laws are observed. However, even for this limiting case, it is a powerful thing to be able to describe the behavior of a physical system with very simple mathematical relationships. Note that, up until this point, we have said nothing about what a gas is made of. All we need to successfully describe the behavior we have seen is a way to quantify temperature, pressure, and volume—which are all macroscopic state variables—for a given amount of gas. Using only the things we can measure macroscopically to arrive at a mathematical description can be described as the "top-down" approach.

*Avogadro's principle*: The final variable we need to allow to change is the amount, $n$. Joseph Louis Gay-Lussac (1800s) did these types of experiments and found that by increasing the amount of gas at a given temperature and pressure, the volume increased proportionately. Amedeo Avogadro took this idea further by arguing that if a sample of gas were made up of molecules, or small bits of matter, then twice the amount of gas would contain twice as many molecules, therefore taking up twice as much space. Avogadro's idea (1811) is known as a principle rather than a law because it is based on a model, the existence of molecules, rather than a direct empirical observation. This concept lets us write

$$V = C'''(T, P)n \qquad (1.5)$$

*Ideal gas law*: All these empirical expressions and Avogadro's principle can now be combined mathematically into a single, unified expression. This is known as the ideal gas law and is typically written

$$\boxed{PV = nRT} \qquad (1.6)$$

where all the constants have been replaced by $R$, the ideal gas constant. Note the simplicity of this expression. It was found experimentally that, in the limit of low pressure and high temperature, the behavior of all gases are described by the same value of $R = 8.3145$ J mol$^{-1}$ K$^{-1}$. Another value of $R$ that we often use is 0.08206 L atm mol$^{-1}$ K$^{-1}$.

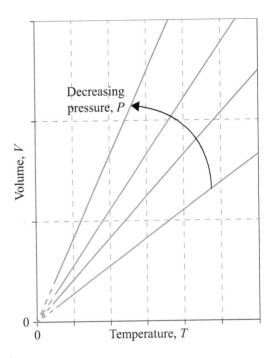

FIGURE 1.4. Isobars for an ideal gas.

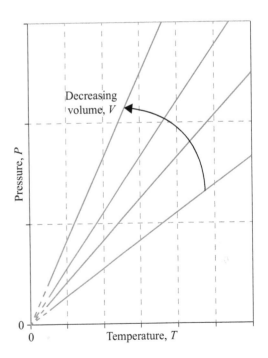

FIGURE 1.5. Isochores for an ideal gas.

### 1.3.3 Equations of State

The ideal gas law is the first of several **equations of state** that we will use. An equation of state (EOS) is a mathematical expression that describes the relationship between the state variables, $n$, $T$, $P$, and $V$. Speaking in mathematical terms, the equation of state serves as a constraint on our freedom to change the values of the different variables. Often we will keep the amount $n$ constant, or we will use molar volume. This leaves three variables, $P$, $V_m$, and $T$. We can plot the equation of state as a surface in $P$, $V_m$, $T$ space, as shown in Figure 1.6. All allowed states of the gas must lie on this surface. We can freely vary any two of these parameters, but the value of the third parameter is constrained by the EOS.

Notice that each of the types of curves we saw previously—the isotherms, isobars, and isochores—are drawn on the EOS surface when the appropriate state variable is kept constant. By slicing through the surface parallel to one axis and projecting that slice onto the plane of the other two axes, we reproduce the plots shown above in Figures 1.2, 1.4, and 1.5.

### 1.3.4 Standard States

At this point, we can introduce the concept of **standard states**, which will be important later on when we develop thermodynamics. A standard state serves as a reference point on the surface defined by the EOS. An example of a standard state you may be familiar with is elevation; we reference elevation to sea level, because that is an agreed-upon standard. We could reference to the center of the earth or the top of Mt. Everest, but those would be less convenient. Standard states for gases are defined in terms of pressure at a stated temperature; note that once the temperature and pressure are set, the molar volume

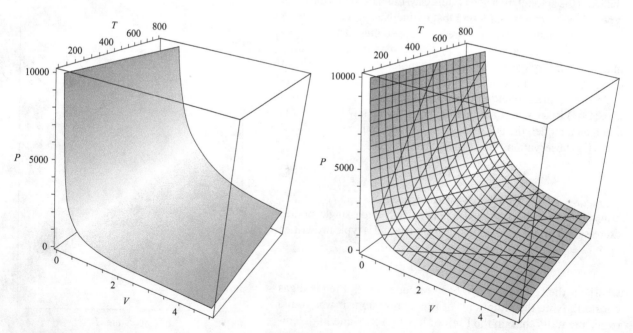

**FIGURE 1.6.** The ideal gas equation of state, plotted in $P$, $V_m$, $T$ space. The curves on the surface in the right panel correspond to the isotherms, isochores and isobars.

is fixed by the EOS. One common standard state is known as Standard Temperature and Pressure (STP). This is 1 atm pressure at 0°C (273.15 K). Another standard state is Standard Ambient Temperature and Pressure (SATP), which is 1 bar pressure at a temperature of 25°C (298.15 K).

## 1.4 Summary, and Where We Go Next

In this chapter, we have introduced the main areas of physical chemistry and discussed some general ideas that will help you in your study of this subject. We have also reviewed the historical development of the ideal gas law. In the next chapter, we will develop the basic ideas of statistics and probability that we will need to build a molecular model of gases in Chapter 3.

## PROBLEMS

Note: The problems for this chapter are designed as a review of material you have previously covered in your mathematics and general chemistry courses. In later chapters, it will be assumed that you have the necessary skills to work these types of problems.

**1.1** Take the derivatives of the following functions:

a) $f(x) = 3x^2 \exp(-3x^2)$

b) $f(x) = 6\ln(2x) + 3x^{-1}$

c) $f(x) = 3\cos^2\left(2\theta - \dfrac{\pi}{4}\right) + \dfrac{1}{2}\sin(3\theta^2)$

**1.2** Evaluate the following integrals:

a) $\displaystyle\int_{298}^{1000} -\dfrac{2000}{T}\, dT$

b) $\displaystyle\int_{5}^{50} (2.3 + 0.05V^{-1} - 3V^3)\, dV$

c) $\displaystyle\int_{0}^{1} (\cos 3t + e^{-kt})\, dt$

**1.3** Taylor series can be very useful in analyzing complex mathematical functions. The formal expression of the Taylor series for a function $f(x)$ in the vicinity of $x = a$ is written

$$f(x) = f(a) + \left(\dfrac{df}{dx}\right)_a (x-a) + \dfrac{1}{2!}\left(\dfrac{d^2 f}{dx^2}\right)_a (x-a)^2 + \ldots = \sum_{n=0}^{\infty} \dfrac{1}{n!}\left(\dfrac{d^n f}{dx^n}\right)_a (x-a)^n$$

Using Taylor series, prove each of the relations in a) through e) for the case where $x \ll 1$.

a) $e^x \approx 1 + x$

b) $\ln(1 + x) \approx x$

c) $(1 + x)^{-1} \approx 1 - x$

d) $\sin(x) \approx x$

e) $\cos(x) \approx 1$

f) Prove this relation: $e^{ikx} = \cos(kx) + i\sin(kx)$. (This is known as Euler's identity.)

**1.4** The volume, in mL, of 1 g of liquid water can be accurately represented as a function of temperature ($t$ = deg Celsius) by the formula:

$$V = 1.000 - 6.4270 \times 10^{-5}t + 8.5052 \times 10^{-6}t^2 - 6.790 \times 10^{-8}t^3$$

Determine the temperature at which the volume of water is at its minimum. What is the density of water at this temperature? Make sure your results are physically meaningful.

**1.5** You are taking a trip to a nearby city. As you drive along, your passenger notes the mileage on the trip odometer every five minutes. Given these data, answer the following questions.

| $t$ (min) | 0 | 5 | 10 | 15 | 20 | 25 | 30 | 35 | 40 | 45 | 50 | 55 | 60 |
|---|---|---|---|---|---|---|---|---|---|---|---|---|---|
| $d$ (miles) | 0 | 3 | 6 | 11 | 16 | 22 | 30 | 37 | 40 | 42 | 45 | 48 | 50 |

a) What was the total distance traveled?

b) What was the average speed for the entire trip?

c) Estimate the speed at the 30- and 45-minute points.

d) How much distance was travelled between minute 30 and minute 45?

**1.6** The volume flow rate, $F$ (in units of L min$^{-1}$), through a pipe was measured over the course of a day and fit to the following function, where $t$ is in hours:

$$F = 8.00 + \sin(1.50t)e^{-0.1t} + \cos(0.25t)$$

a) What is the total volume of fluid (in L) delivered through the pipe over the entire day?

b) What was the average flow rate (in L min$^{-1}$) over the course of the day?

c) What was the flow rate at hour 3 and hour 6?

d) How much fluid was delivered between hour 3 and hour 6?

**1.7** Consider the molecule formaldehyde. Draw the Lewis dot structure and describe the geometry of this molecule. Describe the molecular orbitals and their occupations. Give the bond order of each bond. Finally, is formaldehyde paramagnetic or diamagnetic?

**1.8** The allowed energy levels of the hydrogen atom are described by the following expression:

$$E_n = -2.17868 \times 10^{-18} J\left(\frac{1}{n^2}\right)$$

where $n$ is the quantum number of the energy level, and the energy is in J. The allowed values of $n$ are all positive integers; $n = 1, 2, 3, ...$ . The Balmer series that is observed in the line spectrum of hydrogen corresponds to transitions that end in the $n = 2$ level. Determine the wavelengths of the first five lines in the Balmer series.

**1.9** The enthalpy of combustion of ketene ($CH_2CO$) is $-981.1$ kJ mol$^{-1}$. The enthalpy of combustion of methane ($CH_4$) is $-802.3$ kJ mol$^{-1}$. Both these values are at 25°C. Given this information, calculate the enthalpy of the following reaction at 25°C.

$$2 \, CH_4 \, (g) + 2 \, O_2 \, (g) \rightarrow CH_2CO \, (g) + 3 \, H_2O \, (g)$$

**1.10** 50.0 mL of a 0.100 M solution of hydrazoic acid ($HN_3$, $pK_a = 4.72$) is titrated with 0.100 M NaOH at 25°C. Compute the pH (a) before the addition of any base and after the addition of (b) 25.00 mL, (c) 50.00 mL, and (d) 51.00 mL of base.

**1.11** The following data were obtained for the initial rate of reaction of pyridine ($C_5H_5N$) and methyl iodide ($CH_3I$) in benzene at 25°C.

| $[C_5H_5N]$ (mol L$^{-1}$) | $[CH_3I]$ (mol L$^{-1}$) | rate (mol L$^{-1}$ s$^{-1}$) |
| --- | --- | --- |
| $1.00 \times 10^{-4}$ | $1.00 \times 10^{-4}$ | $7.5 \times 10^{-7}$ |
| $2.00 \times 10^{-4}$ | $2.00 \times 10^{-4}$ | $3.0 \times 10^{-6}$ |
| $2.00 \times 10^{-4}$ | $4.00 \times 10^{-4}$ | $6.0 \times 10^{-6}$ |

a) Write the rate law for this reaction.

b) Calculate the rate constant $k$, and give its units.

c) Predict the initial reaction rate that would be observed in a solution with $[C_5H_5N] = 5.0 \times 10^{-5}$ M and $[CH_3I] = 2.0 \times 10^{-5}$ M.

**1.12** a) What is the volume of 1.00 mol of ideal gas under conditions of standard temperature and pressure (STP), $P = 1.00$ atm and $T = 0.0$°C?

b) What is the volume of 1.00 mol of ideal gas under conditions of standard ambient temperature and pressure (SATP), $P = 1.00$ bar at a temperature of 298.15 K?

c) You've probably seen a baking soda volcano, or even done one yourself. Making reasonable assumptions, estimate the volume of $CO_2$ that would be produced when 100.0 mL of vinegar is added to 50.0 g of sodium bicarbonate if the gas is contained and allowed to reach a pressure of 1.00 atm at a temperature of 25.0°C.

# Introduction to Statistical Mechanics

## Probability and the Boltzmann Distribution

## 2.1 Probability and Statistics

Atoms and molecules are small. They are so small that there about $10^{17}$ atoms in a speck of dust. Even in a gas, where the individual molecules are spread out, there are about $10^{19}$ particles in 1 $cm^3$ of gas at ambient conditions. If we had to keep track of what each of these individual particles were doing, that would be a monumental task in information management more than anything else. Fortunately, we can use the statistics of large numbers (and $10^{17}$ to $10^{19}$ definitely count as large numbers) to approach the problem and concern ourselves only with the average behavior of all these particles. To begin this discussion, we first need to review some aspects of probability and statistics.

### 2.1.1 Populations and Averages

One of the foundational ideas of statistics is that of a **population**. The most obvious example of a population is a group of people. This population will have subsets within it—for example, men and women, or people with brown eyes and people with blue eyes. If we know the exact makeup of this population, we can accurately describe it—for example, in our group of 100 people, we have 56 women and 44 men. If we know this makeup, then we can say that if we were to choose a person at random, 56 out of 100 times, we would choose a woman, and 44 out of 100 times we would choose a man. We can therefore say that the **probability** of selecting a woman is 56 out of 100, or 56%, and the probability of selecting a man is 44 out of 100, or 44%. These values are examples of **descriptive statistics**, or figures that describe the population in question. Note that both probabilities need to add up to 100%; if we choose a person at random and don't care if we choose a man or a woman, we will definitely choose a person.

Many times, we don't know the exact makeup of the population, usually because we can't individually check each member of the population. In this case, we can take a

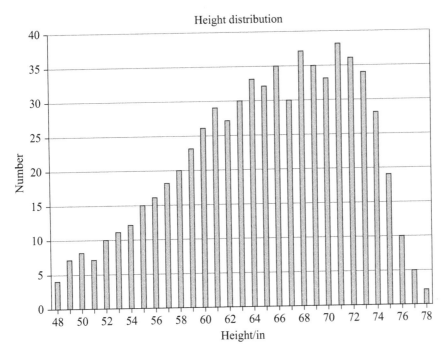

Height distribution

FIGURE 2.1. Histogram of the height of students in our survey.

sample, or a small number of individuals from the population. **Inferential statistics** are used to take what we learn about the sample that we have measured and extend that to the entire population that we haven't measured or can't measure. Assuming our sample is representative of the population, this is a valid approach and is widely used in social and political science, as well as the physical and life sciences.

Instead of talking about the gender of an individual, which is a qualitative parameter, let's consider something we can quantitatively describe, such as the height of an individual. We conduct a survey of $N = 670$ students on campus and determine their heights, then we plot a histogram as shown in Figure 2.1.

This histogram gives us an idea of how the heights are distributed. In other words, it tells us how many students are a certain height. If we select a student at random, our chance of finding a student with height $h$ is $P_h = n_h / N$, where $n_h$ is the number with that height and $P_h$ is the corresponding probability of observing that height. If we want the probability of finding a student within a range of heights, we add up the values for each of the desired heights. Mathematically, we would write this as

$$P(h_1 < h < h_2) = \sum_{h=h_1}^{h_2} P_h = \frac{1}{N} \sum_{h=h_1}^{h_2} n_h \tag{2.1}$$

Note that if we sum over all the heights, $\sum_h n_h = N$, the total number of students, and $\sum_h P_h = 1$.

We compute the **average** height of our student population in the following manner:

$$\bar{h} = \frac{\sum_h n_h h}{\sum_h n_h} = \frac{1}{N} \sum_h n_h h \tag{2.2}$$

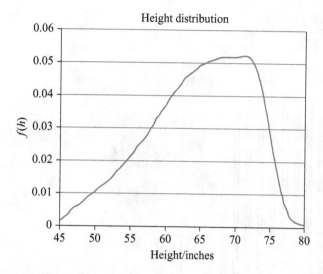

**FIGURE 2.2.** Continuous probability density function (PDF) of the height of students in our survey.

One general notation for an average is to write the variable of interest with a bar over it. Stated in words, we take each height and multiply it by the number of students with that height and add all the numbers up. We then divide by the total number of students. The bar over the $h$ indicates "the average of $h$." We can also show that $\bar{h} = \sum_h P_h h$.

There are other descriptive values we can calculate based on our sample, such as the standard deviation, but we will not go into those at this point in our discussion.

## 2.1.2 Continuous Probability Distributions

In our example of students and their height, we have **discrete** data; we measured the height to the nearest inch, so a student would be measured as 69" or 70", not 69.2". In many cases, the variable of interest is not discrete but is in fact **continuous**; in reality, we could measure the height as precisely as we want. We need to extend the ideas of probability and averages to the case of continuous variables. Instead of a discrete histogram like we have plotted above, we would have a continuous function. Such a function is known as a **probability density function (PDF)**. Let's plot a sample PDF for the height of our students, shown in Figure 2.2. Here we plot the probability of being within $dh$ of a certain height $h$ vs. the height. Notice that the $y$-axis no longer gives us the number at that height. In fact, if you look carefully you will see that the numerical values are much smaller than they were before. This makes sense, since now we are distinguishing between a height of 59" and 59.1" (or even 59.01"), so the number with any given height will necessarily be smaller than if we discretize the results to the nearest inch.

Since we are using a continuous variable, the summations we used before in Eq. 2.2 now become integrals. The probability of the height being in a certain range is given by

$$P(a < h < b) = \frac{\int_a^b f(h)\,dh}{\int_0^\infty f(h)\,dh} \tag{2.3}$$

where $f(h)$ is the PDF. A properly defined PDF should cover all possible values for the variable in question, which would be all positive real numbers, and we also require that the distribution be **normalized**. This means that the probability of finding a value, no matter what that value is within the range of possible values, is equal to 1. Mathematically, we write this normalization condition as

$$\int_0^\infty f(h)\,dh = 1 \tag{2.4}$$

Similar to what we did in Eq. 2.2, we compute the average height as

$$\bar{h} = \frac{\int_0^\infty h f(h)\,dh}{\int_0^\infty f(h)\,dh} = \int_0^\infty h f(h)\,dh \tag{2.5}$$

Remember, the denominator equals 1 for a normalized distribution. Often such integrals must be evaluated numerically, depending on the particular PDF. (Note that these are the limits for this particular variable, the height, which can only be positive. Other variables would be integrated over the appropriate limits for that variable.) An average value computed in this way is also known as an **expectation value**, or the value you would expect to observe on average, based on random sampling of the underlying population.

## 2.1.3 Angled Bracket Notation

It is a common notation to use angled brackets to denote the integral over all possible values. Thus we can write the average as

$$\bar{h} = \int_0^\infty h f(h)\, dh = \langle h \rangle$$

So long as we have an expression for the PDF, we can in principle evaluate the average through this integral. If we want to evaluate the average of a different quantity, say $h^2$, then that is what goes in the integral. Mathematically, we would write this quantity as

$$\langle h^2 \rangle = \int_0^\infty h^2 f(h)\, dh$$

In general, then, we compute the average of a variable $x$ by evaluating

$$\langle x \rangle = \bar{x} = \int x f(x) dx \qquad (2.6)$$

We likewise evaluate the expected value of any function, $g(x)$, of our variable $x$ by evaluating

$$\langle g \rangle = \int g(x) f(x) dx \qquad (2.7)$$

The limits of integration in Eqs. 2.6 and 2.7 need to cover all possible values of the variable $x$. Limits of zero and infinity are appropriate for a variable that can only have positive values. If negative values are also possible, then the correct limits would be from negative infinity to positive infinity.

There are some things to remember with this notation:

- The angled brackets denote an integral over all possible values of the variable in question.
- The function $f(x)$ denotes the probability of the value being between $x$ and $x + dx$.
- The distribution function $f(x)$ should be normalized.

## 2.1.4 Normal (Gaussian) Distribution

A distribution function that is commonly encountered in science is the **normal** (or **Gaussian**) **distribution**. This is the familiar bell-shaped curve, as shown in Figure 2.3. The functional form of a Gaussian distribution is

$$f(x) = \frac{1}{\sigma\sqrt{2\pi}} e^{\frac{-(x-\bar{x})^2}{2\sigma^2}} \qquad \text{where} \quad -\infty < x < \infty \qquad (2.8)$$

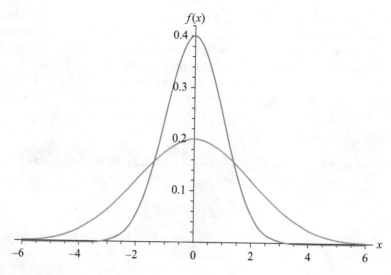

**FIGURE 2.3.** Normal (Gaussian) distributions with a mean of 0 and standard deviation of 1 (blue) and 2 (orange).

The shape of the distribution is controlled by two parameters: $\bar{x}$, the average; and $\sigma$, the standard deviation. The average tells us the center of the distribution and the standard deviation gives the width. This function is normalized and symmetric about the average.

## 2.2 Central Limit Theorem

One of the most useful results of statistics is the **central limit theorem**. This theorem actually forms the basis of much of what is done with statistics. It allows us to use a normal (Gaussian) distribution to describe properties of a sample from a population where the individuals are governed by any distribution function. Let's illustrate this with rolling dice.

When you roll a properly weighted die, you have equal probability of getting any number from 1 through 6. This distribution function is known as a **uniform distribution**. The probability of rolling each value can be plotted in a histogram, just like we did before with the height of students. This histogram, shown in Figure 2.4, looks flat, since there is equal likelihood of obtaining any of the possible outcomes.

But what is the average value? If we add up all the possible results and divide by 6, the total number of results, we obtain 3.5. One way to think of the average is the center of mass of the distribution. You can see that if we had a physical object in the shape of the uniform distribution and we wanted to balance it on a fulcrum, we would need to place the fulcrum beneath the value 3.5. Note also that we can never roll the average value; we can roll a 3 or a 4, but not the value 3.5. The average, or expected value, is what we expect to see on average with multiple attempts. For example, if we roll a 1, then a 6, the average of those outcomes is 3.5. If we roll a die many times, add up all the results, and divide by the number of trials, we will obtain a number very close to 3.5, even though we can never get that result from a single roll of the die.

Now, let's consider the case of rolling two dice and adding up the two values to get a single result. The histogram of results, shown in Figure 2.5, looks very different from the

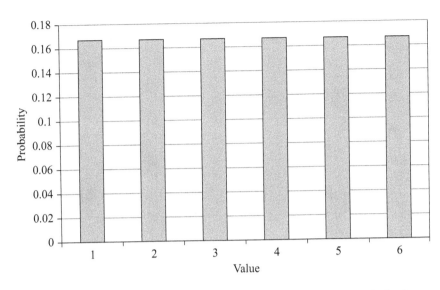

FIGURE 2.4. Uniform probability distribution for the outcome of rolling a single six-sided die.

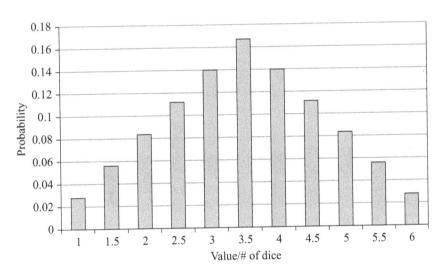

FIGURE 2.5. Probability distribution for the outcome of rolling two 6-sided dice.

uniform distribution of a single roll. Instead of being uniform, it is peaked at the center. This is because there is only one way to roll a value of 2 (1 and 1), but there are six ways to roll a value of 7 (1 and 6, 2 and 5, 3 and 4, 4 and 3, 5 and 2, 6 and 1). Notice that the average value for rolling two dice (7) is twice the average value for rolling one die (3.5).

What if we do this for three dice? The histogram of these outcomes is shown in Figure 2.6. Notice that the distribution is even more sharply peaked than it was for two dice. The average, or expected value, is apparently right between 10 and 11, since those two results have equal probability. In fact, the average of 10.5 is 3 times the average value of rolling a single die, which was 3.5.

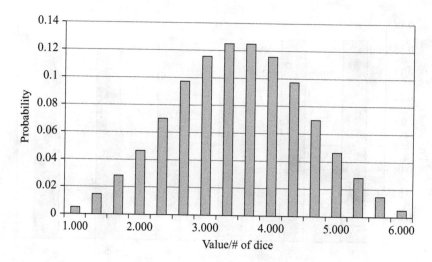

**FIGURE 2.6.** Probability distribution for the outcome of rolling three 6-sided dice.

In order to see how the outcomes tend to concentrate around the average value, we can plot all these results on the same scale by dividing the outcomes by the number of dice that were rolled. This is done in Figure 2.7 for 2, 3, and 10 dice. Now we can see that the average is always 3.5, but the distribution of outcomes narrows as the number of dice increases. In statistics language, the standard deviation decreases relative to the range of possible values. If we rolled a very large number of dice, added up the results, and divided by the number of dice rolled, then we would be quite confident in obtaining a value of 3.5, with very little likelihood of rolling anything significantly different from that value. Likewise, if we just care about the actual result of rolling $N$ dice, then we would expect to obtain a value of $3.5N$.

These results illustrate the central limit theorem, which states that for a large number of random trials, regardless of the underlying distribution function (uniform in the case of rolling a die), the overall results will be distributed according to a normal (Gaussian) distribution. Note that as the number of trials gets very large, the standard deviation from the average decreases and we can be very certain in predicting the overall result. Note also that even though we can predict the overall outcome of rolling $N$ dice, we don't know what the result was for the roll of each individual die.

### Sample Problem 2.1

This problem will deal with the same situation of rolling multiple dice that we have been discussing. For the cases of rolling 2, 3, and 10 dice and dividing the outcome by the number of dice, determine the overall probability of obtaining a result within ±1 of the average.

### Solution

Basically, we need to sum up the results of the histograms for all values between 2.5 and 4.5 for each of the three cases. By taking the raw data, which you could recreate if you so desire, this is a straightforward summation.

For 2 dice, $P(2.5 \leq \text{outcome} \leq 3.5) = 0.667$
For 3 dice, $P(2.5 \leq \text{outcome} \leq 3.5) = 0.676$
For 10 dice, $P(2.5 \leq \text{outcome} \leq 3.5) = 0.949$

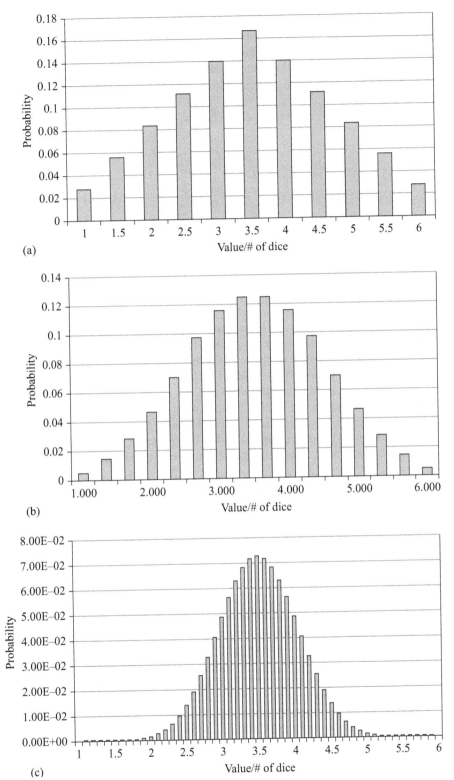

**FIGURE 2.7.** Histograms for rolling a) 2, b) 3 and c) 10 dice. Horizontal axes are rescaled by dividing the outcome by the number of dice to illustrate the central limit theorem.

So, we see that for two or three dice, roughly two thirds of the results are within ±1 of the average, but for 10 dice, 95% of the outcomes fall within this range.

If you wanted to make this determination for the case of 10 dice without generating the raw data, you could actually make a copy of the histogram, cut out the shape generated by the bars, and weigh it. You could then cut off the wings and weigh it again, and you should obtain a similar result. This "cut and weigh" technique of integration was actually very common in the days of strip chart recorders, before we had digital data-acquisition tools.

## 2.3 Permutations and Configurations

The central limit theorem gives us confidence that we can predict the average outcome of multiple random events. So how does that help us understand the behavior of molecules, which can each be in a variety of possible energy states? To begin answering these questions, we need to review another area of probability theory that has to do with permutations and combinations, or the ways we can place objects in various arrangements.

Consider that you have one ball and three boxes, labeled 1 through 3. How many different ways can you arrange the ball in the boxes? Quite obviously, three. Now, what if we have two distinguishable balls to put in the three boxes. How many distinct ways can we arrange the balls if we only allow one ball per box? There are actually six ways to do this, since we can switch the balls between the two occupied boxes. Each arrangement, for example a ball in box 1 and box 2, is called a **configuration**. Each way to obtain a given configuration is known as a **permutation**. So, for this case, we would say we have three configurations but, if we can distinguish between ball 1 and ball 2, there are six permutations.

Let's more formally develop the mathematical description of this type of situation. One of the main tools we'll need is the concept of the **factorial**. Recall that when we evaluate a factorial, we take the product of all integers up to the final number. So, $3! = 3 \times 2 \times 1 = 6$. Likewise, $5! = 5 \times 4 \times 3 \times 2 \times 1 = 120$. (Note that $0! = 1$, by definition.) You can probably see that factorials quickly get very large. Why does this work? If we want to arrange three balls into three boxes, we have three choices of which ball to put in the first box. However, we only have two choices for the second box and no choice, or only one option, for the third one, giving a total of $3! = 6$ permutations. Hopefully, you can see now that if we wanted to put five balls in five boxes, we have five choices for the first box, four for the second, three for the third, two for the fourth, and no choice, or one option, for the fifth, meaning there are $5 \times 4 \times 3 \times 2 \times 1 = 5! = 120$ ways to arrange our five balls in five boxes, one ball per box.

Now, let's make the situation a bit more interesting. Let's suppose that we have five balls, but we are only going to choose three of them to put into three boxes, one ball per box. How many different ways can we do this? Well, to set this idea up, let's actually consider two additional boxes, but they won't count in the final analysis; call them the reject boxes, if you wish. As before, there are $5!$ ways to arrange five balls in the five boxes. But what about the two reject boxes? Does the order of placement here matter? Remember that these two reject boxes hold the balls we're not choosing, so we don't care about the order of placement in the last two boxes. This means that if we have, say ball 3 in the first box, ball 2 in the second box, and ball 5 in the third box, it doesn't matter if we place the last two as 1,4 or 4,1; those arrangements are the same. To avoid double counting these, we simply divide our total number of arrangements by two. Thus, the number of distinct ways,

or permutations, of choosing three balls from a group of five is written as $_5P_3 = \dfrac{5!}{2!} = 60$.

In general, if we are choosing $M$ individuals out of a group of $N$, then the number of permutations is given by

$$_N P_M = \frac{N!}{(N-M)!} \tag{2.9}$$

It is useful to take a minute to talk about this expression. Note that the number in the numerator is the factorial of the total number of individuals in the group you are choosing from. The number in the denominator is the factorial of the number you are not choosing, where *order doesn't matter*. When the order doesn't matter, we have to avoid double counting all the arrangements that are the same.

Now, what if we don't care about the order of the ones we do choose? Let's say we have five balls, and we are choosing three of them, but we don't care in what order we place them. Well, following our pattern, we should also divide by 3!, since the order among the chosen three doesn't matter. So the number of different arrangements of choosing three balls from a group of five is given by $\frac{5!}{3!\,2!} = 10$. If the order of the chosen balls doesn't matter, we go from 60 possibilities to only 10. Each arrangement is called a **combination**. The general way to calculate the number of combinations that arise from choosing $M$ individuals from an overall group of $N$ is

$$_N C_M = \frac{N!}{M!(N-M)!} \tag{2.10}$$

Note that the two values in the denominator, $M$ and $N - M$, add up to the total number we are choosing from, $N$. The main difference between a permutation and a combination is whether the order in which we arrange the chosen items matters or, in other words, if the chosen items are **distinguishable**. If they are distinguishable (meaning that order matters), we have to account for all the different arrangements or permutations. If they are **indistinguishable** (meaning that order doesn't matter), then the number of conformations is (often significantly) smaller. Note that if we choose all the objects from the group, the number of permutations is $N!$, whereas the number of combinations is simply 1.

Let's extend this idea to more balls and more boxes. One way to describe the configuration is with a set of **occupation numbers**, $n_i$, where $i$ is the label of the box and $n_i$ gives us the number of balls in box $i$. It should be fairly obvious that $\Sigma_i n_i = N$, where $N$ is the total number of balls. A result of probability theory tells us that the number of ways to arrange $N$ indistinguishable objects into $M$ different boxes (or states) can be determined from the occupation numbers by the expression

$$W = \frac{N!}{n_1!\,n_2!\,n_3! \ldots n_M!} = \frac{N!}{\prod_{i=1}^{M} n_i!} \tag{2.11}$$

The value $W$ is called the **weight** of the configuration, and this expression is known as a **multinomial distribution**. The larger the weight, the more different ways that particular configuration can be obtained.

For example, how many different ways can we put six balls in three boxes with three balls in box 1, one ball in box 2, and two balls in box 3? The total number of balls is $N = 6$. A convenient notation is to write the configuration as {3,1,2}, where we list the **occupation numbers** in order of the box number. The number of different ways we can reach this configuration is calculated to be $W = \frac{6!}{3!1!2!} = 60$.

What is the weight of the following configurations for placing six indistinguishable balls in three boxes: all the balls in one box; four balls in the first box and two in the third box; five balls in the first box, one in the second, and none in the third; three balls in the first two boxes and none in the third.

Solution

For the first arrangement, our configuration is written as {6,0,0}. We calculate the weight according to the expression $W_{6,0,0} = \dfrac{6!}{6!0!0!} = 1$. (Remember that $0! = 1$.)

The next configuration is written as {4,0,2}. The weight is $W_{4,0,2} = \dfrac{6!}{4!0!2!} = 15$.

For the configuration {5,1,0}, the weight is $W_{5,1,0} = \dfrac{6!}{5!1!0!} = 6$.

For the last configuration {3,3,0}, the weight is $W_{3,3,0} = \dfrac{6!}{3!3!0!} = 20$.

---

We can see in the preceding examples that the number of ways to arrange the balls increases as things are spread out more evenly. What about distributing the balls equally among the boxes in the configuration {2,2,2}? In this case we have $W_{2,2,2} = \dfrac{6!}{2!2!2!} = 90$. As we will be able to definitively prove later on, this arrangement has the greatest weight, or the greatest likelihood, for this situation.

We should note that in order to compute actual probabilities, we would need to determine the weight of all possible configurations and add those values up. We would then divide the weight of a given configuration by that sum. For anything but very small situations, determining absolute probabilities is often not a useful undertaking. Note, though, that if all we care about are *relative* probabilities, knowledge of the statistical weights is sufficient since the incredibly large denominator would divide out in determining this ratio. For example, the relative probability of the {2,2,2} configuration compared to the {3,3,0} configuration is $90/20 = 4.5$; the {2,2,2} configuration is 4.5 times more likely than the {3,3,0} configuration.

Our next step is to extend this reasoning to a collection of molecules, which can be in a wide variety of states. When we start talking about collections of molecules, the numbers become very large very quickly. To help us in this, we will first present a useful approximation for dealing with the factorials of large numbers. Because these numbers become so large, it is often more convenient to deal with the logarithms of those numbers; a logarithmic function increases much more slowly than the original values. In particular, for large numbers we can approximate the logarithm of a factorial as

$$\ln x! = x \ln x - x \tag{2.12}$$

This is known as **Stirling's approximation**, and is quite good for large values of $x$.

# 2.4 Distribution of Molecular States

As you know from general chemistry, the energy states of molecules are quantized. This means that a molecule cannot possess arbitrary amounts of energy, but only certain amounts depending on the energy levels of the molecular system. In a bulk sample, we often can't distinguish these small steps in energy; it looks continuous. This is because of the incredibly large number of molecules in any macroscopic sample. On the molecular level, however, energy is constantly being exchanged as molecules collide. In order to go from the molecular to the bulk level, we need to properly account for how this energy is spread around.

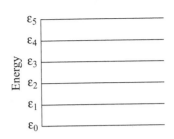

FIGURE 2.8. Energy level diagram with equally spaced states.

Let's consider a small collection, or **microsystem**, of three molecules and allow for equally spaced energy levels labeled $\varepsilon_0$, $\varepsilon_1$, $\varepsilon_2$, etc. We will assign the energy of the zeroth level to be zero. (Where we place the reference point for energy is arbitrary, so we do what is most convenient.) Each higher level has one more unit of energy. (The $\varepsilon_2$ level has two units of energy.) An energy level diagram will look like Figure 2.8.

Now, let's say the total energy in our system must be equal to 3 units of energy. Obviously one way to have an energy of three units would be to give it all to one molecule, leaving the other two with no energy. Or we could spread it out evenly and give each molecule one unit of energy. A third possibility is to give two units to one molecule and one unit to another, leaving the third with no energy. Let's indicate these three different arrangements on our diagram by placing a marker for each molecule at the energy of that molecule, as shown in Figure 2.9.

Each of these three arrangements is known as a **configuration**. Each configuration can be described by the number of molecules at each energy level. It's important also to state that the order in which the molecules are assigned to each state doesn't matter; the molecules are indistinguishable.

As we saw in the last section, the **weight**, or number of ways to obtain a given configuration, is given by Eq. 2.11.

$$W = \frac{N!}{n_0!\,n_1!\,n_2!\,n_3!\ldots}$$

Looking at our diagrams above, we would describe the first configuration by {2,0,0,1,0,0}, where the each of the six numbers represents the number of molecules in the corresponding energy state. We have two molecules in the zeroth state and one in the third state. The second configuration is described by {0,3,0,0,0,0}; all three molecules are in the first state. The third configuration is described by {1,1,1,0,0,0}, with one molecule each in states 0–2. There are actually three different ways we can achieve the first configuration; we can have each of the three molecules in the third energy level. Each of these possible ways to achieve a certain configuration is known as a **microstate**. Likewise, there are 3!, or 6, microstates corresponding to the last configuration. There is only one way to achieve the second configuration; it corresponds to a single microstate.

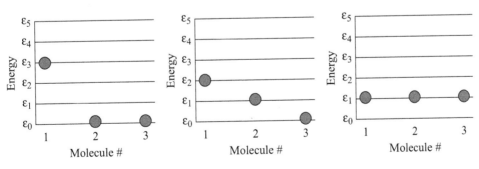

FIGURE 2.9. Possible arrangements of three molecules with three total units of energy.

Now, let's imagine that the molecules are bouncing around and can exchange energy, but the total energy remains in three energy units. In thermodynamic terms, we would say that this system is **isolated**, meaning no matter or energy can leave the system. Which configuration is more likely to be seen? One of the key assumptions in statistical mechanics is the **principle of equal *a priori* probabilities**. This principle states that no particular microstate is to be preferred over any other. In other words, our system of molecules has an equal chance of being in any given microstate. We have determined that there is a total of 10 different microstates, described as three configurations. However, because there are six ways to get the third configuration, we would expect to observe it 60% of the time. We only expect the energy to be equally distributed 10% of the time. 30% of the time, one of the molecules will have all the energy, but a particular molecule will only have all the energy 10% of the time; any of the three could have it. Thus for this system, the most likely configuration is the one where one molecule has 2 quanta of energy, another molecule has 1, and the third has 0. It would be nice if we could predict this arrangement in advance, and that's what we'll work toward in the next section.

## 2.5 The Boltzmann Distribution

Our example of three molecules is really small. However, we can already see that one configuration is preferred over the other two because there are more ways to obtain it. What happens when we have a much larger number of molecules in our microsystem? It should be obvious that as $N$ increases, $W$ increases much more quickly. Not only that, but as we saw in our discussion of the central limit theorem, as the sample size increases there is a particular configuration that will be much more probable than all others. Our goal now is to identify that most probable configuration.

Because the numerical value of $W$ will be large, it is easier to use $\ln W$ than $W$ itself. We can therefore write

$$\ln W = \ln N! - \ln \prod_i n_i! = \ln N! - \sum_i \ln n_i!$$

(Recall the rules of logarithms: $\ln a \cdot b = \ln a + \ln b$ and $\ln \dfrac{a}{b} = \ln a - \ln b$.) For factorials of large numbers, we can use Stirling's approximation $\ln x! = x \ln x - x$. This lets us write

$$\ln W = N \ln N - N - \sum_i (n_i \ln n_i - n_i) = N \ln N - \sum_i n_i \ln n_i$$

(Remember that $\sum_i n_i = N$.)

Now, we want to know where $W$, or $\ln W$, is at its maximum. To find this, we write the total differential with respect to arrangement, where the arrangement is given by all the individual occupation numbers, $n_i$, and set it equal to zero.

$$d \ln W = \sum_i \left( \frac{\partial \ln W}{\partial n_i} \right) dn_i = 0 \tag{2.13}$$

We cannot vary the arrangement at will for our isolated system, however. We have certain constraints that must be obeyed.

The first relates to the fixed number of molecules:

$$N = \sum_i n_i$$

The second relates to the fixed total energy of the microsystem:

$$E = \sum_i n_i \cdot \epsilon_i$$

where $\epsilon_i$ is the energy of state $i$. (Note that the states don't have to be evenly spaced as they were in our example above.) The mathematical technique to solve this problem is the method of undetermined multipliers. To apply this technique, we include these constraints by writing

$$
\begin{aligned}
d \ln W &= \sum_i \left( \frac{\partial \ln W}{\partial n_i} \right) dn_i + \alpha \sum_i dn_i - \beta \sum_i \epsilon_i dn_i \\
&= \sum_i \left\{ \left( \frac{\partial \ln W}{\partial n_i} \right) + \alpha - \beta \epsilon_i \right\} dn_i = 0
\end{aligned}
\tag{2.14}
$$

(The last term is negative because we know the final answer and the minus sign will be an important part of that answer.) We won't show all the details here, but what we get is known as the **Boltzmann distribution**.

$$\frac{n_i}{N} = \frac{e^{-\beta \epsilon_i}}{\sum_i e^{-\beta \epsilon_i}} \tag{2.15}$$

Note that $N$, the total number of molecules, is a key part of this result. The new parameter $\beta$ comes from our constraint of fixed total energy; the quantity $\beta$ has units of energy$^{-1}$. We can write the left-hand side of this equation as $P_i$, the fraction in state $i$. We also define the sum in the denominator as the **partition function**, $q$:

$$q = \sum_i e^{-\beta \epsilon_i} \tag{2.16}$$

The sum is over all the allowed energy states of the molecule; however, we can't get any more specific until we know more about these states. We now write the Boltzmann distribution in its more conventional form

$$P_i = \frac{e^{-\beta \epsilon_i}}{q} \tag{2.17}$$

So, for a given microsystem, the Boltzmann distribution will tell us the fraction of molecules that occupy a given state. Because the number of molecules is so large, we can be almost certain that this distribution of the population is what we will observe at any time, despite the exchange of energy among individual molecules; there are many more ways to achieve this configuration than any other.

Note that the parameter $\beta$, which has to do with our constraint of fixed total energy, has units of energy$^{-1}$. We will not go through the complete derivation, but it can be shown that $\beta = 1/k_B T$. $k_B$ is known as **Boltzmann's constant** and has the value of $1.3807 \times 10^{-23}$ J K$^{-1}$. $T$ is the temperature in Kelvin. This result forces us to rethink what we mean by temperature. In this formulation, $T$ is a fitting parameter to describe how energy is distributed throughout a system at thermal equilibrium. (The whole idea of temperature becomes a bit more complicated for nonequilibrium systems.) As a side note, you should multiply Boltzmann's constant by Avogadro's number and see what you get. (Hint: It will look familiar.)

With the value of $\beta$ determined, we can write the familiar form of the Boltzmann distribution:

$$P_i = \frac{e^{-\epsilon_i/k_B T}}{q} \qquad \text{where} \qquad q = \sum_i e^{-\epsilon_i/k_B T} \tag{2.18}$$

Qualitatively, the partition function is simply a number and can be thought of as the number of states that are important to the system at a given temperature. The value $k_B T$ is sometimes referred to as the **thermal energy**, and is a useful reference for comparison when we talk about the allowed energy states of our molecules. If the energy of the state is much greater than $k_B T$, it doesn't contribute much to the partition function. Likewise, the population in a high-energy state will be very small. On the other hand, a state with energy less than $k_B T$ will fully contribute to the partition function and have a larger population.

There are many cases where multiple states have the same energy; such energy states are said to be **degenerate**. Each of these degenerate states must be included in the partition function. Another way to deal with this is to define a variable, $g_i$, that gives the degeneracy of levels at energy $\epsilon_i$. We can then slightly modify the Boltzmann distribution as follows

$$P_i = \frac{g_i e^{-\epsilon_i/k_B T}}{q} \qquad \text{with} \qquad q = \sum_i g_i e^{-\epsilon_i/k_B T} \tag{2.19}$$

The summation in the partition function is now over energy levels, not the individual energy states. One way to think of this is the rooms in an office building. The energy level is akin to the floor of the building. However, any given floor may be configured into few or many offices; the number of offices on a given floor is the degeneracy of that level.

## 2.6 Entropy

We began this discussion by trying to find the configuration with the greatest weight, or the most probable distribution of the energy amongst the available states. Boltzmann's other great contribution to science was to make the connection between the weight of a configuration and **entropy**, which was originally introduced in classical thermodynamics as a way to deal with the spontaneous flow of heat from a hot body to a colder one. The mathematical expression for this relation is

$$S = k_B \ln W \tag{2.20}$$

where $W$ is the weight of the most probable configuration. What configuration is most likely? The one that can be achieved in the most possible ways, as described by the Boltzmann distribution.

If the system is randomly sampling all possible configurations, it will most likely be found in the most probable one, and that corresponds to the configuration with the highest entropy. Likewise, if a system starts in a configuration that is not the most probable one, and it can randomly sample the configuration space, it will eventually find its way to the most probable configuration, which will increase the entropy of that system. Once it finds that most probable configuration, the chance of it changing to a less probable configuration is very small. We often talk about entropy in terms of "disorder," but what this expression helps us understand is that entropy really has to do with probabilities. This equation is so important that it is engraved on Boltzmann's tombstone.

## 2.7  Summary, and Where We Go Next

In this chapter, we have put together some of the tools of probability and statistics that we will need in order to talk about the behavior of large collections of molecules. We have also developed the Boltzmann distribution, which is one of the most powerful concepts ever developed and is the foundation of statistical mechanics. It will allow us to construct detailed molecular models of a wide variety of phenomena. We'll first use the Boltzmann distribution to develop the kinetic molecular theory of gases and derive the ideal gas law from this molecular model in the next chapter. This will be our first example of the "bottom-up" approach where we derive a mathematical relationship based on a microscopic model. (Recall that we used the "top-down" approach in Chapter 1 in our discussion of the historical development of the ideal gas law.)

## PROBLEMS

**2.1**  You are dealt a hand of five cards from a standard deck of playing cards.

   a)  What is the probability of having only one heart?

   b)  What is the probability of having five hearts?

   c)  What is the probability of having the numbers 5–9, of any suit?

   d)  What is the probability of being dealt the numbers 5–9, of any suit, in numerical order?

**2.2**  Let's assign a point value to the outcome of flipping a coin: heads = 1, tails = 0.

   a)  When flipping a single coin, what is the probability of flipping a heads?

   b)  Given the scores we have assigned, what is the average outcome of flipping a single coin?

   c)  Consider the case of flipping four coins and adding up the total result. Make a chart showing each possible outcome, the number of ways it can be obtained, and the probability of each outcome. Also state the average result for flipping four coins.

   d)  Consider the case of flipping 100 coins and adding up the total result. What is the average outcome?

   e)  Determine the relative probability of obtaining the average outcome and a score equal to half the average outcome when flipping 100 coins. How does this compare to the same relative probability when you flip four coins?

**2.3** You have four balls, labeled *a*, *b*, *c*, and *d*, that can be placed in one of two boxes.

a) Determine the number of permutations for each configuration and write out the explicit configurations that are possible, neglecting permutations within the two boxes.

b) Determine the most probable distribution of the balls in the boxes. Also determine the probability of this most probable distribution.

**2.4** Imagine that you are having a dinner party, but only have space for five additional guests. You have 10 friends from whom you will select your guests. Your place at the table is fixed.

a) How many different seating arrangements can you make?

b) How many different dinner groups can you make, where seating arrangements don't matter?

c) How many different arrangements can you make, where you only care about the people sitting next to you, but not the order of the other three guests?

**2.5** Imagine you have a large box, the floor of which is divided up into 100 separate compartments in a 10 × 10 grid. The walls of the compartments are lower than the walls of the box, such that balls placed in the box can bounce between compartments when the box is shaken. Each compartment is large enough to hold only five balls.

a) You place 100 indistinguishable balls in the box, with five to a compartment; only 20 compartments have any balls in them. Calculate the statistical weight of this arrangement.

b) What if you put two balls per compartment? (There are still only 100 balls total.) Calculate the statistical weight of this arrangement.

c) If you were to pick up the box and shake it, such that the balls can bounce around and land in compartments, what arrangement would you expect to see most of the time? Why?

d) Calculate the statistical weight of this most likely arrangement.

e) Let's start with one ball per compartment. Take one ball from one compartment and put it in another compartment. Calculate the statistical weight of this arrangement and compare it to the weight of the most likely arrangement you proposed in part d).

f) Does this confirm your prediction of the most likely way to arrange the balls in the compartments? Why or why not?

**2.6** Consider a system that consists of *N* molecules to be distributed among *M* states that are all degenerate. For the most probable configuration, prove that the population in each state is the same as all the others.

**2.7** Many systems can be modeled as having only two energy states. This is known as a two-level system. This problem will be your first chance to play with a partition function.

a) Take the first energy state as having zero energy. The second state has energy $\epsilon$. Write an expression for the molecular partition function, $q$, for this system.

b) Evaluate the numerical value of the partition function in the limit of $T \to \infty$ and $T \to 0$.

c) Determine the fraction of molecules that are in each energy state in both temperature limits.

d) In nuclear magnetic resonance (NMR) spectroscopy, we cause the spin state of a proton (or other nucleus) to flip. This can be modeled as a two-level system. NMR spectroscopy operates in the radio frequency range of the electromagnetic spectrum. If the frequency of a transition is 500 MHz, what are the relative populations in each of the two states at room temperature?

**2.8** A certain molecular system is found to have only two allowed energy levels. The degeneracy of the ground level is 2, and the degeneracy of the excited level is 4. The energy spacing between the levels is 0.30 eV.

a) At a temperature of 1000 K, what is the ratio of the population in the two states, $n_1/n_0$?

b) What wavelength of light would be needed to excite a transition from the ground state to the excited state, and in what region of the electromagnetic spectrum does this transition take place?

**2.9** For the same molecular system in the previous problem, determine the temperature at which 25% of the total population would be found at the excited level.

**2.10** Any type of energy can be used in the Boltzmann distribution. For this problem, we will consider only gravitational potential energy, $\epsilon_h = mgh$, where $m$ is the mass of a particle, $h$ is the height, and $g$ is the gravitational acceleration, equal to 9.8 m s$^{-2}$.

a) Derive an expression that you can use to determine the ratio of the number density of a column of gas at two different heights. Assume the temperature is uniform throughout the column.

b) You want to separate methane and ethane gas in a vertical column at a refinery. What is the difference in number density of the two gases at the bottom and top of a 100 m column at a temperature of 135°C?

**2.11** A system consists of two subsystems, which we'll label 1 and 2. The statistical weights of the subsystems are: $W_1 = 2 \times 10^{25}$ and $W_2 = 3 \times 10^{26}$.

a) Calculate the statistical weight of the composite system formed by combining the two subsystems.

b) Calculate the entropy of each subsystem and the total system.

**2.12** In this problem, we'll return to the large box with 100 smaller compartments we explored in Problem 2.5 to get more understanding of statistical entropy.

a) Assuming we can use Boltzmann's formula for this type of situation, calculate the entropy for the two situations described in parts a) and b).

b) Calculate the entropy for the situations described in part d).

c) Briefly describe what it means for a system to "sample its configuration space" in terms of the entropy of a system and what will happen to the entropy over time.

**2.13** Let's go back to a two-level system, where both levels are singly degenerate. The levels are spaced by 0.25 eV. Our system will consist of 100 molecules, each of which will be in one of these two energy states.

a) Let's start under a condition where 99% of the molecules are in the ground state. Determine the temperature of this situation.

b) What is the entropy of the system under the conditions described in part a)?

c) What are the temperature and entropy when 60% of the molecules are in the ground state?

d) For the two situations described in parts a) and c), you add just enough energy to move one more molecule from the ground state to the excited state. What effect does this have on the temperature and entropy for each situation? Report your results as a percent increase in temperature and entropy for both situations.

e) What can you say about how entropy increases with an increase in energy under conditions of low and high temperature?

# Kinetic Molecular Theory

## 3.1 Maxwell–Boltzmann Distribution of Speeds

### 3.1.1 Translational Energy of Gas Particles

In the last chapter, we developed the Boltzmann distribution, which gives us a sense of how likely we are to find a molecule in a state of a given energy at a given temperature. To review, the Boltzmann distribution (Eq. 2.19) is written as

$$P_i = \frac{g_i e^{-\epsilon_i/k_B T}}{q} \quad \text{with} \quad q = \sum_i g_i e^{-\epsilon_i/k_B T}$$

where $P_i$ is the probability of a molecule being at a given energy level (this is also the fractional population in that level), $g_i$ is the degeneracy of that level, $\epsilon_i$ is the energy of the level, $k_B$ is Boltzmann's constant, and $T$ is the absolute temperature. The partition function, $q$, is evaluated by summing over all the energy levels, and can be thought of as the number of levels with a significant amount of the total population.

Up to this point, we haven't said anything specific about the possible energy levels of our molecules. We'll start with the simplest system we can, that of a monatomic gas, such as He or Ne, where the gas particles are individual atoms. We will also ignore any interactions between the atoms in the gas. The only type of motion such gas particles can have is translational motion. We know from classical physics that the kinetic energy of a particle of mass $m$ traveling at velocity $v$ is given by $E_{kin} = \frac{1}{2}mv^2$. In principle, each gas particle (or atom, in this case) could be traveling at a different velocity. But what is the likelihood that a molecule has a particular velocity? To get that answer, we turn to the Boltzmann distribution.

## 3.1.2 The One-Dimensional Velocity Distribution

In the context of the Boltzmann distribution, we can assign an energy to each gas particle. For simplicity, we will initially confine ourselves to motion in one dimension, which we'll call the $x$ direction. So, for a particle with velocity component $v_x$, we have energy $\epsilon_{kin,x} = \frac{1}{2}mv_x^2$. We can then write the probability that a particle has a given kinetic energy in the $x$ direction, or a given $x$ component of velocity, as

$$P_{v_x} = \frac{e^{-\epsilon_{kin,x}/k_BT}}{q} = \frac{e^{-\frac{mv_x^2}{2k_BT}}}{q} \qquad (3.1)$$

To fully evaluate this probability, however, we need to look at the partition function in the denominator. Recall that the partition function is a sum over all the possible energy levels of our particles. Treating our particles classically, the velocity is a continuous variable; we are ignoring any quantization of translational energy states at this point. This means that our partition function, which is formally a sum, can be approximated as an integral, which we can write as

$$q = \sum_{v_x} e^{-\frac{mv_x^2}{2k_BT}} \approx \int_{-\infty}^{\infty} e^{-\frac{mv_x^2}{2k_BT}} \, dv_x = \left( \frac{2\pi k_BT}{m} \right)^{1/2} \qquad (3.2)$$

Note that the limits of integration are from negative to positive infinity, reflecting the fact that the particles can travel in either a forward or reverse direction. Note also that the function we are integrating is a Gaussian function, the integrals of which have a standard form.

Now that we have evaluated the partition function, we can write the probability of having a particular $x$ component of velocity as

$$P_{v_x} = \left( \frac{m}{2\pi k_BT} \right)^{1/2} e^{-\frac{mv_x^2}{2k_BT}} \qquad (3.3)$$

This is basically a probability distribution function (PDF) for the $x$ component of velocity. A more conventional way to write the PDF is as

$$f(v_x)dv_x = \left( \frac{m}{2\pi k_BT} \right)^{1/2} e^{\frac{-mv_x^2}{2k_BT}} \, dv_x \qquad (3.4)$$

where the notation $f(v_x)dv_x$ reminds us that we are talking about the probability of a particle having a $v_x$ value between $v_x$ and $v_x + dv_x$. You should convince yourself that this PDF is normalized.

It is worth spending some time looking at this distribution function. First, we readily recognize it as a normal, or Gaussian, function. (See Eq. 2.8, as well as Figure 2.3 for plots of a Gaussian function.) The average value of $v_x$ is 0. This can be interpreted physically as meaning that the particle is equally likely to be traveling in the forward and the reverse directions. Second, we should consider how this function depends on the two parameters we can adjust, namely the particle mass $m$ and the temperature $T$. Comparing back to Eq. 2.8, we see that the standard deviation is $\sigma = (k_BT/m)^{1/2}$. If we increase the mass, $\sigma$ decreases and the distribution will fall off more quickly. This means there are fewer particles traveling at high velocity for heavy particles than for light particles. The reverse is true if we decrease the mass; we are more likely to find light particles traveling at a high velocity. We can also see that if we increase the temperature, the distribution broadens out (σ increases), meaning we have a greater likelihood of having fast-moving particles at high temperature than at low temperature. The reverse happens if we decrease the temperature; at low temperature, the range of velocities decreases.

### 3.1.3 The Maxwell–Boltzmann Distribution of Molecular Speeds

We now have a way to quantify the motion of gas particles in one dimension. We live, however, in a three-dimensional world. How do we extend this idea to three dimensions? First, we can argue that if a gas is truly **isotropic**, meaning the direction doesn't matter, then there is no preference to be traveling in one direction compared to another. (We are, of course, neglecting the effect of gravity, which does define an up/down direction. But for a container of gas, this is a reasonable approximation.) Another way to describe this is to say that our choice of the $x$ direction is arbitrary. What you call $x$, I could call $y$, and vice versa. But who is right? If direction doesn't matter, then we are both correct and the answers we get must be independent of our choice of coordinate system. In other words, we can use the same one-dimensional distribution function to describe motion in the $x$, $y$, and $z$ directions.

You may recall that when we are looking at the probability of independent events, we multiply the individual probabilities. This means we can write a three-dimensional probability distribution function as

$$f(v_x)f(v_y)f(v_z)\,dv_x\,dv_y\,dv_z = \left(\frac{m}{2\pi k_B T}\right)^{3/2} e^{\frac{-mv_x^2}{2k_B T}} e^{\frac{-mv_y^2}{2k_B T}} e^{\frac{-mv_z^2}{2k_B T}}\,dv_x\,dv_y\,dv_z \tag{3.5}$$

Since we have said we don't care about direction, it makes sense to convert to a spherical coordinate system. Instead of a radius, the equivalent variable becomes the magnitude of the velocity, which we call the speed $v$, mathematically written as

$$v^2 = v_x^2 + v_y^2 + v_z^2 \text{ or } v = \sqrt{(v_x^2 + v_y^2 + v_z^2)} \tag{3.6}$$

(Remember that velocity is a vector symbolized as $\vec{v}$, which has magnitude and direction. Speed is the magnitude of velocity and is a scalar quantity; direction doesn't matter for speed.) Recall that the volume element in Cartesian coordinates is related to that in spherical coordinates by

$$dx\,dy\,dz = r^2 \sin\theta\,dr\,d\theta\,d\phi \tag{3.7}$$

We extend this to our consideration of speed by replacing $r$ with $v$ to write

$$dv_x\,dv_y\,dv_z = v^2 \sin\theta\,dv\,d\theta\,d\phi$$

This lets us write our distribution function as

$$f(v,\theta,\phi)\,dv\,d\theta\,d\phi = \left(\frac{m}{2\pi k_B T}\right)^{3/2} v^2 e^{\frac{-mv^2}{2k_B T}}\,dv \sin\theta\,d\theta\,d\phi$$

Again, we don't care about direction, so we can integrate over the angular coordinates.

$$\int_0^{2\pi} \int_0^{\pi} \sin\theta\,d\theta\,d\phi = 4\pi \tag{3.8}$$

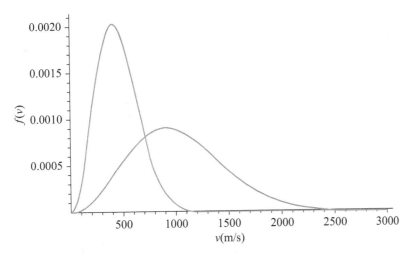

FIGURE 3.1. Maxwell–Boltzmann distributions of speed for (blue) $T/M$ = 10000 and (orange) $T/M$ = 50000.

Therefore, we can write the three-dimensional probability distribution function, known as the Maxwell–Boltzmann distribution of molecular speeds, as

$$f(v)dv = 4\pi \left( \frac{m}{2\pi k_B T} \right)^{3/2} v^2 e^{\frac{-mv^2}{2k_B T}} dv \tag{3.9}$$

This is a very powerful expression because it tells us the relationship between the speed of molecules and their mass at a given temperature. As with the one-dimensional function, if we increase the mass, the distribution narrows and we are less likely to see particles traveling at a high speed. Also, if we increase the temperature, the distribution spreads out and we are more likely to find particles traveling at high speed. See Figure 3.1 for plots of the Maxwell–Boltzmann distribution of speeds. Note in particular that the distribution is no longer a Gaussian distribution; it does not extend to negative speeds, which have no physical meaning.

It is interesting at this point to briefly talk about why this expression has two people's names attached to it, James Clerk Maxwell and Ludwig Boltzmann. We have derived this expression directly from the Boltzmann distribution, but Maxwell actually independently arrived at the same conclusion earlier (in 1860) based primarily on the central limit theorem. Maxwell reasoned that molecules must be traveling in some sort of random fashion and that their statistics would be governed by a normal distribution. Boltzmann developed his more rigorous derivation in 1877. Because they were both involved, the final result bears both their names.

### 3.1.4 Properties of the Maxwell–Boltzmann Distribution

The Maxwell–Boltzmann distribution has some significant differences from the one-dimensional distribution we looked at earlier. Notably, because speed cannot be negative, the range of possible values only goes from 0 to infinity, rather than from negative infinity to positive infinity. In fact, the probability of a particle having a speed of 0 is actually 0;

no particles are going to be strictly at rest. At low speed, the function increases according to $v^2$. At high speed, the distribution decays exponentially. This means there must be a maximum somewhere in between. We can find this **most probable speed** by taking the derivative of the distribution, setting it equal to zero, and solving for the speed at this maximum. Doing so gives us

$$v_{mp} = \left(\frac{2k_B T}{m}\right)^{1/2}$$

(3.10)

While the most probable speed is interesting mathematically, it has very little physical meaning. A more interesting parameter would be the **average speed** at which our gas particles are traveling. We can determine this by evaluating

$$\bar{v} = \langle v \rangle = \int_0^\infty v f(v)\, dv = \left(\frac{8k_B T}{\pi m}\right)^{1/2}$$

(3.11)

Note that the average speed is slightly greater than the most probable speed. This reflects the fact that the distribution is not symmetric, but instead is skewed somewhat toward the high-speed side.

Another parameter we can determine is known as the **root-mean-square, or rms, speed**. This is determined by taking the square root of the mean (or average) of the square of the speed. Mathematically, we write

$$v_{rms} = \sqrt{\langle v^2 \rangle} \quad \text{where} \quad \langle v^2 \rangle = \int_0^\infty v^2 f(v)\, dv$$

(3.12)

The rms speed is readily evaluated to be

$$v_{rms} = \left(\frac{3k_B T}{m}\right)^{1/2}$$

(3.13)

Note that the rms speed is slightly greater than the average speed, which makes sense because squaring the high speeds results in even larger values, and that's what we are averaging over. The relative positions of these various speeds are shown in Figure 3.2.

All of these speed expressions contain the ratio $k_b/m$. In evaluating these expressions, it is important to ensure that the units work out. Thus, the mass must be in kg per particle, which is a rather small value. If we multiply this ratio on top and bottom by Avogadro's number (remember, in algebra, we can always multiply by 1), we obtain a somewhat more convenient form of this ratio:

$$\frac{k_B}{m} = \frac{k_B}{m} \cdot \frac{N_A}{N_A} = \frac{R}{M}$$

(3.14)

where $M$ is now the molar mass in kg mol$^{-1}$ and $R$ is the gas constant, familiar from the ideal gas law. You can use either form—whichever you find most convenient.

Students are often confused when working problems as to which speed they should use. When do we use the most probable, average, or rms speeds? The important thing to keep in mind is that we are talking about the average of a property. If that property depends in some way on speed (or velocity), then we need to appropriately average over the speed. Let's consider the average kinetic energy of a monatomic gas. We know from classical

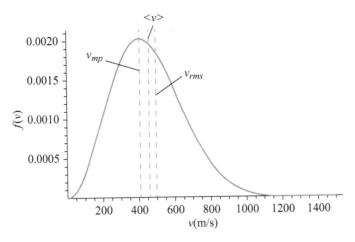

FIGURE 3.2. Indications of the most probable, average, and rms speeds from the Maxwell–Boltzmann distribution.

physics that kinetic energy is given by $E_{kin} = \frac{1}{2}mv^2$. The average kinetic energy is then given by

$$\langle E_{kin} \rangle = \left\langle \frac{1}{2}mv^2 \right\rangle = \frac{1}{2}m\langle v^2 \rangle$$

Because the mass of each molecule is the same as every other, we can pull that quantity out of the average; the same is true of the number 1/2. We can then see that the correct characteristic speed we need to consider is the rms speed. We therefore write the average kinetic energy as

$$\langle E_{kin} \rangle = \frac{1}{2}mv^2_{rms} = \frac{3}{2}k_BT \text{ or } E_m = \frac{3}{2}RT \qquad (3.15)$$

where $E_m$ is the energy per mole of gas. This result matches experimental observations; the average energy per mole of a monatomic gas is $3/2RT$. Note that this average energy is independent of the mass of the particles, which is also observed experimentally. Our simple, molecular approach has accurately predicted an experimental observation. Take some time to think about the importance of this.

To summarize the characteristic speeds that arise from the Maxwell–Boltzmann distribution,

$$v_{mp} = \left( \frac{2k_BT}{m} \right)^{1/2} = \left( \frac{2RT}{M} \right)^{1/2} \quad \bar{v} = \left( \frac{8k_BT}{\pi m} \right)^{1/2} = \left( \frac{8RT}{\pi M} \right)^{1/2} \quad v_{rms} = \left( \frac{3k_BT}{m} \right)^{1/2} = \left( \frac{3RT}{M} \right)^{1/2}$$

As we just discussed, the rms speed is what we should use whenever we are concerned with average energy; kinetic energy depends on the square of the speed. We would use the average speed when the property under consideration depends only on the first power of the speed—for example, momentum. There are very few practical uses of the most probable speed. In the next section, we will use the ideas we have put together to derive the ideal gas law and develop other parameters based on our molecular model of a gas.

You may have heard that when helium gas is released, it can escape from Earth's gravity and dissipate into space. The escape velocity on Earth is 11.2 km s$^{-1}$. For a sample of He gas at 300 K, how does the average speed of a He atom compare to the escape velocity? What does this tell you about the possibility of He escaping the Earth?

Solution

The average speed is readily calculated using Eq. 3.10 to be 1.26 km s$^{-1}$. This is about an order of magnitude less than the escape velocity, so that would suggest that He gas cannot readily escape the atmosphere. However, keep in mind that there is a distribution of speeds. The fastest moving ones may be able to escape. Also the atmosphere is a dynamic structure, so at any given time there are going to be some He atoms that have the ability to escape. Over a sufficiently long time, they will in fact all leave and escape into space. Fortunately for us, the significantly greater mass of gases like $O_2$, $N_2$, and others means that the Earth can maintain a permanent atmosphere.

# 3.2 Kinetic Molecular Theory of Gases

## 3.2.1 Derivation of the Ideal Gas Law From Kinetic Theory

With the Maxwell–Boltzmann distribution of speeds, we are prepared to derive the ideal gas law from a simple molecular model. To begin this derivation, we must first state some important assumptions:

- A gas consists of molecules of mass $m$ in ceaseless, random motion.
- The volume of each molecule is 0; we are treating the particles as point particles.
- Molecules interact only through elastic collisions; there are no attractive or repulsive interactions between the molecules.
- The average of a molecular property corresponds to the experimental observable of that quantity.

We will also make use of some tools from classical physics, namely Newton's second law of motion, $F = ma = \dfrac{dp}{dt}$, and the conservation of energy and momentum. Let's proceed.

First, we will express the speed in terms of the velocity components in a Cartesian coordinate system: $v^2 = v_x^2 + v_y^2 + v_z^2$. The kinetic energy of a gas particle is expressed as

$$\epsilon_{kin} = \frac{1}{2}mv^2 = \frac{1}{2}mv_x^2 + \frac{1}{2}mv_y^2 + \frac{1}{2}mv_z^2$$

We also need to define what we mean by pressure; according to classical physics, pressure is a force per unit area. In the case of a container of gas, the pressure we are talking about is from the walls of the container. We have already seen that force is the time rate of change of the momentum. So it is to the momentum that we will initially turn our attention, in particular the change of momentum of a gas particle colliding with the wall.

Let's consider a gas molecule moving toward a wall in the $-x$ direction. The $x$ component of velocity is $-v_x$. When the particle collides with the wall, the particle reverses direction, and the change in momentum is given by

$$\Delta p_x = mv_x - (-mv_x) = 2mv_x$$

In a given time interval $\Delta t$, more than one molecule could hit the wall. Let's designate the total number of collisions in this time interval as $N_{\Delta t}$. Now, only molecules close to the wall can hit the wall. How many molecules are we talking about? First, the number density of molecules is given by $nN_A/V$, where $n$ is the number of moles in the container, $V$ is the volume of the container and $N_A$ is Avogadro's number. In time interval $\Delta t$, a molecule can travel a distance $v_x \Delta t$. If the wall has an area $A$, then molecules in the volume $Av_x \Delta t$ are close enough to hit the wall. Thus, the number of molecules that can hit the wall in the time interval is given by

$$N_{\Delta t} = \frac{1}{2} \frac{nN_A}{V} Av_x \Delta t$$

We need the factor of 1/2 because half the molecules that are close to the wall are traveling away from it; therefore, they won't hit it at all.

The total change in momentum is therefore given by

$$\Delta p_{x,\,tot} = 2mv_x N_{\Delta t} = 2mv_x \frac{1}{2} \frac{nN_A}{V} Av_x \Delta t = \frac{nmN_A Av_x^2 \Delta t}{V} = \frac{nMAv_x^2 \Delta t}{V}$$

We have combined the mass per molecule and Avogadro's number into the molar mass $M$. Newton's second law defines force as the time derivative of momentum. For our finite time step, we write the force as

$$F_x = \frac{\Delta p_{x,\,tot}}{\Delta t} = \frac{nMAv_x^2}{V}$$

Pressure is defined as the force per unit area, which we write mathematically as

$$P = \frac{F_x}{A} = \frac{nMv_x^2}{V}$$

Now, not every molecule is traveling with the same speed. One of our assumptions was that the average of a molecular property would be the observable value. Mathematically, we write this as

$$P = \langle P \rangle = \left\langle \frac{nMv_x^2}{V} \right\rangle = \frac{nM\langle v_x^2 \rangle}{V}$$

Because the number of moles, the molar mass, and the volume are all the same for every particle, we can pull them out of the averaging operation. Let's look back at our definition of speed. After averaging, we can write

$$\langle v^2 \rangle = \langle v_x^2 \rangle + \langle v_y^2 \rangle + \langle v_z^2 \rangle = 3\langle v_x^2 \rangle$$

We justify this step by saying that there is no preference for one direction over another; the gas is isotropic. Substitution gives us

$$PV = \frac{1}{3}nM\langle v^2 \rangle$$

(3.16)

Let's pause and consider this expression for a moment. Recall from the previous section that the average square speed depends on the mass of the gas particles and the temperature. If we fix the temperature, then this value is a constant for a given gas. That means that at a given temperature, everything on the right-hand side of this equation is a constant, which means that the pressure–volume product is also a constant. This is simply a restatement of Boyle's law, which we have just derived.

Now, let's proceed to the end of the derivation. We already determined an expression for the rms speed (Eq. 3.13), which lets us write

$$\langle v^2 \rangle = \frac{3k_B T}{m} = \frac{3RT}{M}$$

Substituting this in to Eq. 3.16 gives us the ideal gas law

$$PV = nRT \qquad \text{or} \qquad PV = Nk_B T$$

(Recall that $R = N_A k_B$ and $N = nN_A$.)

Consider the importance of what we have just done. We have taken the Maxwell–Boltzmann distribution of speeds, which was based on the Boltzmann distribution, stated some reasonable assumptions to construct a molecular model of a diffuse gas, and from that we have derived the exact same mathematical relationship that resulted from the experimental work of Boyle, Charles, and Gay-Lussac, as well as the molecular hypothesis of Avogadro. That is a fairly significant achievement. This also illustrates the "bottom-up" approach to physical chemistry.

It is useful to briefly consider why this worked. Recall that the ideal gas law is a limiting law and only holds true under conditions of high temperature and low pressure. In the context of our molecular model, high temperature means the molecules are on average moving past one another quickly. Low pressure also means low number density, or few particles per volume. One of our assumptions was that the gas particles take up no space. Now, we know that real molecules have to occupy *some* space and that a point particle is a pure mathematical abstraction. But, if the particles are on average very far apart, then they have effectively zero size. Thus, the assumptions we put into our model correspond to the same physical conditions under which the ideal gas law holds true. If we want to model the behavior of real gases, which show deviations from ideal behavior, then we will have to adjust our model. We'll get there eventually, but let's continue with ideal gases for now.

### 3.2.2 Quantifying Intermolecular Collisions in a Gas–Collision Frequency

As we were developing the Boltzmann distribution, we proposed a simple model of an isolated system where the molecules could exchange energy. How do they do that? They have to collide. It is important, therefore, in developing models for energy transfer and the transport properties of a gas to quantitatively describe the collisions of gas molecules. As with our derivation of the ideal gas law, we need to carefully state our assumptions.

Most of our assumptions from the derivation of the ideal gas law will remain the same. Specifically the molecules will still be thought of as moving randomly, and they will only interact through elastic collisions. The one assumption we need to revisit is the size of the molecules. We initially assumed the molecules had zero size; we treated them as point particles. You may have asked during that derivation, "how can objects of zero size collide?" This is a valid question, and in fact some presentations of the above derivation will consider the molecules not as colliding with each other, but as passing through each other. You obtain the same result either way. The difference, however, is you then have to distinguish between molecules colliding (or passing through) other molecules and molecules colliding with (but not passing through) the wall. It is mathematically possible for point particles to collide, and that treatment simplifies the discussion somewhat. Either way, the idea of point particle molecules is definitely not physical, so we need to relax that constraint and allow the molecules to have a definite size.

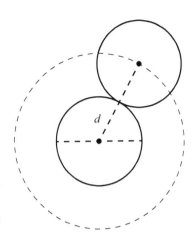

**FIGURE 3.3.** The distance of closest approach between two spherical molecules is the same as the diameter of one of the spheres.

Instead, let's consider the molecules to be hard, rigid spheres of diameter $d$. We generally track a molecule's position by the location of its center of mass which, for a spherical molecule, will be at the center of the sphere. So, if two spherical molecules of the same size collide, how close will their centers of mass be? If the molecules are hard or rigid, which means their shape cannot change as a result of the collision, then the distance between the centers of mass of the two particles will be the same as the molecular diameter $d$, as shown in Figure 3.3. Let's choose one particle as our test particle. No other particle's center of mass can get within a distance $d$ of the test particle's center of mass. This means there is an excluded area of $\pi d^2$ within which the center of mass of another particle cannot enter. This area, which we will symbolize as $\sigma$, we will call the **collisional cross section**. (Unfortunately, we use the same symbol for the cross section and the standard deviation. Be sure to keep them straight.) This collisional cross section accounts for the "size" of the collision. Large particles will have large cross sections, meaning they can collide more easily, and small particles will have small cross sections, meaning they collide less frequently. If we have particles of different size that collide with each other, we consider the distance between the respective centers of mass and write

$$\sigma = \pi d^2 \quad \text{where} \quad d = r_A + r_B \tag{3.17}$$

where $r_A$ and $r_B$ are the individual molecular radii. Note that very few real molecules are actually spherical, and the collisional cross section and molecular radii are "effective" sizes.

Now, let's freeze all the particles in our gas in place. We will then fire our test particle into this stationary gas with the average speed as given by the Maxwell–Boltzmann distribution and ask ourselves how many collisions our test particle will have per second with the stationary gas particles. In time interval $\Delta t$, our particle will travel a distance $\bar{v}\Delta t$. Taking the collisional cross section into account, we can picture the particle sweeping out a volume of $V_{test} = \sigma\bar{v}\Delta t$, as shown in Figure 3.4. In order for there to be a collision, the center of mass of a background gas particle needs to be within this volume. With a number density $N/V$ of our background gas, the number of collisions per second, which we will call the collision frequency $Z'$, is given by

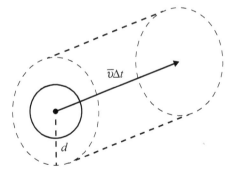

**FIGURE 3.4.** As a test particle travels a distance $\bar{v}\Delta t$, it sweeps out a cylindrical volume given by $V_{test} = \sigma\bar{v}\Delta t$.

$$Z' = \frac{V_{test}N/V}{\Delta t} = \sigma\bar{v}\frac{N}{V}$$

We are using the ' to indicate the artificial constraint of the frozen background gas.

Now, it is not physically reasonable to have the background gas molecules frozen in place. In fact, each particle in the gas is moving with speeds given by the Maxwell–Boltzmann distribution. This means that some particles will be moving into the path of our test particle and some will be moving out of it as the test particle moves along. Taking this relative motion into account, the correct parameter we should use is the relative mean speed, given by

$$\bar{v}_{rel} = \sqrt{2}\bar{v} \tag{3.18}$$

(This is given without proof.) It is also useful to introduce another parameter for talking about collisions known as the **reduced mass**. This quantity is defined as

$$\mu = \frac{m_A m_B}{m_A + m_B} \tag{3.19}$$

where $m_A$ and $m_B$ are the masses of the two collision partners. Note that if the two masses are the same, $\mu = \frac{1}{2}m$. Recall that the average speed in the Maxwell–Boltzmann distribution is given by $\bar{v} = \left(\frac{8kT}{\pi m}\right)^{1/2}$. We can write the relative mean speed for particles of the same mass as

$$\bar{v}_{rel} = \sqrt{2}\bar{v} = \sqrt{2}\left(\frac{8kT}{\pi m}\right)^{1/2} = \left(\frac{8kT}{\pi \mu}\right)^{1/2} \tag{3.20}$$

Thus, we can write the collision frequency of a nonstationary gas as

$$Z = \sigma \bar{v}_{rel} \frac{N}{V} = \sigma \left(\frac{8k_B T}{\pi \mu}\right)^{1/2} \frac{P}{k_B T} \tag{3.21}$$

This quantity can be interpreted as the average number of collisions experienced by a single gas particle per second as it travels through the background gas of a given temperature and pressure.

## Sample Problem 3.2

Estimate the collision frequency for neon gas under STP conditions. Take the cross section to be about 0.4 nm².

### Solution

STP is a pressure of 1 atm, or 101.325 kPa, and a temperature of 0°C, or 273.15 K. The cross section is given as 0.4 nm², or $4 \times 10^{-19}$ m². The last thing we need for Eq. 3.21 is the reduced mass. Since we are considering collisions between molecules of the same type, the reduced mass is determined by Eq. 3.19 to be half the individual mass.

$$\mu = \frac{1}{2} M = 10.0898 \text{ g mol}^{-1}$$

We need to convert this reduced mass, which is in g mol⁻¹, to kg. We do this with the conversion that 1 g mol⁻¹ = 1 amu = $1.66054 \times 10^{-27}$ kg. (Another way to do this is to divide the molar mass by Avogadro's number, then convert g to kg.) This gives us a reduced mass of $\mu = 1.68 \times 10^{-26}$ kg.

Putting all these values into Eq. 3.21 gives us a collision frequency of $Z = 8 \times 10^9$ s$^{-1}$. This is the number of collisions experienced by a *single molecule* every second. The reciprocal of this value gives about $1 \times 10^{-10}$ s, or 0.1 ns, which is the average time between collisions for a single molecule. (Note: It is important when working with these relations that all values be in proper SI units.)

Even at low to moderate pressures, molecules are colliding and exchanging energy very rapidly. The results of Sample Problem 3.2 also give us added confidence in our statistical approach; even if the system were to somehow move away from the most probable arrangement, it wouldn't stay there for very long because there are so many random collisions happening so quickly. On the time scale of even fractions of a second, there have been so many collisions that the system is completely randomized and will follow a Boltzmann distribution.

## 3.2.3 Mean Free Path

We now have a sense of how rapidly molecular collisions happen from our determination of the collision frequency. Another parameter that gives us insight into the molecular world is known as the **mean free path**, which is the average distance a particle travels between collisions. We can determine this quite readily by simply dividing the average speed of a gas molecule by the collision frequency

$$\lambda = \frac{\bar{v}}{Z} = \frac{k_B T}{\sigma P \sqrt{2}} = \frac{V}{\sigma N \sqrt{2}} \tag{3.22}$$

(Eq. 3.18 was used to switch between $\bar{v}_{rel}$ and $\bar{v}$, which is where the factor of $\sqrt{2}$ comes from.) The mean free path is symbolized by the Greek letter lambda, $\lambda$. What values does it typically have? Under the same conditions for which we estimated the collision frequency in Sample Problem 3.2, we can readily compute a mean free path of about $6 \times 10^{-8}$ m, or 60 nm. A typical molecule is a few Å in size, which is 0.1 nm, so we can see that molecules will typically travel a distance equal to several hundred times their size before colliding with another molecule. This gives us added confidence that our original assumption that molecules have zero (or very small) size was not completely unreasonable.

### Sample Problem 3.3
Scuba tanks are typically prepared at a gauge pressure of 3000 psi. Under these conditions, is the ideal gas law a reasonable description of the behavior of the gas? Justify your answer. Use a collisional cross section of 0.43 nm$^2$ for the gas molecules.

### Solution

One way to judge the validity of the ideal gas law is to compare the size of the molecules to the mean free path. From the cross section and Eq. 3.17, we can estimate a molecular diameter of 0.37 nm.

To determine the mean free path, we first need to convert the pressure to SI units. Remember that gauge pressure is the pressure above atmospheric pressure. 3000 psi converts to $2.07 \times 10^7$ Pa. Adding in the atmospheric pressure ($1.03 \times 10^5$ Pa) means we have $P = 2.08 \times 10^7$ Pa. Using Eq. 3.22 gives a mean free path of $3.27 \times 10^{-10}$ m, or 0.327 nm, at 300 K.

The calculated mean free path is about the same as the molecular size, so the molecules are really close to each other on average. The ideal gas law is not going to work well under these conditions because the assumption that the molecules are far apart relative to their size does not hold true. (In fact, our expression for the mean free path may not really be applicable in this case.) Under these conditions, it's hard to really think of this as a gas but rather a compressed fluid.

There is another way we can think of the mean free path, and that has to do with a group of gas molecules traveling through a background gas. Imagine we have a pulsed nozzle that releases a burst of gas containing $N_0$ molecules into a container of the same type of gas molecules. What will happen to this burst of gas as it travels into the background gas? There will be collisions between the molecules in our burst and the molecules in the background. Each of these collisions will cause a molecule in our group to scatter out of the group, and the number remaining in the original burst of gas will necessarily decrease the further that burst travels.

Let's consider this problem more quantitatively. On what will the rate at which molecules scatter out of the original group depend? Obviously, we need to consider the collisional cross section between the molecules; bigger molecules will hit each other more often than smaller molecules. We also need to account for how fast our burst is moving relative to the background gas. The size of our group will matter; the more molecules in the group, the more likely one of them will get hit. And we have the concentration of the background gas. Let's write this into a mathematical expression

$$\frac{dN_g}{dt} = -\sigma \bar{v}_{rel} N_g \left(\frac{N}{V}\right) = -\sigma \bar{v}_{rel} N_g \frac{P}{k_B T} \qquad (3.23)$$

where $N_g$ is the number of gas molecules in our group at any point in time, $\sigma$ is the collisional cross section, and $N/V$ is the number density of the background gas, which we can express as $P/k_B T$ by using the ideal gas law. We include the negative sign because the size of our group will decrease over time as molecules scatter away. We can relate the time element $dt$ to a distance element $dx$ by the following relation, based on Eq. 3.18:

$$\bar{v}_{rel} = \sqrt{2}\bar{v} = \sqrt{2}\frac{dx}{dt} \quad \text{or} \quad dt = \frac{\sqrt{2}}{\bar{v}_{rel}} dx$$

Substituting this into Eq. 3.23 and separating variables gives us

$$\frac{dN_g}{N_g} = -\sigma \bar{v}_{rel} \frac{P}{k_B T} \frac{\sqrt{2}}{\bar{v}_{rel}} dx = \frac{-\sigma P \sqrt{2}}{k_B T} dx$$

If we compare the right-hand side of this equation with our earlier expression, we recognize the reciprocal of the mean free path, from Eq. 3.22. We can now rewrite the right hand side to get

$$\frac{dN_g}{N_g} = \frac{-1}{\lambda} dx$$

Integrating from $x = 0$ to an arbitrary position $x$ gives us

$$\ln\frac{N_g}{N_0} = \frac{-x}{\lambda} \quad \text{or} \quad N_g = N_0 e^{-x/\lambda} \qquad (3.24)$$

Thus, we can see that the mean free path is also the decay constant for the decrease in the size of a group of gas molecules traveling through a background gas. After a group of gas molecules travels a distance equal to the mean free path of the background gas, only the fraction $1/e$, or about 37%, of the group will still be together.

### 3.2.4 Collision Density

So far, we've been talking about the collisions experienced by a single gas molecule, or a small group of gas molecules. Generally, we aren't as concerned about individual molecules; rather, we're concerned about the collection of molecules as a whole. A parameter that lets us talk about this is the **collision density**, which is the total number of collisions taking place per volume of gas per second. This is fairly straightforward to determine; we multiply the collision frequency, which relates to the collisions of a single molecule per time, by the number density of the gas.

$$Z_V = \frac{1}{2} Z \frac{N}{V} = \frac{1}{2} \sqrt{2} \sigma \left( \frac{8 k_B T}{\pi m} \right)^{1/2} \left( \frac{P}{k_B T} \right)^2$$

$$Z_V = 2\sigma \left( \frac{1}{\pi m} \right)^{1/2} \left( \frac{1}{k_B T} \right)^{3/2} P^2 = \frac{1}{2} \sigma \bar{v}_{rel} \left( \frac{N}{V} \right)^2 \tag{3.25}$$

The subscript $V$ reminds us that we are talking about the total collisions per unit volume of one type of gas molecule colliding with others of the same type. We need to include the factor of 1/2 to avoid double counting the collisions. Note that we can write this expression in several different, but equivalent ways, and use whichever one is most suitable for our purposes. Going back to the sample gas we've been talking about since Sample Problem 3.2 and using typical values, we can estimate that there are about $1.4 \times 10^{35}$ collisions s$^{-1}$ m$^{-3}$ in a gas. Once again, this gives us confidence in assuming that these random events will ensure that only the most probable distribution of energy in our gas will be observed.

### 3.2.5 Collision Flux

To this point, we have been talking about collisions between molecules. The molecules also collide with the wall, and we should do something to quantify those collisions as well. In fact, we can also consider the possibility of molecules passing through a hole in that wall with the same procedure. To do this, we follow a process similar to what we did in deriving the ideal gas law.

Consider a test area $A$, which could either be a part of a wall, a hole in a wall, or just an area of concern. We will only consider motion in the direction parallel to the surface normal of our test area. In order to pass through the test area, the molecules have to be fairly close to it. In a time element $\Delta t$, a molecule must be a distance $v_x \Delta t$ from the area and traveling toward the area. Our test volume is once again given by $A v_x \Delta t$. Multiplying this volume by the number density of the gas gives us the total number of collisions with the test area. Of course, not all the molecules are traveling with the same speed, so we need to properly average over the forward $x$ component of the velocity.

$$N_{coll} = \frac{N}{V} A \Delta t \int_0^\infty v_x f(v_x) \, dv_x \tag{3.26}$$

The limits of integration reflect the fact that we only consider the molecules traveling toward the test area. To evaluate this integral, we will use the one-dimensional velocity distribution (Eq. 3.4).

$$f(v_x) = \left( \frac{m}{2\pi k_B T} \right)^{1/2} e^{-mv_x^2/2k_B T}$$

Putting this function into the integral and evaluating it gives us

$$N_{coll} = \frac{N}{V} A\Delta t \left( \frac{k_B T}{2\pi m} \right)^{1/2}$$

We now define the **collision flux** as the number of collisions per area per time, which we write mathematically as

$$Z_W = \frac{N_{coll}}{A\Delta t} = \frac{N}{V} \left( \frac{kT}{2\pi m} \right)^{1/2} = \frac{1}{4} \bar{v} \frac{N}{V} \quad \text{or} \quad Z_W = \frac{P}{(2\pi k_B T m)^{1/2}} \tag{3.27}$$

For neon gas at STP, $Z_W$ is approximately $3.6 \times 10^{23}$ cm$^{-2}$ s$^{-1}$.

If we multiply the collision flux by the test area, we obtain the number of collisions per second with that area. As we said before, the test area could be a hole in the wall of the container, so the collision flux multiplied by the area of the hole gives us the rate at which particles pass through that hole. Notice that this rate is inversely proportional to the square root of the mass of the gas particles. You may recall a relationship like this in general chemistry; in fact, we have just derived Graham's law of effusion. This is one more success for our simple molecular model.

### Sample Problem 3.4

A Knudsen cell consists of a container of molten metal with a small hole at the top to allow the vapor to escape. The vapor pressure of Al at 1333 K is $1 \times 10^{-6}$ atm. If the orifice diameter is 2.5 mm, what mass of Al leaves the cell per hour of operation?

Solution

We have Al atoms passing through or colliding with the orifice, so the ideas behind collision flux relate to this problem. We look to Eq. 3.27 to get started. We can get the mass of an Al atom from the molar mass of 26.98 g mol$^{-1}$. Converting to kg gives us a mass of $4.480 \times 10^{-26}$ kg. Putting everything into Eq. 3.27 gives us a collision flux of $1.40 \times 10^{21}$ m$^{-2}$ s$^{-1}$. This is the rate of departure per unit area.

The hole diameter is 2.5 mm, which, using $A = \pi r^2$, corresponds to an area of $4.9 \times 10^{-6}$ m$^2$. Multiplying the collision flux by the orifice area gives us a rate of departure for Al atoms of $6.9 \times 10^{15}$ s$^{-1}$, or $2.5 \times 10^{19}$ hr$^{-1}$. This may seem like a large number, but remember we are talking about the number of Al atoms. Using Avogadro's number and the molar mass of Al, we can convert back to mass. After doing so, we find that we have lost 1.1 mg Al per hour of operation. (Note: We are assuming that there is sufficient mass of molten Al for the vapor pressure in the cell to remain constant. Once the cell starts to run dry, the rate of departure will necessarily decrease.)

# 3.3 Transport Properties of Gases

Most of what we have discussed about the behavior of gases concerns the static properties of a sample of gas. By *static* we mean not changing over time. For example, if we have a sealed container of a gas, even though the molecules are constantly moving about and exchanging energy with each other, the temperature, pressure, volume, and amount of the gas remain constant over time. It is a consequence of the statistics of large numbers that we can perceive the rapidly moving and random microscopic system as unchanging at the macroscopic level.

We have already seen hints, however, of how a system can change, most notably with the collision flux we just developed. As we described, our test area could be a hole, which means gas molecules are leaving the container and the pressure in the container could be changing over time; as gas molecules leave a container of fixed volume, the pressure must necessarily drop. In this section, we will develop molecular models for other changing properties of a system that we refer to as **transport properties**. There are three properties we will consider: diffusion, the transport of mass; thermal conductivity, the transport of energy; viscosity, the transport of momentum.

## 3.3.1 Diffusion

Imagine that you are sitting in a classroom and your instructor opens a small vial of a very odorous compound. She takes a whiff from the vial and comments on the terrible odor. You, however, smell nothing out of the ordinary. The instructor then sets the open vial on the counter and asks people to raise their hand when they can smell the compound. After a short time, people in the front of the room begin to raise their hands (and cover their noses). Eventually, you also smell the compound and raise your hand, but looking behind you, you can see that the people in the back of the room have not raised their hands. Eventually, everyone in the room has raised their hand, the instructor closes the vial, and someone jumps up to open a door to the hallway.

This transport of odorous molecules through space is a very common phenomenon. You may recall watching television only to suddenly smell the aroma of baking cookies coming from the kitchen. Or you may have seen a droplet of ink slowly spread throughout a glass of water. What all these observations have in common is that one substance is moving through another substance and spreading out from a location of initially high concentration. This transport of matter (odorous fumes or ink) through another medium (air in the room or a glass of water) is called **diffusion**. Our goal now is to develop a molecular model for how diffusion takes place.

To begin, we consider a test area within our sample space, similar to what we did when developing the idea of collision flux. At that position, we have a number density of our molecules of interest. We will represent this number density as $\left(\dfrac{N}{V}\right)_0$. Now, for simplicity, we will consider only a one-dimensional problem and concern ourself only with motion along the direction normal to our test area; we will call this the $y$ direction. In principle, the number density of our molecules could be different as we move away from our test area, and it could be different depending on which direction we move. For example, the number density could be higher on the left than it is on the right. Given the prevailing conditions of the background medium, we know that molecules will on average travel a distance of the mean free path between each collision. So let's describe the number density of our molecules one mean free path away from the test area in either direction. We will represent these quantities as $\left(\dfrac{N}{V}\right)_{\lambda}$ and $\left(\dfrac{N}{V}\right)_{-\lambda}$ where the subscript $\lambda$ denotes a distance of one mean free path away from the test area in the positive $y$ direction and $-\lambda$ denotes a distance of one mean free path away from the test area in the negative $y$ direction.

We can describe the number density at each of these positions in terms of a Taylor expansion centered on our original test area. Doing so lets us write

$$\left(\frac{N}{V}\right)_{-\lambda} = \left(\frac{N}{V}\right)_{0} - \lambda\left(\frac{d(N/V)}{dy}\right)_{0} \qquad \left(\frac{N}{V}\right)_{\lambda} = \left(\frac{N}{V}\right)_{0} + \lambda\left(\frac{d(N/V)}{dy}\right)_{0}$$

where $\left(\dfrac{d(N/V)}{dy}\right)_{0}$ is the spatial derivative of the number density at the location of our test area. We previously developed an expression for collision flux as $Z_W = \dfrac{1}{4}\overline{v}\dfrac{N}{V}$. In the context of mass transport, it is more common to symbolize a mass flux with a capital Greek gamma, $\Gamma$. For the mass flux coming toward our test area from the left, we use the number density one mean free path away in the negative direction, and for the mass flux coming toward our test area from the right we use the number density one mean free path away in the positive direction. Mathematically, we write

$$\Gamma_{L\to R} = \frac{1}{4}\overline{v}\left(\frac{N}{V}\right)_{-\lambda} \qquad \Gamma_{R\to L} = \frac{1}{4}\overline{v}\left(\frac{N}{V}\right)_{-\lambda}$$

The net flux through our test area is the difference between these two quantities.

$$\Gamma = \frac{1}{4}\overline{v}\left[\left(\frac{N}{V}\right)_{0} - \lambda\left(\frac{d(N/V)}{dy}\right)_{0} - \left(\frac{N}{V}\right)_{0} - \lambda\left(\frac{d(N/V)}{dy}\right)_{0}\right]$$

$$\Gamma = -\frac{1}{2}\overline{v}\lambda\left(\frac{d(N/V)}{dy}\right)_{0}$$

What we see is that the mass, or diffusion, flux is of the form

$$\Gamma = -D\left(\frac{d(N/V)}{dy}\right)_{0} \tag{3.28}$$

where $D = \dfrac{1}{2}\overline{v}\lambda$. In words, the diffusion flux is proportional to the negative concentration gradient, meaning mass will move toward the direction of lower concentration. This was observed experimentally and is known as Fick's first law of diffusion. Fick's first law of diffusion is a **phenomenological equation**, meaning it is based on observations of the behavior of macroscopic systems. We have just derived the general form of this law from our molecular model. We also see that the diffusion coefficient is proportional to the product of the mean free path and the average speed.

Our treatment was a bit oversimplified, because we only considered motion in one dimension. In reality, molecules could move through our test area at an angle. A more complete derivation that takes all these geometric factors into account gives the correct form of the diffusion coefficient

$$\boxed{D = \frac{1}{3}\overline{v}\lambda} \tag{3.29}$$

Our simple molecular model has accurately predicted the form of the diffusion coefficient and has predicted the form of Fick's first law of diffusion. What this tells us is that if
we have a gradient (or change) of the number density with position, then the diffusion will
occur toward the direction of lower number density. In other words, if the concentration
is high in one location but low in another, mass will move from the high side to the low
side. Note also that if the concentration is uniform with respect to position, there is no net
movement of mass; we would not expect to have a fully mixed solution of ink in water and
come back later to see that the ink has all collected into a single position.

What is the molecular basis for this diffusion behavior? Probability tells us that there
are more ways to spread the ink molecules throughout the entire container than there are
to put them all in one place. Thus, over time, the random motion of the molecules will
cause the system to move towards a more likely arrangement. Once it has reached the
most likely arrangement, we would never expect the system to leave that arrangement.
Diffusion is simply a matter of moving from a less likely arrangement to a more likely
arrangement of the molecules; it all comes back to probabilities.

## 3.3.2 Thermal Conductivity

We can apply similar reasoning to what was used in our discussion of diffusion to consider
the property of **thermal conductivity**, or the transport of energy within a gas. Consider
a tube of monatomic gas where the number density is uniform, but one side of the tube
is at a higher temperature than the other along the $y$ direction. We have already seen that
the average energy of a monatomic ideal gas is proportional to the temperature, namely
$\langle E_{kin} \rangle = \frac{3}{2} k_B T$ . If we take our test area to be somewhere near the middle of the tube,
molecules coming from one direction will on average carry slightly more energy than the
molecules coming from the other direction. As we did with mass flux, we can write this
energy flux, symbolized by $J$, from each direction as

$$J_{L \to R} = \frac{1}{4} \bar{v} \frac{N}{V} E_{kin}(-\lambda) \qquad J_{R \to L} = \frac{1}{4} \bar{v} \frac{N}{V} E_{kin}(\lambda)$$

where $E_{kin}(\pm\lambda)$ symbolizes the average kinetic energy at a distance of one mean free path
to the right or left of our test area. The net flux through our test area is again

$$J = \frac{1}{4} \bar{v} \frac{N}{V} \left[ E_{kin}(0) - \lambda \left( \frac{dE_{kin}}{dy} \right)_0 - E_{kin}(0) - \lambda \left( \frac{dE_{kin}}{dy} \right)_0 \right]$$

$$J = -\frac{1}{2} \bar{v} \frac{N}{V} \lambda \left( \frac{dE_{kin}}{dy} \right)_0 = -\frac{1}{2} \bar{v} \frac{N}{V} \lambda \left( \frac{dE_{kin}}{dT} \right)_0 \left( \frac{dT}{dy} \right)_0 = -\frac{1}{2} \bar{v} \frac{N}{V} \lambda \frac{3}{2} k_B \left( \frac{dT}{dy} \right)_0$$

$$J = -\frac{1}{4} \bar{v} \frac{N}{V} \lambda 3 k_B \left( \frac{dT}{dy} \right)_0$$

$$J = -\kappa \left( \frac{dT}{dy} \right)_0 \qquad\qquad (3.30)$$

Notice that the energy flux now depends on the gradient of temperature instead of number density. All the parameters in front of this derivative can be grouped into a constant called the **coefficient of thermal conductivity**, symbolized by $\kappa$. We treated this as a one-dimensional problem, as we did with diffusion. Correcting for the geometric aspects of motion in three dimensions again introduces a correction factor of $\frac{2}{3}$, which gives us the more correct form of the coefficient of thermal conductivity

$$\kappa = \frac{1}{6} \bar{v} \frac{N}{V} \lambda f k_B$$

(3.31)

where the factor of 3 has been replaced by the symbol $f$. This represents the **degrees of freedom (DOF)**, or the number of independent ways in which the gas particles can move. For a monatomic gas, this value is clearly 3 because the gas can move in the three physical dimensions. Polyatomic gases, however, have internal motions such as rotations and vibrations that also carry energy, and those would need to be accounted for in the value of $f$. (We will discuss this idea much more extensively in Chapter 7 when we talk about the classical equipartition theorem.) For now, you can think of $f$ as a parameter of the gas.

If we look more carefully at our expression for the coefficient of thermal conductivity, we can spot another prediction. At a given temperature, the mean free path is proportional to $1/P$, whereas the number density is directly proportional to $P$, through the ideal gas law. Thus $\kappa$ would appear to be independent of pressure, which is what is observed experimentally. As the pressure increases, the number density also increases—meaning there are more collisions that could transport more energy. With increasing pressure, however, the distance molecules can travel between collisions—the mean free path—decreases. Thus, these two effects balance out and the thermal conductivity is independent of pressure.

Just as with our treatment of diffusion (or mass transport), we have successfully predicted both the form of the phenomenological equation and the relevant coefficient for energy transport, or thermal conductivity. Note that the energy transport depends on the temperature difference, and energy will flow from the high temperature side to the low temperature side. If there is no difference in temperature with respect to position, then there is no net transport of energy and the system has thermally equilibrated.

### 3.3.3 Viscosity

The last transport property we will consider is **viscosity**, which is the transport of momentum that leads to resistance to flow. To treat this problem, we need to set up a two-dimensional picture. The gas is confined between two plates. The bottom plate is stationary, but the top plate is moving in the $x$ direction with a velocity of $u$. The moving top plate will cause gas molecules near it to also move with a velocity $u$ in the $x$ direction; we will call $u$ the flow velocity. Gas molecules near the bottom plate, however, have nothing causing them to move preferentially in the $x$ direction, so they have a net forward velocity of zero. This means we have a gradient in flow velocity between the top and bottom plates. This condition is called **Newtonian flow**.

Let's consider a test area located somewhere between the top and bottom plates. This area is oriented parallel to the plates, and we will take its normal as being the $y$ direction. Due to collisions, it is possible for molecules to move between layers, but they will have different flow velocities, or momenta, depending on which layer they are coming from.

Taking the $y$ position of our test area as our reference, we can write the momentum in the layer one mean free path above and below the test area as

$$P_{above} = m\left[u_A + \lambda\left(\frac{du}{dy}\right)_A\right] \qquad P_{below} = m\left[u_A - \lambda\left(\frac{du}{dy}\right)_A\right]$$

The momentum flux across the test area is then given by the difference between these two, or

$$J_p = \frac{1}{4}\bar{v}\frac{N}{V}m\left[u_A - \lambda\left(\frac{du}{dy}\right)_A - u_A - \lambda\left(\frac{du}{dy}\right)_A\right]$$

$$J_p = -\frac{1}{2}\bar{v}\frac{N}{V}m\lambda\left(\frac{du}{dy}\right)_A$$

Making the same correction for geometry we have done before, multiplying by ⅔, gives us

$$J_{p_x} = -\eta\frac{du_x}{dy} \quad \text{where} \quad \eta = \frac{1}{3}\frac{N}{V}\bar{v}m\lambda \qquad , \qquad (3.32)$$

As we saw with thermal conductivity, the facts that the mean free path is inversely proportional to pressure and the number density is directly proportional to pressure cause the coefficient of viscosity, $\eta$, to be independent of pressure. This seems counterintuitive, but it is true for the same reasons we discussed above; the number of collisions and the distance traveled between collisions balance out. We can also substitute in our earlier expression for the mean free path and write the coefficient of viscosity as

$$\eta = \frac{2}{3\sigma}\left(\frac{mk_BT}{\pi}\right)^{1/2} \qquad (3.33)$$

This relation shows us that the viscosity of a gas will increase with the mass of the particles, but actually decrease with increasing size of the particles. We also see that the viscosity increases with temperature, counter to what is typically seen with liquids, where strong intermolecular forces are at work. Even though our model has been hard spheres colliding with each other, this expression actually works quite well for dilute real gases and matches experimental observations.

### 3.3.4 Summary of Transport Properties

Hopefully by now you are convinced that our simple model of a gas as hard spheres colliding with each other is quite powerful. In addition to predicting the observed distribution of speeds and the ideal gas law, we have predicted both the phenomenological transport equations and expressions for their respective coefficients. It needs to be noted, however, that these relations will not hold true in all physical situations. As the pressure—and therefore the number density—of a gas increases, nonideal effects are seen. The behavior of real gases depends on the interactions between the gas molecules, which we have to this point ignored. So in the limit of high pressure, our relations will break down. They will also fail if the intermolecular interactions become significant; you could not, for example, use these relations to describe the properties of a liquid.

Likewise, at extremely low pressure we will have problems as well. More specifically, when the mean free path becomes something on the order of the size of the container, our expressions for diffusion, thermal conductivity, and viscosity will fail. This is because molecules do not experience enough collisions; they are likely to travel the entire length or width of the container before hitting another molecule. Therefore, you could not use these expressions to describe the behavior of molecules in a high-vacuum system, where mean free paths of many meters are possible. So long as we stay well away from these extreme limits, however, the expressions we have derived work very well, especially considering the simplicity of the underlying model.

## 3.4 Summary, and Where We Go Next

In this chapter, we have applied the fundamental ideas of the Boltzmann distribution to build a molecular model of the behavior and properties of a gas. From this simple model, we have derived the ideal gas law and quantified several parameters relating to molecular collisions. We have also been able to develop molecular descriptions of diffusion, thermal conductivity, and viscosity. For a model that is very simple in its basic assumptions, we have been able to accurately describe an impressive number of properties and phenomena. This illustrates the power of this "bottom-up" approach.

In the next chapter, we will continue to build on our models of molecular collisions. The main difference we will introduce is the ability of these colliding molecules to react with each other; we'll do some actual chemistry. Based on this collisional foundation, we will survey the field of chemical kinetics more broadly in Chapters 5 and 6.

## PROBLEMS

**3.1** You are given two containers of gas, one with He and one with Ar. Both are at a temperature of 300.0 K and a pressure of 0.100 bar.

   a) Compare the fraction of gas molecules traveling at speeds greater than 500.0 m s$^{-1}$ for the two gases.

   b) Compare the fraction of gas molecules traveling at a speed of 500.0 m s$^{-1}$ for the two gases.

   c) Compare the fraction of gas molecules traveling with a speed between 500.0 and 505.0 m s$^{-1}$ for the two gases.

**3.2** Statisticians define a quantity called the variance, $\sigma^2 = \langle x^2 \rangle - \langle x \rangle^2$, which is used to describe the width of a distribution. (Note: The variance is the square of the standard deviation. Also, although the symbol is the same, this has nothing to do with the cross section.)

   a) Determine an expression for the variance of the Maxwell–Boltzmann distribution of speeds.

   b) Discuss the variance in terms of the molar mass and the temperature. How does the width of the distribution change as the molar mass increases? How does the width of the distribution change as the temperature increases?

**3.3 a)** For $N_2$ at 400.0°C, calculate the most probable speed. Estimate the speeds where the probability drops to half the maximum value.

**b)** Repeat these calculations for $SF_6$ at the same temperature and compare the results to those of $N_2$.

**3.4 a)** Calculate the most probable velocity for the one-dimensional Maxwell–Boltzmann distribution and the most probable speed for the three-dimensional Maxwell–Boltzmann distribution.

**b)** Comment on the differences between your results for the one-dimensional and three-dimensional functions.

**3.5 a)** Calculate the mean speed for both an $SF_6$ and an $O_2$ molecule at 500.0 K.

**b)** For the molecule that travels at the slower speed, what temperature would be required to obtain the same mean speed as the other molecule?

**3.6** Imagine a single argon atom confined to a cubical space with edge length of 25.0 Å at 300.0 K.

**a)** Assuming the atom is traveling back and forth in a straight line, calculate the collision frequency with a single wall of the container.

**b)** Determine the atom's change in momentum per collision.

**c)** From your answer to part b), determine the pressure against the wall.

**d)** Compare your answer in c) to a calculation from the ideal gas law.

**3.7** A model that is useful for talking about reactions on surfaces is the two-dimensional gas. In this model, molecules can move about freely on a surface, but they cannot leave the surface.

**a)** Derive an expression for the distribution of speeds of a two-dimensional gas.

**b)** Determine the most probable, average, and rms speeds for the two-dimensional gas.

**c)** Compare your results to the one-dimensional and three-dimensional cases.

**3.8 a)** For a container of $N_2$ gas at 300.0 K and 1.00 mbar pressure, calculate the collision density. Take the cross section for $N_2$ collisions to be $0.43 \times 10^{-18}$ $m^2$.

**b)** What is the collision density if the temperature is raised to 2000 K, with the pressure still at 1.00 mbar?

**c)** What is the collision density if the pressure is raised to 1 bar, with the temperature still at 300 K?

**d)** What is the collision density if instead of $N_2$ gas, you have benzene ($C_6H_6$) vapor at 300.0 K and 1.00 mbar? The cross section for benzene collisions is $0.88 \times 10^{-18}$ $m^2$.

**3.9 a)** Calculate the mean free path for argon gas at 325.0 K and a pressure of 0.20 bar. The collision cross section for Ar is $1.58 \times 10^{-20}$ $m^2$.

**b)** What is the mean free path for a free electron traveling through the background of Ar gas under the same conditions described in part a)? Assume the electron has the same relative speed as the Ar atoms.

**c)** In a cathode ray tube, beams of electrons travel through a background gas to hit a screen. In order for a fraction of $e^{-1}$ of the electrons to hit the screen over a length of 0.50 m, what must be the background pressure of Ar at an operating temperature of 325.0 K.

**3.10** Semiconductor wafers can be processed with $H_2$ gas to change the surface chemistry of the wafer. A wafer is placed in a chamber that operates at 1500.0 K with a $H_2$ pressure of $10^{-6}$ mbar. How many collisions take place per second across the surface of a 4-inch-diameter wafer?

**3.11** A glass cylinder 10.0 cm in diameter and 20.0 cm tall initially contains water vapor at 300.0 K and a pressure of 100.0 torr. A liquid nitrogen cold finger 1.0 cm in diameter is placed against one face of the cylinder. How long will it take for the pressure in the cylinder to drop to $10^{-5}$ torr?

**3.12** For $N_2$ gas, calculate the coefficients of diffusion, thermal conductivity, and viscosity at 300.0 K and a pressure of 1.00 bar. The cross section for $N_2$ collisions is $0.43 \times 10^{-18}$ m$^2$, and $N_2$ has 5 degrees of freedom.

**3.13** In our discussions of collisions, we have treated the collision cross section as a geometric parameter that is fixed for a particular collision pair. Using a reputable source, find data for the viscosity of ammonia gas at different temperatures and determine if there is a temperature dependence to the collision cross section. Discuss why there is or is not a temperature dependence.

**3.14** Eq. 3.29 technically describes what is known as self-diffusion, or one type of molecule diffusing through a background of the same type. If we have two types of molecules diffusing through each other, it is more correct to use the following expression.

$$D_{1,2} = x_2 D_{1,1} + x_1 D_{2,2} = \frac{1}{3}\bar{v}_1 \lambda_1 x_2 + \frac{1}{3}\bar{v}_2 \lambda_2 x_1$$

where $x$ is the mole fraction. In the limit that the two molecules are very similar in terms of mass and size, show that this expression reduces to the self-diffusion expression we started with.

# CHEMICAL KINETICS

How Chemical
Reactions Happen

# Collisional Theory of Chemical Kinetics

## 4.1 Kinetics of a Bimolecular Reaction

One of the goals of physical chemistry is to describe chemical reactions and how they take place at the most fundamental level. We will start down that road in this chapter, beginning with the idea of molecules colliding with each other.

### 4.1.1 Collision Density for Two Types of Molecules

In the last chapter, we developed several ideas with which to quantify collisions between gas molecules. To review, some of the important parameters we considered were:

- The collisional cross section, symbolized by $\sigma$ and calculated by $\sigma = \pi d^2$, where $d = r_A + r_B$.
- The reduced mass of the collision partners, symbolized by $\mu$ and calculated by $\mu = \dfrac{m_A m_B}{m_A + m_B}$.
- The relative mean speed between collision partners, written as $\bar{v}_{rel} = \left( \dfrac{8kT}{\pi\mu} \right)^{1/2}$.

Some other parameters we developed include the collision frequency, the mean free path, and the collision flux, however these won't be as useful for us in developing expressions for chemical reactions. Rather, we are going to revisit the collision density (Eq. 3.25), written as

$$Z_V = \frac{1}{2}\sigma\bar{v}_{rel}\left(\frac{N}{V}\right)^2$$

Recall that we included the factor of 1/2 to avoid the possibility of counting a molecule colliding with itself.

What if we have molecules of two different types (we will label them A and B) colliding with each other? In this case, the number of collisions will depend on the number density of each type of molecule. This lets us write the collision density for A–B collisions as

$$Z_{AB} = \sigma\bar{v}_{rel}\frac{N_{(A)}}{V}\frac{N_{(B)}}{V} \tag{4.1}$$

where $N_{(A)}$ and $N_{(B)}$ are the numbers of each molecule type. (Note: It is important not to confuse the number of molecule A with Avogadro's number in this expression. This is why the A and B appear in parentheses.) Notice that the factor of 1/2 has been removed from this expression because we are only counting the collisions of A molecules with B molecules; we are not counting collisions of each type with other molecules of the same type. If we wanted to account for all the possible collisions in our container of gas, we would need to sum up all the respective collision densities between all the different types of molecules.

Before moving on to chemical reactions, let's briefly restate the physical model we are working with. We are treating our gas molecules as structureless hard spheres that interact only through elastic collisions. There are no attractions or repulsions between the molecules. We justify these assumptions by recalling that molecules are on average separated by a distance much greater than their size, and that the interaction time of a collision is very short. As we build our model of chemical reactions, we will revise and modify this simple model as needed to better account for what we actually observe.

### 4.1.2 Simple Model of a Bimolecular Reaction

Let's consider a simple bimolecular chemical reaction that is described by

$$A + B \rightarrow P$$

This reaction takes place by a molecule of type A reacting with a molecule of type B. As we will see in the next chapter, it is important to distinguish between the overall chemical reaction and the actual molecular steps or mechanism by which that reaction takes place. In this simple case, they are one and the same.

Now, we are interested in quantifying how quickly we can form our reaction product, P. How is the product formed? In order for two molecules to react and form a product, the first thing they must do is *collide* with each other. Thus, the rate of formation of product should have something to do with the rate at which the molecules collide. The collision density for different types of molecules we just developed (Eq. 4.1) will serve as our starting point.

$$Z_{AB} = \sigma\bar{v}_{rel}\frac{N_{(A)}}{V}\frac{N_{(B)}}{V}$$

If we look at the units in this expression, we see that it has units of $m^{-3}\,s^{-1}$. If we assume that every collision leads to formation of product, then we can write the rate of formation of product molecules as the product of the collision density and the total volume of the system.

$$\frac{dN_{(P)}}{dt} = VZ_{AB}$$

where $N_{(P)}$ is the number of product molecules. Reaction rate is more conventionally written as the time rate of change of the number density (or concentration) of the product, so we can divide by the volume to obtain

$$\frac{dN_{(P)}/V}{dt} = Z_{AB} = \sigma \overline{v}_{rel} \frac{N_{(A)}}{V} \frac{N_{(B)}}{V} \tag{4.2}$$

This expression gives us the number of product molecules formed per unit volume per unit time.

- To write our expression in terms of the rate of change of the molar concentration rather than the number density, we recall that $N = nN_A$, where $N_A$ is Avogadro's number. Making this change lets us write

$$\frac{d[P]}{dt} = \frac{Z_{AB}}{N_A} = \sigma \overline{v}_{rel} N_A [A][B] \tag{4.3}$$

where $[P] = \dfrac{n_P}{V}$, likewise for A and B. In this expression, $N_A$ is Avogadro's number. The form of this expression should look familiar to what you saw in general chemistry, especially if we collect the cross section, relative mean speed, and Avogadro's number into a single value. Doing so lets us write

$$\frac{d[P]}{dt} = k[A][B] \quad \text{where} \quad k = \sigma \overline{v}_{rel} N_A \tag{4.4}$$

Eq. 4.4 has the form of a second-order rate law, with $k$ as the rate constant. (We'll formally define rate laws and rate constants in the next chapter, but the basic ideas should already be familiar from what you saw in general chemistry.)

Once again, our simple molecular model has produced something that has been observed experimentally, in this case the form of a second-order rate law. It is useful to spend some time determining whether the values we predict for the rate constants are reasonable. Using values similar to what we used in Sample Problem 3.2 (reduced mass of 0.010 kg $mol^{-1}$, cross section of $0.4 \times 10^{-18}\,m^2$, temperature of 273 K) we estimate a rate constant of about $k = 1.8 \times 10^8\,m^3\,mol^{-1}\,s^{-1}$. Different communities use different units in reporting rate constants, and typical units are $L\,mol^{-1}\,s^{-1}$ and $cm^3\,s^{-1}$ where instead of moles we consider the number of molecules. In these units, our estimated rate constant would be written as $1.8 \times 10^{11}\,L\,mol^{-1}\,s^{-1}$ and $3.0 \times 10^{-10}\,cm^3\,s^{-1}$. Other more specialized disciplines may use even more varied units, such as $ppm^{-1}\,min^{-1}$.

A fairly quick comparison of our predicted rate constants with experimental values will find that we have greatly overestimated the rate constant. This shouldn't be a surprise; we have assumed that every collision leads to reaction. This would mean that a head-on collision between rapidly moving molecules is just as likely to lead to reaction as a glancing blow between slow molecules. So it should be no surprise that our predicted values are too high. We have another problem with our simple model, and that is in our prediction of the temperature dependence of the rate constant. Recall that the relative mean speed depends on $T^{1/2}$ (see Eq. 3.20), so the rate constant should increase with increasing temperature with this same dependence. Experimental observations do show an increase in $k$ with $T$, but not as the square root; $k$ increases according to $e^{-1/T}$. Clearly, we need to revise our model to better account for these experimental observations.

### 4.1.3 Energy Requirement for Chemical Reactions

The discussion to this point has revealed another requirement that we need to include in our molecular model of chemical reactions. The first requirement is that the molecules need to collide with each other. The second requirement is that this collision needs to have *sufficient energy*; otherwise, a reaction will simply not occur. This is because a reaction usually involves the breaking of one or more chemical bonds, which always requires an input of energy. We therefore need to account for the energy of the collision in our model. Starting from our expression for the bimolecular rate constant, we really only have two parameters that we can adjust: the relative mean speed and the collisional cross section. The relative mean speed accounts for the motion of the molecules, whether they collide or not, so we probably don't want to make any changes there. This leaves the collisional cross section, which is where we now turn our focus.

How can we account for our energy requirement in terms of the collisional cross section? First, we can state that if a reaction does not occur, because the energy of the collision is insufficient, then it is as if the molecules did not collide. In other words, if the energy of the collision is below some threshold for a reaction to take place, the collisional cross section is effectively zero. On the other hand, a highly energetic collision is more likely to lead to reaction, and we should approach the value for the rate constant we determined in the last section. What we need is a mathematical expression for an energy-dependent cross section, which we will now call the **reaction cross section**, symbolized as $\sigma^*$.

Let's begin with a geometric argument based on two spherical particles colliding, as illustrated in Figure 4.1. In a relative frame of reference, we can consider one of the particles to be at rest and the second particle moving towards it with speed $v_{rel}$. If the particles collide head on, as shown in Figure 4.1a, the energy of the collision is

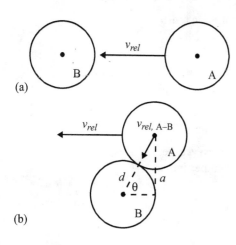

(a)

(b)

FIGURE 4.1. Collision between two spherical molecules. a) The collision occurs head on. b) The collision occurs at an angle, thus $v_{rel,\ A-B}$ is less than $v_{rel}$.

$$\epsilon_c = \frac{1}{2}\mu v_{rel}^2 \tag{4.5}$$

This is the maximum energy the collision can have. If the particles collide at some angle, the collision is less energetic. How do we account for that? We can define the component of the speed directed between centers of mass as

$$v_{rel,\ A-B} = v_{rel}\cos\theta = v_{rel}\frac{(d^2 - a^2)^{1/2}}{d}$$

where $\theta$ is the angle of the collision ($0°$ is head on, and $90°$ is a glancing blow), $d$ is the minimum distance between centers of mass and $a$ is the displacement of collision trajectories. If we multiply the square of this expression by $1/2\mu$, we can write the actual collision energy $\epsilon_\theta$ as

$$\epsilon_\theta = \frac{1}{2}\mu v_{rel,\,A-B}^2 = \epsilon_c\left(\frac{d^2 - a^2}{d^2}\right)$$

Above a certain threshold angle $\theta$, or a certain distance $a$, the chemical reaction will not occur. We will call this maximum distance $a_{max}$, and the corresponding threshold energy $\epsilon_a$.

$$\epsilon_a = \epsilon_c\left(\frac{d^2 - a_{max}^2}{d^2}\right)$$

We can now solve for $a_{max}^2$ and write

$$a_{max}^2 = \left(1 - \frac{\epsilon_a}{\epsilon_c}\right)d^2$$

Multiplying this expression by $\pi$ gives us an expression for an energy-dependent cross section, the reactive cross section, which we write as

$$\sigma^* = \pi a_{max}^2 = \left(1 - \frac{\epsilon_a}{\epsilon_c}\right)\pi d^2 = \left(1 - \frac{\epsilon_a}{\epsilon_c}\right)\sigma$$

$$\sigma^*(\epsilon_c) = \left(1 - \frac{\epsilon_a}{\epsilon_c}\right)\sigma \quad \text{for} \quad \epsilon_c \geq \epsilon_a \qquad (4.6)$$

In Eq. 4.6, $\sigma$ is the same geometric cross section we developed in the last chapter. This expression only holds if the collision energy is at least as great at the threshold energy, $\epsilon_a$. If the collision energy is less than the threshold energy, then the reactive cross section is zero. Note that for an energy close to the threshold energy, the reaction cross section is almost zero, whereas the reaction cross section approaches the geometric cross section as the energy of the collision increases. The function describing the reaction cross section is shown in Figure 4.2.

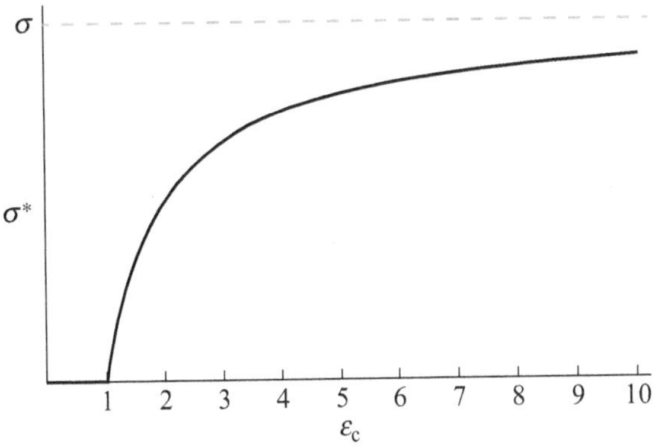

Keep in mind that not all molecules are traveling at the same speed; in other words, not all collisions happen with the same energy. To develop a full expression for the rate constant, we need to properly average over both the reactive cross section and the relative speed of the collision partners.

$$k = \langle k \rangle = \langle \sigma^* v_{rel} N_A \rangle = N_A \langle \sigma^* v_{rel} \rangle$$

FIGURE 4.2. Functional form of the reaction cross section. Both $\epsilon_a$ and $\sigma$ are taken to be equal to 1 in this figure. Below $\epsilon_a$, the reactive cross section has a value of 0. As the collision energy increases, the collision cross section approaches the geometric cross section, indicated by the dashed blue line.

To evaluate this average, we need a probability distribution function for the relative speed of collision partners. For this, we return to the Maxwell–Boltzmann distribution, now using the reduced mass of the collision partners instead of the individual molecular mass

$$f(v_{rel})dv_{rel} = 4\pi\left(\frac{\mu}{2\pi k_B T}\right)^{3/2} v_{rel}^2 e^{\frac{-\mu v_{rel}^2}{2k_B T}} dv_{rel} \qquad (4.7)$$

We can convert this distribution over relative speed to one over collision energy with Eq. 4.5.

$$\epsilon_c = \frac{1}{2}\mu v_{rel}^2 \text{ or } v_{rel} = \sqrt{\frac{2\epsilon_c}{\mu}}$$

Taking the derivative of this expression lets us write

$$d\epsilon_c = \mu v_{rel} dv_{rel} \quad \text{or} \quad dv_{rel} = \frac{1}{\mu v_{rel}} d\epsilon_c = \frac{1}{(2\mu\epsilon_c)^{1/2}} d\epsilon_c$$

Making these substitutions into Eq. 4.7 lets us write

$$f(\epsilon_c)d\epsilon_c = 4\pi\left(\frac{\mu}{2\pi k_B T}\right)^{3/2} \frac{2\epsilon_c}{\mu} e^{\frac{-\epsilon_c}{k_B T}} \frac{1}{(2\mu\epsilon_c)^{1/2}} d\epsilon_c$$

$$f(\epsilon_c)d\epsilon_c = 2\pi\left(\frac{1}{\pi k_B T}\right)^{3/2} \epsilon_c^{1/2} e^{\frac{-\epsilon_c}{k_B T}} d\epsilon_c \qquad (4.8)$$

Now, the average we need to evaluate is

$$k = N_A \int_0^\infty \sigma^*(\epsilon_c) v_{rel} f(\epsilon_c) d\epsilon_c$$

$$= N_A 2\pi\left(\frac{1}{\pi k_B T}\right)^{3/2} \int_0^\infty \sigma^*(\epsilon_c)\left(\frac{2\epsilon_c}{\mu}\right)^{1/2} \epsilon_c^{1/2} e^{-\epsilon_c/k_B T} d\epsilon_c$$

$$= N_A\left(\frac{8}{\mu\pi k_B T}\right)^{1/2}\left(\frac{1}{k_B T}\right)\int_0^\infty \sigma^*(\epsilon_c)\epsilon_c e^{-\epsilon_c/k_B T} d\epsilon_c$$

To evaluate the integral, we need to recall our model of the reactive cross section. Below the threshold energy, the reactive cross section is zero; and above the threshold energy, the reactive cross section is described by Eq. 4.6. This lets us write the integral as

$$\int_0^\infty \sigma^*(\epsilon_c)\epsilon_c e^{-\epsilon_c/k_B T} d\epsilon_c = \int_{\epsilon_a}^\infty\left(1 - \frac{\epsilon_a}{\epsilon_c}\right)\sigma\epsilon_c e^{-\epsilon_c/k_B T} d\epsilon_c = \sigma(k_B T)^2 e^{-\epsilon_a/k_B T}$$

Putting this all together gives us

$$k = N_A\sigma\left(\frac{8k_B T}{\pi\mu}\right)^{1/2} e^{-\epsilon_a/k_B T} = N_A\sigma\bar{v}_{rel}e^{-\epsilon_a/k_B T} \qquad (4.9)$$

Notice that this is very similar to the expression for the rate constant we obtained from our simple collisional model. The key difference is the exponential term that depends on our threshold energy. Some slight cosmetic alterations to this expression will show how important this idea of a threshold energy really is. If we collect all the parameters before the exponential into a single preexponential factor, $A$, and convert our threshold energy to an energy per mole (which will also turn $k_B$ into $R$), we can write the rate constant as

$$k = Ae^{-E_a/RT} \qquad (4.10)$$

which you may recognize as the **Arrhenius equation**. Our threshold energy—the minimum energy necessary for a reaction to take place—can now be called the **activation energy**.

Now that we have modified our collisional model to account for the energy of the collision, we have predicted the Arrhenius equation. (Svante Arrhenius proposed this equation in 1889.) This very important relationship helped form the mathematical foundation of chemical kinetics. It is worthwhile to spend a little time to consider why this works and what this relation tells us. First, we have correctly determined the exponential dependence of the rate constant on temperature. This arises naturally from the probabilistic nature of molecular motion and the recognition that low-energy, glancing-blow collisions are unlikely to lead to reactions. We have also gained insight into the preexponential factor from the Arrhenius equation. It depends on the relative size of the colliding molecules through the collisional cross section, and the relative motion of the molecules. The bigger they are, the more likely they are to collide, whereas heavier molecules on average move more slowly and therefore collide less often.

If you look closely, you will see that the preexponential factor contains the relative mean speed, which increases at $T^{1/2}$. Wasn't the whole point of accounting for the energy of the collisions to fix the temperature dependence of our rate constant? This is formally correct; however, in the product of two functions, one an exponential and another a square root, the exponential function has much greater influence on the behavior of the function, particularly in the limit of very high temperature.

If we treat the preexponential factor as (approximately) a constant, we can see that in the limit of infinite temperature, the exponential term approaches 1 and $A$ becomes the rate constant at that high temperature limit. Thinking of the preexponential factor in this way can actually allow us to approximate collisional cross sections from kinetic data. If we determine the rate constant at several temperatures, we can plot our data as $\ln k$ vs $1/T$, which should yield a straight line. The slope of this line is $-E_a/R$ and the intercept is $\ln A$. Using a temperature value in the middle of our experimental range, and knowing the molecular weights of the reactant molecules, we can approximate the effective collisional cross section.

## Sample Problem 4.1

An important reaction in atmospheric chemistry is the reaction of NO and $O_3$ to produce $NO_2$ and $O_2$. NO and $NO_2$ are known as $NO_x$ species, and are important in the reactions that lead to formation of smog in urban environments. The following table contains measurements of the second-order rate constant for this reaction over a range of temperatures. From these data, calculate a) the activation energy and b) the effective collisional cross section.

| T (K) | k (cm³ mol⁻¹ s⁻¹) |
|---|---|
| 275 | $8.03 \times 10^9$ |
| 300 | $1.12 \times 10^{10}$ |
| 325 | $1.60 \times 10^{10}$ |
| 350 | $2.15 \times 10^{10}$ |
| 400 | $3.38 \times 10^{10}$ |

Solution

The first thing we do is make a plot of ln $k$ vs $1/T$ and perform a linear fit to this plot. The slope of the best fit line is equal to $-E_a/R$, and the slope is equal to ln $A$. The plot and best fit parameters are shown in Figure 4.3.

a. From the best fit line, the slope is −1281.3. Multiplying by $-R$ gives us an activation energy of 10.7 kJ/mol.

b. The intercept from the best fit line of 27.443 is equal to ln $A$. Taking the exponential of this value gives us an Arrhenius prefactor of $A = 8.28 \times 10^{11}$ cm³ mol⁻¹ s⁻¹. (Note: The units of the prefactor will always be the same as the rate constants you are working with.) From Eqs. 4.9 and 4.10, we can write an expression for the prefactor.

$$A = N_A \sigma \left( \frac{8k_B T}{\pi \mu} \right)^{1/2}$$

The collision partners are NO, with a molar mass of 30.006 g mol⁻¹, and $O_3$, with a molar mass of 47.998 g mol⁻¹. These give a reduced mass of 18.464 g mol⁻¹, or $3.066 \times 10^{-26}$ kg. Solving for $\sigma$, using $T = 325$ K, gives a value of $2.25 \times 10^{-21}$ m² for the collisional cross section. (This value may seem rather small compared to others we have seen. The next section will explain why that is the case.)

### 4.1.4 Steric (Orientation) Requirement for Chemical Reactions

This discussion of the effective collisional cross section leads us to the last factor we need to consider in our collisional model of chemical reactions. Suppose that we have a reaction between a diatomic molecule and a free radical atom, as follows:

$$H + HCl \rightarrow H_2 + Cl$$

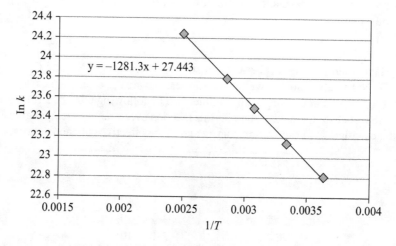

FIGURE 4.3. Arrhenius plot for the data from Sample Problem 4.1.

Such a reaction could be an important step in an atmospheric chemistry context. Does it matter how the H atom collides with the HCl molecule? If the H approaches from the H side, then we can imagine forming the desired product. What if the collision happens from the Cl side? Then we will end up with a new HCl molecule and release an H atom, but these are the same as the initial products; it would be as if the reaction didn't happen. For reasons of the *orientation* of the collision, we would expect the reaction to proceed at roughly half the rate we predict from our simple collisional model, even taking energy into account.

This discussion allows us to add one more item to our collisional model of chemical reactions: chemical reactions happen when molecules 1) collide 2) with sufficient energy 3) and the correct orientation. These requirements form the crux of our model. We have been able to adequately account for the number and energy of the collisions, however our ability to deal with the orientation of the collision is severely limited by other aspects of our model. Recall that we have been considering our molecules as structureless, hard spheres. How do we account for an orientation effect with such a model? Simply put, we include a parameter, known as the **steric factor**, to compensate for it. With the inclusion of a steric factor, symbolized as $P$, we write our expression for the bimolecular rate constant as

$$k = PN_A \sigma \bar{v}_{rel} e^{-\epsilon_a/k_B T} \tag{4.11}$$

As we can see in our simple H + HCl reaction, we could estimate that the steric factor should be approximately 0.5. (The actual value is 0.039, showing that the orientation requirement is even more strict than our simple model would suggest.) For more complicated molecules, steric factors can be quite small, even on the order of $10^{-6}$. Geometric arguments can be made based on structural calculations to estimate both the steric factor and the collisional cross section, but those methods are beyond the scope of this text. There are even a few mechanisms where $P$ is greater than 1, which indicates very strong attractive interactions between the collision partners. In practice, the steric factor is estimated by comparing the simple, predicted rate constant based on known molecular sizes to measured values.

## Sample Problem 4.2

Let's revisit the NO + $O_3$ reaction from Sample Problem 4.1. Estimates of the diameters of these molecules are 360 and 436 pm for NO and $O_3$, respectively. From these values, estimate the steric factor for this reaction.

## Solution

In Sample Problem 4.1, we calculated an effective collisional cross section of $2.25 \times 10^{-21}$ m² for this reaction. This value can be considered to be the product of the true collisional cross section and the steric factor.

$$\sigma_{eff} = P\sigma$$

From the molecular diameters, we can calculate the geometric cross section according to Eq. 3.17, $\sigma = \pi d^2$ where $d = r_A + r_B$. Each radius is equal to half the respective diameter, so the value of $d$ we will use is 398 pm. This value of $d$ gives a geometric cross section of $4.98 \times 10^{-19}$ m². Taking the ratio of this geometric cross section and the effective collisional cross section we calculated earlier gives a steric factor of $P = 0.0045$.

## 4.2 Reactions in Liquid Media

Our treatment thus far has only dealt with chemical reactions in (diffuse) gas. Many important processes, however, take place in a liquid medium. Can we apply the ideas we have developed here to liquid phase reactions? Some of the basic ideas still apply, but there are important differences between a gas and a liquid that need to be considered.

The most obvious difference between a gas and a liquid is the density of the medium, which relates to the average distance between molecules. In a gas, the distance between molecules is generally a few hundred times the molecular size. This is not at all true in a liquid, where molecules are practically touching all the time. The other key difference between liquid- and gas-phase reactions is the presence of a solvent. Even though the solvent molecules may not be involved in the chemical reactions, they will come between the reaction partners and can limit the likelihood that the desired collisions even take place. The solvent molecules also make it more difficult for any of the reactant molecules to achieve high speeds, meaning the energy of the collisions is less likely to be high than in gas phase reactions.

A full quantitative treatment of the molecular details of liquid phase reactions cannot be presented at this point; we need to more fully develop the formalism of chemical kinetics first. We can, however, construct a reasonable, qualitative picture of two important limiting scenarios for liquid-phase reactions. Recall that the first thing that needs to take place in a chemical reaction is a collision between the reactants. In a liquid environment, however, reactant molecules do not move about as freely as in a gas. For reactions with fairly low activation energies, the fundamental limitation is not the reactive encounter itself, but how quickly the reactant molecules can move through the solvent to find each other. This is known as the **diffusion-controlled limit**. Rate constants for diffusion-controlled reactions are typically around $10^9$ L mol$^{-1}$ s$^{-1}$.

The other limit that is often encountered is when the activation energy of the reaction is significantly greater than the average kinetic energy of the reactants in solution. This condition is known as the **activation-controlled limit**. In this case, the solvent can actually help the reaction rather than hinder it. In the gas phase, if two molecules collide with insufficient energy to react, they will quickly move apart from each other. In solution, the solvent molecules can help keep the reactants close together because of the **cage effect**. This may allow the reactants to collide multiple times before one of them diffuses away. Collisions with solvent molecules can even help temporarily increase the energy of the collision between reactants. For reversible reactions, however, the cage effect can also slow things down by keeping the products in close proximity and allowing the back reaction to occur more readily.

## 4.3 Summary, and Where We Go Next

In this chapter, we have developed a model of chemical reactions at the most fundamental level, in terms of collisions between molecules. We have also explored the energy and orientation requirements of these reactions. In the course of developing our molecular model, we have predicted the Arrhenius equation, which was originally developed based on observations at the macroscale. Once again, our simple molecular model has shown its power. In the next chapter, we will more fully develop the concepts and tools of classical chemical kinetics and learn more about how we can make connections between macroscopic observations and the detailed molecular processes that govern chemical reactions.

# PROBLEMS

**4.1** a) Treating neon as an ideal gas at STP, calculate the collision density. Use a collisional cross section of $0.4$ nm$^2$.

b) For a mixture of Ne and Ar at STP where the Ar is present at 1% concentration, calculate the collision density between majority and minority species. [Use the same collisional cross section from part a) for this calculation.]

c) For the same mixture as described in part b), calculate the total collision density that includes each type of collision. Compare your results to part a).

**4.2** Eq. 4.8 describes the probability distribution function for the energy of a bimolecular collision.

a) Calculate the fraction of collisions that have an energy greater than an activation energy of $200$ kJ mol$^{-1}$ at temperatures of 300 K and 1000 K.

b) Repeat the calculations for an activation energy of 20 kJ mol$^{-1}$.

c) What is the percent increase in the fractions calculated in parts a) and b) for a temperature increase of 10 K?

**4.3** The gas phase reaction of NO and $Cl_2$ to produce NOCl and Cl follows a second-order rate law. The preexponential factor has a value of $4.0 \times 10^9$ L mol$^{-1}$ s$^{-1}$ at 298.15 K. The activation energy is $84.9$ kJ mol$^{-1}$.

a) Calculate the reaction cross section.

b) Calculate the rate constant at 300 K and 500 K, assuming the preexponential factor is temperature independent.

**4.4** For the reaction of atomic oxygen with $N_2$ to produce NO and N, the prefactor has a value of $1 \times 10^{14}$ cm$^3$ mol$^{-1}$ s$^{-1}$ and an activation energy of $315$ kJ mol$^{-1}$. The similar reaction with atomic S has a prefactor of $4 \times 10^{12}$ cm$^3$ mol$^{-1}$ s$^{-1}$ and an activation energy of $459$ kJ mol$^{-1}$. Use this information to estimate the relative size of atomic S and O. Comment on the interpretation of your results and if anything else should be included to make such an estimate.

**4.5** a) The decomposition of two molecules of NOCl into two molecules of NO and a $Cl_2$ molecule is found to proceed by a collision between the two NOCl molecules. The Arrhenius prefactor was estimated from theory to be $5.9 \times 10^{10}$ L mol$^{-1}$ s$^{-1}$. The experimental value was determined to be $9.4 \times 10^9$ L mol$^{-1}$ s$^{-1}$. The activation energy was found to be 102 kJ mol$^{-1}$. Estimate the value of the steric factor for this reaction.

b) For the hydrogenation of ethene to form ethane, the theoretical and experimental values of the Arrhenius prefactor are $7.4 \times 10^{11}$ L mol$^{-1}$ s$^{-1}$ and $1.24 \times 10^6$ L mol$^{-1}$ s$^{-1}$, respectively. The activation energy is 180 kJ mol$^{-1}$. Estimate the value of the steric factor for this reaction.

c) Compare your results for parts a) and b) and comment on why they are the same or different. Justify your results in terms of molecular structures.

**4.6** For the reaction

$$2\ NO_2\ (g) \rightarrow 2\ NO\ (g) + O_2\ (g)$$

bimolecular rate constants were determined over a range of temperatures, as summarized in the table. (Source: Park, J., *et al.*, J. Phys. Chem. A **102**, 10099 (1998).)

| $T$ (K) | $k$ (cm$^3$ s$^{-1}$) |
|---|---|
| 602 | $7.16 \times 10^{-22}$ |
| 650 | $3.91 \times 10^{-21}$ |
| 700 | $1.79 \times 10^{-20}$ |
| 750 | $6.69 \times 10^{-20}$ |
| 800 | $2.12 \times 10^{-19}$ |
| 850 | $5.86 \times 10^{-19}$ |
| 900 | $1.45 \times 10^{-18}$ |
| 950 | $3.25 \times 10^{-18}$ |

a) From these data, calculate the activation energy, assuming you can treat the Arrhenius prefactor as a constant.

b) Calculate the activation energy again, this time taking into account the explicit temperature dependence of the prefactor. Compare your results to those in part a).

c) Assuming a geometric cross section of 0.60 nm$^2$, estimate the steric factor for this reaction.

**4.7** Oxygen atoms are very reactive in the atmosphere. One possible mechanism for the destruction of ozone involves a collision between an oxygen atom and ozone to produce two $O_2$ molecules. The NIST chemical database reports a rate constant of $1.2 \times 10^{-10}$ cm$^3$ s$^{-1}$ for this reaction at 298 K. The "diameters" of these species are 304 pm for O and 436 pm for $O_3$. Given these data, estimate the activation energy for this reaction. State any assumptions in your calculation.

# Rate Laws and Reaction Mechanisms

## 5.1 Reaction Rate and Rate Laws

In the last chapter, we developed a model of chemical reactions based on the concept of molecular collisions. This model was highly successful; however, we cannot actually observe the individual molecular collisions that lead to reactions. We can, however, measure the concentrations of reactants and products over the course of the reaction. Thus, we need to define the rate of a reaction in terms of what we can measure. In other words, we need a "top-down" formulation of chemical kinetics, which is what we will develop in this chapter.

### 5.1.1 Formal Definition of Reaction Rate

Consider a generic chemical reaction of the form

$$A + 2B \rightarrow 3C + D$$

We can see from the stoichiometry of this reaction that as we lose compound A, we gain the same amount of compound D but 3 times the amount of compound C. We also lose compound B twice as fast as compound A. Mathematically, we can write expressions for the time rate of change of the concentration of each compound as

$$\frac{d[D]}{dt} = \frac{1}{3}\frac{d[C]}{dt} = -\frac{d[A]}{dt} = -\frac{1}{2}\frac{d[B]}{dt}$$

Note that the concentrations of A and B decrease with time, meaning those derivatives are negative, and we need to include the minus sign for those two terms in writing the equations. Note also that the stoichiometric coefficients are included as their reciprocals to make all the expressions equal; the rate of formation of C is 3 times that of D, therefore the rate of formation of D is ⅓ that of C.

We will use this example, and some basic logical reasoning, to develop a more general definition of reaction rate. First, we introduce a quantity known as the **extent of reaction**, $\xi$. This is defined as

$$\xi \equiv \frac{n_J - n_{J,0}}{v_J} \tag{5.1}$$

where $n_J$ is the number of moles of compound $J$ at any point in time, $n_{J,0}$ is the initial number of moles of compound $J$, and $v_J$ is the **stoichiometric coefficient** of compound $J$. The value of $v_J$ is the numerical value in the balanced chemical equation and is positive for products and negative for reactants. Thus, in our example above, $v_C = 3$ and $v_D = 1$, whereas $v_A = -1$ and $v_B = -2$. Note that the value of the extent of reaction is the same for each compound at any point in time, and that the value of $\xi$ ranges from 0 to 1. The extent of reaction also has units of moles, although we are talking about moles of the entire reaction, not any particular reactant or product.

The extent of reaction changes with time, and we can write its time derivative as

$$\frac{d\xi}{dt} = \frac{1}{v_J}\frac{dn_J}{dt} \quad \text{or} \quad \frac{dn_J}{dt} = v_J \frac{d\xi}{dt} \tag{5.2}$$

($n_{J,0}$ drops out of the derivative because it is a time-independent initial value.) We now formally define the **rate of reaction** as

$$\boxed{rate \equiv \frac{1}{V}\frac{d\xi}{dt}} \tag{5.3}$$

Using Eq. 5.2, we can write the rate in a more readily usable format

$$rate = \frac{1}{V}\left(\frac{1}{v_J}\frac{dn_J}{dt}\right) = \frac{1}{v_J}\frac{d[J]}{dt} \tag{5.4}$$

Note that with this definition, the rate of reaction is always a positive quantity. The time rate of change of a particular concentration, however, can be either positive or negative depending on whether it is a product or reactant.

It is useful to point out that we rarely measure rate of reaction directly. More likely, we measure the concentration of a reactant or product as a function of time. If we have time-dependent concentration data, we can then approximate the instantaneous rate through a variety of numerical methods. Note that the rate of reaction should be the same for all reactants and products. It is therefore good practice to measure as many concentrations as possible to reduce any experimental error. Also, the rate of reaction will change as the reaction proceeds, generally slowing down over time. Once a reaction reaches completion—that is, the system comes to equilibrium—the rate of reaction goes to zero.

## Sample Problem 5.1

Consider the combustion of ethane. Write rate expressions for every species in this reaction.

Solution

The first thing we need to do is write the balanced reaction for the combustion of ethane.

$$C_2H_6 + \tfrac{7}{2}O_2 \rightarrow 2\,CO_2 + 3\,H_2O$$

$CO_2$ and water are our products, so their stoichiometric coefficients are positive; ethane and oxygen are the reactants, so their stoichiometric coefficients are negative. We therefore write the rate expressions as

$$\text{rate} = \frac{1}{2}\frac{d[CO_2]}{dt} = \frac{1}{3}\frac{d[H_2O]}{dt} = -\frac{d[C_2H_6]}{dt} = -\frac{2}{7}\frac{d[O_2]}{dt}$$

## 5.1.2 Rate Laws

The rate of reaction is really nothing more than what it claims to be; a measure of how fast that reaction is proceeding at any point during the reaction. It changes during the course of the reaction, and will vary depending on how the reaction was set up. It would be more useful if we had some descriptive factors that related to fundamental aspects of the reaction and were independent of how the reaction was done or who did it. How would the reaction rate be affected by an increase or decrease in the concentration of one of the reactants? How is the rate affected by temperature? What we want is a mathematical description for how the rate of reaction depends on these factors. The general form of such a function would be written as

$$\text{rate} = f(T,[A],[B],[C],\ldots)$$

An expression of this form is called a **rate law**, and generally has the form

$$\text{rate} = k(T)[A]^a[B]^b[C]^c \ldots \tag{5.5}$$

where $k$ is the (temperature-dependent) **rate constant** and the exponent for each concentration term is the **order of reaction** with respect to that compound.

Unlike expressions for the rate of reaction in terms of the time rate of change of concentration, a rate law *cannot* be written down simply by looking at the overall stoichiometry of the reaction. Rate laws *must* be determined experimentally. This is because the rate law reflects an overall relationship between the concentrations of various compounds and the rate of reaction, but it does not tell us all the steps whereby the reaction happens. This sequence of molecular events is called the **mechanism** of the reaction. Some reaction mechanisms—even for what appear to be simple overall reactions—can be very complicated, leading to complicated rate laws. Later in this chapter, we'll make connections between mechanisms and rate laws and learn how to determine the rate law for a particular reaction mechanism.

One common way to determine the order of reaction with respect to a given compound is the **isolation method**, whereby all reactants except one are present in excess. This means that the concentration of these compounds will not change by much, and can therefore be assumed to be roughly constant. If we take our test reaction of $A + 2B \rightarrow 3C + D$ and run the reaction with an excess of B, we can rewrite our proposed rate law as

$$\text{rate} = k'[A]^a$$

where the $[B]^b$ has been folded into the rate constant. We then perform the experiment under a variety of initial concentrations of A, or determine the rate of reaction at various points of known concentration. We can take the logarithm of our expression and write

$$\log \text{rate} = \log k' + a \log[A] \tag{5.6}$$

Plotting the logarithm of the rate vs. the logarithm of the concentration will then give a straight line, where the slope of that line is the order of reaction with respect to that compound. Repeating this process with an excess of A will allow us to determine the order of reaction with respect to compound B, and so forth. Once we know the order of reaction for each compound, we can readily determine the value of the rate constant, $k$, at the temperature of the experiments.

Another way to determine order of reaction for various species is the **method of initial rates**. In this approach, multiple experiments are performed with different initial concentrations of the reactants. Typically, only one concentration at a time is changed. The rate is determined for each set of initial conditions. By comparing the results, the order of reaction can be determined. For example, if doubling the concentration of A results in a doubling of the rate, we know the order of reaction for A is 1. On the other hand, if doubling the concentration of B quadruples the rate, then we know that the order of reaction for B is 2. (Problem 1.11 can be solved with this approach.)

For many reactions, the rate laws contain terms with first or second order. Noninteger orders are a possibility, however, as well as negative reaction orders. The rate law can depend on the concentration of one or more of the products, so that possibility should be considered as well in performing these experiments. Some reactions even have much more complicated rate laws. For example, the relatively simple reaction $H_2 + Br_2 \rightarrow 2\,HBr$ (all species gas phase) has the fairly complicated rate law

$$\text{rate} = \frac{k[H_2][Br_2]^{3/2}}{[Br_2] + k'[HBr]}$$

As we will see throughout the remainder of this chapter, the rate law can provide much insight into the mechanism by which a reaction takes place. Before exploring these mechanisms further, however, we will develop some useful mathematical relations for the simplest rate laws.

### Sample Problem 5.2

The following reaction is investigated to determine its rate law.

$$NO_2\,(g) + CO\,(g) \rightarrow NO\,(g) + CO_2\,(g)$$

When the concentration of $NO_2$ is doubled in excess CO, the rate is found to quadruple. When the concentration of CO is doubled in excess $NO_2$, the rate of reaction is unchanged. What is the rate law for this reaction?

### Solution

We could use the approach outlined in connection with Eq. 5.6; however, the numbers here are simple enough we can determine the rate law by inspection. We are told that the rate quadruples when the concentration of $NO_2$ doubles. This suggests that the order of reaction for $NO_2$ is 2; squaring a factor of 2 gives us a factor of 4 increase in the rate, holding [CO] constant. When the concentration of CO is doubled while holding $[NO_2]$ constant, however, we find no increase in the rate of reaction. This suggests that the reaction is zeroth order with respect to CO. The correct rate law is then written as

$$rate = k[NO_2]^2$$

### 5.1.3 First-Order Kinetics

Consider a reaction of the form

$$A + B \rightarrow C + D$$

that exhibits a first-order rate law,

$$rate = k[A] \tag{5.7}$$

(Remember: Rate laws *cannot* be written down simply by looking at the stoichiometry of the overall reaction.) If we express the rate in terms of the time rate of change of the concentration of A, we can write the following mathematical expression

$$\frac{-d[A]}{dt} = k[A] \quad \text{or} \quad \frac{d[A]}{dt} = -k[A] \tag{5.8}$$

This expression is readily integrated to give what we call the first-order **integrated rate law**

$$\ln\frac{[A]}{[A]_0} = -kt \quad \text{or} \quad [A] = [A]_0 e^{-kt} \tag{5.9}$$

where $[A]_0$ is the initial concentration of compound A.

For a reaction that exhibits first-order kinetics, we see that the concentration of the reactant decays exponentially, as shown in Figure 5.1a. Note that the time constant of the decay is simply the reciprocal of the rate constant, $\tau = 1/k$. If we plot the ln of the concentration as a function of time, we can see that the slope of that line will equal $-k$. See Figure 5.1b. This is a fairly common way to determine the rate constant for first-order

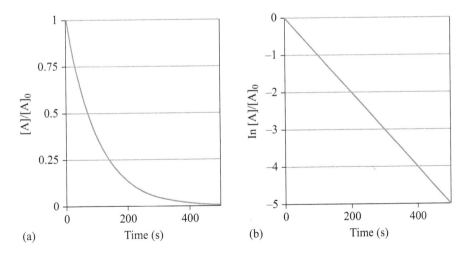

**FIGURE 5.1.** First-order reaction kinetics. a) Plot of concentration vs. time shows exponential decay. b) Plot of ln of concentration is linear, with a slope of $-k$.

reactions. The units of a first-order rate constant are simply per time, e.g. $s^{-1}$. Keep in mind that rate constants are temperature dependent; therefore, experiments of this type need to be performed under conditions of well-controlled temperature.

Another characteristic of first-order reactions can be seen by considering what is known as the **half-life**. The half-life is the time it takes for the concentration of the reactant to drop to a factor of one half the initial value. Mathematically, we write

$$[A]_{1/2} = \frac{1}{2}[A]_0 \text{ at } t_{1/2} \tag{5.10}$$

If we substitute this relation into the integrated rate law, we obtain the following

$$kt_{1/2} = -\ln \frac{\frac{1}{2}[A]_0}{[A]_0} = -\ln \frac{1}{2} = \ln 2$$

$$t_{1/2} = \frac{\ln 2}{k} \tag{5.11}$$

Note that the half-life is independent of the initial concentration. Our choice of initial time is somewhat arbitrary; therefore, we can choose any point during the reaction as the "initial" time. At a time of one half-life later, the concentration will be one half that "initial" value.

The idea of half-life is often discussed in connection with the decay of radioisotopes. This is because radioactive decay always follows first order kinetics. If we have 10 g of a radioactive material with a half-life of 10,000 years, then after 10,000 years we will have 5 g of that material. After another 10,000 years, we will have 2.5 g remaining, and so forth. The constancy of the half-life, which reflects the constancy of the rate constant for a radioactive decay process, provides the basis for radiometric dating. If we can determine the fraction of a radioisotope that has decayed, typically by determining the amount of decay products that are present, we can work backwards to determine the age of that sample.

It should also be mentioned that there is nothing special about the ratio of one half. We could just as easily determine the time it takes to have one third of our initial concentration, or four fifths. Chose any fraction you want, and you will find that the time it takes to lose that fraction is the same throughout the course of the reaction. As we will see, this constancy is a special feature of first-order kinetics.

### Sample Problem 5.3

Iodine-131 ($^{131}$I) is a radioactive isotope, useful for radiation therapy and medical imaging. $^{131}$I decays by beta emission, which follows first-order kinetics. The half-life of $^{131}$I is 8.02 days. If a patient is given a dose of $^{131}$I, how long will they have to wait until the amount of the radioisotope in their body has dropped to 5% of the initial amount?

### Solution

Because the radioactive decay of $^{131}$I follows first-order kinetics, we can use the first order integrated rate law (Eq. 5.9) to solve this problem. We want to know the time it takes for the amount to decrease to 5% of the initial amount. The rate constant in Eq. 5.9 can be replaced by Eq. 5.11. This gives us

$$\ln\frac{[A]}{[A]_0} = \ln 0.05 = \frac{-\ln 2}{t_{1/2}}t$$

Solving for $t$ gives us a time of 35 days.

It is good practice to check that our answers make sense. After 8 days, we would have 50% remaining, 25% after 16 days, 12.5% after 24 days, and 6.25% after 32 days. Our answer makes sense.

### 5.1.4 Second-Order Kinetics

Consider now a reaction of the form

$$A \rightarrow C + D$$

that exhibits a second-order rate law,

$$\text{rate} = k[A]^2 \tag{5.12}$$

If we express the rate in terms of the time rate of change of the concentration of A, we can write the following mathematical expression

$$\frac{-d[A]}{dt} = k[A]^2 \quad \text{or} \quad \frac{d[A]}{dt} = -k[A]^2 \tag{5.13}$$

This expression is readily integrated to give the second-order integrated rate law

$$\frac{1}{[A]} - \frac{1}{[A]_0} = kt \quad \text{or} \quad [A] = \frac{[A]_0}{1 + kt[A]_0} \tag{5.14}$$

where again $[A]_0$ is the initial concentration of compound A. For a second-order reaction, we can determine the value of the rate constant by plotting $1/[A]$ as a function of time. Figure 5.2

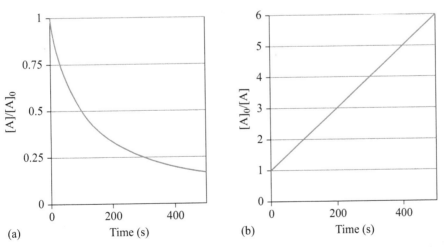

(a)      Time (s)        (b)      Time (s)

FIGURE 5.2. Second-order reaction kinetics. a) Plot of concentration vs. time. b) Plot of $[A]_0/[A]$ is linear, with a slope of $k$. ($[A]_0$ is taken to be 1.)

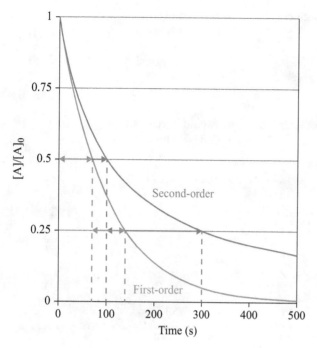

**FIGURE 5.3.** Comparison of first- and second-order kinetics. The numerical value of the rate constant is the same for both cases. Note that the half-life for the first-order reaction, indicated by the orange double arrow, is the same as the reaction proceeds; whereas the half-life for the second-order reaction, indicated by the blue double arrow, increases as the reaction proceeds.

shows the behavior of a second order reaction. Note that the units of the second-order rate constant are per concentration per time, e.g. L mol$^{-1}$ s$^{-1}$.

Consideration of the half-life of a second-order reaction shows an important distinction from a first-order reaction. As before, the half-life is the time that it takes for the initial concentration to drop to half the initial value. Using this definition, we can write

$$kt_{1/2} = \frac{2}{[A]_0} - \frac{1}{[A]_0} = \frac{1}{[A]_0}$$

$$t_{1/2} = \frac{1}{k[A]_0} \tag{5.15}$$

Notice that the half-life now depends on the initial concentration of A. Of course, we can restart our clock whenever we choose to, which means if we let the reaction run for one half-life, the time required for the next 50% decrease in concentration will increase, as can be seen in Figure 5.3. Thus, a second-order reaction will generally take longer to reach completion than a first-order reaction with similar rate constants. This can be an issue, for example, with environmental contaminants that decay by second-order kinetics; low-level concentrations will persist for a long time in the environment.

The second-order rate law we have considered thus far is second order in a single reactant, but it is also possible to have a second-order rate law that is first order in two different reactants. For example, a reaction of the form

$$2A + B \rightarrow C$$

is found to have the rate law

$$\text{rate} = k[A][B] \tag{5.16}$$

Determination of an integrated rate law in this case involves coupled differential equations, since both [A] and [B] are changing in time, and the solution to this problem is more than we are going to take on at this point.

### 5.1.5 Zero-Order Kinetics

It is entirely possible that the rate law of a reaction could be independent of the concentration of one or more of the reactants. (We saw this in Sample Problem 5.2.) An extreme example of this would be a reaction such as

$$A \rightarrow C + D$$

that exhibits a rate law,

$$\text{rate} = k \tag{5.17}$$

The integrated rate law in this case is found by integrating

$$-\frac{d[A]}{dt} = k \quad \text{or} \quad \frac{d[A]}{dt} = -k \tag{5.18}$$

to obtain

$$[A] = [A]_0 - kt \tag{5.19}$$

The concentration of A decreases linearly over time, so we can simply plot concentration as a function of time to determine the rate constant. (What happens to the half-life of a zero-order reaction as the reaction proceeds?)

Note that for both first- and second-order reactions, the concentration approaches its final value asymptotically. In the case of a zero-order reaction, the concentration could in principle hit zero and keep going to negative values. This, of course, makes no physical sense. What is typically seen, however, is that a reaction only exhibits zero-order kinetics when the reactant is present in relatively large amounts. When the concentration drops below a certain threshold, the reaction will switch over to exhibit first- or second-order kinetics. This means something has changed in how the reaction takes place; there has been a change in the reaction mechanism.

## 5.1.6 Effect of Temperature

As was mentioned earlier, care must be taken when determining the rate law to keep the temperature constant. This is because rate constants themselves are temperature dependent. We saw this in the last chapter in our discussion of the collisional model of reactions and the derivation of the Arrhenius equation, Eq. 4.10.

$$k = Ae^{-E_a/RT}$$

In order to determine the effect of temperature on the rate of reaction, the values of the preexponential factor, $A$, and the activation energy, $E_a$, need to be determined. As was discussed in Section 4.1.3 and illustrated in Sample Problem 4.1, these parameters can be determined by plotting $\ln k$ vs $1/T$. The slope is then equal to $-E_a/R$, and the intercept is equal to $\ln A$.

It is worth mentioning at this point that not all reactions follow the Arrhenius equation. In some cases, an increase in temperature can lead to a decrease in reaction rate. In other cases, the effect of temperature will not follow the simple exponential behavior of the Arrhenius equation. Such non-Arrhenius behavior is one indication that a reaction may not be proceeding by simple collisions between reactants, but rather involves a more complicated reaction mechanism. The consideration of reaction mechanisms is where we now turn our focus.

## 5.2 Reaction Mechanisms

The determination of a rate law by experimental methods gives us some ability to predict how the rate of a reaction will depend on a variety of conditions. The rate law tells us very little, however, about the detailed, molecular-level events that actually take place during the reaction. This sequence of molecular steps is called the **reaction mechanism**. In this section, we develop the tools necessary to take a proposed reaction mechanism and determine the resultant rate law. Comparison of the proposed and actual rate laws can then be used to judge the feasibility of the proposed mechanism. If the proposed rate law does not match experiment, then the mechanism is clearly flawed. A match between a proposed rate law and experiment does not guarantee that the mechanism is correct, however. Rather, such agreement merely demonstrates that the mechanism is *plausible*. Science proceeds by falsifying a hypothesis—in this case a mechanism—so plausibility is often the best we can hope for until additional experiments can be done.

## 5.2.1 Elementary Reaction Steps

Recall that for an overall reaction, we cannot simply look at the stoichiometric coefficients of each reactant and write down the rate law. This is because the reaction often proceeds through more than a single event. This is particularly true for reactions with complicated stoichiometry. Recall from our discussion in the last chapter that, at the molecular level, chemical reactions proceed due to collisions between molecules. Thus, most steps in a reaction mechanism involve only one or two molecules at a time.

Let's consider a hypothetical reaction

$$2A + B \rightarrow E + F$$

A possible mechanism could look like the following.

Step 1:  $A + B \rightarrow C + D$
Step 2:  $A + G \rightarrow E$
Step 3:  $C + D \rightarrow F + G$

This mechanism is made up of individual steps that only involve two molecules at a time, even though the overall reaction involves three reactant molecules. Each of these steps in the mechanism is known as an **elementary step**. Note that the three steps taken together add up to the overall reaction; this is the first requirement of any proposed mechanism.

This example contains other molecules that are part of the mechanism, but not part of the overall reaction. These molecules fall into two types. A molecule that is produced in one step and then consumed in another is called an **intermediate**; in this mechanism, compounds C and D are intermediates. Intermediate species should not appear in overall rate laws. Compound G is consumed in step 2 but then produced again in step 3. A molecule that does this is actually a **catalyst**. Its concentration is unchanged over the course of the reaction, but the reaction cannot proceed without it, and thus it may appear in the final rate law.

Unlike for an overall reaction, where we cannot simply write the rate law based on the stoichiometry, we can write the rate law for an individual elementary step. These steps are characterized in terms of their **molecularity**, which is the number of molecules involved in the step. A **unimolecular** step, involving only one molecule, will always have a first-order rate law.

$$A \rightarrow P \qquad \text{rate} = k[A] \tag{5.20}$$

Examples of unimolecular steps include an isomerization or an elimination step. (Radioactive decay is also unimolecular.) Many steps are **bimolecular**, meaning they involve two molecules and will have a second-order rate law.

$$A + B \rightarrow P \qquad \text{rate} = k[A][B] \tag{5.21}$$

Examples of a bimolecular elementary step are the $S_N2$ and E2 mechanisms you learned about in organic chemistry. **Termolecular** steps that involve three molecules are possible, but they are fairly rare, since they involve the simultaneous collision of three molecules all at the same time, and that is a fairly unlikely event.

In some cases, we can very easily tell if a reaction can be described by a single elementary step or not. For example, if we have a reaction where the overall stoichiometry involves two molecules, but the rate law is first order, then it clearly cannot take place in a single step. If it did, that single step would be a bimolecular event and therefore be described by a second-order rate law. A mismatch between reaction stoichiometry and rate law is a clear indication that a multistep mechanism needs to be developed and analyzed. However, a match between overall stoichiometry and rate law does not necessarily guarantee that the reaction proceeds in a single elementary step. In the following sections, we develop procedures for determining the overall rate law that corresponds to a particular mechanism.

## 5.2.2 Reversible Reaction Approaching Equilibrium

Let's consider a reversible reaction of the form

$$A \rightleftarrows B$$

where each step is elementary and unimolecular. (As mentioned above, this could be some sort of isomerization reaction, such as *cis*-2-butene to *trans*-2-butene.) In analyzing a proposed reaction mechanism, it is useful to write down the rate law that corresponds to each step in the reaction. The forward rate law for this reaction is written as

$$\text{rate}_f = k[A]$$

The reverse rate law is written as

$$\text{rate}_r = k'[B]$$

The ' in the second rate constant helps us distinguish it from the rate constant of the forward reaction. In general, we can write the total rate of change of the concentration of compound A as

$$\frac{d[A]}{dt} = -k[A] + k'[B] \tag{5.22}$$

A similar expression for B would be written as

$$\frac{d[B]}{dt} = k[A] - k'[B] \tag{5.23}$$

It is worth pointing out a few details about these expressions, since we will be seeing many expressions of this type. When writing an expression for total rate of change for a given chemical species, we need to look at the mechanism and identify all the steps that contain the species of interest. In this case, both steps involve A, so we have two terms in our expression. Next, we need to determine if our species is consumed or produced as a result of that step. If it is consumed, then that term will be negative; whereas if it is produced, it will be positive. In this case, the forward step reduces the amount of A present, so that is represented by a negative term. The reverse step produces A, so it is positive. We then include the relevant rate constant for that step and all the species that you find at

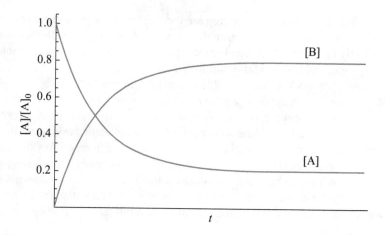

FIGURE 5.4. Plots of concentration vs. time for the reaction A $\rightleftarrows$ B with $k = 4\,k'$.

the back end of the arrow for that step. Note that the reduction of A in the forward step depends on [A], but the formation of A in the reverse step depends on [B].

Now that we have expressions for the total time rate of change of [A] and [B], we want to develop general expressions for [A] and [B] as a function of time. Solving these differential equations will require that we stipulate a boundary condition. The simplest condition we can impose is that there is no B initially. We can also see by the stoichiometry of the reaction that at all times,

$$[A] + [B] = [A]_0 \tag{5.24}$$

must be true; this is just a mathematical statement that matter must be conserved. Applying these boundary conditions leads to solutions of the form

$$[A] = \frac{k' + ke^{-(k+k')t}}{k' + k}[A]_0 \quad \text{and} \quad [B] = 1 - \frac{k' + ke^{-(k+k')t}}{k' + k}[A]_0 \tag{5.25}$$

These functions are plotted in Figure 5.4.

After solving a differential equation, it is good practice to evaluate those solutions in certain limits to make sure the answers make physical sense. At $t = 0$, the exponential term becomes one and $[A] = [A]_0$ and $[B] = 0$. This matches the initial conditions we imposed when solving the problem. As we go to equilibrium at late time, or as $t \rightarrow \infty$, we have

$$[A]_{eq} = \frac{k'[A]_0}{k + k'} \quad \text{and} \quad [B]_{eq} = \frac{k[A]_0}{k + k'}$$

You should recall from general chemistry that we can write an equilibrium constant for this reaction as

$$K = \frac{[B]_{eq}}{[A]_{eq}} \tag{5.26}$$

If we insert the expressions for the equilibrium concentrations of A and B, we have

$$K = \frac{k}{k'} \tag{5.27}$$

The value of the equilibrium constant is simply the ratio of the forward and reverse rate constants. Thus, if the forward rate constant is larger than the reverse, the system at equilibrium will have more of the product than the reactant, whereas the reverse is also true. If the forward and reverse rate constants are basically the same, then we would have roughly equal amounts of reactant and product at equilibrium.

This result gives us some additional insight into what we mean by a chemical equilibrium. At the macroscale, we can say that the reaction has reached equilibrium once the concentrations of reactants and products are no longer changing. What about at the microscale? Molecules are still colliding with each other, so individual reactive collisions could still be happening. How can we have reactive collisions at the molecular level but see no change in concentration at the bulk level? This can be true if the rate of the forward reaction and the rate of the reverse reaction are the same. Mathematically, we write the equilibrium condition as

$$k[A]_{eq} = k'[B]_{eq} \qquad (5.28)$$

Simple algebra with this relation will give us the same result as above in Eqs. 5.26 and 5.27.

It is also useful at this time to build another mental picture of a chemical reaction that involves the concept of activation energy we developed in the last chapter. Recall that we were able to use our collisional model to derive the Arrhenius equation, Eq. 4.10, which tells us how the rate constant depends on the activation energy, $E_a$, and the temperature.

$$k = Ae^{-E_a/RT}$$

where $A$ is the preexponential factor that accounts for the frequency of molecular collisions. In a particular sample of gas, the frequency of collisions will be basically the same for all the different molecules present. The rate of reaction will therefore depend more on how much energy is required for those collisions to lead to reaction. One way to represent the energy of reaction is with an energy "hill," as shown in Figure 5.5. The reactants start out on one side of the hill. In order to cross over to the product side, a collision has to have enough energy to get over the hill. The molecular arrangement at the top of this energy hill is known as the **transition state**; it gets this name because chemical bonds are in transition and some bonds are forming and some are breaking. (We will fully consider transition state theory, one of the triumphs of physical chemistry, in Chapter 21 after we have covered quantum mechanics and thermodynamics.) Collisions on the product side can also send molecules back over to the reactant side. If the reactants start out at a higher energy than the products, then the hill they have to cross over is smaller than the hill to come back from the product side; therefore, the forward rate constant is greater than the reverse rate constant.

Eventually, when the reaction comes to equilibrium, the rate of passage over the hill will be the same for both directions. Note that the rate constant only depends on the energy barrier and the temperature, but the rate itself includes the concentration of reactant or product. In order for those two rates to be equal, the concentrations need to have the relationship we derived above for the equilibrium constant. As we will see much later in the book, thermodynamic equilibrium is only concerned with the initial and final energy of

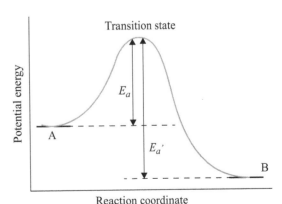

FIGURE 5.5. Plot of potential energy with reaction coordinate for the reaction A $\rightleftarrows$ B. The activation for the reverse step is greater than for the forward step.

reactants and products, not the process of moving from one side of the reaction to the other. Thus, we would expect equilibrium to favor the more stable side of the reaction. That is exactly the same situation we see here in the context of the rate constants; if the products are more stable than the reactants, then the energy barrier to go back from product will be larger than the forward barrier and more molecules will be found on the product side at equilibrium. We can also see how this is true in the context of the Boltzmann distribution, which tells us that we will have more molecules in a lower energy state, in this case the product, than in a higher energy state, the reactant. It is always comforting when different descriptions of a reaction—in this case thermodynamics, kinetics, and statistical mechanics—all come to the same physical conclusions.

### 5.2.3 Consecutive Elementary Reactions

Let's now consider a reaction that proceeds through two elementary steps.

$$A \rightarrow I \rightarrow P$$

where we have rate constants $k_a$ for the first step and $k_b$ for the second step. The species I in this mechanism is an intermediate, because it is created and then consumed over the course of the reaction. Note that the intermediate does not appear in the overall reaction, $A \rightarrow P$. If we do not allow back conversion of I to A, then we have for the rate of change of concentration of A

$$\frac{d[A]}{dt} = -k_a[A] \tag{5.29}$$

This expression is readily integrated to give the concentration of A as a function of time.

$$[A] = [A]_0 e^{-k_a t} \tag{5.30}$$

The total time rate of change of the concentration of the intermediate is given by

$$\frac{d[I]}{dt} = k_a[A] - k_b[I] \tag{5.31}$$

The rate of formation of product only depends on [I], and is written as

$$\frac{d[P]}{dt} = k_b[I] \tag{5.32}$$

Using our function for [A], we can readily proceed to a full expression for [P] with time.

$$[P] = \left(1 + \frac{k_a e^{-k_b t} - k_b e^{-k_a t}}{k_b - k_a}\right)[A]_0 \tag{5.33}$$

As we did before, it is useful to look at this expression, Eq. 5.33, in certain limits. At very short time, close to $t = 0$, [P] = 0, which we expect; the reaction hasn't had time to produce any product. At very late time, or as $t \rightarrow \infty$, the exponential terms all approach zero and [P] = $[A]_0$; all the reactant has been converted into product. At times before the reaction reaches equilibrium, the function is a bit more complicated, and will depend on the relative magnitudes of $k_a$ and $k_b$, as shown in Figure 5.6.

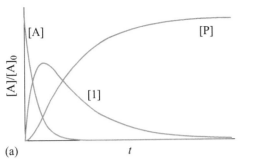
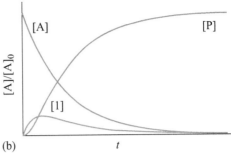

FIGURE 5.6. Plots of concentration with time for the reaction A → I → P. In a) $k_a = 4k_b$ and in b) $k_b = 4k_a$

It is particularly useful to think about what happens if one of the rate constants is significantly larger than the other one. Let's consider the case where $k_b \gg k_a$. This allows us to simplify our expression for [P] as a function of time to

$$[P] = (1 - e^{-k_a t})[A]_0$$

Note that this expression only depends on the rate constant for the first step. Thus, the first step is known as the **rate-limiting step**. The first step is slow (it has the smaller rate constant), and therefore more energy is required to get over the activation barrier. Once the reacting molecule has crossed that barrier, there is easily enough energy to get over the second, smaller barrier, so the reaction proceeds quickly to the formation of product.

What if the first step is fast, but the second step is slow? Mathematically, $k_a \gg k_b$ would be true, and our function for [P] would simplify to

$$[P] = (1 - e^{-k_b t})[A]_0$$

Now, the second, slow step is the rate-limiting step, and it is the only one that shows up in the final expression. Energy diagrams for these two cases are shown in Figure 5.7.

This discussion raises some interesting points about validating reaction mechanisms. Note that both cases of the rate-limiting step lead to first-order rate laws. If we were to measure concentrations as a function of time, however, we would have no way of knowing if we had determined $k_a$ or $k_b$, thus we wouldn't actually know what the mechanism

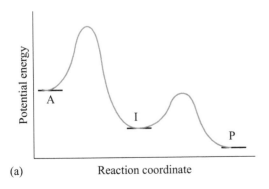
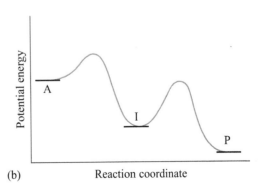

FIGURE 5.7. Potential energy diagrams for the reaction A → I → P with a) $k_b > k_a$ and b) $k_a > k_b$.

was. Either hypothesis would fit the experimental results. So what could be done to get more information? One thing we could do would be to try to identify the presence of the intermediate species, either by **quenching** (or stopping) the reaction before it reaches completion, or through some sort of spectroscopic characterization.

### 5.2.4 Branching Elementary Reactions

Let's now consider the possibility of a branching reaction where one reactant can form two different products:

$$A \rightleftharpoons C \qquad \text{forward } k_1, \text{ reverse } k_1'$$

$$A \rightleftharpoons D \qquad \text{forward } k_2, \text{ reverse } k_2'$$

A plausible energy diagram for this situation is shown in Figure 5.8. At early time, the rate of formation of C will be given by

$$\frac{d[C]}{dt} = k_1[A]$$

(Note that at early time we are not allowing for the back reaction, since there is no C present initially.) Likewise, for D we can write

$$\frac{d[D]}{dt} = k_2[A]$$

Doing a bit of algebra and integrating with respect to time lets us write the ratio of the concentration of the two products at early time as

$$\frac{[D]}{[C]} = \frac{k_2}{k_1} \tag{5.34}$$

So, we can see that at early time, we will have more of whichever product is formed faster. This situation is said to be under **kinetic control**.

What about at long time, as the reaction approaches equilibrium? Let's first consider each branch separately. This means that, at long time, there will be an equilibrium between A and C, as well as an equilibrium between A and D. For each of these, we can write an equilibrium constant

$$K_1 = \frac{[C]_{eq}}{[A]_{eq}} = \frac{k_1}{k_1'} \qquad K_2 = \frac{[D]_{eq}}{[A]_{eq}} = \frac{k_2}{k_2'}$$

We can now write the ratio of products at equilibrium as

$$\frac{[D]_{eq}}{[C]_{eq}} = \frac{K_2}{K_1} \tag{5.35}$$

Under these conditions, the reaction is said to be under **thermodynamic control**.

Let's consider some numbers, where we'll just use relative values for rate constants. We will take $k_1 = 1$, and $k_1' = 0.01$, $k_2 = 0.1$ and $k_2' = 0.0005$. The initial ratio of products is $[D]/[C] = 0.1$. So C is formed 10 times as

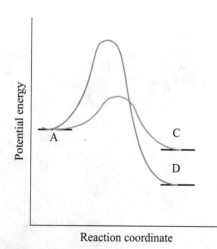

**FIGURE 5.8.** Potential energy diagrams for a branching reaction where C is the kinetic product and D is the thermodynamic product.

fast as D initially, in the kinetic limit. However, in the thermodynamic limit, $K_1 = 100$ and $K_2 = 200$, so $[D]_{eq}/[C]_{eq} = 2$. Initially, we have more C, but as the reaction proceeds, we eventually have more D present among our products. If your goal is to isolate the C product, what would you do? Remove it from the reacting system and quench any back reaction as quickly as possible. If you want D, however, you need to allow the reaction to approach equilibrium—then you can start removing it, which will cause even more formation of D. (Remember Le Châtelier's principle from general chemistry.)

## 5.2.5 Steady State Approximation

The reaction mechanisms we have considered so far are relatively simple. Clearly, we need to be able to deal with more complicated mechanisms in a systematic manner. It is possible to have multiple elementary steps—some of which are reversible, and others not—as well as multiple intermediates. In this section, we will develop an approximation that can be very useful in analyzing more complicated mechanisms.

We will take as our test reaction one with a mechanism given by

$$A + B \rightleftarrows I \rightarrow P$$

where the first step is reversible, and the last step is rate limiting. We will label the rate constants as $k_a$ for the first forward reaction, $k_a'$ for the reverse of the first step, and $k_b$ for the last step. In determining the overall rate law for a mechanism, we generally want to start with the rate of formation of the desired product. This is written as

$$\frac{d[P]}{dt} = k_b[I] \tag{5.36}$$

The main reason we don't stop here is that the intermediate is not a part of the overall reaction; a well-formed rate law should only include reactants and possibly products or any catalytically active species. (One other consideration is for liquid-phase reactions that are pH dependent. In this case, $[H^+]$ or $[OH^-]$ can show up, even though those species may not be present in the overall reaction. Their presence in the rate law tells us that the mechanism involves those ions, which are always present in aqueous solutions.)

The next step is to write an expression for the total rate of change of the intermediate, since that shows up in our expression for the rate of formation of product. For this mechanism, we would write this expression as

$$\frac{d[I]}{dt} = k_a[A][B] - k_a'[I] - k_b[I] \tag{5.37}$$

Here is where we will make an (often justifiable) assumption, known as the **steady state approximation**. This is based on the assumption that, after a short incubation time, the concentration of a short-lived intermediate does not significantly change. Mathematically, the steady state approximation is written as

$$\boxed{\frac{d[I]}{dt} \approx 0} \tag{5.38}$$

We now apply the steady state approximation to the reaction we are discussing.

$$\frac{d[I]}{dt} = k_a[A][B] - k_a'[I] - k_b[I] \approx 0$$

Solving this expression for [I] lets us write

$$[I] = \frac{k_a[A][B]}{k_a' + k_b}$$

Substitution of this into the rate of formation of product (Eq. 5.36) gives us

$$\frac{d[P]}{dt} = \frac{k_a k_b}{k_a' + k_b}[A][B] \tag{5.39}$$

This looks like a second-order rate law, with an effective rate constant $k_r = \frac{k_a k_b}{k_a' + k_b}$.

The steady state approximation only works if an intermediate is short lived, meaning that when an intermediate molecule is formed, it fairly quickly undergoes another reaction. Thus, the concentration of intermediate will never be very large. Note that the approximation does not say that the concentration of intermediate is zero, just that it doesn't change much over time. In the context of the mechanism we are discussing, there are two possible reactions that an intermediate molecule can undergo: It can either go back to form the initial reactants, or it can go forward to form product. Let's look at the rate law in the two limits where one of these steps is significantly faster than the other.

If the reverse of the first reaction happens much more quickly than the formation of products, then we can say that $k_a' \gg k_b$. We would then write Eq. 4.39 as

$$\frac{d[P]}{dt} = \frac{k_a k_b}{k_a'}[A][B] \tag{5.40}$$

If we only consider the first step and its reverse, we can think of those two reactions coming to an equilibrium, and the equilibrium constant would be given by

$$K_a = \frac{k_a}{k_a'}$$

This would let us write the rate law as

$$\frac{d[P]}{dt} = k_b K_a[A][B] \tag{5.41}$$

The presence of $k_b$ indicates that the second step is the rate-limiting step. Again, the reaction looks like a second-order rate law, with effective rate constant $k_r = k_b K_a$. This situation is sometimes described as a **preequilibrium**; the reactants establish an equilibrium with the intermediate, which then slowly bleeds away to form product.

The other limiting case that would lead to a short-lived intermediate is if the formation of product is very rapid, meaning $k_a' \gg k_b$. Making this assumption lets us write Eq. 4.39 as

$$\frac{d[P]}{dt} = k_a[A][B] \tag{5.42}$$

Now, the first step is the rate-limiting step, and $k_a$ governs the overall rate law. If we observe a second-order rate law, it may not be obvious which limiting case is the more correct mechanism, so we would have to do some additional experiments to more definitively determine the mechanism of the reaction.

## Sample Problem 5.4

The decomposition reaction

$$2 \, NO_2 \rightarrow 2 \, NO + O_2$$

is suggested to occur by means of the following mechanism.

$$NO_2 + NO_2 \rightleftarrows N_2O_4 \qquad K_1 \text{ (fast equilibrium)}$$
$$N_2O_4 \rightarrow NO + NO_3 \qquad k_2 \text{ (slow)}$$
$$NO_3 \rightarrow NO + O_2 \qquad k_3 \text{ (fast)}$$

Determine the overall rate law that would correspond to this mechanism.

### Solution

We begin by looking at the rate of formation of a product. Because NO is produced in two of the steps, let's consider the rate of formation of $O_2$. We can't form $O_2$ without forming both NO molecules, so that will be characteristic of the whole reaction. We write the rate of formation of $O_2$ as

$$\text{rate} = \frac{d[O_2]}{dt} = k_3[NO_3]$$

We can't stop here, because $NO_3$ is an intermediate in this reaction. We therefore write an expression for the total rate of change of $[NO_3]$ and apply the steady state approximation.

$$\frac{d[NO_3]}{dt} = k_2[N_2O_4] - k_3[NO_3] \approx 0$$

Solving this for $[NO_3]$ gives us

$$[NO_3] = \frac{k_2[N_2O_4]}{k_3}$$

Substitution back into our initial rate expression gives us

$$\text{rate} = \frac{d[O_2]}{dt} = k_3 \frac{k_2[N_2O_4]}{k_3} = k_2[N_2O_4]$$

We have just replaced one intermediate with another, so we need to write an expression for the total rate of change of $N_2O_4$ and apply the steady state approximation again.

$$\frac{d[N_2O_4]}{dt} = k_1[NO_2]^2 - k'_1[N_2O_4] - k_2[N_2O_4] \approx 0$$

Solving for $[N_2O_4]$ gives us

$$[N_2O_4] = \frac{k_1[NO_2]^2}{k'_1 + k_2}$$

Substituting in to our rate of formation of product gives us

$$\text{rate} = \frac{d[O_2]}{dt} = \frac{k_1 k_2}{k'_1 + k_2}[NO_2]^2 = k_{eff}[NO_2]^2$$

The reaction is predicted to be second order in $NO_2$ concentration.

---

We can also use the temperature dependence of the rate constant to gain some additional insight into the mechanism. Recall the Arrhenius equation (Eq. 4.10) for how the rate constant changes with temperature.

$$k = Ae^{-E_a/RT}$$

We derived this from our simple collisional model, and it is also found to hold true for simple overall reactions and elementary steps. What about the effective rate constant for the preequilibrium condition? We could write this as

$$k_r = \frac{k_a k_b}{k'_a} = \frac{\left(A_a e^{-E_{a,a}/RT}\right)\left(A_b e^{-E_{a,b}/RT}\right)}{\left(A'_a e^{-E_{a,a'}/RT}\right)} = \frac{A_a A_b}{A'_a}e^{-(E_{a,a}+E_{a,b}-E_{a,a'})/RT} \tag{5.43}$$

The effective activation energy for this reaction is therefore

$$E_a = E_{a,a} + E_{a,b} - E_{a,a'} \tag{5.44}$$

and, depending on the relative magnitude of $(E_{a,a} + E_{a,b})$ and $E_{a,a'}$, it can either be positive or negative. A negative effective activation energy would mean that the reaction would actually *slow down* with an increase in temperature, because the reverse step would become favored relative to the formation of product. Non-Arrhenius kinetics are often a sign that the reaction mechanism is more complicated than a single elementary step.

## 5.3 Lindemann–Hinshelwood Mechanism of Unimolecular Reactions

There are many reactions in atmospheric and combustion chemistry that have unimolecular stoichiometry where one reactant molecule either rearranges into a new product or decomposes into multiple products. It seems unreasonable, however, that this single molecule would undergo dissociation in a single elementary step. What would cause an otherwise stable molecule to simply rearrange or fall apart? What makes these reactions even more interesting is that they exhibit first-order kinetics at high pressure, but second-order kinetics at low pressure. Clearly, a single-step, unimolecular mechanism cannot explain such behavior.

A mechanism was developed by Frederick Lindemann and Charles Hinshelwood in 1922 to describe these types of reactions. The Lindemann–Hinshelwood mechanism consists of three steps: (1) collisional activation of the reactant molecule, whereby a reactant molecule gains sufficient energy to react to form product; (2) collisional deactivation, where the excited reactant molecule loses the excess energy through another collision before it can react; (3) reaction to form product, where the excited reactant molecule moves to the product side of the reaction. We write these elementary steps as follows:

$$A + A \rightarrow A + A^* \qquad \text{Collisional activation, rate constant } k_a$$
$$A^* + A \rightarrow A + A \qquad \text{Collisional deactivation, rate constant } k_a' \qquad (5.45)$$
$$A^* \rightarrow P \qquad \text{Reaction, rate constant } k_b$$

In this notation, $A^*$ signifies a reactant molecule that has received sufficient energy such that it could react to form product; the $^*$ denotes that A is in an excited energy state.

To analyze the kinetics and determine the rate law for this mechanism, we begin by writing the rate law for the third step, the one that leads to formation of product.

$$\frac{d[P]}{dt} = k_b[A^*] \qquad (5.46)$$

The excited reactant molecule is the intermediate in this reaction, so we write the total rate of change of the intermediate concentration and apply the steady state approximation

$$\frac{d[A^*]}{dt} = k_a[A]^2 - k_a'[A][A^*] - k_b[A^*] = 0 \qquad (5.47)$$

Solving Eq. 5.47 for $[A^*]$ gives

$$[A^*] = \frac{k_a[A]^2}{k_b + k_a'[A]} \qquad (5.48)$$

Substitution of Eq. 5.48 into Eq. 5.46 gives the general rate law as

$$\frac{d[P]}{dt} = k_b[A^*] = \frac{k_a k_b[A]^2}{k_b + k_a'[A]} \qquad (5.49)$$

This rate law doesn't fit our normal definitions of first- or second-order kinetics, and looks much more complicated. The main feature is the presence of [A] in the denominator.

As we've done before, however, we will explore this rate law in certain limits. Under conditions of high pressure, the rate of collisional deactivation is greater than the rate of unimolecular decay

$$k_a'[A^*][A] \gg k_b[A^*] \qquad \text{or} \qquad k_a'[A] \gg k_b \qquad (5.50)$$

Substituting Eq. 5.50 into Eq. 5.49 lets us write the rate of production of products as

$$\frac{d[P]}{dt} = k[A] \quad \text{with} \quad k = \frac{k_a k_b}{k_a'} \qquad (5.51)$$

which looks like a first-order rate law. Collisional deactivation will dominate at high pressure, thus the rate law is first order at high pressure, as seen in the experiments. This is because the rate-limiting step is the unimolecular formation of product; most excited molecules don't get the chance to form product because they experience a deactivating collision first.

The other limit would be low pressure, where collisional deactivation is less likely than formation of products. Mathematically, we write this condition as

$$k_a'[A] \ll k_b \qquad (5.52)$$

which, on substitution back into Eq. 5.49, gives us a rate law of

$$\frac{d[P]}{dt} = k_a[A]^2 \tag{5.53}$$

Thus, we have second-order kinetics at low pressure, again as seen in the experiments. At low pressure, collisions are fairly infrequent, so the rate-limiting step is the initial activating collision; a second deactivating collision is unlikely to occur at low pressure before reaction can take place.

The Lindemann–Hinshelwood mechanism was an early triumph in physical chemistry and, although it has been superseded by more sophisticated approaches, still serves as a useful example of the development of a rate law from a reaction mechanism. The fact that a simple mechanism of just three steps can explain observed rate laws over a wide range of pressures is quite impressive. Many reactions in atmospheric chemistry involve up to a dozen steps with several intermediates, but even though they can't be analyzed as readily as this mechanism, the same fundamental ideas are used to understand them.

## 5.4 Kinetics in Solution

As we discussed at the end of the last chapter, the presence of a solvent significantly changes how a chemical reaction proceeds in solution compared to the gas phase. Rather than encountering each other in ballistic collisions, reactant molecules are jostled about by the solvent molecules. Diffusion through the solvent is now a very important consideration, as is the amount of energy the reactants can gain from collisions with the solvent molecules. We now develop more quantitative descriptions of the conditions of diffusion control and activation control.

### 5.4.1 Diffusion-Controlled Reactions

The first step in a bimolecular elementary reaction that takes place in solution is the formation of an **encounter pair**. This step is written as

$$A + B \rightarrow AB \qquad \text{rate} = k_d[A][B] \tag{5.54}$$

The subscript $d$ on the rate constant denotes that it relates to the diffusion of the reactants in the liquid medium. We will not fully derive this here, but use of the Stokes–Einstein equation leads to an expression for the diffusion-controlled rate constant as

$$k_d = \frac{8RT}{3\eta} \tag{5.55}$$

where $\eta$ is the viscosity of the liquid and $R$ is the ideal gas constant.

Once the encounter pair forms, there are two options; the two reactants can diffuse away from each other without reacting, or the pair can move to formation of product. Those steps, and their rate laws, are written as

$$AB \rightarrow A + B \qquad \text{rate} = k_d{'}[AB]$$

$$AB \rightarrow P \qquad \text{rate} = k_a[AB]$$

Our intermediate is the encounter pair, AB, so as we have done before, we write an expression for the total rate of change of [AB] and apply the steady state approximation.

$$\frac{d[AB]}{dt} = k_d[A][B] - k_d'[AB] - k_a[AB] = 0$$

The rate of formation of product is then written as

$$\frac{d[P]}{dt} = k_a[AB] = \frac{k_a k_d}{k_a + k_d'}[A][B] = k_r[A][B] \tag{5.56}$$

where we write $k_r$ as the effective rate constant.

In the limit that encounter pairs quickly react to form product, $k_a \gg k_d'$ and the effective rate constant becomes

$$k_r = \frac{k_a k_d}{k_a} = k_d \tag{5.57}$$

Thus, the limit for reaction taking place is the diffusion of the two reactant molecules to find each other and form an encounter pair. This is the limit of diffusion-controlled reactions, and is often seen with free-radical reactions where the activation energy is rather small.

## 5.4.2 Activation-Controlled Reactions

The other limit of our effective rate constant is when $k_a \ll k_d'$. In this case, we write the effective rate constant from Eq. 5.56 as

$$k_r = \frac{k_a k_d}{k_d'} = k_a K_d \tag{5.58}$$

where $K_d$ represents an equilibrium constant for the formation of an encounter pair. In this case, the limit to reaction is the ability of the reactant molecules to gain enough energy from the solvent once they have formed an encounter pair. The temperature dependence of this type of reaction may also be more complicated than simple Arrhenius kinetics would suggest, because both $k_a$ and $K_d$ will have their own temperature dependence. Increasing the temperature will lead to more energy available to the encounter pair, but it may also make it easier for the reactant molecules to move away from each other before they react.

# 5.5 Summary, and Where We Go Next

In this chapter, we have developed the formalism of chemical kinetics in terms of rate laws and reaction mechanisms. We have also introduced the steady state approximation, which allows us to develop rate laws for complicated reaction mechanisms. It is important to keep in mind that a mechanism is only plausible if the rate law predicted by that mechanism matches what is determined experimentally. In the next chapter, we will consider reactions taking place on surfaces and discuss some important ideas relating to heterogeneous catalysis, a very important area in the chemical industry.

**5.1** The isomerization of $CH_3NC$ to $CH_3CN$ has a rate constant of $k = 1.07 \times 10^{-5}$ $s^{-1}$ at 450 K.

a) What order kinetics does this reaction exhibit?

b) What fraction of $CH_3NC$ will have decomposed after a time of 2 hours?

**5.2** In the decomposition of NOBr, two molecules of NOBr react to form two molecules of NO and a $Br_2$ molecule. The following data were obtained by measuring the pressure of NOBr as a function of time at 298 K.

| Time (hr) | P of NOCl (kPa) |
|:---:|:---:|
| 0 | 25 |
| 2 | 5.8 |
| 5 | 2.5 |
| 8 | 1.9 |
| 10 | 1.5 |
| 15 | .9 |
| 20 | .7 |

Determine whether the reaction follows first- or second-order kinetics. Determine the value of the rate constant, in appropriate units.

**5.3** At an archaeological dig site, a wooden object is found that looks like some sort of tool. The $^{14}C$ radioactivity (which reflects the number of radioactive atoms present) of the artifact is 35.3% of that of wood from a living tree in the same area. Given that the half-life of $^{14}C$ is 5,730 years, estimate the age of the wooden object.

**5.4** A reaction is described by a second-order rate law in a single species. The rate constant has a value of $3.4 \times 10^{-2}$ L $mol^{-1}$ $s^{-1}$. The reaction starts with $[A] = 0.0050$ mol $L^{-1}$.

a) What is the half-life of the reaction at the initial time and after a duration of 1 hour and 2 hours?

b) How long will it take for the concentration of A to be reduced to 10% of its initial value?

c) What is the half-life at the time you determined in part b)?

**5.5** The thermal decomposition of $N_2O_5$ to form $NO_2$ and $NO_3$ has been found to follow first-order kinetics at 298 K. The Arrhenius prefactor has a value of $6.3 \times 10^{14}$ $s^{-1}$, and the activation energy is 88 kJ $mol^{-1}$.

a) What is the half-life of this reaction at 298 K?

b) At what temperature would the reaction have a half-life equal to 10% of the value you determined in part a?

c) Discuss what your results to parts a) and b) suggest about the need for precise temperature control in performing kinetics experiments.

**5.6** In section 5.1.4, we considered rate laws that are second order in only a single chemical species. Here, we will broaden our horizons a little.

    a) Consider an elementary reaction described by the rate law rate = $k[A][B]$. If the reaction starts with equal concentrations of A and B, derive the integrated rate law.

    b) For the same reaction and rate law described in part a), derive a more general integrated rate law where the initial concentrations of A and B are not necessarily the same. (Hint: You may need to review the technique of integration by partial fractions to complete the derivation.)

**5.7** Ethyl mercaptan ($C_2H_5SH$) decomposes by first-order kinetics to produce ethene and $H_2S$. For this reaction, the Arrhenius prefactor is $1.0 \times 10^{13}$ $s^{-1}$ and the activation energy is 215 kJ $mol^{-1}$. A stream containing $C_2H_5SH$ passes through a 2 m pipe of 50 mm diameter at 2 L $min^{-1}$. What is the highest temperature at which you can operate to deliver 90% of the initial amount of $C_2H_5SH$ to a downstream reactor?

**5.8** Consider a reaction described by the following mechanism:

$$A + B \rightleftarrows C$$

$$B + C \rightarrow D$$

    a) Write the overall reaction described by this mechanism.

    b) What role does compound C play in this reaction?

    c) Derive a rate law for the formation of compound D, assuming that compound C is relatively unstable. Justify any assumptions in your derivation.

    d) Simplify your rate law for the two cases where either the reverse reaction of step 1 or the forward reaction of step 2 dominates the kinetics. What type of rate law is observed in each case? Also which step is rate limiting in each case?

    e) Sketch plausible energy diagrams for the two cases described in part d).

**5.9** Atomic iodine readily combines to form molecular iodine in the presence of inert argon by the reaction

$$I + I + Ar \rightarrow I_2 + Ar$$

    a) Assuming this reaction takes place in an elementary step, write the rate law.

    b) What is the role of the Ar atoms in this reaction mechanism?

    c) At 298 K, the rate constant for this reaction has a value of $7.1 \times 10^{14}$ $cm^6$ $mol^{-2}$ $s^{-1}$. The vapor pressure of iodine is 40 Pa at 298K. A chamber is prepared with only solid $I_2$ and 100 mbar of Ar. A laser is used to photodissociate 25% of the $I_2$ vapor. Estimate the time it will take for the atomized $I_2$ vapor to recombine. Justify any assumptions or approximations you make.

**5.10** Consider a reaction of the form

$$A \rightleftarrows B \rightleftarrows C$$

with rate constants $k_1$ and $k_{-1}$ for the first reaction (forward and reverse) and $k_2$ and $k_{-2}$ (forward and reverse) for the second reaction.

a) Sketch plots of the concentration of each species as a function of time with $k_{-1} = 0$, $k_1 = k_2$, and $k_{-2} = 2 k_2$. Sketch a potential energy diagram for this situation.

b) Make similar plots and a potential energy diagram for the case where $k_{-1} = 1/2 k_1$, $k_1 = 2 k_2$, and $k_{-2} = 2 k_2$.

**5.11** The following mechanism has been proposed for the addition of hydrogen chloride to an alkene.

$$HCl + HCl \rightleftarrows (HCl)_2 \qquad\qquad K_1$$

$$HCl + RCH=CHR' \rightleftarrows complex \qquad K_2$$

$$(HCl)_2 + complex \rightarrow RCH_2CHClR' + 2\,HCl \qquad k_r\ (slow)$$

a) Write the overall reaction that corresponds to this mechanism.

b) Derive the rate law that corresponds to this mechanism.

**5.12** Exchange of oxygen between hypochlorite ion ($ClO^-$) and iodide ion in aqueous solution to form chloride ion and hypoiodite ion ($IO^-$) is proposed to occur according to the following mechanism:

$$ClO^- + H_2O \rightleftarrows HOCl + OH^- \qquad K_1$$

$$I^- + HOCl \rightarrow HOI + Cl^- \qquad k_2\ (slow)$$

$$OH^- + HOI \rightarrow H_2O + IO^- \qquad k_3\ (fast)$$

a) Derive the rate law that corresponds to this mechanism.

b) What effect will an increase in the pH of the solution have on the rate of this reaction?

## CHAPTER 6

# Catalysis and Surface Reactions

## 6.1 Catalysis

### 6.1.1 Role of a Catalyst

In the last chapter, we developed a mathematical formalism for describing reaction kinetics. We also learned how we can take a proposed reaction mechanism and analyze it to determine the corresponding rate law. The rate law tells us how the rate of reaction changes with different concentrations of the various reactants and products. In most cases, we can speed a reaction up by increasing the concentration of a reactant. But this is not the only way we can speed up a reaction. As we saw in Chapter 4 and with the Arrhenius equation (Eq. 4.10),

$$k = Ae^{-E_a/RT}$$

we can usually speed up a reaction by increasing the temperature, which causes the molecules to move faster and collide with more energy.

The Arrhenius equation actually gives us another hint as to how we can increase the rate of a chemical reaction, which is by decreasing the activation energy, $E_a$. The activation energy has to do with the energy required for a collision to lead to reaction, and therefore depends on the types of bonds that are forming and being broken. Because of this, you may think that there is not much we can do to affect such fundamental aspects of a reaction. This is precisely what a catalyst does, however. A **catalyst** is something that increases the rate of a reaction without itself being consumed during the course of the reaction. Most catalysts operate by reducing the activation energy for the reaction,

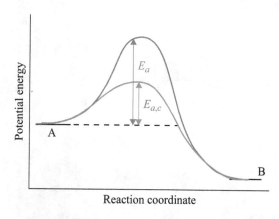

**FIGURE 6.1.** Uncatalyzed and catalyzed reaction pathways with activation energies of $E_a$ and $E_{a,c}$, respectively.

generally through stabilization of the transition state, leading to orders-of-magnitude increases in reaction rates even at moderate temperatures. Activation barriers for a catalyzed and uncatalyzed reaction are shown in Figure 6.1. It is important to note that a catalyst does not change the final distribution of products and reactants at equilibrium; rather, it reduces the time required to reach equilibrium.

### 6.1.2 Homogeneous and Heterogeneous Catalysis

Catalysts generally fall into one of two classes. If the catalyst is in the same physical state as the reactants—for example, dissolved in solution—then we call it a **homogeneous catalyst**. Many catalysts used in synthetic organic chemistry are transition metal complexes that are dissolved in the same solution as the reactants; therefore, these are homogeneous catalysts. Enzymes, which are proteins that catalyze specific biochemical reactions, are also homogeneous catalysts. Because the catalyst is in the same environment as the reactants, it interacts with reactant molecules very frequently. One of the challenges of using a homogeneous catalyst, however, is recovering the catalysts for reuse once the reaction has completed. This can be a significant concern if the catalyst contains a precious metal, which they often do.

If the catalyst is in a different physical state than the reactants, we call this a **heterogeneous catalyst**. Most commonly, the heterogeneous catalyst is a solid and the reaction takes place in a gas or liquid phase. One example of a heterogeneous catalyst is the catalytic converter in the exhaust system of a car, which has a honeycomb structure to maximize the surface area on which the reactions take place. An advantage of heterogeneous catalysts is that the ability to recover and reuse the material is often much greater than for a homogeneous catalyst. Many of these catalysts require very expensive metals, however, and they can even become ineffective over time through a process called **poisoning**, whereby the surface chemistry changes due to buildup of undesirable compounds. To better understand heterogeneous catalysis, we need to develop a model for reactions that take place on a surface.

## 6.2 Model of Molecular Adsorption to a Surface

### 6.2.1 Adsorption

In order for a reaction to take place on a surface, reactant molecules first have to interact with the surface. If a molecule interacts strongly with a surface and remains there for some time, we say that the molecule has **adsorbed** to the surface. The word "adsorbed" looks very similar to the word "absorbed," so it is important to distinguish between the two. **Adsorption** is the process whereby a molecule attaches to the surface but does not penetrate into the bulk of the solid. **Absorption** involves incorporation of the molecule into the bulk solid material. A molecule that has adsorbed to a surface can **desorb**, or leave the surface. Leaving the solid is more difficult if the molecule has been absorbed into the bulk.

There are generally two types of adsorption: **physisorption** and **chemisorption**. A molecule that physisorbs to the surface is held in place by noncovalent interactions, such as van der Waals (vdW) forces or dipole interactions. A physisorbed molecule is not permanently attached to the surface and can potentially desorb and move away from the surface. Physisorbed molecules can also move across the surface without leaving. Chemisorption involves the formation of a covalent bond with the surface; therefore, the interaction is much stronger, and it is more difficult to remove the molecule from the surface. Chemisorption is often preceded by physisorption; a molecule first interacts weakly with the surface before exchanging electrons and forming a covalent bond. Chemisorbed molecules are also not very mobile on the surface.

## 6.2.2 Thermodynamic Considerations of Adsorption

We will formally cover thermodynamics later in the book. You have, however, already been exposed to some of the important ideas in your general chemistry courses. These will be sufficient to discuss some of the thermodynamic considerations that are relevant to the adsorption process. One of the most important things you learned about chemical thermodynamics is that bond formation is always exothermic, and that bond breaking is always endothermic. Mathematically, we write $\Delta H < 0$ for a bond-formation process and $\Delta H > 0$ for a bond-breaking process. Because the adsorption process involves the formation of a "bond" between the molecule and the surface, adsorption is always exothermic, or $\Delta H_{ads} < 0$. (We have put the word "bond" in quotation marks here because, for physisorption, there is no formation of an actual chemical bond. However, the exothermic requirement still holds for an interaction that is mediated by weaker forces such as vdW and dipole interactions.) When a molecule adsorbs to the surface, heat is released, which typically flows away into the solid material.

In general chemistry, you also learned about Le Châtelier's principle and how a chemical system at equilibrium responds to a perturbation. For an exothermic reaction, heat is, in a sense, a product; thus if the temperature is increased, the reaction will shift to the reactant side—that is, the gas phase, not surface-bound molecule. This means that adsorption is more likely at low temperatures than at high temperatures, which matches our common experience with dew on a cool morning. Conversely, if we want to reduce the likelihood of molecules sticking to our surface, we can increase the temperature.

Enthalpy is not the full story of thermodynamics; we also need to consider what is happening with entropy. In Chapter 2, we developed a statistical definition of entropy in terms of the number of ways we can arrange the molecules in our system. For an adsorption process, we go from molecules that are moving about freely in the gas phase to molecules that are attached to the surface. Clearly, there are many more ways to arrange the molecules in the gas relative to being on the surface, so we can say that adsorption results in a decrease in entropy. Mathematically, we write $\Delta S_{ads} < 0$.

Enthalpic and entropic considerations are balanced if we consider the change in Gibbs energy for a process. You should recall from general chemistry that (at constant pressure and temperature) $\Delta G = \Delta H - T\Delta S$. For the adsorption process, we therefore can write

$$\Delta G_{ads} = \Delta H_{ads} - T\Delta S_{ads} \qquad (6.1)$$

Recall that a process is spontaneous if $\Delta G < 0$. Since $\Delta H_{ads}$ and $\Delta S_{ads}$ are both negative, we can see that the sign of $\Delta G_{ads}$ will depend on the temperature. At low temperature, the enthalpy term will be larger and $\Delta G_{ads}$ will be negative and spontaneous. At high temperature, the $T \Delta S_{ads}$ term will dominate, making the overall sign of $\Delta G_{ads}$ positive and not spontaneous. This does not mean that no molecules will adsorb to the surface, but that the equilibrium will favor the desorption side of the process. The amount of molecules sticking to the surface will thus be temperature dependent.

## 6.2.3 Langmuir Model of Surface Adsorption

We now begin to develop the simplest quantitative model of adsorption of molecules on a surface. This model was first developed by the grand pioneer of surface science, Irving Langmuir, in 1916. In developing this model, Langmuir stated three assumptions to describe the simplest case of adsorption:

- The surface consists of uniform adsorption sites with uniform energy of adsorption, $\Delta H_{ads}$.
- The adsorption energy of one site is independent of the coverage of a neighboring site.
- Only one molecule can adsorb per site (monolayer coverage).

These three assumptions form the basis of the model, so let's discuss them in more detail. We first think of the surface as consisting of sites where molecules can adsorb, and the energy of adsorption is the same for each site. Each site can accept at most one molecule, and then that site is covered. One way to think of the surface is as a checkerboard where all the squares are the same and you can only place one checker per square. As for independence of sites, this means that the presence of a checker on a square has no effect on the ability to place one on a neighboring square. Figure 6.2 depicts the Langmuir model of adsorption.

More complicated models will adjust one or more of these assumptions. For example, we could allow more than one molecule per site, or we could have different types of sites that exhibit different preferences for adsorption. We could also require that once one site has been occupied, it is more likely or less likely for a molecule to adsorb on a neighboring site. It is important, though, that we start with the simplest model, just as we did in developing the kinetic molecular theory of gases, and see what we can do with it before trying

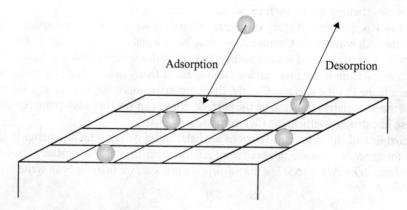

**FIGURE 6.2.** Adsorption and desorption from a surface that follows the Langmuir model. As depicted, the fractional coverage $\theta = 0.25$.

to build a complicated model to describe all possible phenomena. This simple model will of course have limitations, but it can actually describe many things quite well.

We can describe the adsorption/desorption process by the reversible reaction

$$A\,(g) + S \rightleftarrows AS$$

where AS signifies the molecule A bound to the surface S. The adsorption rate constant we will call $k_a$, and the desorption rate constant we will call $k_d$. Instead of writing rate expressions in terms of concentration, since we are talking about gas-phase molecules, we will use pressure. It is also useful to define a new parameter called the **fractional surface coverage**, represented by $\theta$. This parameter ranges from 0, for a completely bare surface, to 1, for a completely covered surface. The rate of adsorption can be written in terms of $\theta$ as

$$\text{rate}_a = k_a P(1-\theta) = \frac{d\theta}{dt} \tag{6.2}$$

where $k_a$ is the rate constant for adsorption and $P$ is the pressure of A in the gas phase. Note that the rate of adsorption depends on $1-\theta$, since we are really concerned with the number of open sites on which new molecules can attach; if the surface is covered, no additional molecules can adsorb to the surface. The rate of desorption is similarly written as

$$\text{rate}_d = k_d \theta = -\frac{d\theta}{dt} \tag{6.3}$$

Note that there is no dependence of the desorption rate on the pressure in the gas phase; there is always room in the gas for one more molecule.

Once the gas-surface system has come to equilibrium, the rate of adsorption and the rate of desorption will be the same. Put another way, the fractional surface coverage will not change because it has reached a steady state. This means we can write

$$k_a P(1-\theta) = k_d \theta \tag{6.4}$$

It is helpful to define an equilibrium constant of adsorption as the ratio of $k_a$ and $k_d$.

$$K_{ads} = \frac{k_a}{k_d} \tag{6.5}$$

Solving for the fractional coverage gives us

$$\boxed{\theta = \frac{PK_{ads}}{1 + PK_{ads}}} \tag{6.6}$$

Because the two rate constants, and therefore the adsorption equilibrium constant, depend on temperature, it is typical to evaluate this expression at a fixed temperature. Partly for this reason, Eq. 6.6 is known as the **Langmuir isotherm**. At a given temperature, it gives us the relationship between gas phase pressure and fractional surface coverage.

The shape of the Langmuir isotherm is clearly nonlinear, with a fairly steep rise at low pressure and saturation at some higher pressure, as shown in Figure 6.3. How quickly the surface reaches saturation depends on the value of $K_{ads}$; if $K_{ads}$ is large, the surface will saturate at fairly low gas pressure because of the strong interactions between the molecules and the surface, and the reverse is true for small $K_{ads}$. We have already discussed that adsorption is favored at low temperatures, thus the value of $K_{ads}$ will increase with a decrease in temperature, meaning the surface will be saturated at a lower pressure than

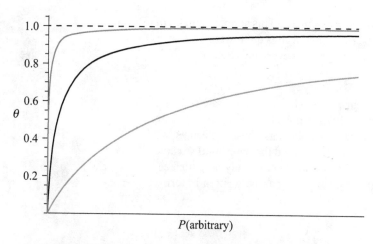

**FIGURE 6.3.** Langmuir isotherms with values of $K_{ads}$ of 1-black, 10-blue, and 0.1-orange. (The units of $K_{ads}$ and $P$ are arbitrary.)

at high temperature. Obtaining Langmuir isotherms at multiple temperatures can give us significant insight into the thermodynamics of the adsorption process, which will be revisited later in the text.

These ideas are also relevant to solid materials with a reasonably high vapor pressure, meaning they can sublime. Mass loss of a solid due to sublimation is greatly reduced in an ambient atmosphere, primarily because the escaping atoms or molecules collide with background gas and eventually arrive back at the surface from which they escaped. This is one reason why incandescent light bulbs are filled with a low pressure of argon or other inert gas. Otherwise, the filament would completely evaporate in a fairly short time, and you'd have to replace the light bulb. The inside of the bulb would also darken as the tungsten deposits on the glass. Irving Langmuir was the one who figured this out.

### 6.2.4 Uses of the Langmuir Isotherm

As we have just discussed, the Langmuir isotherm can give us insights into the thermodynamics of the adsorption process. There are other uses for this type of data that we will now discuss. In particular, we can learn about the size of molecules and the effective surface area of materials. To begin this discussion, we need to slightly rearrange the mathematical expression of the Langmuir isotherm, Eq. 6.6.

$$\theta + PK_{ads}\theta = PK_{ads}$$

Recall that the parameter $\theta$ represents the fractional surface coverage. We can think of this as the number of molecules on the surface divided by the maximum number of molecules that could possibly be on the surface. Mathematically, we write this idea as

$$\theta = \frac{N}{N_{sat}} \tag{6.7}$$

where $N_{sat}$ is the maximum number of adsorbed molecules on a fully saturated surface. We can substitute this into our expression and rearrange things a bit to write

$$\frac{P}{N} = \frac{P}{N_{sat}} + \frac{1}{K_{ads}N_{sat}} \tag{6.8}$$

Before doing anything else with this expression, we need to be clear what the different variables represent. Here, $P$ is the pressure in the gas phase above the surface on which molecules have attached, and $N$ is the number of molecules adsorbed on the surface. $N_{sat}$ is the maximum number of molecules that can possibly be on the surface. One way to determine $N$ is to take the surface and quickly move it from the chamber in which it has established an equilibrium with the gas and place it in a high-vacuum chamber. In this new environment, the equilibrium will shift to cause most of the gas to desorb. The pressure that results from this desorption can then be measured and, through the ideal gas law, be converted into a number of molecules. If we then make a plot of $P/N$ vs. $P$, we can fit those results to a line, the slope of which is $1/N_{sat}$ and the intercept is $1/K_{ads}N_{sat}$.

Knowledge of $N_{sat}$ can tell us some interesting things both about the surface and the adsorbing molecules. If we know the effective surface area of the material to which molecules are adsorbing, then by knowing how many molecules we can adsorb on that surface, we can obtain an effective surface area of each molecule. On the other hand, if we have a good sense of the size of the adsorbing molecules, determining $N_{sat}$ will allow us to calculate the effective surface area of the solid, which may otherwise be hard for a highly porous material or a powder sample.

Sample Problem 6.1
A new powdered material is being tested for use as a drying agent, or desiccant. It is found that 0.025 g of material has a saturation coverage of $N_2$ of $2.30 \times 10^{20}$ molecules. The effective surface area of $N_2$ is 16.2 Å$^2$, and that of $H_2O$ is about 14 Å$^2$. How much water, in grams, can be adsorbed per gram of this material?

Solution

The saturation coverage is readily converted to an effective total surface area

$$\left(2.30 \times 10^{20}\, \text{molecules}\right) \times \left(16.2 \text{Å}^2/\text{molecule}\right) \times \left(10^{-20}\, \text{m}^2/\text{Å}^2\right) = 37.3 \text{m}^2$$

$$\frac{37.3 \text{ m}^2}{0.025 \text{ g}} = 1500 \text{ m}^2\text{g}^{-1}$$

The effective surface area of this material is 1500 m$^2$ g$^{-1}$, which may seem large but is actually not unreasonable for high-surface-area materials. With an effective size of a water molecule of 14 Å$^2$, we can readily determine the amount of water we can adsorb with this material.

$$1500 \text{ m}^2\text{g}^{-1} \times \frac{1 H_2O \text{ molecule}}{14 \times 10^{-20}\, \text{m}^2} \times \frac{1 \text{ mol}}{6.022 \times 10^{23}\, \text{molecules}} \times \frac{18.0 \text{ g } H_2O}{1 \text{ mol } H_2O}$$

$$= 0.32 \text{ g } H_2O/\text{g}$$

Thus, we can adsorb 320 mg of water per gram of desiccant material.

# 6.3 Mechanisms of Reactions at Surfaces

## 6.3.1 Unimolecular Surface Reactions

The simplest reaction mechanism we can have on a surface would be a simple unimolecular reaction of a surface-bound species. We write the reaction steps as follows:

$A + S \rightleftarrows AS$      Adsorption $k_a$, desorption $k_d$

$AS \rightarrow P + S$      Reaction $k_r$

As we did before, we start by writing the rate expression for the formation of product.

$$\frac{dP_P}{dt} = k_r' N_{AS} = k_r \theta$$

(6.9)

(It is generally more convenient to use pressure rather than concentration for gas phase reactions.) The rate of formation of product depends on the amount of surface-bound reactant we have, which we can either represent as a number or as a fractional coverage, $\theta$. We have made a distinction between $k_r$ and $k_r'$ because the units of the rate constant will necessarily be different depending on our choice. If we assume that the rate constant for reaction is small compared to the rate constant for desorption, then we can argue that the reactant molecules A in the gas phase will come to an equilibrium with the molecules that are adsorbed to the surface. If we assume that adsorption of A follows the Langmuir model, then we can use the expression for the Langmuir isotherm (Eq. 6.6) to write

$$\frac{dP_P}{dt} = \frac{k_r K_{ads} P_A}{1 + K_{ads} P_A}$$

(6.10)

This rate expression is readily evaluated in two limits, either low or high reactant pressure. If the reactant pressure is low, then the denominator simplifies to a value of 1 and the rate of formation of product will be first order in the reactant pressure.

$$\frac{dP_P}{dt} \approx k_r K_{ads} P_A \quad \text{if} \quad K_{ads} P_A \ll 1$$

(6.11)

On the other hand, if the reactant pressure is high, then the rate of formation of product becomes independent of reactant pressure.

$$\frac{dP_P}{dt} \approx k_r \quad \text{if} \quad K_{ads} P_A \gg 1$$

(6.12)

This is another example of a zero-order reaction. Thus, if we want the reaction to proceed quickly, we want to ensure that our surface is always covered, which requires that the reactant pressure be high. There are cases, however, where a reaction on a surface leads to an isomerization or decomposition that is undesirable. To avoid this side reaction, we need to keep the reactant pressure fairly low, which of course slows down the desired reaction. Such trade-offs are common in science and engineering.

## 6.3.2 Eley–Rideal Mechanism of Surface Reactions

The next most complicated surface reaction mechanism we will consider is the reaction of a gas-phase molecule with a surface-bound reactant. The first thing that happens is that reactant A comes to an equilibrium on the surface, as described by the Langmuir model. Reactant B then collides with a surface-bound A to lead to formation of product.

$$A + S \rightleftarrows AS \qquad \text{Adsorption } k_a, \text{ desorption } k_d$$
$$B + AS \rightarrow P + S \qquad \text{Reaction } k_{ER}$$

The rate of formation of product will therefore depend on the pressure of B and the amount of surface-bound A.

$$\frac{dP_P}{dt} = k_{ER}\theta_A P_B \qquad (6.13)$$

We use the expression for the Langmuir isotherm (Eq. 6.6) to write

$$\frac{dP_P}{dt} = \frac{k_{ER}K_{ads,\,A}P_A P_B}{1 + K_{ads,\,A}P_A} \qquad (6.14)$$

Again, we can look at this expression in two limits. If we have low pressure of reactant A, then the rate law becomes

$$\frac{dP_P}{dt} \approx k_{ER}K_{ads,\,A}P_A P_B \quad \text{if} \quad K_{ads,\,A}P_A \ll 1 \qquad (6.15)$$

The rate law then looks second order overall, and first order in each reactant. On the other hand, if the pressure of reactant A is high, we have

$$\frac{dP_P}{dt} \approx k_{ER}P_B \quad \text{if} \quad K_{ads,\,A}P_A \gg 1 \qquad (6.16)$$

and the reaction is now simply first order in B. To maximize the formation of product, we want to keep the surface covered in A, because the rate limiting step is collisions of B molecules with the A-covered surface.

## 6.3.3 Langmuir–Hinshelwood Mechanism of Surface Reactions

The Eley–Rideal mechanism is one limit for a bimolecular surface reaction where only one of the reactants needs to be bound to the surface. The other limit would be a reaction between two surface-bound reactant molecules. This is the basis of the Langmuir–Hinshelwood mechanism. Both A and B attach to the surface, where the reaction takes place. Keep in mind that physisorbed molecules are not covalently attached to the surface, so they can move about on the surface before desorbing. Thus, they can encounter each other and react. The steps in this mechanism are as follows:

$$A + S \rightleftarrows AS \qquad \text{Adsorption } k_{aA}, \text{ desorption } k_{dA}$$
$$B + S \rightleftarrows BS \qquad \text{Adsorption } k_{aB}, \text{ desorption } k_{dB}$$
$$AS + BS \rightarrow P + S \qquad \text{Reaction } k_{LH}$$

Within this model, we will assume that there is only one type of adsorption site, and that the sites have no preference for either A or B molecules. This means that both A and B molecules are competing with each other for surface sites, and we need to write

$$\theta_A = \frac{K_{ads,\,A}P_A}{1 + K_{ads,\,A}P_A + K_{ads,\,B}P_B} \quad \text{and} \quad \theta_B = \frac{K_{ads,\,B}P_B}{1 + K_{ads,\,A}P_A + K_{ads,\,B}P_B} \qquad (6.17)$$

The rate of reaction is thus written as

$$\frac{dP_P}{dt} = k_{LH}\theta_A\theta_B = \frac{k_{LH}K_{ads,A}P_A K_{ads,B}P_B}{[1 + K_{ads,A}P_A + K_{ads,B}P_B]^2}$$

(6.18)

Because the rate constant and the respective equilibrium constants are all temperature dependent, it should come as no surprise that the Langmuir–Hinshelwood mechanism often leads to non-Arrhenius kinetics. One of the reasons for this complication is that low temperature favors adsorption of the reactants; however, the surface needs to be warm enough for the surface-bound reactants to have sufficient surface mobility to encounter each other and react. If the surface is too cold, the reactants stick but don't move around much. If the surface is too hot, they don't stick in the first place. Temperature optimization is thus very important.

### 6.3.4 More Complicated Mechanisms of Surface Reactions

The Eley–Rideal and Langmuir–Hinshelwood mechanisms represent two limits of surface reactivity, and examples of each have been found experimentally. In reality, most surface reactions lie somewhere between these two extremes. There are other, more complicated mechanisms for surface reactions, particularly if we relax the assumptions of the Langmuir model of surface adsorption. For example, allowing molecules to form multilayers (multiple molecules per site) will certainly affect the kinetics of a surface reaction.

More sophisticated models also try to take the nature of the surface sites into account. A surface is not in reality an atomically flat checkerboard. Rather, there are steps, terraces, edges, and other features on any real surface. Often it is these types of sites, rather than flat regions, that are catalytically active. Surface morphology becomes even more important when working with nanoparticles, where only certain crystalline facets may be catalytically active. Identifying the types of surface sites that are active for specific reactions is an active area of research.

Another factor that needs to be considered in many catalytic models is the possibility of the surface being **poisoned**. Poisoning occurs when a compound attaches to the surface and remains there, thus blocking the surface sites from accepting other reactant molecules. If a catalyst is poisoned too greatly, the material may simply need to be replaced. Given that many heterogeneous catalysts consist of expensive metals such as palladium or platinum, preventing poisoning is a very real factor in using these catalysts effectively.

## 6.4 Summary, and Where We Go Next

In this chapter, we have developed a useful model for considering chemical reactions on surfaces, the Langmuir model. This is central to our understanding of heterogeneous catalysis, an important process in the chemical industry. This concludes our coverage of chemical kinetics, but you should be aware that there is much more to this field that you may explore in future courses. We will now return to our simple molecular models and see how well we can use them to model the property of heat capacity. What we find will eventually lead us into the development of one of the triumphs of 20th-century physics, quantum mechanics.

**6.1** This problem will investigate the effect of lowering the activation energy on the rate constant.

a) Consider a homogeneous catalyst that lowers the activation energy by 13 kJ mol$^{-1}$. What effect will this have on the rate of reaction? State any assumptions in your calculation.

b) When considering the effect of a heterogeneous catalyst, are there any other aspects of the situation besides the activation energy that should be considered in a full analysis?

**6.2** You work with a company that designs catalytic converters for automobiles. Without the catalyst, only 5% of the $N_2O$ in the automobile exhaust decomposes after traveling through the catalytic converter system. If the exhaust is at 800 K, by how much does the catalyst need to reduce the activation energy in order for 75% of the $N_2O$ to decompose? Assume the decomposition of $N_2O$ follows first-order kinetics.

**6.3** Enzymes are a very important class of catalysts, as they catalyze biological processes. In this problem we will explore a widely used mechanism of enzyme kinetics, known as the Michaelis–Menten mechanism. In this mechanism, E is the enzyme, S is the substrate (a molecule that binds to the enzyme), ES is the bound enzyme–substrate complex, and P is the product.

$$E + S \rightleftharpoons ES \qquad k_a, k_a' \qquad \text{(forward, reverse)}$$
$$ES \rightarrow P + E \qquad k_b$$

Because all the enzyme is either free or bound, we can always write

$$[E] + [ES] = [E]_0$$

where $[E]_0$ is the initial concentration of enzyme. Because there is generally a high concentration of substrate relative to enzyme, we can assume that the substrate concentration doesn't change much, or $[S] \approx [S]_0$.

a) Derive an expression for the rate of formation of product that depends only on the initial concentrations of enzyme and substrate, $[E]_0$ and $[S]_0$. (Do not include any intermediates in your expression.) You may find it helpful to use the Michaelis constant, $K_M = (k_a' + k_b)/k_a$, in your expression. The Michaelis constant is characteristic of each enzyme. (Note that $K_M$ has units of concentration.) Clearly state any assumptions.

b) This mechanism was developed based on the following observations.

- For a given $[S]_0$, the initial rate is proportional to $[E]_0$
- When $[S]_0 \ll K_M$, the rate is proportional to $[S]_0$
- When $[S]_0 \gg K_M$, the rate reaches a maximum value, $v_{max}$, independent of $[S]_0$

Demonstrate that the rate expression you derived in part a) agrees with these observations.

c) Similar to the poisoning of a heterogeneous catalyst, an enzyme can be blocked by a molecule that occupies the active site and doesn't leave. This process is known as enzyme inhibition. (Many medications act by intentionally inhibiting certain enzymes.) Write mechanistic steps to include the effect of the inhibitor and make the necessary modifications to the rate expression you derived in part a). Make sure that you recover the original expression in the limit that the inhibitor concentration goes to zero.

**6.4** For a polyatomic molecule adsorbing on a surface, there is the possibility that the molecule dissociates in some way as it adsorbs. Consider the dissociative adsorption of $H_2$ on a surface.

a) Derive an expression for the Langmuir isotherm for this case, treating each separate H atom as occupying its own surface site.

b) Compare the isotherms for dissociative and nondissociative adsorption when $K_{ads} = 0.1$, 1, and 10 bar$^{-1}$.

**6.5** a) For a gas that adsorbs nondissociatively on a surface where $K_{ads} = 2.5$ bar$^{-1}$, by what percentage does the pressure need to increase in order for the fractional coverage to increase from 0.4 to 0.5?

b) Repeat this calculation for the case where $K_{ads} = 0.25$ bar$^{-1}$.

**6.6** A new formulation of silica gel (porous $SiO_2$) is being investigated for its adsorbent properties. Oxygen gas was adsorbed onto the powdered material at various pressures, and then the amount of adsorbed gas was measured. The following data were obtained at 298 K.

| P (bar) | N of $O_2$ ($\times 10^{18}$ molecules g$^{-1}$) |
|---------|--------------------------------------------------|
| 0.10    | 6.93                                             |
| 0.20    | 12.81                                            |
| 0.40    | 26.34                                            |
| 0.60    | 39.14                                            |
| 0.80    | 49.57                                            |
| 1.00    | 63.11                                            |
| 1.20    | 72.73                                            |
| 1.50    | 88.11                                            |

a) Calculate the value of the adsorption equilibrium constant and the saturation coverage.

b) Assuming the $O_2$ molecule has an effective area of 19.8 Å$^2$, calculate the effective surface area per gram of the powdered silica gel.

c) If we take the effective area of a $H_2O$ molecule to be 14 Å$^2$, what mass of water can be taken up per gram of this material?

**6.7** The idea of the collision flux that we introduced in Section 3.2.5 can be applied to the sublimation of a solid. This is justified as follows. Assume that the solid is confined in a sealed container and heated until equilibrium between the vapor and the solid has been reached. A small hole is opened, and the gas is allowed to escape. As long as there is solid material in the container, and the rate of effusion is reasonably slow, the vapor pressure will remain constant. Now, we remove the container, making the surface area from which the gas will escape equivalent to the total surface area of the solid. The rate of sublimation will still be proportional to what the vapor pressure would have been in the sealed container.

a) For tungsten wire at 2700 K, the vapor pressure is $2.85 \times 10^{-9}$ bar. For a wire that is 20 cm long and 0.50 mm thick, what is the mass loss per hour?

b) The primary ingredient in moth balls is naphthalene, often in the form of flakes. The vapor pressure of naphthalene at 20°C is 6.5 Pa. A sample of naphthalene flakes is weighed before and after sublimation takes place in a vacuum chamber. The loss of mass after 5 min exposure to vacuum is 85 g. Assuming all mass loss takes place from the surface of the flakes, estimate the effective surface area of the original naphthalene sample.

**6.8** In Section 6.3.2, we showed that for reactions that follow the Eley–Rideal mechanism, it is desirable to have strong adsorption of one of the reactants on the surface. Is this also true for the Langmuir–Hinshelwood mechanism? Derive an expression for the rate of reaction for the L–H mechanism where one of the reactants adsorbs much more strongly than the other one. What is the observed rate of reaction with respect to each reactant in this limit? Discuss how this would affect the design of a reactor for a reaction that follows Langmuir–Hinshelwood kinetics.

**6.9** Our derivation of Eq. 6.18 assumed that there was only one type of adsorption site that either A or B could attach to, meaning they can displace each other.

    a) Derive an expression for the case where there are two types of adsorption sites, and each reactant can only attach to one of them. In other words, the two reactants cannot displace each other from the surface.

    b) Evaluate the rate law in the limit that one reactant adsorbs to its site much more strongly than the other does.

    c) Briefly describe the ideal distribution of the two types of adsorption sites on the surface.

# QUANTUM MECHANICS

How Things Really Are

# Classical Equipartition Theorem, Heat Capacity, and the Need for a Better Approach

## 7.1 Modeling How Energy Is Distributed Throughout a System

In Chapter 2, we developed the Boltzmann distribution, which tells us the most probable way to distribute energy amongst available states. Other than translational energy, which we used to derive the Maxwell–Boltzmann distribution of molecular speeds, we did not go into any specifics about what those energy states might be. From Newtonian physics, there are two types of energy: kinetic energy (energy of motion) and potential energy (energy of position). Later in the course, we'll define a new type of energy, the chemical potential, that drives everything from phase transitions to chemical reactions. Each of these types of energy needs to be accounted for in a complete treatment of any molecular system.

Energy is conserved and can be interchanged. We see this as an object initially at rest (zero kinetic energy) but at a large height (high potential energy) starts to fall, converting that potential energy into kinetic energy. There are even different types of kinetic energy, relating to different types of motion such as traveling in a ballistic trajectory or rotating about a fixed point. What interests us now is how the available energy is distributed throughout our molecular system. We will first consider kinetic and potential energy of atoms and molecules in a purely classical picture and see how far this approach can take us. We will also ignore certain macroscopic effects such as gravitation, external electric or magnetic fields, and the motion of the earth.

### 7.1.1 Energy of a Monatomic Ideal Gas

Let's start with a volume of ideal monatomic gas, such as helium or argon. The only type of energy to consider is translational kinetic energy; there are no interactions between atoms in an ideal gas, so there is no potential energy. The only type of motion these particles can undergo is **translational motion**, or motion in a straight line. The energy associated with translational motion, which we will call **translational energy**, can be exchanged through elastic collisions. Even though energy is exchanged between atoms, the total energy within an isolated system stays the same.

Let's define a quantity $U$ as the total internal energy of the system. In this case, all internal energy is translational kinetic energy. We know from Newtonian mechanics and the Maxwell–Boltzmann distribution, which we explored in Chapter 3, that the average internal (kinetic) energy per atom is

$$\langle U \rangle = \langle E_{kin} \rangle = \frac{1}{2}m\langle v^2 \rangle = \frac{3}{2}k_B T \tag{7.1}$$

Recall that $\langle v^2 \rangle = \dfrac{3k_B T}{m}$. It is generally more useful to talk about more than one atom; if we have $N$ atoms, the total average internal energy is

$$\langle U \rangle = \frac{3}{2}Nk_B T \tag{7.2}$$

If we recall that $N = nN_A$, and that $k_B N_A = R$, we can write the internal energy per mole as

$$\frac{U}{n} = U_m = \frac{3}{2}RT \tag{7.3}$$

where the subscript $m$ denotes *per mole*. This molar energy was already known and, once again, we have arrived at an experimentally observed result purely from our molecular model. Because of the statistics of large numbers and the central limit theorem, we are justified in dropping the angled brackets in Eq. 7.3 when talking about energy per mole.

Now we need to discuss the concept of **degrees of freedom**. These are the independent directions in which something can move. For free translational motion of an object, such as an atom of monatomic ideal gas, we have 3 degrees of freedom, one for each direction $x$, $y$, and $z$. Since the total molar internal energy is $3/2RT$, we can reasonably say that each translational degree of freedom imparts $1/2RT$ to the molar internal energy. This statement also implies that there is no internal energy that is independent of $T$; at $T = 0$, there is no motion. We will derive the energy per translational degree of freedom more rigorously in Section 7.1.3.

### 7.1.2 Energy of a Polyatomic Gas

The relation we just derived holds for atoms. Now we need to consider molecules that consist of more than one atom. First, we can readily see that each atom in the molecule can move in three directions ($x$, $y$, and $z$), or that each molecule possesses 3 degrees of freedom per atom.

$$\text{DOF} = 3n \tag{7.4}$$

where $n$ is the number of atoms in the molecule. If the molecule is translating in the $x$ direction, then that takes 1 DOF from the total. The same holds for the $y$ and $z$ directions. Thus, translation of the whole molecule accounts for 3 DOFs. One of these is shown in Figure 7.1a. What about the remaining degrees of freedom?

If not for the bonds that hold the molecule together, each atom could move independently of the others. The bonds, however, act as constraints on the ways the atoms can move. Consider a diatomic molecule and allow one atom to move up while the other moves down. This motion would stretch the bond, and eventually the bond would have to break, as shown in Figure 7.1b. If we want the molecule to stay together, we can't allow this type of motion. We could however, allow the molecule to rotate about the center of mass, as shown in Figure 7.1c; now, both atoms are moving but the bond is intact. The same is true for a vibration of the molecule; the atoms can move apart as long as they are able to return without breaking the bond. Rotational and vibrational motions are known as **internal motion**, because the center of mass does not move. We can therefore break the degrees of freedom up as follows:

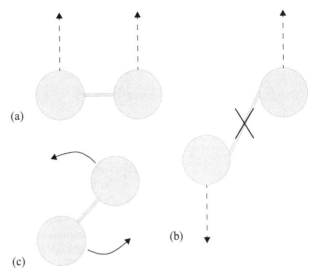

(a)

(b)

(c)

**FIGURE 7.1.** a) Translational motion of a diatomic molecule. b) If both atoms try to move in opposite directions, the bond would eventually break. c) Rotation about the center of mass preserves the integrity of the bond.

$$DOF = 3n = 3 \text{ (translational)} + (3n - 3) \text{ (rotational, vibrational)}$$

Let's first consider the rotational motion of a molecule. Here we need to distinguish between linear and nonlinear molecules. For a linear molecule, rotation about only two axes can be measured. Those axes are perpendicular to the molecular axis; rotation about the molecular axis cannot be measured and has no energy associated with it. For a nonlinear molecule, rotation about all three axes is possible. The remaining degrees of freedom are described by vibrations. We can rewrite our expression for the degrees of freedom as follows:

$$DOF = 3n = 3 \text{ (trans)} + 2 \text{ (rot)} + (3n - 5) \text{ (vib) linear} \tag{7.5}$$

$$DOF = 3n = 3 \text{ (trans)} + 3 \text{ (rot)} + (3n - 6) \text{ (vib) nonlinear} \tag{7.6}$$

## Sample Problem 7.1

Determine the DOFs and describe them for CO, $H_2O$, and $CS_2$.

### Solution

CO has two atoms, so total DOF = 6. There are 3 translational DOFs, 2 rotational DOFs (all diatomics are linear), and 1 vibrational DOF.

$H_2O$ has three atoms and is nonlinear with 9 DOFs: 3 translational DOFs, 3 rotational DOFs (nonlinear), and 3 vibrational DOFs.

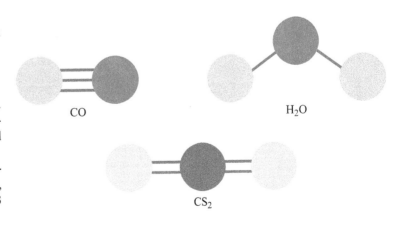

CO

$H_2O$

$CS_2$

$CS_2$ is a linear triatomic, so it has 9 DOFs: 3 translational DOFs, 2 rotational DOFs (linear), and 4 vibrational DOFs.

---

## 7.1.3 Classical Equipartition Theorem

These are the different ways that energy can be stored in the motion of the molecules. Now, how is that energy spread around? For example, is there more vibrational energy than translational energy, or do those types of motion carry the same amount of energy? Classically, we allow for equal distribution of the available energy into all possible types of motion. This idea is known as the **classical equipartition theorem**. In the formal statement of the theorem, every energy term with a square dependence on a variable of either motion or position contributes $1/2RT$ to the molar internal energy, or $1/2k_BT$ to the average energy per molecule. What follows is a formal derivation of this result.

We have already seen this demonstrated for translational motion via the Maxwell–Boltzmann distribution, but let's generalize the discussion to include rotational and vibrational motion. In all cases, we have energy that depends on the square of some parameter, $s$.

$$\epsilon_s = cs^2 \qquad \text{where } c \text{ is some constant}$$

We will assume that the possible values of $s$ form a continuum; there are no discrete states. (Remember, this is a classical theorem.) The probability of the molecule having a given value of $s$ is written by the Boltzmann distribution

$$P_s(s) = \frac{e^{-cs^2/k_BT}}{\int_{-\infty}^{\infty} e^{-cs^2/k_BT}\,ds}$$

where we integrate over all values of $s$. The average energy is calculated by evaluating the expression

$$\langle\epsilon_s\rangle = c\langle s^2\rangle = c\int s^2 P_s(s)\,ds = \frac{c\int_{-\infty}^{\infty} s^2 e^{-cs^2/k_BT}\,ds}{\int_{-\infty}^{\infty} e^{-cs^2/k_BT}\,ds} = \frac{\frac{1}{2}c\sqrt{\pi\left(\frac{k_BT}{c}\right)^3}}{\sqrt{\frac{\pi k_BT}{c}}}$$

$$\langle\epsilon_s\rangle = \frac{1}{2}k_BT$$

or, per mole:

$$\boxed{\langle E_{m,s}\rangle = \frac{1}{2}RT} \qquad (7.7)$$

Important note: *This only works if the states of $s$ are continuous!*

As we have already seen, translational energy goes as

$$E_{trans} = \frac{1}{2}mv^2 \qquad (7.8)$$

and each translational DOF contributes $1/2RT$ to the molar internal energy. Rotational energy goes as

$$E_{rot} = \frac{1}{2}I\omega^2 \qquad (7.9)$$

where $I$ is the moment of inertia and $\omega$ is the angular frequency. Each rotational DOF also contributes $1/2RT$ to the molar internal energy. Vibrational motion, as modeled by a Hooke's law spring, involves both translational and potential energy, written as

$$E_{vib} = \frac{1}{2}mv^2 + \frac{1}{2}kx^2 \qquad (7.10)$$

Here, $k$ is the force constant of the spring and $x$ is the displacement from the equilibrium position. Each vibrational DOF, therefore, contributes $1/2RT$ of kinetic energy and $1/2RT$ of potential energy, for a total of $RT$ for each vibration. We summarize these results in Table 7.1.

TABLE 7.1 Contributions to internal energy according to the equipartition theorem.

| | Linear | Nonlinear |
|---|---|---|
| $U_{m, trans}$ | 3/2RT | 3/2RT |
| $U_{m, rot}$ | RT | 3/2RT |
| $U_{m, vib}$ | $(3n - 5)RT$ | $(3n - 6)RT$ |

# 7.2 Heat Capacity

## 7.2.1 General Concepts of Heat Capacity

It now needs to be mentioned that it is very difficult to directly measure the internal energy of a gas. What we can measure, however, are *changes* in internal energy as we change the temperature of the gas. To do this, we define a quantity known as the **heat capacity**, which is the change in energy divided by the change in temperature, formally written as a derivative:

$$C = \frac{dU}{dT} \qquad (7.11)$$

This definition is somewhat oversimplified, because the energy can depend on $P$ and $V$, but we'll use it for the time being. Similarly, the heat capacity can be considered under conditions of either constant volume or constant pressure; we are actually concerned with the former, the constant-volume heat capacity, at this point. (The more formal definition of the heat capacity is as a partial derivative, as we'll see in Chapters 13 and 16.) Heat capacity is an extensive property, and therefore changes with the amount of material present. To simplify matters, and remove the size considerations, chemists generally work with the molar heat capacity. Note that if we divide by grams, not moles, we call this quantity the *specific heat*, a term that is often favored by physicists.

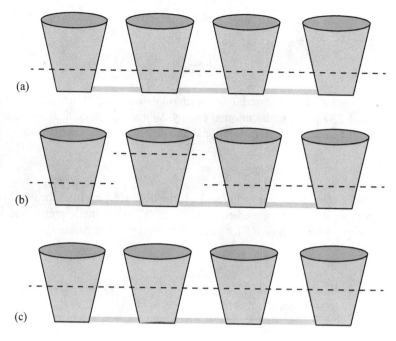

**FIGURE 7.2.** a) A system of four buckets connected at their bases. The water level in all four is initially the same. b) Water is added to the second bucket, raising the water height. c) Water flows through the tubes at the base to equalize the height in all buckets.

Our discussion of heat capacity is also helpful in revisiting our understanding of energy and temperature. As we saw in our development of the Boltzmann distribution, temperature gives us a sense of how the energy of a system is spread around among the available states. Heat capacity has to do with the different states into which energy can be put. Imagine a collection of buckets, as shown in Figure 7.2. The water in the bucket represents the energy. The height of the water in the bucket is representative of the temperature. Each bucket represents a different type of motion, or degree of freedom.

If we add water to a single bucket, the height of the water in that bucket increases. But can we have different heights in different buckets? Or, in other words, can we have different temperatures for different types of motion? If the system is at thermal equilibrium, then there can only be a single temperature value to describe the entire system. This means that we have to add the same amount of water to all of the buckets or allow water to flow between them. You can think of the buckets being connected at the base so that water can move between them to keep all the levels the same. In a classical model, we can add arbitrarily small amounts of energy (water) to the system (the collection of buckets). According to the equipartition theorem, any energy added to the system will spread out equally amongst all the various types of motion, or in our bucket model, any amount of water will spread out equally amongst all the various buckets. The height of the water (representing the temperature) will then be the same in all the buckets.

Now, let's consider two sets of buckets, one with only 3 and one with 15 buckets. The initial level of water in all the buckets is the same, so we could say that both systems are at the same temperature. But what about the energy of the two systems? Clearly, the system of 15 buckets has more water (energy) than a system of only three, even though the level of the water (the temperature) is the same. This is an important distinction between energy and temperature; temperature is not the same thing as average energy.

**TABLE 7.2**  Contributions to heat capacity according to the equipartition theorem.

|  | Linear | Nonlinear |
|---|---|---|
| $C_{m, trans}$ | 3/2R | 3/2R |
| $C_{m, rot}$ | R | 3/2R |
| $C_{m, vib}$ | $(3n - 5)R$ | $(3n - 6)R$ |

Now, we can extend this analogy to heat capacity. If we want to raise the level of water in both systems of buckets by the same amount, how much water has to be added to each system? Clearly, we will need to add more water to the system of 15 buckets than to the system of three buckets. The change in height (increase in temperature) is the same for the two systems, but more water (energy) has to be added to the system with 15 buckets (degrees of freedom) than to the system of only three. Thus, we would say that the system of 15 buckets has a higher heat capacity than the system of three buckets. This is because there are more places to put the water.

This analogy of buckets and water gives us some valuable insight into the fundamental ideas of energy, temperature, and heat capacity. If two systems have different numbers of degrees of freedom, or "buckets" in which to put energy, then the total energy of each system will be different, even when they are at the same temperature. Likewise, a system with more degrees of freedom will have a higher heat capacity than a system with fewer degrees of freedom; more total energy needs to be added to achieve the same increase in the temperature, or more energy needs to be withdrawn to lower the temperature. Anyone who lives in a humid climate experiences this every summer evening. Water vapor in the air has a much higher heat capacity than oxygen or nitrogen, and so moist air stays warmer longer than dry air. Even though deserts can get just as hot in the day, the nights are much cooler because the dry air has a fairly low heat capacity and so cools off much more quickly once the sun sets.

## 7.2.2 Heat Capacity of Ideal Gases

Let's see how well our equipartition model can predict the heat capacity of a gas where the molecules have an arbitrary number of atoms. First, we revise our table to be for heat capacity rather than energy, as shown in Table 7.2. (We have taken the temperature derivative of each element in Table 7.1 to arrive at these results.)

Sample Problem 7.2

Using the equipartition theorem, predict the heat capacity for Ar, CO, $H_2O$, $CO_2$, and $CH_4$. (These predictions will only hold in the high-temperature limit.)

Solution

Ar is a monatomic gas, so it only has 3 DOF, all of them translational. The heat capacity is predicted to be $C_m = 3/2R$.

CO is a linear diatomic with 3 translational DOFs, 2 rotational DOFs (all diatomics are linear), and 1 vibrational DOF. The predicted heat capacity is $C_m = (3/2 + 1 + 1)R = 7/2R$.

$H_2O$ is a nonlinear triatomic with 3 translational DOFs, 3 rotational DOFs (nonlinear), and 3 vibrational DOFs. The predicted heat capacity is $C_m = (3/2 + 3/2 + 3)R = 6R$.

$CO_2$ is a linear triatomic, with 3 translational DOFs, 2 rotational DOFs (linear), and 4 vibrational DOFs. The predicted heat capacity is $C_m = (3/2 + 1 + 4)R = 13/2R$.

$CH_4$ is a nonlinear molecule with five atoms. It has 3 translational DOFs, 3 rotational DOFs, and 9 vibrational DOFs. The predicted heat capacity is $C_m = (3/2 + 3/2 + 9)R = 12R$.

---

Now we need to ask: how does the equipartition theorem do in describing the actual heat capacity of gases at moderately high temperatures? We can readily look up the heat capacity for a monatomic gas, and we find a value of $C_m = 1.5R$. So far, so good. If we look up the heat capacity at 298 K of a diatomic gas, such as $N_2$ or $O_2$, we find a value of $2.5R$; we had predicted $3.5R$. The experimental values for triatomic $H_2O$ and $CO_2$ are $3.0R$ and $3.5R$, respectively; we had predicted $6.0R$ and $6.5R$, respectively. What about a polyatomic gas, such as $CH_4$? Our prediction would be $12R$, but the experimental value is $3.2R$.

Classical equipartition clearly works well for monatomic gases, but the predictions become much worse as the number of atoms in the molecule increases. Why is this? The problem comes from the vibrational energy; the equipartition assumption does not properly describe the energy of intramolecular vibrations. This is explained by quantum mechanics, which, as we will see, tells us that the allowed energies of translations, rotations, and vibrations are all quantized into particular levels. Classical mechanics, however, models the energy as continuous. Going back to our bucket analogy, for a real molecular system, we can't add energy in arbitrarily small amounts. As we will see, the spacing of the levels is closer for translations and rotations than for vibrations, which means if we only add small amounts of energy, there may not be enough to raise a vibrational "bucket" to the next-highest-allowable level. That energy will instead have to go into translations and rotations, so it's as if the vibrational "bucket" isn't available and the heat capacity is lower than predicted. We clearly need a better model to take all of this into account.

### 7.2.3 Dulong and Petit Law for Heat Capacity of Solids

All forms of matter have a heat capacity. In the early 1800s, Pierre-Louis Dulong and Alexis-Thérèse Petit measured the heat capacities of a number of monatomic solids, such as copper metal. These measurements were rather primitive and suggested that all monatomic solids have the same heat capacity, about 25 J mol$^{-1}$ K$^{-1}$. This came to be known as the Dulong and Petit law. We can understand why they saw what they did in terms of classical equipartition theory.

Let's consider the atomic motions of a monatomic solid. Each atom can be considered to be at a point on the crystal lattice and connected to neighboring atoms by "springs." The only motion these atoms exhibit is vibrational motion about their lattice positions in each of the three spatial dimensions. Classical equipartition theory predicts that each vibrational degree of freedom will contribute $R$ to the molar heat capacity, giving a total molar heat capacity of $3R$, or 24.9 J mol$^{-1}$ K$^{-1}$. This agrees well with Dulong and Petit's observations. However, with developments in refrigeration, it soon became apparent that the Dulong and Petit law broke down at low temperatures. In fact, as $T$ approaches zero, the heat capacity also goes to zero. Once again, the classical model has failed us.

# 7.3 The Limits of Classical Physics and the Need for a New Approach

Before we can address the problems we have encountered in predicting heat capacity of ideal gases and monatomic solids, we need to revisit the world of physics at the end of the 19th century. Newton's laws of motion had been successfully used for about 200 years. With the more recent development of Maxwell's equations in the 1860s for the description of electricity and magnetism, as well as the development of thermodynamics at about the same time, many more phenomena were now understood. Physics was a very powerful scientific enterprise. In fact, some felt that all the hard problems had already been solved and that the challenge of the 20th century would be improving the precision of fundamental constants. There were, however, a few unanswered questions that lurked on the horizon, specifically blackbody radiation and the photoelectric effect, which we now explore.

## 7.3.1 The Blackbody Radiation Problem

The problem of blackbody radiation has to do with the light emitted by a hot object. Consider the heating element of an electric stove or oven. You can tell when the element is warm because it has a dull, red glow. As the element gets hotter, the red color gets brighter. If something gets hotter still, it will have an orange or even yellow color. If something is "white hot," then it is emitting light over the entire visible spectrum, and so it looks white. If we take the light emitted by our object and analyze it with a spectrometer, where the different colors of light are dispersed, we can measure an emission spectrum—the intensity of each color of light emitted by the object. We see that as an object gets hotter, more light is emitted at shorter wavelengths, as shown in Figure 7.3. We also see that the maximum in the emission spectrum shifts to shorter wavelengths as the temperature increases.

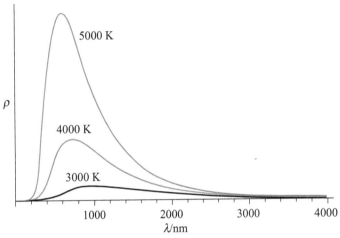

FIGURE 7.3. Emission spectra of blackbodies heated to 3000 K, 4000 K, and 5000 K.

In 1893, Wilhelm Wien developed a mathematical relation between the absolute temperature of the object and the wavelength of the maximum in the emission spectrum.

$$\lambda_{max} = \frac{b}{T} \qquad b = 2.8978 \times 10^{-3} \text{ m K} \qquad (7.12)$$

This was known as Wien's displacement law and, while it correctly determines the emission maximum, it does not explain the entire shape of the emission spectrum. The challenge for physicists was to model this behavior more quantitatively.

First, we need to formally define what we mean by a blackbody. A blackbody has perfect absorptivity, meaning any light incident on it is absorbed and it will appear black, as well as perfect emissivity, meaning nothing prevents radiated light from leaving the object. To maintain a balance between absorption and emission, the typical blackbody model consists

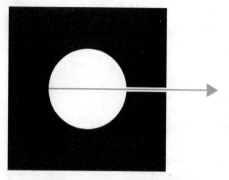

FIGURE 7.4. Cross section of a theoretical blackbody. Light can only escape through the pinhole.

of a hollow, spherical cavity inside of a solid object. When the energy contained by the light waves inside the cavity is in thermal equilibrium with the walls of the object, we can learn about temperature of the object by measuring the emitted light. A small pinhole through the side allows us to measure the spectrum of the light inside without disturbing this equilibrium. Figure 7.4 shows a cross section of a blackbody.

It was already known from Maxwell's equations that light is an electromagnetic wave, where the product of the wavelength and the frequency gives the speed of light, which is a fundamental constant of the universe.

$$\lambda v = c \tag{7.13}$$

Each possible wavelength of light can be thought of as a mode of motion characterized by a certain frequency. Also in the Maxwell model, the energy associated with light depends on the intensity of that light. Therefore, looking at the intensity of an emission spectrum of a blackbody tells us about the spectral energy density, which is the energy per volume per wavelength, at each wavelength of light. We symbolize the spectral energy density as $\rho(\lambda, T)$, which has units of energy/length⁴ (three powers of length for the volume, one for the wavelength of light). If we integrate the spectral energy density over all the possible wavelengths of light, we obtain the energy density in the cavity.

$$\frac{E}{V} = \int_0^\infty \rho(\lambda, T)\, d\lambda \tag{7.14}$$

Knowledge of the spectral density function will enable us to determine the energy density of the blackbody at a given temperature.

The first approach that was taken to determine the spectral energy density function was based on an equipartition analysis. We can imagine that each electromagnetic wave of light corresponds to an oscillator with frequency $v$, and therefore wavelength $\lambda$. Because this light can be polarized in one of two directions, there are two degrees of freedom associated with each mode of oscillation. (Light is a transverse wave, which means that the electric field oscillates at a right angle to the direction the wave propagates. If we take the wave as moving in the $z$ direction, the electric field can oscillate in either the $x$ or $y$ directions.) According to equipartition, then, the average energy associated with each mode of oscillation is $2 \times 1/2\, k_B T = k_B T$. Now, we need to know how many oscillator modes are associated with each wavelength of light.

Consider a standing wave on a string and its harmonics, where the end points of the string do not move. The lowest frequency (longest wavelength) mode will have a wavelength of $\lambda = 2L$, where $L$ is the length of the string. Any higher order harmonics will have a wavelength given by $\lambda_n = 2L/n$, where $n$ is a positive integer. The value of $n$ is also the number of modes with this shorter wavelength, and is given by

$$n = \frac{2L}{\lambda}$$

The number of modes changes with wavelength according to

$$dn = \frac{-2L}{\lambda^2}\, d\lambda$$

Since this is a classical, continuum approach, we also allow all possible wavelengths to be present. Note that the number of modes will increase as the wavelength decreases proportional to the square of the wavelength, and the number of modes approaches infinity as the wavelength approaches zero.

Our simple model only holds for a one-dimensional situation. The extension to three dimensions involves a bit of complicated geometry that will not be shown here. The end result of a three-dimensional analysis is a prediction of the spectral energy density function, known as the Rayleigh–Jeans law, first proposed in 1900 and further refined in 1905.

$$\rho(\lambda, T) = \frac{8\pi k_B T}{\lambda^4} \qquad (7.15)$$

This expression does a very good job at matching the experimental spectra at long wavelengths but has serious problems as the wavelength decreases. In this expression, as the wavelength decreases, the spectral energy density increases. This means that any object, at any temperature, should be producing lots of visible, ultraviolet, and even X-ray radiation. In fact, if we use this function in the integral of Eq. 7.14, we obtain an infinite energy density *at any temperature*. This was known as the **ultraviolet catastrophe**. Keep in mind, however, that this is not a problem with the physical world, but with an inadequate attempt to model the physical world. We clearly need a better model than a classical, equipartition approach provides.

## 7.3.2 Planck's Hypothesis and a Solution for Blackbody Radiation

The solution to this theoretical conundrum was provided by Max Planck in 1900. Planck recognized that part of the problem was in assuming that we can have light of any wavelength in the cavity. He argued that instead of allowing light at all wavelengths or frequencies, we should only allow harmonics of a fundamental frequency that is determined by the size of the cavity in the blackbody. He also proposed that the energy associated with this light is proportional to that fundamental frequency.

$$\epsilon_n = nh\nu = \frac{nhc}{\lambda} \qquad (7.16)$$

The constant $h$, known as Planck's constant, is the proportionality constant to convert between frequency and energy. We now want to redetermine the spectral energy density based on this model, which will be of the form

$$\rho(\lambda, T) = \frac{8\pi}{\lambda^4} f(\lambda, T) \qquad (7.17)$$

where the function $f(\lambda, T)$ replaces the equipartition result of $k_B T$ in the Rayleigh–Jeans law (Eq. 7.15). We will use the Boltzmann distribution to determine this function.

Let's designate the number of oscillators with energy $\epsilon_n = \frac{nhc}{\lambda}$ as $N_n$. The total number of oscillators and the total energy are then given by

$$N = \sum_{n=0}^{\infty} N_n \quad \text{and} \quad E = \sum_{n=0}^{\infty} N_n \epsilon_n \qquad (7.18)$$

The Boltzmann distribution gives us the number of oscillators with a given wavelength

$$P_n = \frac{N_n}{N} = \frac{e^{-\epsilon_n/k_B T}}{q} = \frac{e^{-nhc/\lambda k_B T}}{q} \qquad (7.19)$$

At this point, we don't have a closed expression for the partition function, $q$, so let's instead take the lowest energy state as our reference. We can divide Eq. 7.19 by the equivalent expression for $n = 0$, with $\epsilon_0 = 0$, which gives us

$$N_n = N_0 e^{-nhc/\lambda k_B T} \tag{7.20}$$

Now we can write our expression for the total number of oscillators as

$$N = N_0 \sum_{n=0}^{\infty} e^{-nhc/\lambda k_B T} \tag{7.21}$$

Similarly, the total energy of the system is given by

$$E = N_0 \sum_{n=0}^{\infty} \frac{nhc}{\lambda} e^{-nhc/\lambda k_B T} = N_0 \frac{hc}{\lambda} \sum_{n=0}^{\infty} n e^{-nhc/\lambda k_B T} \tag{7.22}$$

We can simplify Eqs. 7.21 and 7.22 with the following geometric series for a number less than 1:

$$\sum_{n=0}^{\infty} x^n = 1 + x + x^2 + x^3 + \dots = \frac{1}{1-x} \tag{7.23}$$

$$\sum_{n=0}^{\infty} n x^n = x + 2x^2 + 3x^3 + \dots = \frac{x}{(1-x)^2} \tag{7.24}$$

Let's take $x = e^{-hc/\lambda k_B T}$, so $x < 1$, as required for these series. Now we have

$$N = N_0 \frac{1}{1 - e^{-hc/\lambda k_B T}} \quad \text{and} \quad E = N_0 \frac{hc}{\lambda} \frac{e^{-hc/\lambda k_B T}}{\left(1 - e^{-hc/\lambda k_B T}\right)^2} \tag{7.25}$$

and we can write the average energy as the ratio of the total energy and the total number.

$$\langle E \rangle = \frac{E}{N} = \frac{hc}{\lambda} \frac{e^{-hc/\lambda k_B T}}{1 - e^{-hc/\lambda k_B T}} = \frac{hc}{\lambda \left(e^{hc/\lambda k_B T} - 1\right)} = f(\lambda, T) \tag{7.26}$$

Putting this into our expression for the spectral energy density (Eq. 7.17) gives us

$$\rho(\lambda, T) = \frac{8\pi hc}{\lambda^5 \left(e^{hc/\lambda k_B T} - 1\right)} \tag{7.27}$$

This function is known as the Planck distribution, and it perfectly matches the observed emission spectrum of a blackbody. We now have a model that fits the observations.

The significance of this result was not readily apparent at the time, but it helped set the stage for one of the most significant upheavals ever in the history of science: the advent of quantum mechanics. Planck was not trying to revolutionize physics; rather, he was attempting to solve a very specific scientific problem. In order to do this, he needed to make a new hypothesis—that of discrete, or quantized, possible values of the energy of the light in the cavity of a blackbody. We accept this as a good hypothesis because it provided a much better match to experimental data than any previous attempt. No one at the time, least of all Planck himself, could have foreseen the consequences of this new way of thinking about energy.

### 7.3.3 The Photoelectric Effect

The second cloud on the horizon of late 19th-century physics was the photoelectric effect. This was the observation that when light was incident on a metal surface in a vacuum, electrons were ejected from that metal surface. The existence of electrons, negatively charged particles of very small mass, had been verified by J. J. Thomson in 1896. The idea that light—which according to classical models is an electromagnetic wave—could impart energy to a particle like an electron is not unexpected; energy is exchanged all the time. However, there were certain aspects of the observations that could not be resolved in the classical model. According to Maxwell's equations, the energy of a beam of light depends on its intensity, but it was found that the energy of the ejected electrons did not depend on the intensity of the light but rather the wavelength; short-wavelength light produced more energetic electrons than long-wavelength light. In fact, if the wavelength of light were longer than a certain value, no electrons were ejected at all. There was an effect of the intensity of the light, but this related to the number of electrons produced, not their energy. The classical model clearly could not adequately account for all the observations.

In 1905, Albert Einstein published an explanation for the photoelectric effect, based to a large extent on Planck's hypothesis of quantized amounts of energy. Einstein postulated that light energy is conveyed in small packets, or "quanta" (which would later be given the particle-sounding name of **photons**), where the energy of each packet follows Planck's relation (Eq. 7.16 with $n = 1$).

$$E_{photon} = \frac{hc}{\lambda} = h\nu \tag{7.28}$$

In order to eject an electron, a certain binding energy that holds the electron inside the metal needs to be overcome. If the wavelength of the light is too long, then each quantum of light has insufficient energy to overcome this binding energy, called the **work function**, and no electrons are ejected. If the wavelength of light is shorter than this threshold, then the electron will have kinetic energy equal to the difference between the light energy and the work function, $\Phi$. Mathematically,

$$E_K = \frac{hc}{\lambda} - \Phi \tag{7.29}$$

At the time Einstein proposed this model, there was not enough experimental evidence to fully validate his hypothesis. Guided by his theoretical model, however, it wasn't long before more-careful experiments were performed that matched Einstein's predictions. It was for this work that Einstein was awarded the Nobel Prize in 1922.

Einstein's explanation of the photoelectric effect was one more hint that our understanding of the physical world at its most fundamental level was about to change. Classical theory clearly described matter as being made of particles and light as being a wave. The idea of quantized energy, however, means that light can be thought of as coming in small packets of energy, almost like a particle. All the rules for exchange of energy by collisions between particles now worked to describe the interaction of light with electrons. Coupled with the solution to the blackbody problem, the explanation of the photoelectric effect threw open the door to the development of quantum mechanics.

### 7.3.4 Einstein Formula for the Heat Capacity of Solids

The explanation of the photoelectric effect was not the last thing that Einstein would do to pave the way for the development of quantum mechanics. In 1907, he proposed a new model for the heat capacity of solids that was a vast improvement over the law of Dulong and Petit. Instead of the equipartition model that allows for all possible frequencies, Einstein described the solid as a collection of oscillators (balls and springs) that vibrate with a particular frequency, $v_E$ (called the Einstein frequency). He then allowed the oscillators to only have energy in steps of $jhv_E$ where $j$ is an integer that ranges from 0 to $\infty$. We now need to know the total energy of all the oscillators and the total number of oscillators in the system.

Let's designate the number of oscillators with energy $jhv_E$ as $N_j$. The total number of oscillators and the total energy are then given by

$$N = \sum_{j=0}^{\infty} N_j \quad \text{and} \quad U = \sum_{j=0}^{\infty} N_j jhv_E \tag{7.30}$$

Now we need to know how many oscillators are in each energy state. To do this, we go back once again to the Boltzmann distribution.

$$P_j = \frac{N_j}{N} = \frac{e^{-\epsilon_j/k_B T}}{q} = \frac{e^{-jhv_E/k_B T}}{q} \tag{7.31}$$

As we did for the blackbody radiation expression, we can divide the above expression by the equivalent expression for $j = 0$, with $\epsilon_j = 0$, which gives us

$$N_j = N_0 e^{-jhv_E/k_B T} \tag{7.32}$$

Now we can write our expression for the total number of oscillators as

$$N = N_0 \sum_{j=0}^{\infty} e^{-jhv_E/k_B T} \tag{7.33}$$

Similarly, the total energy of the system is given by

$$U = N_0 \sum_{j=0}^{\infty} jhv_E e^{-jhv_E/k_B T} = N_0 hv_E \sum_{j=0}^{\infty} je^{-jhv_E/k_B T} \tag{7.34}$$

We again use the geometric series (Eqs. 7.23 and 7.24) we used for the spectral energy density of a blackbody to obtain

$$N = N_0 \frac{1}{1 - e^{-hv_E/k_B T}} \quad \text{and} \quad U = N_0 hv_E \frac{e^{-hv_E/k_B T}}{\left(1 - e^{-hv_E/k_B T}\right)^2} \tag{7.35}$$

and we write the average internal energy as the ratio of the total energy and the total number.

$$\langle U \rangle = \frac{U}{N} = hv_E \frac{e^{-hv_E/k_B T}}{1 - e^{-hv_E/k_B T}} = \frac{hv_E}{e^{hv_E/k_B T} - 1} \tag{7.36}$$

If we have 1 mole of oscillators, the average total energy is then

$$U_m = 3N_A \left( \frac{hv_E}{e^{hv_E/k_B T} - 1} \right) \tag{7.37}$$

(The factor of 3 accounts for the three spatial dimensions in which each atom can move.)

The molar heat capacity is defined as the temperature derivative of this molar internal energy.

$$C_m = \frac{dU_m}{dT} \tag{7.38}$$

Thus, we can get the heat capacity by taking the derivative of the internal energy with respect to $T$. It's actually easier to use $\beta = 1 / k_B T$, which lets us write the molar internal energy as

$$U_m = 3N_A \left( \frac{h\nu_E}{e^{h\nu_E \beta} - 1} \right)$$

We can take the derivative by using the relation

$$\frac{d}{dT} = \frac{d\beta}{dT} \frac{d}{d\beta} = -\frac{1}{k_B T^2} \frac{d}{d\beta} = -k_B \beta^2 \frac{d}{d\beta} \tag{7.39}$$

Now for the heat capacity, we have

$$C_m = \frac{dU_m}{dT} = -k_B \beta^2 \frac{dU_m}{d\beta}$$

Upon evaluating the derivative and making the necessary substitutions, we have

$$C_m = 3N_A k_B \left( \frac{h\nu_E}{k_B T} \right)^2 \frac{e^{\frac{h\nu_E}{k_B T}}}{\left( e^{\frac{h\nu_E}{k_B T}} - 1 \right)^2} \tag{7.40}$$

We can define the Einstein temperature as

$$\Theta_E = \frac{h\nu_E}{k_B} \tag{7.41}$$

and rearrange things to get the Einstein heat capacity formula

$$\boxed{C_m = 3R \left( \frac{\Theta_E}{T} \right)^2 \frac{e^{\frac{-\Theta_E}{T}}}{\left( 1 - e^{\frac{-\Theta_E}{T}} \right)^2}} \tag{7.42}$$

Figure 7.5 shows the functional form of this relation. Note that this formula is written in a reduced fashion, meaning the temperature only appears as a ratio. In other words, it is a universal law. The value of the Einstein temperature will change for different substances, but the function stays the same. This expression is readily evaluated in the limits of high and low temperature and gives the proper results.

## 7.3.5 Debye Formula for Heat Capacity of Solids

There is actually a problem with Einstein's result. In particular, it was observed experimentally that as $T$ approaches zero, the heat capacity goes as $T^3$; the Einstein formula goes to zero faster than observed. Peter Debye improved on Einstein's model by allowing the

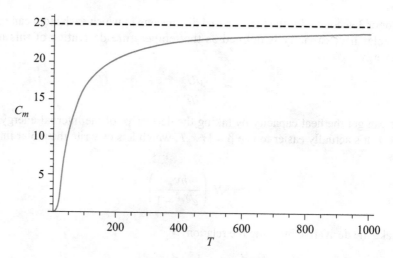

**FIGURE 7.5.** Einstein heat capacity relation for a value of $\Theta_E = 20$ K. Dashed line indicates the Dulong–Petit limit of $3R$.

atoms to oscillate over a range of frequencies, up to a certain limit known as the Debye frequency, $\nu_D$. His result is summarized in the Debye formula

$$C_{V,m} = 9R\left(\frac{T}{\Theta_D}\right)^3 \int_0^{\Theta_D/T} \frac{x^4 e^x}{(e^x - 1)^2}\, dx \tag{7.43}$$

where the Debye temperature is defined as

$$\Theta_D = \frac{h\nu_D}{k_B} \tag{7.44}$$

This result is not as easy to interpret analytically but can be handled quite readily with modern computers and numerical analysis. One additional complication of this model is that the Debye temperature itself is temperature dependent; more frequencies become accessible as the temperature increases. What started out as a fairly straightforward application of classical physics to predict a material property like heat capacity has fairly quickly become more complicated. Analysis of the heat capacity, however, can provide a great deal of insight into the structure of a material and the types of motion its atoms and molecules can experience. We can also learn about electronic, magnetic, and other properties with heat capacity measurements.

## 7.4 Summary, and Where We Go Next

At the beginning of this chapter, we returned to a simple, classical model to try to predict the property of heat capacity, which is the relationship between energy and temperature changes. This model was based on the assumption that energy can be distributed throughout the system in arbitrarily small amounts and would spread out, or partition, equally. For the monatomic ideal gas, this treatment works fine, but for even a diatomic molecule, this model no longer works. In attempting to apply the equipartition model to the heat capacity of solids, we again meet with difficulties.

We also saw the limitations in using classical models to describe blackbody radiation and the photoelectric effect. Only by giving up the classical idea that energy can come in arbitrarily small amounts were more satisfactory models of these phenomena developed. This new idea of the quantization of energy was also extended by Einstein to better describe the heat capacity of solids. We have reached the limit of what we can do with the simple, classical approach. In the next chapter, we will begin the formal development of quantum mechanics.

# PROBLEMS

**7.1** There are actually two forms of heat capacity that are used in thermodynamics: the constant volume heat capacity $C_{V,m}$, and the constant pressure heat capacity, $C_{P,m}$. Strictly speaking, the expressions we developed with the classical equipartition theorem give values for the constant volume heat capacity. When working with a gas, we need to clearly specify which value we are using, however for a liquid or a solid the distinction doesn't matter so much. (For an ideal gas, the relationship between the two is $C_{P,m} = C_{V,m} + R$.) Justify why there is a significant difference in the two heat capacities for a gas but not for a liquid or solid.

**7.2** Consider a diatomic molecule that is physisorbed to a surface and must stay within a close distance from the surface. Describe the degrees of freedom for this molecule and the kinds of motion it can experience.

**7.3** Pick your favorite organic molecule that consists of four or more atoms and is a gas at room temperature.

a) Using your knowledge of the structure of this molecule, estimate the heat capacity by using the classical equipartition theorem.

b) Find a literature value for the constant volume heat capacity for your molecule. (You may only be able to find constant pressure values. See Problem 7.1 for a discussion of the difference between the two.) Compare the literature value and your estimate from part a) and comment on any differences.

c) Identify one of the fundamental vibrational frequencies for your molecule. Using the Boltzmann distribution, estimate the fraction of molecules in the first excited vibrational state at $T = 298.15$ K and 1000 K.

d) Discuss how the results of your calculation in part c) can help explain the discrepancies between the equipartition value and literature value of the heat capacity.

**7.4** a) The peak in the solar emission spectrum occurs at about 480 nm. Estimate the surface temperature of the sun, assuming the sun can be treated as a blackbody.

b) A red giant star is found to have its maximum emission at a wavelength of 640 nm. Estimate the surface temperature of this star.

c) The heating element of an electric oven glows red at $450°$ F. Estimate the wavelength of the maximum of the emission spectrum, treating the heating element as a blackbody. Does this value match with what you visually see?

**7.5** Planck's model of blackbody radiation did a much better job of matching experimental data than the previous models did. The previous models weren't completely wrong, however. They described some parts of the problem, but not as much as Planck's did. In evaluating the quality of Planck's model, it is important that we also show consistency with what was done before.

a) In the limit that the energy spacing between allowed oscillator states is small, show that the Planck distribution (Eq. 7.27) reduces to the Rayleigh–Jeans law (Eq. 7.15).

b) From the Planck distribution, derive Wien's displacement law (Eq. 7.12).

**7.6** a) Calculate the energy for a photon of the following wavelengths: 650 nm, 532 nm, 400 nm.

b) In photochemistry, chemical reactions are initiated by the absorbance of a photon of light. For a laser source that produces light continuously at 514 nm with a power of 2.0 W, how long will it take to deliver 1 mole of photons to the reaction?

**7.7** Experiments were performed to measure the kinetic energy of electrons ejected from a metallic surface by UV light. The following data were collected.

| $\lambda$ (nm) | $E_k$ (eV) |
|---|---|
| 210 | 1.63 |
| 225 | 1.18 |
| 250 | 0.64 |
| 275 | 0.22 |
| 285 | 0.06 |

Using these results, calculate the value of Planck's constant and the work function for this metal. From the value of the work function, suggest a possible identity of the metal.

**7.8** Show that the Einstein heat capacity formula (Eq. 7.42) gives the proper results in the limits of very high and very low temperature.

**7.9** a) Assuming that each atom in an Al crystal carries 3 quanta of vibrational energy, what would be the energy per mole for Al? The vibrational frequency is $5.8 \times 10^{12}$ s$^{-1}$.

b) Within the limits of the Einstein theory of solids, calculate the average vibrational energy per mole for Al metal at 300 K. The Einstein temperature for Al is ~280 K.

c) Repeat the calculation from part b) for a temperature of 3000 K. In addition, calculate the molar internal energy at both temperatures using an equipartition analysis. Comment on how well the two models, Einstein and equipartition, compare to each other at the two temperatures.

## CHAPTER 8

# Fundamentals of Quantum Mechanics

## Wavefunctions, Operators, and the Schrödinger Equation

## 8.1 Wave–Particle Duality

### 8.1.1 Momentum of Photons

As we saw in the last chapter, Albert Einstein's explanation of the photoelectric effect required that we revise our picture of light as simply an electromagnetic wave. Rather, Einstein showed that the energy of light is conveyed in small packets, or quanta, where the energy of each packet depends on the frequency—and therefore the wavelength—of the light.

$$E = h\nu = \frac{hc}{\lambda} \tag{8.1}$$

Conservation of energy is something we take very seriously in physics and chemistry, and this explanation satisfies that principle. But there is another equally important physical concept, and that is the conservation of momentum. How can light, as a wave, impart linear momentum to a particle like an electron? Einstein provided an answer to this question as well, based on another of his 1905 papers—the paper on special relativity. (1905 is known as Einstein's "miracle year" because it saw the publication of three fundamentally important papers: the explanation of the photoelectric effect, the presentation of special relativity, and a molecule-based explanation of Brownian motion. He received the Nobel Prize for the paper on the photoelectric effect, but the others are just as important in the development of science.)

One of the results of special relativity is an expression for the square of the total energy of a particle

$$E^2 = (pc)^2 + (mc^2)^2$$

If a particle is at rest, then it has no momentum, and we obtain Einstein's most famous expression, $E = mc^2$. A quantum of light, however, has no mass; but according to this relation, it can have momentum; if $m = 0$, we can write $E = pc$. From now on, we will call light quanta **photons**. The momentum of a photon is therefore

$$p = \frac{E}{c} = \frac{hc}{c\lambda} = \frac{h}{\lambda} \quad \text{or} \quad P_{photon} = \frac{h}{\lambda} \tag{8.2}$$

where $h$ is again Planck's constant with a value of $6.6261 \times 10^{-34}$ Js. For light at optical wavelengths, say 500 nm, this means a single photon has a momentum of only $1.33 \times 10^{-27}$ kg m/s. This looks quite small; however, the mass of an electron is only $9.1094 \times 10^{-31}$ kg; therefore, photons can impart a significant velocity to an electron—just as was observed in the photoelectric effect. We have now gone from thinking about light as purely a wave to thinking of it as energy packets—photons—that carry momentum, just like particles do.

### 8.1.2 De Broglie's Hypothesis

In 1924, a French doctoral student, Louis de Broglie, took Einstein's idea of the momentum of a photon and literally turned it on its head. In his doctoral thesis, he argued that if light—which we think of as a wave—can have momentum, then could not a particle have a wavelength? The de Broglie wavelength is calculated by inverting Einstein's relation and writing

$$\lambda_{particle} = \frac{h}{p} \tag{8.3}$$

At the time, this was something of a conjecture, but not without reason. For a macroscopic object, like a rock or a baseball, where the momentum is on the order of 1 kg m/s, this de Broglie wavelength would be on the order of $10^{-34}$ m, which is ridiculously small and would be impossible to measure. But what about an electron? Now, because of the very small mass, the de Broglie wavelength could be on the order of nm, which is measurable.

It wasn't long before there was experimental evidence to back up de Broglie's hypothesis. In 1926, Clinton Davisson in the United States and George Paget Thomson in Scotland independently led teams that observed diffraction of electron beams by crystals. The wavelengths associated with the diffraction patterns exactly matched de Broglie's predictions. De Broglie received the Nobel Prize in 1929 for his theoretical work, and Davisson and Thomson shared the prize in 1937 for their experimental work on electron diffraction. Once again, we were forced to rethink our basic understanding of the physical world.

This idea that light can act like a particle and that electrons have a wavelength is often referred to as **wave–particle duality**. This term is somewhat misleading, however, because it attempts to use macroscopic terms to describe microscopic phenomena. The question is often posed, "What is an electron?" to which students will hem and haw and give answers such as "A particle, or a wave, depending on what you're doing to it." The best answer to the question, however, is simply "An electron is an electron." It is neither a particle nor a wave; it is an electron. We can describe some of the properties of an electron in terms of what we call particle-like properties, and other properties are described by what we call wavelike properties. But an electron is just an electron, and it doesn't really matter what you call it. Only by letting go of some of our preconceptions can we gain a more correct understanding of the world at the atomic level. Now you can see why the early 20th century was such an exciting time in physics; a whole new way of looking at the world was being developed.

Sample Problem 8.1

A handgun can have a muzzle velocity of 400 m s$^{-1}$. A typical bullet weighs about 16 g. Compare the de Broglie wavelength of the bullet to that of an electron produced by an electron gun with an energy of 1 keV.

Solution

The momentum of the bullet is simply calculated as

$$p = 0.016 \text{ kg} \times 400 \text{ m s}^{-1} = 6.4 \text{ kg m s}^{-1}$$

The de Broglie wavelength is calculated from Eq. 8.3 to be

$$\lambda = \frac{h}{p} = \frac{6.6261 \times 10^{-34} \text{ J s}}{6.4 \text{ kg m s}^{-1}} = 1.0 \times 10^{-34} \text{ m}$$

This is a very small—and impossible to measure—value.

For the electron gun, the momentum of the electron is

$$p = \sqrt{2mE} = \sqrt{2(9.1094 \times 10^{-31} \text{ kg})(1000 \text{eV})(1.6022 \times 10^{-19} \text{ J eV}^{-1})}$$

$$= 1.7 \times 10^{-23} \text{ kg m s}^{-1}$$

The de Broglie wavelength is

$$\lambda = \frac{h}{p} = \frac{6.6261 \times 10^{-34} \text{ J s}}{1.7 \times 10^{-23} \text{ kg m s}^{-1}} = 3.9 \times 10^{-11} \text{ m}$$

This is small but measurable and significantly larger than the value for the bullet.

## 8.2 The Schrödinger Equation

Phenomena such as blackbody radiation, the photoelectric effect, and electron diffraction showed that classical physics with Newtonian particles and fields described by Maxwell's equations are not fully adequate to describe the behavior of electrons and other small objects. To describe these things, a new type of physics was developed in the early 20th century. As we will see, the idea of quantized (or discrete amounts of) energy is central to this new type of physics. Partly for this reason, this new field came to be called **quantum mechanics**.

### 8.2.1 The Quantum-Mechanical "Free Particle"

We will now consider the simplest possible quantum-mechanical system, that of a free "particle," such as an electron, moving in one dimension. (We are using the term *particle* loosely, for reasons we just discussed.) By *free*, we mean that there are no outside forces acting on this particle and it is unaffected by any other particles. It exists in its own universe. What is the energy of such a particle? Since there are no forces acting on it, there is no potential energy—only kinetic energy. And since it has nothing to interact with, the kinetic energy will not change over time. If this particle has kinetic energy, then it also has linear momentum as given by

$$E_K = \frac{1}{2}mv^2 = \frac{p^2}{2m}$$

Since it has a linear momentum, it also has a wavelength, given by de Broglie's relation (Eq. 8.3).

$$\lambda = \frac{h}{p} = \frac{h}{\sqrt{2mE_K}}$$

Since we know our particle has wavelike properties, we choose to mathematically describe that aspect of the particle. We can do so by writing a **wavefunction**, which tells us how the wavelike aspect of our particle varies with position. The simplest wavefunction, symbolized by the Greek letter ψ, that we can write for a pure wave is a sine or cosine function.

$$\psi(x) = \sin\left(\frac{2\pi}{\lambda}x\right) \quad \text{or} \quad \lambda(x) = \cos\left(\frac{2\pi}{\lambda}x\right)$$

Recall that a sine or a cosine function repeats over a distance of the wavelength such that

$$\cos\left(\frac{2\pi}{\lambda}(x+\lambda)\right) = \cos\left(\frac{2\pi}{\lambda}x\right)$$

A similar expression can be written for the sine function. It will become somewhat tiresome to write the quantity $2\pi/\lambda$ all the time, so we define a quantity called the **angular wavenumber**, symbolized by $k$ and written as

$$k = \frac{2\pi}{\lambda} \tag{8.4}$$

This lets us write our proposed wavefunctions in the form

$$\psi(x) = \sin kx \quad \text{or} \quad \psi(x) = \cos kx$$

We can actually write a more general form of our wavefunction by using the Euler relation for a complex exponential

$$e^{ikx} = \cos kx + i \sin kx \quad \text{where} \quad i = \sqrt{-1} \tag{8.5}$$

We now write the proposed wavefunction for a quantum-mechanical free particle as

$$\psi(x) = e^{ikx} \tag{8.6}$$

## 8.2.2 The Momentum Operator

You may wonder why we took a perfectly good sine or cosine function and turned it into a complex exponential, which may not be as familiar to you. There are very good reasons, which we will now explore. The first reason has to do with the derivative of our wavefunction. Recall that taking the derivative of an exponential function always returns the same exponential. Taking the derivative of our free-particle wavefunction lets us write

$$\frac{d}{dx}\psi(x) = ike^{ikx}$$

Recall that $k$ is the angular wavenumber, defined in terms of the wavelength, which then relates back to the momentum through de Broglie's relation. Putting all this together lets us write

$$k = \frac{2\pi}{\lambda} = \frac{2\pi p}{h} \quad \text{or} \quad p = \frac{hk}{2\pi}$$

The quantity $h/2\pi$ shows up a lot in quantum mechanics, so it is given its own symbol, $\hbar$, called "$h$ bar." Using this new symbol lets us write

$$p = \hbar k \tag{8.7}$$

Thus, we can see that the angular wavenumber of our wavefunction relates back to the momentum of our particle.

Now, let's add some constants to our derivative operation. Specifically, if we multiply by $\hbar/i$, we have

$$\frac{\hbar}{i}\frac{d}{dx}\psi(x) = \hbar ke^{ikx} = p_x\psi(x)$$

Multiplying the derivative of the wavefunction by $\hbar/i$ returns the same wavefunction multiplied by the momentum of the particle the wavefunction is describing. In other words, doing this mathematical operation returns the numerical value of the momentum. We now define the **momentum operator** as

$$\boxed{\hat{p}_x \equiv \frac{\hbar}{i}\frac{\partial}{\partial x}} \tag{8.8}$$

The "hat" over the symbol $p_x$ tells us that this is an operator. An operator conveys a set of mathematical instructions, in this case, "take the derivative with respect to $x$, and multiply by $\hbar/i$." Note that we have formally defined the momentum operator in terms of a partial derivative, which will be important as we extend to multidimensional systems. In the one-dimensional case we are considering, the conventional derivative and the partial derivative are identical.

## 8.2.3 Operators, Eigenfunctions, and Eigenvalues

Operators are at the heart of the mathematical formalism of quantum mechanics, so it is worth spending a little time to become more familiar with them and how they work. Basically, an operator is a set of instructions for a mathematical procedure to be performed on a function. The momentum operator we just introduced tells us to take the derivative of our function with respect to a position variable and then multiply by the constant value $\hbar/i$. Other operators will involve different mathematical instructions.

Sometimes, when we operate on a particular function, we get the same function back, multiplied by a constant. This was the case when we used the momentum operator on our free-particle wavefunction. In general, when the result of using an operator on a function returns the same function back, multiplied by a constant, we say that the function is an **eigenfunction** of that operator. The constant is referred to as the **eigenvalue**. The term *eigen* comes from a German word meaning *characteristic*. Consider the function $f(x) = e^{ax}$ and the derivative operator, $\hat{D} = \dfrac{d}{dx}$. If we operate with the derivative operator on our exponential function, we obtain

$$\hat{D}f(x) = \hat{D}e^{ax} = \frac{d}{dx}e^{ax} = ae^{ax} = af(x)$$

Thus, the function $f(x) = e^{ax}$ is an eigenfunction of the derivative operator, with eigenvalue $a$. If we try a sine function of the form $f(x) = \sin kx$, we obtain

$$\hat{D}f(x) = \hat{D}\sin kx = \frac{d}{dx}\sin kx = k\cos kx \neq kf(x)$$

In this case, we did not get the same function back; the sine function became a cosine function. Thus, $f(x) = \sin kx$ is not an eigenfunction of the derivative operator.

Mathematically, we write the relationship between an operator and its eigenfunctions as

$$\hat{A}f = af$$

(8.9)

where $\hat{A}$ represents the operator, $f$ is an eigenfunction of that operator, and $a$ is the corresponding eigenvalue. You may notice a similarity between this terminology and the eigenvectors and eigenvalues of a matrix that you encountered in linear algebra. (There are some fundamental similarities here. In fact, there is an entire formalism of quantum mechanics based on linear algebra where the operators are represented as matrices, but we won't be developing that in this text.)

We can now see why we prefer the complex exponential to either the sine or cosine functions as our choice of wavefunction for the free particle. The complex exponential is an eigenfunction of the momentum operator, but the sine and cosine functions are not. One of the postulates of quantum mechanics is that each operator has a set of eigenfunctions and corresponding eigenvalues, and those tell us about the possible states of our quantum-mechanical system. Therefore, we are very interested in the eigenfunctions of any given operator.

Even though we motivated our choice of the momentum operator by using an appropriate wavefunction for our free particle, the definition of the momentum operator is formally a postulate. Recall that a postulate is an idea that cannot be proven to be correct but is assumed to be so and then used as the basis for further reasoning. If predictions that arise from reasoning based on the postulate are verified, then we have greater assurance that our postulate is correct. We now need to postulate another operator, this time the **position operator**

$$\boxed{\hat{x} \equiv x \times}$$

(8.10)

The mathematical instructions conveyed by the position operator simply tell us to multiply a function by $x$, the position variable. We can define similar operators for the $y$ and $z$ position variables.

## 8.2.4 The Hamiltonian Operator and the Schrödinger Equation

With the momentum and position operators, we can now define other quantum-mechanical operators. Classically, kinetic energy in the $x$ direction relates back to momentum by the relation

$$E_{K,x} = \frac{p_x^2}{2m} \tag{8.11}$$

We will define a quantum-mechanical kinetic energy operator for motion in the $x$ direction, symbolized as $\hat{T}_x$, by writing

$$\hat{T}_x = \frac{1}{2m}\hat{p}_x^2 = \frac{-\hbar^2}{2m}\frac{\partial^2}{\partial x^2} \tag{8.12}$$

Note that when we square an operator, we perform the operation twice, hence the second derivative. The total kinetic energy is the sum of the kinetic energy associate with the motion in all three spatial directions. Therefore, we write the total kinetic energy operator as

$$\hat{T} = \frac{-\hbar^2}{2m}\left[\frac{\partial^2}{\partial x^2} + \frac{\partial^2}{\partial y^2} + \frac{\partial^2}{\partial z^2}\right] = \frac{-\hbar^2}{2m}\nabla^2 \tag{8.13}$$

where the sum of second partial derivatives is represented by $\nabla^2$, known as *del squared* or the *Laplacian operator*. Potential energy is a function of position, so we will define the potential energy operator $\hat{V}$ by

$$\hat{V} = V(x,y,z) \tag{8.14}$$

Use of the potential energy operator simply involves multiplying our wavefunction by the potential energy function, which is a function of the spatial variables $x$, $y$, and $z$.

The formalism of classical physics that you are probably the most familiar with is known as Newtonian mechanics. It is based on Newton's laws of motion and principally involves determining all the forces acting on a body. Another approach to classical mechanics was developed by W. R. Hamilton in the 1830s that instead focuses on the total energy of the system. Based on his work, we define the **Hamiltonian operator** as

$$\hat{H} = \hat{T} + \hat{V} = \frac{-\hbar^2}{2m}\nabla^2 + V(x,y,z) \tag{8.15}$$

The Hamiltonian operator is also known as the **total energy operator**, since it is constructed from the kinetic and potential energy operators. The exact form of the Hamiltonian operator will depend on the particular system under study, specifically the potential energy of that system; the kinetic energy part is always the same, although its exact mathematical form will be different depending on the choice of coordinate system.

As we said before, each operator has a set of eigenfunctions. The set of functions we are generally most concerned with are the eigenfunctions of the Hamiltonian, or total energy, operator. Written mathematically, we want functions such that

$$\hat{H}\psi = E\psi \tag{8.16}$$

These functions represent the available energy states of our system, and the corresponding eigenvalues are the energies of those states. This equation, published in 1926, is known as the **Schrödinger equation**, and solving it for a particular system is at the heart of quantum mechanics. Erwin Schrödinger shared the 1933 Nobel Prize with Paul Dirac, another pioneer in quantum mechanics. (The Dirac equation includes relativistic effects and is beyond the scope of this book.)

Let's now use the Schrödinger equation to directly solve for the wavefunction of a free particle moving in one dimension. The first thing we need to do is construct the Hamiltonian operator for this situation. Because we are talking about a free particle, there is no potential energy anywhere and we can write $V(x) = 0$ for all $x$. The kinetic energy operator need only contain the $x$ term, since we are not allowing motion in the $y$ or $z$ directions. This lets us write the Schrödinger equation as

$$\frac{-\hbar^2}{2m} \frac{\partial^2 \psi(x)}{\partial x^2} = E\psi(x) \tag{8.17}$$

Slightly rearranging things gives us

$$\frac{\partial^2 \psi(x)}{\partial x^2} = \frac{-2mE}{\hbar^2} \psi(x) = -k^2 \psi(x) \quad \text{where} \quad k = \frac{\sqrt{2mE}}{\hbar} \tag{8.18}$$

So, we need a function that, when we take its second derivative, we get the same function back multiplied by a negative number ($k^2$ must be positive). The general functions that satisfy this differential equation are sines, cosines, and complex exponentials. As we have seen with the Euler relation, complex exponentials can be written in terms of sines and cosines, so we use the complex exponentials as our general solutions. There are two possibilities we need to consider:

$$\psi_1(x) = e^{ikx} \quad \text{and} \quad \psi_2(x) = e^{-ikx} \tag{8.19}$$

The energy of our particle is then given by

$$E = \frac{\hbar^2 k^2}{2m} \tag{8.20}$$

Because the value of $k$ relates back to the momentum of the particle, which is a physically observable quantity, it needs to be a real number. Note that the value of $k$ can be either positive or negative. Physically, we can think of these two solutions, $\psi_1$ and $\psi_2$, as describing a particle traveling in either the positive or negative $x$ direction, respectively. Energy, however, doesn't depend on direction. It relates to the square of momentum and must therefore be nonnegative; any positive value of the energy, as well as an energy of zero, is allowed. You may have been expecting some restrictions, or quantization, of the allowed energies; this is quantum mechanics, after all. The reason that all energies are possible is because there are no restrictions on the particle. Remember, it's free. As we will see in the next chapter, quantization or restriction of the possible energy levels comes about when the particle is spatially confined. The free particle experiences no confinement, so there is no quantization of the energy states.

You might think we engaged in a bit of circular reasoning here in the way we have developed the Schrödinger equation and then used it to get back to our original wavefunctions. You are partially correct. We have done it this way to show the logical connections between the various ideas. Fundamentally, however, the Schrödinger equation is a postulate—just like the definitions of the position and momentum operators—and we can't prove that it's correct. Showing consistency doesn't hurt, however. Now that we have the Schrödinger equation, we can move to more interesting situations than a particle that exists in its own universe with nothing acting on it. Before moving on to other systems, however, we want to more fully develop some of the formalism of quantum mechanics and explore its meaning. Once we have all our tools on the table, we'll tackle more interesting problems, starting in the next chapter.

## 8.3 The Postulates of Quantum Mechanics

We now have some of the most important pieces we need to work with quantum mechanics, namely wavefunctions, operators, and the Schrödinger equation. Before moving on to different systems than the free particle, we are going to develop a few more ideas that will be important as we continue our study of quantum mechanics. At the end of this section, we formally present the postulates of quantum mechanics that form the basis for everything we will do hereafter.

### 8.3.1 The Born Interpretation of the Wavefunction

We have developed a wavefunction for a free particle, and we will see many other wavefunctions as we continue in our study of quantum mechanics. You may have asked yourself, "But what does the wavefunction *mean*?" This is a valid question, and one that we will now explore. First, it is important to clarify what the wavefunction does *not* mean. For our one-dimensional free particle, there can only be motion in that one direction. Therefore, the particle should not be thought of as oscillating up and down in some perpendicular direction. There is an oscillation, but it's not one of position. So what is oscillating?

The physical interpretation of the wavefunction was proposed by Max Born in 1928. Born postulated that the modulus square of the wavefunction should be interpreted as a probability density function for the location of the particle. Mathematically, the quantity $\psi^*\psi \, dx$ represents the probability of finding the particle between position $x$ and $x + dx$. The $^*$ indicates the complex conjugate of the wavefunction, where all occurrences of the imaginary number $i$ are replaced by $-i$. (You may recall that multiplying a complex number by its complex conjugate always produces a real number.) The probability of finding the particle in a region of space between $a$ and $b$ would then be determined by evaluating the integral

$$P(a < x < b) = \int_a^b \psi^*\psi \, dx \tag{8.21}$$

If we have a particle in a three-dimensional space, we integrate over the appropriate boundaries in that space. The oscillations of the wavefunction now relate to oscillations of probability.

This interpretation of the wavefunction moves it from a purely mathematical abstraction into the physical world, and therefore imposes some limitations on the kinds of functions we can use. First of all, the wavefunction needs to be *continuous*, since probabilities can't instantaneously change from one position to another. We also generally require that the first derivative of the wavefunction be continuous, although there are certain situations where this may not hold true. Just like any true function, we can't have two different values of the probability at a single location, so the wavefunction must be *single valued*. The wavefunction also needs to be *finite* over its spatial range. Some examples of valid and invalid wavefunctions are shown in Figure 8.1.

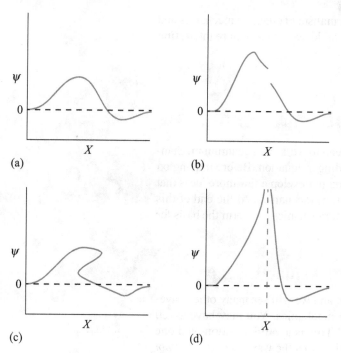

FIGURE 8.1. Proposed wavefunctions a) An acceptable wavefunction. b) An unacceptable wavefunction because of the discontinuity. c) An unacceptable wavefunction because it is not single valued. d) An unacceptable wavefunction because it goes to infinity; the vertical dashed line shows the vertical asymptote.

There is one more condition that our wavefunction must satisfy, and this has to do with the way we determine the probability of finding the particle within a certain spatial range. Let's extend the limits of the integral above to include all space. What is the probability that we find our particle somewhere in that space? Well, if we have a particle, then there has to be unit, or 100%, probability of finding our particle somewhere. Mathematically, we write

$$\int_{-\infty}^{\infty} \psi^* \psi \, dx = 1 \qquad (8.22)$$

A wavefunction that satisfies this condition is said to be **normalized**. An integral over any smaller range of space yields the probability of finding the particle in that region, which must of necessity return a value less than 1.

Let's summarize the mathematical requirements of a well-defined wavefunction:

- $\psi$ must be continuous.
- The first derivative of $\psi$ must (usually) be continuous.
- $\psi$ must be single valued.
- $\psi$ must be finite over its spatial range.
- $\psi$ must be normalizable, meaning the integral of $\psi^* \psi$ must be real.

Now that we have these conditions, let's see how our wavefunction for the free particle behaves. Our wavefunction of $\psi(x) = e^{\pm ikx}$ is clearly continuous, single valued, and finite. The derivative of an exponential is also an exponential, so the first derivative is also continuous. What about normalizing the wavefunction? Here, because we are allowing the particle to move anywhere along its one dimension, we need to be a little bit careful.

Let's first consider the product of the wavefunction with its complex conjugate, which gives the probability distribution for the location of the particle. We write the wavefunction, its complex conjugate, and the product of the two as

$$\psi(x) = e^{ikx} \quad \psi^*(x) = e^{-ikx} \quad \psi^* \psi = e^{-ikx} e^{ikx} = e^0 = 1$$

Note that the value of $\psi^* \psi$ is independent of position. This tells us that the probability distribution for the position of the free particle is a uniform distribution; we are equally likely to find the particle at any position. The probability of finding the particle within a given region of space, say within a distance of $\pm l$ about the origin, is then given by

$$P(-l < x < l) = \int_{-l}^{l} \psi^* \psi \, dx = \int_{-l}^{l} dx = 2l \qquad (8.23)$$

Right away, we see a problem; our probability could be greater than 1, depending on the value of $l$, which cannot be the case. The integral also has units of length, which doesn't make physical sense either.

Many times, when solving the Schrödinger equation, the wavefunction is not automatically normalized. One way to fix this is to multiply the wavefunction by a constant such that it is. Consider the case where

$$\int_{-\infty}^{\infty} \psi^* \psi \, dx = N \neq 1 \tag{8.24}$$

We multiply the wavefunction by a constant, $a$, and require

$$\int_{-\infty}^{\infty} (a\psi)^* (a\psi) \, dx = 1 \tag{8.25}$$

If the constant is real, then $a^*a$ is a real number, and we can write it as $a^2$. This step lets us write

$$a^2 \int_{-\infty}^{\infty} \psi^* \psi \, dx = a^2 N = 1 \tag{8.26}$$

The normalization constant $a$ can then simply be written as

$$a = \frac{1}{\sqrt{N}} \tag{8.27}$$

In other words, if the integral of $\psi^* \psi$ over all space is not equal to 1, we can divide the wavefunction by the square root of that integral, and we will have a normalized wavefunction.

Let's return to our free-particle wavefunction. If we want to insist that the particle be found between $-l$ and $l$, then we would write the wavefunction as

$$\psi(x) = \frac{1}{\sqrt{2l}} e^{ikx} \tag{8.28}$$

If we integrate $\psi^* \psi$ over the limits of $-l$ to $l$, we will indeed obtain a result of 1. However, by limiting where the particle can be, there must be something interacting with it—which would mean the particle was not truly free. If we extend the range where the particle can be found, by gradually removing our restrictions, we really need to evaluate the limit

$$\lim_{l \to \infty} \frac{1}{2l} \int_{-l}^{l} dx = 1 \tag{8.29}$$

Because the two infinities approach each other at the same rate, the limit is well defined and we can write our normalized wavefunction as

$$\psi(x) = a e^{ikx} \quad \text{where} \quad a^2 = \frac{1}{2l} \quad \text{in the limit that } l \to \infty \tag{8.30}$$

The free-particle wavefunction is not the best example of a normalized wavefunction, but this is because of the somewhat artificial nature of the system; it is a free particle and is equally like to be anywhere. As we will see in the next chapter, once we constrain our particle to being in a particular region, normalization becomes much easier to deal with.

Now is also a good time to mention that the wavefunction has units, and they are somewhat unconventional units. For a one-dimensional system, like our free particle, the Born expression requires that $\int_{-\infty}^{\infty} \psi^* \psi \, dx = 1$. The right-hand side of this expression represents a probability, which is unitless. The integration on the left-hand side, however, imparts a unit of length. The only way to make the left-hand side unitless is for the product $\psi^*\psi$ to have units of length$^{-1}$. This means that the wavefunction itself has units of length$^{-1/2}$. These are rather strange units indeed, but they are necessary for the meaning of $\psi^*\psi$ as a probability density, or probability per unit length. For a wavefunction in three-dimensional space, we write the normalization condition as

$$\int_{-\infty}^{\infty} \psi^*\psi \, d\tau = 1 \tag{8.31}$$

where $d\tau$ is the appropriate volume element; in a Cartesian system, $d\tau = dx \, dy \, dz$, whereas in spherical coordinates $d\tau = r^2\sin\theta \, dr \, d\theta \, d\phi$. The wavefunction must now have units of volume$^{-1/2}$ to preserve the meaning of $\psi^*\psi$ as the probability per unit volume of finding the particle. It is a good idea when you finish a problem to check the units of your normalized wavefunction and make sure they are correct.

## 8.3.2 Expectation Values

We have now learned about the meaning of the wavefunction, but what about the meaning of the operators? We have developed certain operators that sound a lot like physical properties, such as momentum, position, and energy. One of the postulates of quantum mechanics is that for every physical observable, there is a corresponding operator. Another postulate is that we can determine the expectation value of that physical quantity by evaluating the integral

$$\boxed{\langle J \rangle = \int_{-\infty}^{\infty} \psi^* \hat{J} \psi \, dx} \tag{8.32}$$

where $\hat{J}$ is the operator that corresponds to the physical property $J$.

Let's see how this works for the momentum operator and our free particle. Consider a free particle moving in the $+x$ direction with the wavefunction $\psi(x) = ae^{ikx}$. We would determine the expectation value of a momentum measurement on this particle by evaluating

$$\langle p_x \rangle = \int_{-\infty}^{\infty} \psi^* \hat{p}_x \, \psi \, dx$$

We can first look at the result of using the momentum operator on the wavefunction and write

$$\hat{p}_x \psi(x) = \frac{\hbar}{i} \frac{\partial}{\partial x} ae^{ikx} = \hbar k ae^{ikx} = \hbar k \, \psi(x)$$

Putting this back into the integral gives us

$$\langle p_x \rangle = \int_{-\infty}^{\infty} \psi^* \hat{p}_x \, \psi \, dx = \hbar k \int_{-\infty}^{\infty} \psi^*\psi \, dx = \hbar k \tag{8.33}$$

(Recall that we normalized the wavefunction.) Thus, the expected value of the momentum is simply $\hbar k$, or $h/\lambda$, which matches de Broglie's relation (Eq. 8.3) and our expectations.

What about the energy of our free particle? Now we use the Hamiltonian, or total energy, operator and write

$$\langle E \rangle = \int_{-\infty}^{\infty} \psi^*(x) \hat{H}\psi(x) \, dx$$

As before, let's see what the Hamiltonian operator does to our wavefunction. For the free particle, the Hamiltonian is simply the kinetic energy operator and we can write

$$\hat{H}\psi(x) = \frac{-\hbar^2}{2m}\frac{\partial^2}{\partial x^2} ae^{ikx} = \frac{\hbar^2 k^2}{2m} ae^{ikx} = \frac{\hbar^2 k^2}{2m}\psi(x)$$

(Recall that $i^2 = -1$.) Putting this back into the integral gives us

$$\langle E \rangle = \frac{\hbar^2 k^2}{2m} = \frac{p_x^2}{2m} \tag{8.34}$$

Again, this matches our expectations.

    We have been fortunate in evaluating these expectation values in that the wavefunction $\psi(x) = ae^{ikx}$ is an eigenfunction of both the momentum and Hamiltonian operators. Whenever we are evaluating the expectation value of a system that is described by an eigenfunction of the operator corresponding to the physical quantity we are measuring, we are guaranteed to obtain the corresponding eigenvalue. But what if our wavefunction is not an eigenfunction of the operator, which is often the case? We'll look at that next.

## 8.3.3 Superposition

Early on in our discussion of the free particle, we briefly toyed with the possibility of using a sine or cosine function as our wavefunction. We ultimately settled on the complex exponential, and we can see that this has been a useful function. Let's return to the cosine function, though, and see what it tells us. First, we need to see if it meets all the requirements of a valid wavefunction. It is continuous, has a continuous first derivative, and is finite and single valued. Normalization would need to be done in a fashion similar to what we did with the complex exponential, but there is no reason to reject it as a valid wavefunction for the free particle.

    We now want to know about the expectation values of energy and momentum for a particle described by the wavefunction

$$\psi(x) = a \cos kx$$

(The $a$ is the normalization constant, similar to what we did before.) Let's start with the energy. We obtain the expectation value of the energy by writing

$$\langle E \rangle = \int_{-\infty}^{\infty} (a\cos kx)^* \hat{H}(a\cos kx)\, dx$$

Since the cosine function is real, the complex conjugate is just the function itself. Now we need to see if this wavefunction is an eigenfunction of the Hamiltonian, which will make evaluating the integral trivial, since we have already established the wavefunction to be normalized.

$$\hat{H}\psi(x) = \frac{-\hbar^2}{2m}\frac{\partial^2}{\partial x^2} a\cos kx = \frac{\hbar^2 k^2}{2m} a\cos kx = \frac{\hbar^2 k^2}{2m}\psi(x)$$

This wavefunction is an eigenfunction of the Hamiltonian operator; therefore, the expectation value of the energy is simply

$$\langle E \rangle = \frac{\hbar^2 k^2}{2m}$$

Note that this is what we had before with the complex exponential as our wavefunction.

Now, what about the momentum? Well, let's first check to see if our new wavefunction is an eigenfunction of the momentum operator.

$$\hat{p}_x \psi(x) = \frac{\hbar}{i}\frac{\partial}{\partial x} a \cos kx = -\frac{\hbar}{i} k \, a \sin kx$$

Our new wavefunction is not an eigenfunction of the momentum operator. This means we can't just jump to the answer and write down the eigenvalue, because there isn't one. We now have two options. The first option is just to evaluate the integral directly, using the result of operating on the wavefunction with the operator.

$$\langle p_x \rangle = \int_{-\infty}^{\infty} a \cos kx \, \hat{p}_x (a \cos kx) \, dx = \frac{-\hbar}{i} ka^2 \int_{-\infty}^{\infty} \cos kx \, \sin kx \, dx$$

The integral of the product of the sine and cosine functions over any integer multiple of wavelengths is zero, therefore we have

$$\langle p_x \rangle = 0$$

This result is somewhat difficult to interpret. How can a particle that is moving (it has kinetic energy) have an expected momentum of zero?

We can gain additional physical insight by taking the second approach to evaluating this expectation value. If we have a function that is not an eigenfunction of the appropriate operator, we can write that function as a **linear combination** of other functions that are eigenfunctions of the operator. Such a linear combination is also called a **superposition**. Recall the relations about complex exponentials and trigonometric functions.

$$\cos kx = \frac{e^{ikx} + e^{-ikx}}{2} \quad \text{and} \quad \sin kx = \frac{e^{ikx} - e^{-ikx}}{2i} \tag{8.35}$$

Each of the two complex exponentials is an eigenfunction of the momentum operator, with eigenvalues of $\pm k$, respectively. Thus we can write

$$\hat{p}_x a \cos kx = \frac{a}{2}\hat{p}_x(e^{ikx} + e^{-ikx}) = \frac{a}{2}(\hbar k e^{ikx} - \hbar k e^{-ikx}) = \frac{a\hbar k}{2}(e^{ikx} - e^{-ikx})$$

Once again, we do not obtain the same function after applying the operator. Putting this back into the integral gives us

$$\langle p \rangle = \int_{-\infty}^{\infty} \frac{a}{2}(e^{ikx} + e^{-ikx})^* \hat{p}_x \frac{a}{2}(e^{ikx} + e^{-ikx}) \, dx$$

$$= \frac{a^2 \hbar k}{4} \int_{-\infty}^{\infty} (e^{-ikx} + e^{ikx})(e^{ikx} - e^{-ikx}) \, dx$$

$$= \frac{a^2 \hbar k}{4}\left[ \int_{-\infty}^{\infty} e^{-ikx} e^{ikx} \, dx + \int_{-\infty}^{\infty} e^{2ikx} \, dx - \int_{-\infty}^{\infty} e^{-2ikx} \, dx - \int_{-\infty}^{\infty} e^{ikx} e^{-ikx} \, dx \right]$$

The first and last terms in this expression cancel out. The middle two terms are readily evaluated by

$$\int_{-\infty}^{\infty} e^{\pm 2ikx} \, dx = 0$$

Thus, we again arrive at the result that the expectation value of the momentum is zero. We can now, however, give some added physical insight into why this is so.

We expressed our wavefunction as a superposition of two complex exponentials with positive and negative terms. This corresponds to a particle traveling in both the positive and negative directions. When we combine those ideas, we have a particle that is equally likely to be traveling in either direction. Thus, the average of those outcomes is zero. This is the same as flipping a coin and assigning a value of +1 to heads and −1 to tails. Even though each flip will either be +1 or −1, on average the result will be 0. Note that the energy doesn't depend on direction, so regardless of which way the particle may be traveling, we get the same value for the energy.

This result leads us to another key idea of quantum mechanics, which relates to the result of a measurement of a quantum-mechanical system. One of the postulates of quantum mechanics is that when we perform a measurement on a system, the only possible values we can measure are the eigenvalues of the eigenfunctions of the corresponding operator. If we have a system that is already described by one of those eigenfunctions, then we know the value we will obtain. However, if the system is not described by an eigenfunction, we need to express it as a superposition, or linear combination, of those eigenfunctions. A single measurement can only return one of those corresponding eigenvalues, but we don't know which one. If we have multiple identical systems and perform the measurement on each one then average the results, we will obtain the expectation value. Let's express these ideas more rigorously and mathematically.

Consider a quantum-mechanical operator $\hat{J}$ that has a set of eigenfunctions $\phi_n$ with corresponding eigenvalues $j_n$. For each of these functions we can write

$$\hat{J}\phi_n = j_n\phi_n \qquad (8.36)$$

The label $n$ here is just an index to keep track of the eigenfunctions and corresponding eigenvalues. We will not prove this here, but one of the characteristics of the eigenfunctions of a quantum-mechanical operator is that they are **orthogonal** to each other. You are probably familiar with the idea of orthogonality from geometry and vector math. Orthogonal lines are perpendicular to each other, and the dot product of two orthogonal vectors is zero. But what does this mean for functions? Two functions are taken to be orthogonal if, for two different functions of the set indexed as $m$ and $n$, we have

$$\int_{-\infty}^{\infty} \phi_m^*(x)\phi_n(x)\, dx = 0$$

If the two functions are the same, and that function is properly normalized, we have

$$\int_{-\infty}^{\infty} \phi_n^*(x)\phi_n(x)\, dx = 1$$

These two conditions can be combined through use of the **Kronecker delta**, $\delta_{m,n}$ which is equal to 1 if $m = n$ and equal to zero if $m \neq n$. We can put this all together into a single expression as

$$\int_{-\infty}^{\infty} \phi_m^*(x)\, \phi_n(x)\, dx = \delta_{m,n} \qquad (8.37)$$

Functions that satisfy this condition are said to be **orthonormal**. *The eigenfunctions of a quantum-mechanical operator form a set of orthonormal functions.* Remembering this will make the evaluation of integrals much easier.

Let's take an arbitrary wavefunction, $\psi$, and express it as a linear combination of two of the eigenfunctions of the operator. We write this as

$$\psi = c_1\phi_1 + c_2\phi_2 \qquad (8.38)$$

If we want our wavefunction to be normalized, there are going to be certain constraints on the values of the two coefficients in this sum. Let's quickly determine what those constraints are. We want to be sure that

$$\int_{-\infty}^{\infty} \psi^*\psi \, dx = 1$$

Substituting in the sum gives us

$$\int_{-\infty}^{\infty} (c_1\phi_1 + c_2\phi_2)^*(c_1\phi_1 + c_2\phi_2) \, dx = 1$$

Expanding out the terms gives us

$$c_1^*c_1\int_{-\infty}^{\infty} \phi_1^*\phi_1 \, dx + c_1^*c_2\int_{-\infty}^{\infty} \phi_1^*\phi_2 \, dx + c_2^*c_1\int_{-\infty}^{\infty} \phi_2^*\phi_1 \, dx + c_2^*c_2\int_{-\infty}^{\infty} \phi_2^*\phi_2 \, dx = 1$$

Now we can use the orthonormality condition to evaluate the individual integrals, making them all either 1 or 0; the first and last terms are 1, and the middle two are 0. This lets us write

$$\left|c_1\right|^2 + \left|c_2\right|^2 = 1 \qquad (8.39)$$

If the coefficients are real numbers (which they don't have to be, but often are), then we can just take the sum of their squares.

Now, let's evaluate the expectation value of the property $J$. We do this by evaluating

$$\langle J \rangle = \int_{-\infty}^{\infty} \psi^* \hat{J} \psi \, dx$$

After substituting in the linear combination (Eq. 8.38), we have

$$\langle J \rangle = \int_{-\infty}^{\infty} (c_1\phi_1 + c_2\phi_2)^* \hat{J}(c_1\phi_1 + c_2\phi_2) \, dx$$

We again expand out the terms inside the integral.

$$\langle J \rangle = c_1^*c_1\int_{-\infty}^{\infty} \phi_1^* \hat{J}\phi_1 \, dx + c_1^*c_2\int_{-\infty}^{\infty} \phi_1^* \hat{J}\phi_2 \, dx$$
$$+ c_2^*c_1\int_{-\infty}^{\infty} \phi_2^* \hat{J}\phi_1 \, dx + c_2^*c_2\int_{-\infty}^{\infty} \phi_2^* \hat{J}\phi_2 \, dx$$

Now we recall that each of the functions in the sum is an eigenfunction of the operator, described by Eq. 8.36. Making these substitutions lets us write

$$\langle J \rangle = c_1^*c_1 j_1\int_{-\infty}^{\infty} \phi_1^*\phi_1 \, dx + c_1^*c_2 j_2\int_{-\infty}^{\infty} \phi_1^*\phi_2 \, dx$$
$$+ c_2^*c_1 j_1\int_{-\infty}^{\infty} \phi_2^*\phi_1 \, dx + c_2^*c_2 j_2\int_{-\infty}^{\infty} \phi_2^*\phi_2 \, dx$$

Once again, orthonormality tells us that the first and last terms integrate to 1, and the middle terms integrate to 0, giving us

$$\langle J \rangle = \left| c_1 \right|^2 j_1 + \left| c_2 \right|^2 j_2 \qquad (8.40)$$

Thus the expectation value is a weighted average of the eigenvalues of the functions we used in constructing the linear combination. Extension of these ideas to a sum of more than two terms is left to the student.

## 8.3.4 Heisenberg's Uncertainty Principle

Let's return to our quantum-mechanical free particle. As we found, the free particle can have any nonnegative value for its kinetic energy, which means it has a well-defined linear momentum. We also saw that the probability distribution particle's location was uniform, meaning it was equally likely to be found anywhere in its one-dimensional space. How can we construct a wavefunction that localizes the particle in one particular region of space? To do this, we need to briefly explore the idea of a Fourier series.

Somewhere along the line in your mathematics courses, you likely encountered Fourier's theorem, which states that any repeating mathematical function can be represented as a sum of sine and cosine functions

$$f(x) \approx c_0 + \sum_{n=1}^{N} \left[ a_n \sin\left(\frac{2\pi nx}{\lambda}\right) + b_n \cos\left(\frac{2\pi nx}{\lambda}\right) \right] \tag{8.41}$$

where $\lambda$ is the period over which the function repeats and $N$ is the number of terms in the series; we get better representations of the real function as $N$ approaches infinity. By using complex exponentials, we can write this in a more compact notation

$$f(x) \approx \sum_{n=-N}^{N} c_n e^{\frac{i2\pi nx}{\lambda}} = \sum_{n=-N}^{N} c_n e^{inkx} \tag{8.42}$$

Recall that we defined the angular wavenumber as $k = 2\pi/\lambda$, and that $k$ relates to the momentum of the particle. So we basically have a series of functions with momenta that are multiples of some fundamental momentum, and this would produce a periodic function with fundamental wavelength $\lambda$.

If we want a wavefunction that is localized in a single position and not periodic, we can do this by extending the fundamental wavelength to infinity, which means the fundamental value of $k$ approaches zero and our multiples of that small number become infinitely close together. The sum then becomes an integral, and we can write the position function as a **Fourier transform** of a function of $k$, or momentum, values

$$f(x) = \int_{-\infty}^{\infty} F(k) e^{ikx} \, dk \tag{8.43}$$

where $F(k)$ is a function that tells us how much of each momentum function we need for our construction of the spatial function. Note that if $F(k)$ is zero except at a single value, then the only thing that survives the integration is the function $e^{ikx}$, which is our wavefunction for a particle with a well-defined momentum. As we have already seen, a particle described by this wavefunction is equally likely to be at any position; it has no well-defined position.

We won't spend a lot of time with Fourier transforms here, but one of the interesting things about them is the inverse relationship between the widths of $F(k)$ and $f(x)$. If the range of the momentum function is very narrow, then the range of the position function is very large. The reverse is also true; if we want a narrowly defined position function, we need a very broad momentum function. In fact, we can define a width parameter for the two functions, which we'll call $\delta k$ and $\delta x$, and the product of those two values will always be greater than or equal to some constant.

$$\delta k \, \delta x \geq C \tag{8.44}$$

The more we tighten up one of these two **conjugate variables**, $k$ or $x$, the less tightly we can constrain the other one.

The mathematics behind Fourier series and Fourier transforms was developed in the 1820s, so it was well known to the physicists working on quantum theory 100 years later. It was Werner Heisenberg who, in 1927, incorporated these ideas into what became known as the **uncertainty principle**. Heisenberg received the Nobel Prize in 1932. To fully develop Heisenberg's ideas, though, we need to return to our quantum-mechanical operators. We also need to think about what these operators represent and how they relate to actual experimental observations.

Consider a baseball coach working with a pitcher who is trying to improve his fastball. How can the coach tell how fast the pitcher is throwing? He uses a radar gun, which bounces radar signals (microwaves) off the incoming fastball. The returning signal is Doppler shifted by the speed of the ball, which the gun can detect and interpret as the speed of the pitch. This assumes that the radar gun and the microwave radiation (light) it emits have no effect on the velocity of the baseball. Now, what if you want to determine the velocity of an electron? Similarly, we can shine light on the traveling electron and measure a Doppler shift. But does the incident light have any effect on the electron? We saw early on in this chapter that the momentum of a photon and that of an electron were of roughly the same order of magnitude. Thus, the interaction of an electron and a photon *can* alter the behavior of that electron; we already saw this with the photoelectric effect. At the quantum level, the act of measuring affects the system being measured.

Now, back to operators. We have already postulated that an operator corresponds to a physically observable quantity, such as position, momentum, or energy. The mathematical use of an operator on a wavefunction is analogous to performing a physical measurement in a laboratory. Using a different operator would correspond to performing a different measurement. The question we need to ask is, does the order in which we perform our measurements matter? Can we, for example, measure the position and then the momentum and get the same answers as if we first measured the momentum and then the position?

If the order of mathematical operations doesn't matter, those operations are said to **commute**. You learned early on in arithmetic about the commutative property of addition and multiplication, which means that

$$a + b = b + a \quad \text{and} \quad ab = ba$$

The same is not true of subtraction and division:

$$a - b \neq b - a \quad \text{and} \quad a/b \neq b/a \ (\text{unless } a = b)$$

In linear algebra, multiplication of matrices generally does not follow a commutative law. What about quantum-mechanical operators? To see if their order matters, we define the **commutator** of two operators as

$$\left[\hat{J}_1, \hat{J}_2\right] = \hat{J}_1\hat{J}_2 - \hat{J}_2\hat{J}_1 \tag{8.45}$$

If the result of evaluating the commutator operating on some arbitrary function is zero, then the operators commute and the order doesn't matter. However, if the commutator is not zero, then the order does matter. Let's evaluate the commutator of the position and momentum operators to see how this works.

Recall that the position and momentum operators are defined as

$$\hat{p}_x \equiv \frac{\hbar}{i}\frac{\partial}{\partial x} \quad \text{and} \quad \hat{x} \equiv x \times$$

To evaluate the commutator, we need to use both operators on an arbitrary function, but in both orders.

$$\left[\hat{x}, \hat{p}_x\right] f = \hat{x}\,\hat{p}_x f - \hat{p}_x \hat{x}\, f$$

Operators, like matrices, work from right to left, so we write the two terms on the right as

$$\hat{x}\,\hat{p}_x f = x \times \frac{\hbar}{i}\frac{df}{dx} \qquad \hat{p}_x \hat{x}\, f = \frac{\hbar}{i}\frac{d}{dx}(xf) = \frac{\hbar}{i}\left(f + x\frac{df}{dx}\right)$$

Putting these together in the commutator gives us the result

$$\left[\hat{x}, \hat{p}_x\right] = \frac{-\hbar}{i} = i\hbar \qquad\qquad (8.46)$$

Since this is not equal to zero, it matters in what order we measure position and momentum. Heisenberg formally defined his uncertainty principle with the following expression

$$\delta J_1 \delta J_2 \geq \frac{1}{2}\left|\left[\hat{J}_1, \hat{J}_2\right]\right| \qquad\qquad (8.47)$$

For two physical properties, $J_1$ and $J_2$, the product of the uncertainty to which we can know the value of those two properties must be greater than or equal to one half the absolute value of the commutator of those two operators. If the operators commute, then we can know both values precisely. If the two operators do not commute, the more precisely we know one value, the less precisely we can know the other. For position and momentum, we have the relation

$$\delta x \,\delta p_x \geq \frac{\hbar}{2} \qquad\qquad (8.48)$$

We won't prove this here, but there is a similar relationship for the variables of energy and time

$$\delta E \,\delta t \geq \frac{\hbar}{2} \qquad\qquad (8.49)$$

Thus, for a state that is very short lived, the energy of that state is not well determined. This relation also has implications for ultrashort pulses of laser light; the shorter the pulse, the less defined the energy and—since energy of light relates to frequency—the pulse will cover a broad range of frequencies.

The reason for all of this is that the act of measuring disturbs the system under investigation. If we want to measure the position of an electron with light, our precision can be no greater than the wavelength of the light we are using. If we want to know the position very precisely, we need to use short-wavelength light. But remember that short-wavelength light will carry more momentum; thus it will have a greater effect on the electron. We may be able to tell where it was at the point in time of the measurement, but the "kick" of the photon will change its trajectory so we have no idea where it went. We could use longer wavelength light, which would provide less of a kick, but then we wouldn't know the position as precisely. There are fairly deep philosophical implications to the uncertainty principle which we will discuss more fully in Chapter 22, but to keep things brief, we need to give up the idea of a passive observer at the quantum level. The act of measurement can affect the system, and we need to keep that in mind.

### 8.3.5 The Postulates of Quantum Mechanics

Throughout this chapter, we have developed and explored the postulates that govern the formalism of quantum mechanics. It is useful to bring them all together. Stated briefly, they are:

1. The state of the system is described by a wavefunction that must satisfy certain mathematical conditions: continuous, continuous first derivative, finite, single valued, normalizable.
2. The product $\psi^*\psi d\tau$ gives the probability of finding the particle within a volume element $d\tau$.
3. All physical observables have a corresponding mathematical operator; specifically the linear momentum operator is written as $\hat{p}_x = \dfrac{\hbar}{i}\dfrac{\partial}{\partial x}$ and the position operator is written as $\hat{x} = x \times$. Operators for other physical quantities can be constructed from these operators.
4. Each operator has an orthonormal set of eigenfunctions. Only the eigenvalues for a given operator can be observed during an experimental measurement.
5. The expectation value of an observable $J$ is given by $\langle J \rangle = \int \psi^* \hat{J}\, \psi d\tau$.

There are different ways to state these postulates, but the central ideas are always the same. For example, it is sometimes stated that the Schrödinger equation is a postulate; however, it arises quite naturally from the third and fifth postulates listed above. The Heisenberg uncertainty principle is also sometimes included in this list. The important thing to remember is that these postulates form the basis for what we will do with quantum mechanics. We can't prove that they are correct, but what arises from them agrees with every experiment that has been performed, so they are judged to be very reasonable postulates.

## 8.4 Summary, and Where We Go Next

We have covered a lot of very difficult terrain in this chapter. At this point, you may be wondering what you have gotten yourself into. It's worth taking a step back and recalling why we have taken this plunge into the world of quantum mechanics. At the beginning of the 20th century, the only way to explain several previously confounding problems was to give up some of the most basic assumptions of classical physics, such as the constancy of distance and time (Einstein had to abandon these in formulating relativity), and the idea that energy could be added to or taken away from a system in arbitrarily small amounts (Planck broke from this to explain blackbody radiation). The ideas developed in the first decades of the last century have had lasting impacts not only on our understanding of the physical world, but also in the realm of daily life. GPS systems wouldn't work at all if they didn't correct for relativistic effects. The laser, the transistor, and in fact most of modern technology—including integrated circuitry and cellular communication—are based on principles that arise from quantum mechanics. As a scientist or engineer in the modern era, you should have more than just a passing familiarity with these important ideas.

Quantum mechanics also enriches our understanding of chemistry, which is really driven by the electrons that surround atomic nuclei. Over the next few chapters, we will use quantum mechanics to develop model systems for describing the structure and properties of molecules. We will gain a better understanding of why atoms are stable—which classical physics couldn't explain—why molecules exist, and how we can use light to investigate their properties. Admittedly, the road will be somewhat bumpy as we continue to use a great deal of mathematics, which is really the language of quantum mechanics, but the results will be very fulfilling. So strap yourself in and prepare for an exciting journey through the quantum realm!

# PROBLEMS

**8.1** The idea of "light propulsion" has been around for some time. Consider a spacecraft with a mass of 5 kg powered by a light beam with a wavelength of 500 nm. If the beam has a power of 100 watts, what is the total change to the velocity of the spacecraft if it is illuminated by the light for 5 years?

**8.2** a) Calculate the de Broglie wavelength of an $O_2$ molecule at 300 K.

b) Based on the ideal gas law, estimate the distance between $O_2$ molecules at 300 K and 1 bar. Compare this distance to the de Broglie wavelength.

**8.3** In order to use a beam of electrons for electron-diffraction measurements, the de Broglie wavelength of those electrons must be comparable to the lattice spacings in the crystal under study. Determine the energy of the electron beam required to perform diffraction measurements in a crystal where the atoms are spaced ~100 pm apart.

**8.4** a) The nucleus of an atom is not a mathematical point but has a finite volume. The diameter of a nucleus is ~$10^{-14}$ m. To confine an electron to this volume requires that the de Broglie wavelength be comparable to this dimension. What would be the kinetic energy of an electron confined to the dimension of the nucleus?

b) The ionization energy of a hydrogen atom is 13.6 eV. How does your calculated energy from part a) compare to this value?

c) Use the ionization energy of H to estimate the size of the H atom.

**8.5** The hydrogen-alpha (Hα) spectral line occurs at 656.28 nm and is used by astronomers to identify the presence of hydrogen in the universe. The source of this light is the transition of an electron between two of the possible electronic states in the hydrogen atom.

a) Calculate the recoil velocity imparted to a single hydrogen atom by the emission of a Hα photon.

b) Calculate the percent change in average velocity due to this photon emission if the hydrogen atoms are in a gas cell at standard ambient temperature and pressure.

**8.6** For each of the following functions, state whether they can be used as quantum-mechanical wavefunctions for a one-dimensional system. If they cannot, provide a justification for why not.

a) $\psi(x) = ax^2 + 2$

b) $\psi(x) = ae^{-\alpha x^2}$

c) $\psi(x) = ae^{-|x|}$

d) $\psi(x) = e^{ikx}$ for $x > 0$; $\psi(x) = 0$ for $x \le 0$

e) $\psi(x) = \tan x$

f) $\psi(x) = \pm\sqrt{ax}$

**8.7** The normalized wavefunction for the $1s$ electron of the hydrogen atom is

$$\psi_{1s} = \frac{1}{\pi^{1/2} a_0^{3/2}} e^{-r/a_0}$$

where $a_0$ is the Bohr radius. (Note that $r$ can only range from 0 to infinity, and you need to evaluate the necessary integrals in spherical coordinates.)

a) Calculate the expectation value of the radius for the $1s$ electron of hydrogen.

Calculate the probability of finding the electron:

b) within a distance of $a_0$ from the nucleus.

c) between 0.7 $a_0$ and 1.3 $a_0$ from the nucleus.

d) at a distance greater than 2 $a_0$ from the nucleus.

**8.8** The following functions are used for various one-dimensional systems. (You will see them in subsequent chapters.) Normalize each wavefunction.

a) $\psi(x) = N \sin\dfrac{2\pi x}{L}$ for a particle confined to $0 < x < L$; outside this region, $\psi = 0$.

b) $\psi = Nxe^{-x^2/2a^2}$

c) $\psi = Ne^{2i\phi}$ for a particle confined to a ring; $\phi$ ranges from 0 to $2\pi$.

**8.9** For each of the following functions, determine whether they are eigenfunctions of the one-dimensional momentum and kinetic energy operators. If the function is an eigenfunction, give the eigenvalue.

a) $ae^{-\alpha x}$

b) $\sin kx$

c) $ax^2 + 2$

d) $ae^{-\alpha x^2}$

**8.10** A free particle is described by the following wavefunction:

$$\psi(x) = 0.56e^{2.5ix} + 0.83e^{-1.6ix}$$

a) In units of $\hbar$, what are the possible values of energy and momentum that could be measured for this particle?

b) In units of $\hbar$, what are the expectation values of energy and momentum?

c) What is the expectation value of position for this wavefunction? Provide a physical interpretation of your result.

**8.11** a) A baseball player has just watched a documentary on quantum mechanics and thinks the uncertainty principle can explain why he can't hit fastballs. Is there any basis for this idea? The mass of a baseball is 145 g. Assume the pitcher can throw a 95±1 mph fastball.

b) A physicist wants to measure the location of a proton moving with a speed of 100±10 m s$^{-1}$ to a precision of 10 nm. Is this feasible?

**8.12** a) Electronic states of atoms and molecules can have lifetimes on the order of 1 ps. Estimate the uncertainty in the energy of this state.

b) Ultrashort laser pulses can be produced that are shorter than 10 fs ($10^{-14}$ s). Determine the range of frequencies and wavelengths that such a pulse must contain if the center wavelength is at 800 nm.

**8.13** We showed that the probability of finding a free particle was uniform with position when that particle is described by the wavefunction $\psi(x) = ae^{\pm ikx}$. Describe the probability density function for a free particle described by the wavefunction $\psi(x) = a \sin kx$. How is the probability density for this wavefunction the same or different from the particle described by the complex exponential? Are there any positions where the particle is more or less likely to be located?

# The Quantum-Mechanical Particle in a Box

## 9.1 The Particle in a Box

In the last chapter, we developed the tools that we need to approach problems in quantum mechanics. Specifically, we introduced wavefunctions and operators, learned about eigen-functions and eigenvalues, and presented the Schrödinger equation. We also discussed expectation values, superposition, and uncertainty. Finally, we formally codified the postulates of quantum mechanics. We are now prepared to tackle our first real quantum-mechanical system; the free particle is useful for demonstrating fundamentals but has no practical application because, by definition, nothing can happen to it.

This first physically meaningful system that we will explore is known as the particle in a box, which is basically a single particle confined to a particular region of space. You might wonder why we should care about such a system. There are actually two physical systems that can be approximated by this model. The first is a real molecule—say, of an ideal gas—confined within a container or a room. The second use of this model is to treat electrons in molecules; for nonconducting systems, the electrons are confined to the physical dimensions of the molecule. Both applications of the model will be important to us later in the text. The other reason that this system is important is that it will allow us to introduce a few more ideas that will extend the power of quantum mechanics. Our tools are in place, so let's get to work.

### 9.1.1 Solving the Schrödinger Equation for the One-Dimensional Particle in a Box

In order to solve the Schrödinger equation for our particle confined in a one-dimensional region of space, from $x = 0$ to $x = L$, we first need to construct the Hamiltonian operator for this situation. A Hamiltonian operator in one dimension is written as

$$\hat{H} = \frac{-\hbar^2}{2m}\frac{\partial^2}{\partial x^2} + V(x) \tag{9.1}$$

The Schrödinger equation in one dimension is written as

$$\hat{H}\psi(x) = \frac{-\hbar^2}{2m}\frac{\partial^2 \psi(x)}{\partial x^2} + V(x)\psi(x) = E\psi(x) \tag{9.2}$$

In order to proceed further, we need to properly define the potential energy function. If the particle can't leave the confines of the box, then something must be preventing the particle from doing so. That something is a potential barrier, which we will take to be infinite outside the dimensions of the box, as shown in Figure 9.1. Within the box, we will conveniently set the potential energy to zero. Mathematically, we write

$$V(x) = 0 \quad \text{for } 0 < x < L$$
$$V(x) = \infty \quad \text{for } x \leq 0, \ x \geq L \tag{9.3}$$

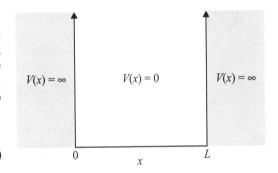

**FIGURE 9.1.** Potential energy function for a particle in a one-dimensional box of length $L$.

This definition of the potential presents a bit of a problem in solving the Schrödinger equation; infinities often do. We can address this by asking ourselves a question: If the particle is confined to the length of the box, what is the probability of finding it outside the box? Clearly, if the particle can't exist outside the box, then the probability of finding it there must be zero. Recall that $\psi^*\psi \, dx$ is the probability distribution function for the location of the particle. If the particle can't be outside the box, then $\psi^*\psi$, and by extension $\psi$ itself, must be zero outside the box. If the wavefunction is zero where the potential is infinite, then the term $V(x)\psi(x)$ in the Schrödinger equation simply equals zero. The second derivative of zero is zero, so the entire left-hand side of the equation is zero. The right-hand side is also zero, regardless of the value of the energy, $E$. You may think that $0 = 0$ is a rather unsatisfactory solution, but it is actually quite helpful in this case. We now have a solution for the wavefunction for the regions outside the box

$$\psi(x) = 0 \quad \text{for} \quad x \leq 0, \ x \geq L$$

We have now solved two thirds of the problem and need to turn our attention to the region inside the box.

Inside the box, we have defined the potential to be zero. This means that the Schrödinger equation in this region can be rewritten as

$$\frac{-\hbar^2}{2m}\frac{\partial^2 \psi}{\partial x^2} = E\psi$$

This looks just like the Schrödinger equation for the free particle; and in fact it is, since we chose the potential inside the box to be zero. Since there is no reason to repeat work we've already done (that's called efficiency, not laziness), we can just write the general solution as

$$\psi(x) = c_1 e^{ikx} + c_2 e^{-ikx} \qquad \text{where} \qquad k = \frac{\sqrt{2mE}}{\hbar}$$

We found the complex exponentials to be very convenient for the free particle, but we could just as easily have chosen to use the sine and cosine. It turns out in this case that the sine and cosine will actually be more convenient for us, so we'll rewrite our general solution to the Schrödinger equation inside the box as

$$\psi(x) = A \sin kx + B \cos kx \qquad \text{with} \qquad k = \frac{\sqrt{2mE}}{\hbar}$$

where $A$ and $B$ are constants that we still need to determine. We also need to determine the allowed energies for our system, which affect the values of $k$.

In order to proceed further, we need to recall one of the requirements we have stated for a valid wavefunction; the wavefunction must be continuous. We provided a justification for the value of the wavefunction being zero outside the box, and we need to make sure the solution inside the box is consistent with that result. Mathematically, we need to set boundary conditions to our solution inside the box. These are simply

$$\psi(0) = 0 \qquad \text{and} \qquad \psi(L) = 0$$

Let's start with the left side of the box, $x = 0$. Putting this value into our general solution for the wavefunction gives us

$$\psi(0) = A \sin 0 + B \cos 0 = B = 0$$

Because $\sin 0 = 0$ and $\cos 0 = 1$, we can see that the only way to satisfy this expression is for $B$ to equal 0.

Now, let's look at the right boundary, $x = L$, incorporating what we have just learned.

$$\psi(L) = A \sin k L = 0$$

There is a temptation to just set $A$ equal to 0 and be done with it. This choice, however, would make the wavefunction zero everywhere, including inside the box. That would mean we have no particle anywhere. Thus we reject $A = 0$ on physical, rather than mathematical, grounds. We need to try something else, so let's look at the sine function. If the sine is to equal 0, then the argument of the sine must be some integer multiple of $\pi$. Mathematically,

$$kL = n\pi \qquad \text{with} \qquad n = 1, 2, 3, \dots$$

A value of $n = 0$ is not physically acceptable, since it would again make the wavefunction equal to 0 for all $x$. Now we can write our solution inside the box as

$$\psi(x) = A \sin \frac{n\pi x}{L} \qquad \text{with} \qquad n = 1, 2, 3, \dots \text{ for } 0 < x < L$$

The integer $n$ is called the **quantum number** and serves as an index for the various solutions of the Schrödinger equation inside the box.

We still don't know the value of $A$, so let's determine that quickly. We can do so by normalizing the wavefunction. Recall that we normalize the wavefunction by requiring that the integral of $\psi^*\psi$ over all space be equal to 1. In this case, because the wavefunction is identically zero outside the box, we just need to evaluate

$$1 = \int_0^L \psi^*\psi \, dx = A^* A \int_0^L \sin^2 \frac{n\pi x}{L} \, dx = A^2 \frac{L}{2}$$

$$A = \sqrt{\frac{2}{L}}$$

We now write the full solution for the wavefunction as

$$\psi(x) = \sqrt{\frac{2}{L}} \sin \frac{n\pi x}{L} \quad n = 1, 2, 3 \dots \text{ for } 0 < x < L$$

$$\psi(x) = 0 \quad \text{for } x \le 0, \; x \ge L$$

(9.4)

The wavefunctions inside the box are integer multiples of half-periods of a sine wave, with the value of the wavefunction equal to 0 at the edges, as shown in Figure 9.2a. (In Problem 9.6 you will show that the functions for different values of $n$ are orthogonal to each other, as required by Postulate 4.) The astute reader will note that the derivative of the wavefunction is not continuous across the edges of the box. This is because of the infinite potential and is one of the exceptions to the conditions we stated in the last chapter. Note that for all $n > 1$, there will be locations somewhere inside the box where the wavefunction is equal to 0. Such points are called **nodes** and represent places where the particle cannot be. This is particularly clear if we look at the plots in Figure 9.2b, which show $\psi^*\psi$. Already we see a difference between the quantum-mechanical solution and its classical analog. If we had a marble in a box with a flat bottom, are there any positions where the marble cannot be? No, the marble can be anywhere along the bottom of the box with equal likelihood. A quantum-mechanical particle, however, is more likely to be found at some locations than at others, as indicated by the maxima in $\psi^*\psi$, whereas it cannot be found at the positions of the nodes. This is the first difference we see in comparing the classical and quantum-mechanical systems.

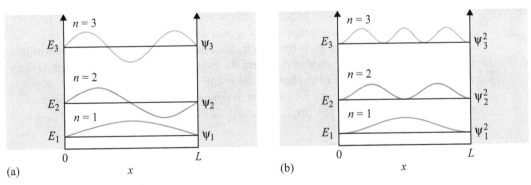

(a)                    (b)

FIGURE 9.2. Plots of a) $\psi$ and b) $\psi^*\psi$ for the particle in a one-dimensional box. All plots are shifted vertically by the energy of the corresponding state.

The second major difference is seen as we consider the energy of the system. Earlier, we wrote

$$k = \frac{\sqrt{2mE}}{\hbar} \quad \text{or} \quad E = \frac{\hbar^2 k^2}{2m}$$

In order to satisfy the boundary conditions, we put limitations on the value of $k$. Specifically, $kL = n\pi$ must be true. Putting this in gives us

$$E_n = \frac{\hbar^2 k^2}{2m} = \frac{\hbar^2 n^2 \pi^2}{2mL^2} \qquad n = 1, 2, 3 \ldots$$

or, more conveniently

$$E_n = \frac{h^2 n^2}{8mL^2} \qquad n = 1, 2, 3 \ldots \tag{9.5}$$

where we used the definition of $\hbar = h / 2\pi$. Thus we see that only certain values of energy are possible for our particle in a box; the energy states have been quantized!

Another interesting quantum-mechanical result is that we cannot have a particle with zero energy, even though we took the potential energy inside the box to be equal to zero; for $n = 1$, we have a lowest possible energy of $E_1 = \dfrac{h^2}{8mL^2}$. This lowest allowable energy above the minimum in the potential is called the **zero-point energy**; the energy of the system can go no lower than this value. Note that as the box becomes smaller—or as $L$ decreases—the energy of a given level, even the lowest, will increase. Confinement leads to quantization, and the more we try to confine a particle, the more spacing we will observe in the allowed energy levels. Also, with more confinement (smaller $L$), the energy of the lowest possible level increases relative to the bottom of the box.

There are some important features of the plots in Figure 9.2 that need to be pointed out to avoid potential confusion. Notice that the individual functions are shifted along the vertical axis by the energy of the corresponding state. This is done for clarity and convenience, so that all the functions are not plotted on top of each other. But you should not think of the wavefunctions as being spatially separated from each other. Remember, this is a one-dimensional problem; the only spatial dimension that exists is the horizontal direction. What we are plotting is the amplitude of the wavefunction as a function of this position. The vertical axis can also represent the energy of the barrier, which jumps from zero to infinity at the walls of the box, or the energy of the state of the particle, which is described by Eq. 9.5. There is a lot going on in figures of this type, and you'll see more of them, so take a moment to familiarize yourself with these conventions.

## 9.1.2 The Correspondence Principle

We now have quantized energy states for our particle confined to a one-dimensional region of space. Note, however, that if we increase the size of the box—that is, if we relax the confinement—the energy levels will space more closely together. If we extend the width of the box infinitely, then we go back to the free-particle solution of a continuum of allowed energies. As we saw with the solutions to problems in kinetics, it is generally good practice to consider what happens to our solutions in certain extreme limits. The fact that we recover the free-particle solution with infinitely spaced walls is encouraging, since it agrees with a result we have already seen.

The fact that we recover a continuum of energy states in the limit that the box is infinitely wide is comforting for another reason. When we remove the confinement of our particle, we regain the classical solution. This is a manifestation of the **correspondence principle** that, in certain limits, any solution to a quantum-mechanical problem must return to the classical result. The correspondence principle was put forth by Niels Bohr in 1920, and helps to bridge quantum mechanics with classical, Newtonian physics. Newton wasn't wrong; his approach is simply limited in its range of applicability, and it breaks down at atomic length and mass scales. As the parameters of a quantum-mechanical system approach those of a Newtonian (classical) system, we need to recover Newton's answers. (Incidentally, the equations of relativity also exhibit correspondence; as the speeds become significantly less than the speed of light, all the equations go back to their classical versions.)

We can consider the allowed states of our quantum system in other limits as well by looking at our expression for the energy. We have already discussed changing the value of $L$, the length of the box. What if we increase the mass of the particle? We can see that the energy levels, and the spacing between them, will decrease as the mass increases. Thus, as we approach macroscopic length and mass scales, our quantum-mechanical solution will begin to look classical.

The third parameter in our energy expression we need to consider is the quantum number $n$. This is also accounted for in the correspondence principle; at large values of $n$, the solutions must look classical. Classically, there is no quantization of energy and the allowable energies form a continuum. The evaluation of the energy spacing in terms of the correspondence principle is done in Problem 9.5. We will, however, consider the shape of the wavefunction, or more properly $\psi^*\psi$, in the limit of large quantum numbers. We can see that $\psi^*\psi$ will have $n$ maxima; therefore, as the quantum number becomes large, so will the number of maxima in $\psi^*\psi$. The number of nodes also increases with $n$; however, there is always more of the wavefunction that is not a node than there are nodes. Also, in any sort of measurement, we cannot resolve distance to arbitrary precision. Thus, if we were to measure the probability distribution of a particle in a state with very large $n$, it would resemble a uniform distribution, exactly as the classical model predicts.

## 9.2 Introduction to Spectroscopy

Spectroscopy involves the use of light to understand the structure of matter. We can do this because light and matter interact in well-defined ways. A full treatment of light-matter interactions is beyond the scope of this text, but we can use what we have learned from the particle-in-a-box system to discuss some of the fundamental ideas of spectroscopy, which we will apply to additional model systems. Spectroscopy is a very powerful tool, and it is largely how we know so much about molecular systems. Molecules are much too small to be observed directly, but spectroscopy can tell us important things about molecular structure and the composition of complicated samples. Activities from process monitoring to product characterization involve one form of spectroscopy or another, making it a vital part of the engineer's toolbox.

## 9.2.1 Time-Dependent Schrödinger Equation

Everything we have done so far with quantum mechanics has involved solving the time-independent Schrödinger equation. This means that the solutions we have evaluated do not change in time. Of course, time is a fundamental variable in the universe, so it should come as no surprise that there is a time-dependent form of the Schrödinger equation. We will not spend much time with this, but you should see it for the sake of completeness. The time-dependent Schrödinger equation is written in the form

$$ i\hbar \frac{\partial \Psi(x,t)}{\partial t} = \hat{H} \Psi(x,t) \tag{9.6} $$

The time-dependent wavefunction is commonly written with a capital $\Psi$ and it is a function of a set of position coordinates, represented by $q$, and time, $t$. The Hamiltonian operator used here is the same as what is used in the time-independent Schrödinger equation. (In some presentations of the postulates of quantum mechanics, the time-dependent Schrödinger equation is presented as its own postulate. That would make it #6 on our list in Section 8.3.5. In this book, however, we will not make much use of it. There are cases where the Hamiltonian is time dependent, but we won't deal with any of those.)

In general, we are interested in so-called **stationary states**, which are states that do not change in time. In these cases, the Hamiltonian does not depend on time and we can separate the spatial and time variables of the wavefunction to write

$$ \Psi(q,t) = \psi(q) f(t) \tag{9.7} $$

The most general solution to the time-dependent Schrödinger equation is then

$$ \Psi(q,t) = \psi(q) e^{-iEt/\hbar} \tag{9.8} $$

The function $\psi(q)$ is the same spatial wavefunction we discussed before. You should verify for yourself that a wavefunction of this form, with a time-independent Hamiltonian, leads to the time-independent Schrödinger equation. The complex exponential is an oscillating amplitude factor, where the frequency of the oscillation increases with the energy of the state. This is why we often talk about the stationary states as standing waves; the amplitude changes periodically in time, but the wave doesn't change position. Note that for this type of wavefunction, the probability of where to find the particle does not change in time. Mathematically, we write

$$ \Psi^*(q,t)\Psi(q,t) = \psi^*(x)e^{iEt/\hbar}\psi(q)e^{-iEt/\hbar} = \psi^*(q)\psi(q) $$

(As a side note, the factor $Et$ in the exponential function should be a good hint at the existence of a time–energy uncertainty relationship.)

## 9.2.2 Light–Matter Interactions

Let's return to the particle in a box. We have determined that the stationary-state wavefunctions are of the form

$$ \psi(x) = \sqrt{\frac{2}{L}}\sin\frac{n\pi x}{L} \qquad n = 1, 2, 3 \ldots \text{ for } 0 < x < L \text{, and zero elsewhere} $$

The energy of each state is given by

$$E_n = \frac{h^2 n^2}{8mL^2} \qquad n = 1, 2, 3 \ldots$$

Recall that a photon of light has energy equal to

$$E = h\nu = \frac{hc}{\lambda}$$

So, by conservation of energy arguments, we should be able to cause a transition between two states if the energy of the photon equals the energy difference between the two states. In other words, if we start in state $i$ and want to go to state $j$, we need to have photons of energy $\Delta E = E_j - E_i = h\nu = hc/\lambda$. If the incident light is not of the correct frequency (wavelength), then the transition cannot occur.

There is actually more to the story than just the photons having the right energy. Recall that light is an oscillating electromagnetic wave, meaning that it is changing in time. To fully describe light–matter interactions, we have to take this time dependence into account. The technique used is known as **time-dependent perturbation theory**. Again, a full treatment is beyond the scope of this text. The short story is that the light, acting as a time-dependent disturbance on the system, can allow the individual stationary states—which are otherwise orthogonal—to couple, or connect, to each other. This is how the system can transition from one state to another; without the light interacting with the two states, the transition wouldn't happen.

A key result of this analysis is a quantity known as the **transition dipole moment**. We can motivate this quantity in the following way. To a first approximation, we can describe the electric field of the light interacting with the electric dipole of the molecule as a dot product of the electric field vector and the dipole moment vector. In this one-dimensional model, we describe the molecular dipole by the relation $\mu_x = \mu_0 x$. The electric field also only has an $x$ component in this model. According to our postulates, we can define a **dipole moment operator** as

$$\hat{\mu}_x = \mu_0 E_0 \hat{x} \qquad (9.9)$$

Because the electric field of the light oscillates, the $x$ value in Eq. 9.9 will actually oscillate in time, but we can ignore that part of the depiction. The transition dipole moment is written as

$$\mu_{ji} = \int \psi_j^* \hat{\mu}_x \psi_i dx = \mu_0 E_0 \int \psi_j^* x \psi_i dx \qquad (9.10)$$

where $j$ and $i$ label the two different states. (Remember, without the $x$, $\int \psi_j^* \psi_i dx = 0$. Also, the integral is only over spatial coordinates, which is why we can ignore the time dependence.) If this quantity is nonzero, we can have a transition; such a transition is called **allowed**. It is possible, however, that this quantity is zero. In such a case, even if our light is of the correct frequency, no transition will take place; we call this a **forbidden** transition.

Let's look at this for the first three states of our particle in a box. We can learn a lot by visually plotting the functions that go into this integral. The $n = 1$, 2, and 3 states are plotted in Figure 9.3a, b, and c. Recall that any two of these states are orthogonal, meaning the integral of the product of any two of their wavefunctions is 0. Figure 9.3d shows this for the $n = 1$ and 2 wavefunctions. (Because we are using purely real functions, we don't have to worry about the complex conjugates in this case.) You can see visually that there is just as much of the function that is positive as negative, so they cancel each other out in the integral. Now, what about the product

$$\psi_2 x \psi_1 = \frac{2}{L}\left(\sin\frac{2\pi x}{L}\right) x \left(\sin\frac{\pi x}{L}\right)$$

shown in Figure 9.3e? Notice that this product is not symmetric, and its integral will not be 0. This means that the transition dipole moment is *not* zero, and a transition between the $n = 1$ and $n = 2$ states *is* possible. The sign of the transition dipole moment doesn't matter; the fact that it is nonzero is enough for the transition to be allowed. The magnitude of this quantity—that is, its absolute value—tells us about the strength of the transition, or the likelihood that it takes place.

What about the transition between $n = 1$ and $n = 3$? Let's look at the product $\psi_3 x \psi_1$, shown in Figure 9.3f. It may not be as obvious, but the integral of this function is identically 0. So a photon of energy $h\nu = E_2 - E_1$ can cause the system to transition from the $n = 1$ state to the $n = 2$ state. But a photon of energy $h\nu = E_3 - E_1$ cannot cause a transition from the $n = 1$ state to the $n = 3$ state; even though the energy is correct, the transition is forbidden. This is one example of a **selection rule**. In this case, a transition is allowed if $\Delta n = +1$. If $\Delta n = +2$, the transition is not allowed. (Actually, a transition will occur if $\Delta n$ is any odd number, but the magnitude of the transition dipole moment decreases as the states get further apart, meaning those transitions are much less likely than for $\Delta n = +1$.) Every form of spectroscopy has a set of selection rules that tell us what states can be connected to each other by light or, in other words, what transitions are allowed.

It is also possible for a photon to be emitted from an excited state, returning the system to a lower energy state; energy must always be conserved. In this case, we change the

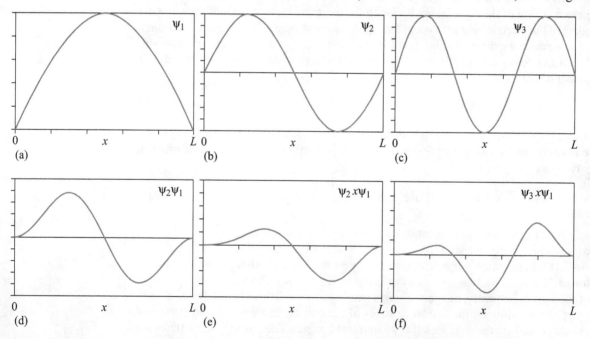

**FIGURE 9.3.** Plots of a) $\psi_1$, b) $\psi_2$, and c) $\psi_3$ for the particle in a one-dimensional box. d) The product of $\psi_1$ and $\psi_2$. e) The product $\psi_2 x \psi_1$, which will not integrate to zero. f) The product $\psi_3 x \psi_1$, which does integrate to zero.

order of the wavefunctions when evaluating the transition dipole moment. Because the operator doesn't actually do anything to the function, and the functions (in this case) are real, their order in the integral doesn't matter. Therefore, $\mu_{ji} = \mu_{ij}$ and the same selection rule applies for going down as for going up. (This is actually true in general, even with complex wavefunctions, although the proof is somewhat beyond this text.) The full selection rule is therefore written as $\Delta n = \pm 1$. Absorption of a photon of the correct energy can cause a transition to an energy level one step higher, and emission of a photon will cause the particle to drop to an energy state one step lower, with the emitted photon carrying away that difference in energy.

### 9.2.3 Electronic States of Conjugated Linear Molecules

Let's apply what we have learned to a molecular system that we can treat with the particle in a box model, the electronic states of a long, conjugated organic molecule. Recall from your organic chemistry classes that the $\pi$ electrons in a conjugated molecule can delocalize along the entire length of that molecule. Thus we can take the length of the molecule as our box, and the electrons as our particles. Let's consider the molecule 1,3-butadiene. There are two double bonds in this molecule, so that means we have $4\pi$ electrons in our system.

Recall also from general chemistry that we can only have two electrons in each state. We will put these four electrons in the first two states, $n = 1$ and $n = 2$. The first allowable transition we can have is for an electron to move from the $n = 2$ state to the $n = 3$ state. The difference in energy between these two states is given by

$$\Delta E_{2,3} = \frac{h^2 3^2}{8\ mL^2} - \frac{h^2 2^2}{8\ mL^2} = \frac{5h^2}{8\ mL^2} = \frac{hc}{\lambda}$$

The measured electronic absorption spectrum of this molecule has a peak at about 290 nm, well into the UV region of the spectrum. We can use this result to solve for the length of the molecule. Doing so gives a value of 6.6 Å, which is a reasonable approximation. Note that as the molecule gets longer and has more double bonds, the spacing between the levels will decrease. For a much longer conjugated molecule like β-carotene, which has 11 double bonds, the wavelength of the absorbed light moves into the blue region, which is why this compound appears orange. By changing the length of these conjugated molecules, we can affect the electronic states, which in turn affects their colors. By tuning the length, and some other functional groups, dye chemists can make any color of the rainbow (and some that aren't in the rainbow).

## 9.3 Variations of the Particle in a Box

### 9.3.1 Particle in a Finite Well

Now that we have our solution to the particle in the box, where the potential barriers to leaving the box are infinite, let's modify the situation somewhat by lowering the walls. Instead of having the potential be infinite, let's make the height of the wall finite, as shown in Figure 9.4.

$$V(x) = 0 \quad \text{for } 0 < x < L$$

$$V(x) = V \quad \text{for } x \leq 0, x \geq L$$

(9.11)

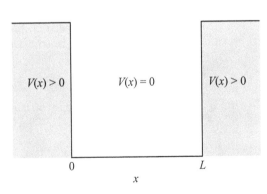

**FIGURE 9.4.** Potential energy function for a particle in a one-dimensional well of length $L$.

As before, we will look at our solution to the Schrödinger equation in three regions, one inside the well and the two regions outside the well.

Let's start with the region on the left side of the well, or where $x < 0$. It is helpful to rewrite the Schrödinger equation as

$$\frac{-\hbar^2}{2m} \frac{\partial^2 \psi}{\partial x^2} = [E - V]\psi$$

If we bring all the constants over to the right-hand side, we have

$$\frac{\partial^2 \psi}{\partial x^2} = \frac{2m[V - E]}{\hbar^2}\psi = \alpha^2 \psi \quad \text{where} \quad \alpha = \frac{\sqrt{2m(V - E)}}{\hbar} \tag{9.12}$$

We will only consider states where the energy of the particle is less than the height of the walls; if the energy of the particle were greater than $V$, then it could escape the well and it would be free again. Such states are called **bound states**, because they are spatially confined to the well. This means that $V - E > 0$, and the right-hand side of the equation is positive. To solve this differential equation, we need a function whose second derivative returns the same function multiplied by a positive constant. When the constant was negative, we had solutions that involved sines, cosines, or complex exponentials. Now the solutions will involve real exponentials, and the general solution is of the form

$$\psi_{\text{left}}(x) = c_1 e^{\alpha x} + c_2 e^{-\alpha x}$$

If we look at the right-hand side, where again $V > E$, we will have the same general solution, but the coefficients could be different.

$$\psi_{\text{right}}(x) = d_1 e^{\alpha x} + d_2 e^{-\alpha x}$$

Inside the box, we have $V = 0$, so we have the same general solution we had for the infinite-walled box.

$$\psi(x) = A \sin kx + B \cos kx \quad \text{where} \quad k = \frac{\sqrt{2mE}}{\hbar}$$

Now, we have six unknown coefficients to determine, and the energy may also be different than before. To obtain a complete solution, we need to apply all of our boundary conditions. Let's first consider the wavefunction at $\pm\infty$. If the particle is confined to the region of the well, then it can't be a long distance outside the well, so we require that $\psi(\pm\infty) = 0$ be true. Using this for our solution to the left-hand side gives us

$$\psi_{\text{left}}(-\infty) = c_1 e^{-\infty} + c_2 e^{\infty} = c_2 e^{\infty} = 0$$

which can only be true if $c_2 = 0$. (Recall that $e^{-\infty} = 0$.) For the right-hand side, we have

$$\psi_{\text{right}}(\infty) = d_1 e^{\infty} + d_2 e^{-\infty} = d_1 e^{\infty} = 0$$

which can only be true if $d_1 = 0$. Two down, four to go. We can get these by enforcing continuity at the walls of the well, continuity of the first derivative at the walls, and normalization. (Because we no longer have an infinity in the potential, the continuity requirement for the first derivative is back in force.) The details of this process are not that informative, so we won't take the time to formally go through it.

What is important is the general shape of the new wavefunctions. Note that just outside the left edge of the box, the wavefunction has the form

$$\psi_{\text{left}}(x) = c_1 e^{\alpha x} \tag{9.13}$$

where the value of $\psi$ is increasing exponentially as we approach the wall from the left. This means that the oscillating function inside the well does not have to go to zero at the walls. We see the same thing on the other side; the oscillating function does not go to zero at the wall and, once we cross the wall, the wavefunction begins to decay exponentially as

$$\psi_{\text{right}}(x) = d_2 e^{-\alpha x} \tag{9.14}$$

Inside the box, the wavefunction will still have oscillations and nodes, depending on the quantum number $n$. The bound wavefunctions for a particle in a finite well are shown in Figure 9.5. Note that for this well, only the first three states are bound; the next highest energy state will have an energy greater than the height of the walls, so it, and all higher energy states, will be unbound.

These new wavefunctions have one striking feature that we need to point out. Remember that $\psi^* \psi$ tells us the probability of finding the particle in a particular location. Well, now that the wavefunction is not zero outside the well, *there is a finite chance of finding the particle outside the well*. This means the particle can spread out more than it would in the infinite well, or in other words the particle is less confined. Confinement affects quantization, so the energy levels in the finite well are lower than they would be in the equivalent infinitely walled box, as indicated in Figure 9.5.

Remember also that the energy of the particle is less than the potential of the barrier. Since the total energy of the particle is the sum of its kinetic and potential energy, when the particle is outside the well we obtain the following result

$$E = T + V < V$$

$$T < 0$$

The kinetic energy of our particle in the region outside the well is *negative*. How can a particle have negative kinetic energy? Classically, that doesn't make sense, but we're not

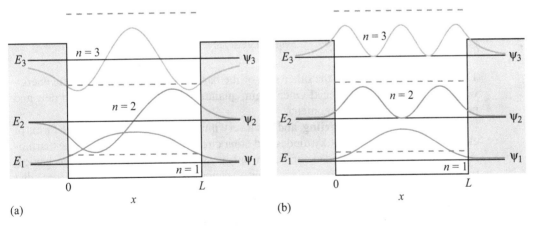

FIGURE 9.5. Finite well with three bound states. Dashed lines indicate the energies of equivalent states in the infinite-walled box. a) Plots of $\psi$ for the bound states. b) Plots of $\psi^* \psi$ for the bound states.

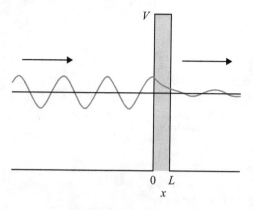

**FIGURE 9.6.** Wavefunction for a particle tunneling through a barrier of height $V$ and width $L$. The lower amplitude on the right of the barrier indicates the finite probability of passing through; most particles reflect.

doing classical mechanics here. This is just one more sign that things are very different in the quantum world. The region near the barrier, where the particle has no right to be, is known as the **classically forbidden region**. Note that the coefficient $\alpha$ (see Eq. 9.12) in the wavefunction for the regions outside the well depends on the difference in energy between the walls and the particle. Thus, for a low-energy state in a deep well, the wavefunction will not penetrate much into the classically forbidden region. As the energy of the particle increases, however, the wavefunction bleeds out of the box more and more. Eventually, once the energy of the particle is greater than the barrier, the wavefunction can spread out over all space; the particle is free again. Once again, we see that it is good practice to consider the solution to our problem in different limiting situations.

## 9.3.2 Tunneling

The existence of the classically forbidden region for a particle confined in a finite well raises some interesting possibilities, which we now explore. Instead of the particle being confined to a well, let's consider an otherwise free particle, traveling to the right, that encounters a potential barrier with a height $V > E$, as shown in Figure 9.6. To the left of the barrier, we have no potential; therefore, we have the free-particle solution we used before

$$\psi_{\text{left}}(x) = ae^{ikx} \quad \text{where} \quad k = \frac{\sqrt{2mE}}{\hbar}$$

(We only use the positive exponential to represent a particle traveling to the right.) Once the particle encounters the barrier, however, we have a situation similar to the right side of our finite well, where the wavefunction will begin to decay away according to the function

$$\psi_{\text{barrier}}(x) = be^{-\alpha x} \quad \text{where} \quad \alpha = \frac{\sqrt{2m(V - E)}}{\hbar}$$

If the barrier is thin enough, such that the wavefunction does not completely decay to zero, then we have to resume the free-particle solution on the other side of the barrier.

$$\psi_{\text{right}}(x) = ce^{ikx}$$

The particle can appear on the other side of the barrier, even though its kinetic energy was insufficient to cross over it! Once again, quantum mechanics has revealed new and previously unthought-of phenomena.

This effect is called **tunneling**, and it is a very important phenomenon. Some forms of electron microscopy—Schottky diodes and other circuit elements—and even the thermonuclear fusion that takes place in our sun are only possible because of quantum-mechanical tunneling. Tunneling can also accelerate certain chemical reactions, particularly those that involve electron or proton transfer.

Determining the coefficients $a$, $b$, and $c$ in our wavefunctions is beyond the scope of this text. We can, however, note a few important things about the solution. First, not every particle that encounters the barrier will tunnel through it; most will bounce off and head back in the direction they came. This means that the coefficient $c$ must be less than $a$. This relates to the fact that not all the particles will make it through the barrier. The ratio of $c$ to *a* reflects the probability that a particle tunnels through the barrier. Note, however, that the energy of the particle—likewise, the value of *k*—is unchanged after passage through the barrier. (A full solution to this problem shows that for particles with energy greater than the barrier height, there is a finite chance they don't make it over but instead "bounce" back. I think that shows an interesting symmetry to the universe; some particles get through when they shouldn't, and others don't get over when they should.)

For thin barriers, the tunneling probability is given by the expression

$$P_t = e^{-2\alpha L} \tag{9.15}$$

where $L$ is the length of the barrier and $\alpha$ is the same decay constant from Eq. 9.12. Note that as the energy difference between the barrier and the particle increases, the tunneling probability decreases; more energetic particles have a better chance of getting through. The tunneling probability also decreases as the length of the barrier increases, so it's easier to get through a thin barrier than a thick one. In designing electronic devices, the engineer will carefully tune the thickness and height of the potential barrier to regulate the tunneling current. Lastly, the tunneling probability also decreases as the mass of the particle increases, so electrons tunnel much more readily than protons. Once we get to macroscopic objects and lengths, the tunneling probability is infinitesimally small; there's that correspondence principle again.

## 9.3.3 The Three-Dimensional Box and Degeneracy

We have spent quite a bit of time now in a one-dimensional world, but this has been time well spent. We've learned about energy quantization for confined particles, the basics of spectroscopy, and the phenomenon of tunneling. Our world, however, isn't confined to just one dimension. How can we apply what we have learned to a more realistic three-dimensional problem? We can do so quite easily, and we will do so now.

Let's define a rectangular space in three dimensions with a potential given by

$$V(x,y,z) = 0 \quad \text{for } 0 < x < L_x,\ 0 < y < L_y,\ 0 < z < L_z$$
$$V(x,y,z) = \infty \quad \text{for } x \le 0,\ y \le 0,\ z \le 0,\ x \ge L_x,\ y \ge L_y,\ z \ge L_z \tag{9.16}$$

where $L_x$, $L_y$, and $L_z$ are the lengths of the rectangular box in the $x$, $y$, and $z$ directions, respectively. As before, the wavefunction will be zero outside the box. Inside the box, we need to solve the Schrödinger equation, written in this case as

$$-\frac{\hbar^2}{2m}\left[\frac{\partial^2}{\partial x^2} + \frac{\partial^2}{\partial y^2} + \frac{\partial^2}{\partial z^2}\right]\psi(x,y,z) = E\psi(x,y,z)$$

$$\frac{\partial^2 \psi}{\partial x^2} + \frac{\partial^2 \psi}{\partial y^2} + \frac{\partial^2 \psi}{\partial z^2} = -\frac{2mE}{\hbar^2}\psi \tag{9.17}$$

At first glance, this appears to be a daunting equation to solve. However, note that each of the derivatives on the left-hand side only involves a single spatial variable. We can therefore try the technique of **separation of variables** to solve this differential equation. We propose a wavefunction and total energy of the forms

$$\psi(x,y,z) = X(x)Y(y)Z(z) \quad \text{and} \quad E = E_x + E_y + E_z \tag{9.18}$$

This reduces our single, three-dimensional differential equation to 3 one-dimensional differential equations that we have already solved.

$$\frac{\partial^2 X}{\partial x^2} = \frac{-2mE_x}{\hbar^2}X \qquad \frac{\partial^2 Y}{\partial y^2} = \frac{-2mE_y}{\hbar^2}Y \qquad \frac{\partial^2 Z}{\partial z^2} = \frac{-2mE_z}{\hbar^2}Z$$

We can then readily jump to the solution. The wavefunction is written as

$$\psi(x,y,z) = \left(\frac{8}{L_x L_y L_z}\right)^{1/2} \sin\frac{n_x\pi x}{L_x}\sin\frac{n_y\pi y}{L_y}\sin\frac{n_z\pi z}{L_z} \tag{9.19}$$

where we now have three separate quantum numbers, one for each direction. The energy is written as

$$E_{n_x,n_y,n_z} = \frac{h^2}{8m}\left(\frac{n_x^2}{L_x^2} + \frac{n_y^2}{L_y^2} + \frac{n_z^2}{L_z^2}\right) \tag{9.20}$$

This approach of separating the variables can be used whenever the potential can be written as a sum; in this case the potential is a sum of zeros, so that's easy.

Now, let's change the system a bit and make our box cubic. This means the lengths of the three sides are all the same, and we can write our expression for the energy as

$$E_{n_x,n_y,n_z} = \frac{h^2}{8m}\left(\frac{n_x^2}{L^2} + \frac{n_y^2}{L^2} + \frac{n_z^2}{L^2}\right) = \frac{h^2}{8mL^2}\left(n_x^2 + n_y^2 + n_z^2\right) \tag{9.21}$$

The lowest energy state clearly has a value of

$$E_{1,1,1} = \frac{3h^2}{8mL^2}$$

The next-highest state will have an energy of

$$E_{2,1,1} = \frac{h^2}{8mL^2}(4+1+1) = \frac{3h^2}{4mL^2}$$

Note, though, that there are three different states that will have the same energy, depending on which quantum number has a value of 2.

$$E_{2,1,1} = E_{1,2,1} = E_{1,1,2}$$

When we have more than one state with the same energy, we say those states are **degenerate**. The first excited state is thus threefold degenerate. What about the set of quantum numbers (2, 2, 1)? That energy level will also be threefold degenerate. What about the set (3, 2, 1)? Now the degeneracy is 6.

The degeneracy of these states comes about because of the symmetry of the system, in this case cubic. What if we stretch one side of our box, so that $L_z > L_x = L_y$? Now,

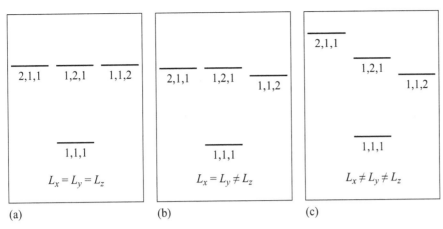

FIGURE 9.7. a) First two energy levels for a cubic three-dimensional box. b) Here, the $z$ dimension has been changed, but the $x$ and $y$ dimensions are still the same. c) All three dimensions are different.

$E_{1,1,2} \neq E_{1,2,1} = E_{2,1,1}$, and we have broken the degeneracy of the system. What were once three states with the same energy are now split into a set of two states and a third state of a different energy, as shown in Figure 9.7a and b. If we were to change one of the other sides such that all three lengths were different, we would not have any symmetry to our system and we would have three states of different energy, as shown in Figure 9.7c.

Symmetry is very important in quantum mechanics. Whenever there is symmetry, there will be degeneracy. We can also often use symmetry to aid us in solving problems, as we will see in the next two chapters.

### 9.3.4 Relative Spacing of Energy Levels

Back in Chapter 7, we made the assumption that we could treat the translational motion of molecules classically. We can now revisit that assumption and check its validity. Let's consider the spacing of levels for a gas molecule, such as $CH_4$, in a 1 m cubic box. With our expression for the energy of the states of the particle in a cubic box, Eq. 9.21, we can easily derive an expression for the difference in energy between two states, where we only change one of the quantum numbers by one step.

$$\Delta E = E_{n_x+1, \, n_y, \, n_z} - E_{n_x, \, n_y, \, n_z} = \frac{h^2}{8mL^2}(2n_x + 1) \tag{9.22}$$

The mass of $CH_4$ is about 16 g mol$^{-1}$, or $2.6 \times 10^{-26}$ kg for a single molecule. This means the spacing of energy levels is on the order of $10^{-42}$ J. This definitely looks like a small number, but we need something to compare it to. For this comparison, we use the **thermal energy**, symbolized as $k_B T$, which always appears in the Boltzmann distribution. At room temperature, $k_B T$ is about $10^{-21}$ J, so the translational energy states are spaced about 21 orders of magnitude closer together than the thermal energy. Assuming we could treat the translational states as continuous was thus a very good approximation.

We have also used the particle in a box model to treat the electronic energy states of highly conjugated organic molecules. Now, the length of the box is a few nm and the mass of the particle is the mass of an electron, $9.1094 \times 10^{-31}$ kg. How close together are those states relative to $k_B T$? We know that the transitions for these molecules occur in the UV and visible regions of the spectrum. Let's take a wavelength of 500 nm as typical. This gives an energy of about $4 \times 10^{-19}$ J. Thus, electronic energy levels are about 100 times further apart than the thermal energy and must be treated quantum mechanically. We should never be tempted to treat electronic states classically.

When using the particle-in-a-box model to describe a system, there are two questions you should always ask yourself: What is my particle?, and what is my box? If you are not careful in setting up your solution to a problem, you can get answers that don't make physical sense.

## 9.4  Summary, and Where We Go Next

In this chapter, we have explored the model system of the quantum-mechanical particle in a box. Even though it is obviously an abstraction, our investigation of this model system has been very fruitful. We have learned about energy quantization, nodes in the wavefunction, penetration into the classically forbidden region and tunneling, symmetry and degeneracy, as well as some of the basic ideas of spectroscopy. The particle-in-a-box model also has many real-world applications. As we saw, it can be used to model the electronic states of long conjugated molecules. It can even be applied to the photophysics of vision due to the molecule retinal, which is found in our vision receptors. As we return to statistical mechanics in Chapter 13, we will also use the particle-in-a-box model to describe the translational states of gas molecules in a closed container. In the next chapter, we will construct quantum-mechanical models for rotational and vibrational motion and explore their applications.

## PROBLEMS

**9.1** For an electron in a one-dimensional box of length 10 Å, calculate the following:

a) The zero-point energy in units of J, eV, and $cm^{-1}$.

b) The probability of finding the electron within a distance $dL$ of the center of the box for the first three energy states.

**9.2** a) Calculate the expectation value and the most probable value of the position for the first two states of the particle in a box.

b) How do these compare to each other? Provide a physical interpretation of the results.

c) For either of these states, is it ever impossible for the particle to be at the expected location?

**9.3** a) Calculate the expectation value of the energy for the first three states of the one-dimensional particle in a box.

b) How do these compare to the solution of the Schrödinger equation? Explain the basis of any comparison.

**9.4** a) Calculate the expectation value of the momentum for the first three states of the particle in a box.

    b) Provide a physical interpretation of these results.

**9.5** Validate the correspondence principle for the particle in a box. Looking at the expression for the energy (Eq. 9.5), it is obvious that the energy will go to infinity as the quantum number gets large. Therefore, we need to take a slightly different approach. Consider instead the ratio of the spacing between adjacent levels to the energy of the lower state in the limit of large quantum number. Physically, this can be thought of as the percent increase in the energy to go up one level relative to the amount of energy already present.

**9.6** In the last chapter, we discussed how the solutions to the Schrödinger equation are orthogonal to each other. Verify this for any two particle-in-a-box wavefunctions.

**9.7** a) Write a general formula for the wavelength of a transition between any two levels for an electron in a one-dimensional box.

    b) Calculate the wavelength for the transition of an electron from the $n = 4$ to $n = 5$ levels in a 10 Å box.

    c) Calculate the transition dipole moment for this transition. Is this transition allowed or forbidden?

    d) Calculate the wavelength and transition dipole moment for the transition from $n = 4$ to $n = 6$ in the same 10 Å box. Is this transition allowed or forbidden?

**9.8** Consider the molecule 1,3,5,7-octatetraene. If we take the length of a C–C bond to be 1.53 Å and the length of a C=C bond to be 1.34 Å, estimate the wavelength of the first allowed electronic transition for this molecule. What would be the wavelength of the transition for 1,3,5,7,9-decapentaene?

**9.9** a) Calculate the tunneling probability for both an electron and a proton to penetrate a 1 Å barrier if the difference between barrier potential and kinetic energy is 1 eV.

    b) Tunneling is a very real effect in chemical reactions that involve proton transfer. If the hydrogen atom is replaced with a deuterium atom, what will be the relative effect on the reaction rate? (This is one example of the kinetic isotope effect.)

**9.10** a) For a particle confined in a three-dimensional cubic box, what possible degeneracies can be observed? Show an example of each.

    b) If the cubic box is distorted such that the lengths of the sides are no longer the same, what will happen to degenerate energy levels?

**9.11** Pores in zeolites can be only a few nm in size.

    a) Consider a $H_2$ molecule confined to a cubic pore 5 Å on a side. Calculate the spacing between the first two energy levels. Give this energy in J, eV and $cm^{-1}$.

    b) What is the wavelength of this transition, and in what range of the electromagnetic spectrum does this transition occur?

**9.12** Set up and solve the Schrödinger equation for a particle confined in a two-dimensional box. Write the general solutions and comment on the type of degeneracy if the box is square.

# The Rigid Rotor and Harmonic Oscillator; Rotational and Vibrational Spectroscopy

## 10.1 Rotational Motion

In the last chapter, we developed the particle-in-a-box model, which can be used to model the translational energy states of a molecule. Recall from our discussion of heat capacity and the equipartition theorem in Chapter 7 that there are two other kinds of internal motion wherein a molecule can store energy. These are **rotations** and **vibrations**. In this chapter, we will construct models for those types of motion. We begin with an overview of rotational motion from a classical perspective.

### 10.1.1 The Classical Rigid Rotor

Before constructing a quantum-mechanical model of rotational motion, we first need to review some of what was known about rotational motion in classical physics. To begin, we make a model of a **rigid rotor**, which is an object that rotates at a fixed distance about a center point. This could be a dumbbell spinning about its center of mass, or a ball on a tether, as shown in Figure 10.1. These two pictures can in fact be directly related if we reintroduce the reduced mass from Chapter 3. The physics are identical for two bodies, of masses $m_1$ and $m_2$, separated by a fixed distance $r$ spinning about the center of mass and a single body of the reduced mass $\mu$ spinning a distance $r$ from a fixed point. Recall that **angular momentum**, just like linear momentum, is properly described as a vector

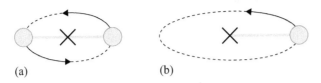

**FIGURE 10.1.** a) Two masses separated by a rod spinning about the center of mass. b) A single mass spinning about a fixed point.

quantity. The angular momentum, $\vec{l}$, is written as the cross product of the position and momentum vectors. Mathematically, we write

$$\vec{l} \equiv \vec{r} \times \vec{p} = \begin{vmatrix} \hat{i} & \hat{j} & \hat{k} \\ x & y & z \\ p_x & p_y & p_z \end{vmatrix} \tag{10.1}$$

$$= (yp_z - zp_y)\hat{i} + (zp_x - xp_z)\hat{j} + (xp_y - yp_x)\hat{k}$$

For simplicity in our initial discussion, we will restrict ourselves to motion in the $x$–$y$ plane; $z$ and $p_z$ are both zero. In this case, the angular momentum is only along the $z$ axis.

$$l_z = xp_y - yp_x$$

For motion on a circular orbit, $\vec{r}$ , the position, and $\vec{p}$ , the momentum, are perpendicular to each other, so the magnitude of $l_z$ is given by

$$l_z = r\ p\ \sin 90° = r\ p$$

In a rotating system, it makes more sense to use cylindrical coordinates $(r, \phi, z)$, where $r$ is the distance from the origin, and $\phi$ is the azimuthal angle, as shown in Figure 10.2.

We also define new variables for angular motion that correspond to the variables for linear motion. For example, we define the angular velocity as

$$\omega \equiv \frac{d\phi}{dt} \tag{10.2}$$

The instantaneous linear velocity relates to the angular velocity by the expression

$$v = r\omega$$

The kinetic energy can be written in terms of the angular velocity as follows:

$$E_{kin} = \frac{1}{2}mv^2 = \frac{1}{2}mr^2\omega^2$$

We now define a quantity called the **moment of inertia**:

$$I \equiv mr^2 \tag{10.3}$$

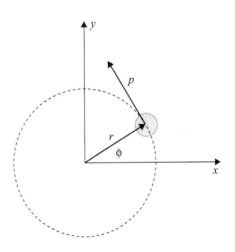

**FIGURE 10.2.** Rotation about the origin, indicating the position, momentum, and angle $\phi$. The angular momentum points out of the page.

This is the expression for a single mass spinning a distance $r$ from a central point. If we have two masses a fixed distance apart, we write the moment of inertia as

$$I \equiv \mu r^2 \tag{10.4}$$

where $\mu$ is the reduced mass. This lets us write an expression for the energy of a rotating body

$$E_{rot} = \frac{1}{2} I \omega^2 \tag{10.5}$$

(We saw this expression back in Chapter 7.) Calculating a moment of inertia for more complex collections of masses gets more complicated, but Eq. 10.5 still holds. Remember also that the kinetic energy (in one dimension) can be written in terms of the linear momentum

$$E_{kin} = \frac{1}{2m} p_x^2$$

For motion on a circular orbit, we can write

$$E_{rot} = \frac{1}{2m} p^2 = \frac{1}{2m} \left( \frac{l}{r} \right)^2 = \frac{1}{2mr^2} l^2$$

$$E_{rot} = \frac{1}{2I} l^2 \tag{10.6}$$

Note that the moment of inertia plays the same role as the mass in linear motion.

One other aspect of this physical situation merits some brief attention, and that is the dimensionality of the problem. We have constrained our rotating particle to motion in a single plane, which is a two-dimensional space. For this reason, this situation is sometimes called the 2-D rigid rotor. However, because the distance from the center of the rotation is fixed, we only have one variable of motion, the azimuthal angle $\phi$. Thus, this is actually a one-dimensional problem.

## 10.1.2 Quantum-Mechanical Two-Dimensional Rotor

As we did for linear motion, we can construct a quantum-mechanical operator for angular momentum by recalling that $\hat{p}_x = \frac{\hbar}{i} \frac{\partial}{\partial x}$ and $\hat{x} = x$. We therefore write

$$\hat{l}_z = \hat{x}\hat{p}_y - \hat{y}\hat{p}_x = \frac{\hbar}{i} \left( x \frac{\partial}{\partial y} - y \frac{\partial}{\partial x} \right) \tag{10.7}$$

If we make the switch to cylindrical coordinates $(r, \phi, z)$ and keep $r$ constant, we express our operator as

$$\hat{l}_z = \frac{\hbar}{i} \frac{\partial}{\partial \phi} \tag{10.8}$$

We likewise write the total energy, or Hamiltonian, operator as

$$\hat{H} = \frac{1}{2I} \hat{l}_z^2 = \frac{-\hbar^2}{2I} \frac{\partial^2}{\partial \phi^2} \tag{10.9}$$

The Schrödinger equation is then written as

$$\frac{-\hbar^2}{2I}\frac{\partial^2 \psi}{\partial \phi^2} = E\psi \qquad (10.10)$$

In this case, the potential is zero only at a fixed value of $r$, but infinity elsewhere, thus $\phi$ is the only variable that can change. Other than the change of a few symbols, $I$ instead of $m$ and $\phi$ instead of $x$, this looks just like the Schrödinger equation for the free particle. So let's propose a solution of the form

$$\psi = ce^{im_l\phi} \quad \text{where} \quad m_l^2 = 2IE/\hbar^2$$

In this expression, we have used the symbol $m_l$ instead of $k$; our reasons for this will become clear shortly.

We now need to consider boundary conditions, which are different from what we had for the particle in a box. In that case, we had to ensure that the wavefunction went to zero at the edges of the box. In this case, the wavefunction needs to repeat every time around the circle, or every $2\pi$ radians; in other words, the wavefunction must be single valued and can't have a different value for different trips around the ring. We express this mathematically by writing

$$\psi(\phi + 2\pi) = \psi(\phi)$$

$$ce^{im_l(\phi+2\pi)} = ce^{im_l\phi}e^{im_l 2\pi} = ce^{im_l\phi}$$

which requires that

$$e^{im_l 2\pi} = 1$$

If we slightly rewrite this expression and use Euler's formula $e^{i\pi} = -1$, we have

$$e^{im_l 2\pi} = (e^{i\pi})^{2m_l} = (-1)^{2m_l} = 1$$

which is only true if $m_l$ is a positive or negative integer, or zero. Once again, we have quantized values of the energy and only certain possibilities for our wavefunctions.

Normalization of the function requires that

$$1 = \int_0^{2\pi} \psi^*\psi\, d\phi = c^2\int_0^{2\pi} e^{-im_l\phi}e^{im_l\phi}\, d\phi = c^2\int_0^{2\pi} d\phi = c^2 2\pi$$

Therefore, the normalization constant is $c = 1/\sqrt{2\pi}$. The normalized wavefunction for the two-dimensional rotor is then written as

$$\psi_{rot} = \frac{1}{\sqrt{2\pi}}e^{im_l\phi} \quad \text{with} \quad m_l = 0,\pm 1,\pm 2,\ldots \qquad (10.11)$$

The energy is given by

$$E_{m_l} = \frac{m_l^2\hbar^2}{2I} \qquad (10.12)$$

There is an important difference between the solutions for the 2-D rotor and the other solutions we have seen before. First, we can have a value of zero for our quantum number $m_l$. For the particle in a box, a quantum number of 0 meant there was no particle. It means something very different here. If $m_l = 0$, then the complex exponential simply has the value of 1, and $\psi^*\psi$ just equals $1/2\pi$, regardless of the angle; there is uniform probability of finding our particle at any angle. As the value of $|m_l|$ increases, we again have nodes in our wavefunction. These nodes are now angular nodes, and the wavefunctions have the appearance of standing waves on a ring.

We also have both positive and negative values for our quantum number. To understand this, we need to apply our angular momentum operator to our wavefunctions. Doing so gives us

$$\hat{l}_z \psi = \frac{\hbar}{i} \frac{\partial}{\partial \phi} \frac{1}{\sqrt{2\pi}} e^{im_l\phi} = m_l \hbar \frac{1}{\sqrt{2\pi}} e^{im_l\phi} = m_l \hbar \psi$$

Notice that the wavefunction is also an eigenfunction of the angular momentum operator, with eigenvalues $l_z = m_l\hbar$. So not only is the energy quantized, but so is the angular momentum. Note that the smallest possible amount of angular momentum is $\hbar$ and our quantum number $m_l$ gives the number of units of angular momentum the system has; this is the justification for our earlier choice in notation, rather than using $k$. Notice also that the angular momentum can be either positive or negative, which accounts for the two directions of motion about the axis; or it can be zero, meaning there is no angular momentum and hence no rotational energy. The energy, of course, can't be negative. Also, because the energy depends on $m_l^2$, all levels except the $m_l = 0$ level are twofold degenerate.

Now, you may be wondering what we can use this model for. The first situation is a molecule that is spinning in a plane, such as a surface, but this doesn't have a lot of application. The more common use of this model is for the electronic states of ringlike molecules, such as benzene. In this case, we typically talk about this as the **particle-on-a-ring** model; the electrons are our particles, and the molecule itself is the ring. The potential energy on the ring is zero, but off the ring it is infinite. Just as we saw for the absorption spectra of long, conjugated molecules when we used the particle-in-a-box model, the particle-on-a-ring model does quite well at predicting the absorption spectra of aromatic molecules. (See Problem 10.2.)

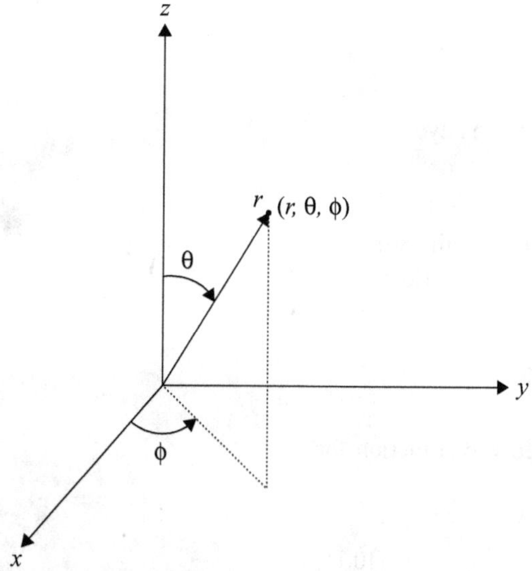

### 10.1.3 Quantum-Mechanical 3-D Rotor

Rotational motion takes place in a single plane, but the orientation of that plane of rotation relative to the $x$–$y$ plane can in principle vary. Therefore, we need a quantum-mechanical solution for a particle that can spin with any orientation. We call this the **3-D rigid rotor**. As we have done before, we need to set up our Hamiltonian operator. It now makes the most sense to use a spherical coordinate system with variables $(r, \theta, \phi)$: $r$ and $\phi$ are the same as in cylindrical coordinates and $\theta$ is the tilt from the $z$ axis, as shown in Figure 10.3. Just as the 2-D rotor was equivalent to a particle on a ring, the 3-D rotor is actually identical to a particle that is constrained to move on the surface of a sphere of radius $r$. On the surface of the sphere, $V = 0$, but off that surface $V = \infty$.

FIGURE 10.3. Spherical coordinate system.

Motion in all three Cartesian directions must be considered, so we write the Hamiltonian as

$$\hat{H} = \frac{-\hbar^2}{2m} \nabla^2 = \frac{-\hbar^2}{2m} \left( \frac{\partial^2}{\partial x^2} + \frac{\partial^2}{\partial y^2} + \frac{\partial^2}{\partial z^2} \right)$$

When we convert to spherical coordinates, again keeping $r$ constant, we have

$$\hat{H}_{rot} = \frac{-\hbar^2}{2I}\left[\frac{1}{\sin\theta}\frac{\partial}{\partial\theta}\left(\sin\theta\frac{\partial}{\partial\theta}\right) + \frac{1}{\sin^2\theta}\frac{\partial^2}{\partial\phi^2}\right] \tag{10.13}$$

(Making these substitutions is messy, so we have skipped the details. Note that for the case of the 2-D rotor we considered in the last section, the value of the angle $\theta$ is fixed at $90°$, so its derivatives are zero and the only term that survives is the last one. Also, $\sin\theta = 1$.) Analogous to the classical energy, as described in Eq. 10.5, we can define an operator for the square of the total angular momentum by removing the factor of $2I$ to get

$$\hat{l}^2 \equiv -\hbar^2\left[\frac{1}{\sin\theta}\frac{\partial}{\partial\theta}\left(\sin\theta\frac{\partial}{\partial\theta}\right) + \frac{1}{\sin^2\theta}\frac{\partial^2}{\partial\phi^2}\right] \tag{10.14}$$

Again, our wavefunctions must satisfy the Schrödinger equation. The form of this equation is obviously more complex, but the solutions were already well known to mathematicians and physicists. The solutions are known as **spherical harmonics**, typically symbolized as $Y_l^{m_l}(\theta,\phi)$. These functions are characterized by two quantum numbers, $l$ and $m_l$. We have two quantum numbers because this is a two-dimensional problem; motion is allowed in terms of the angles $\theta$ and $\phi$. The total angular momentum quantum number, $l$, can take on values $l = 0, 1, 2, \ldots$, or all nonnegative integers. The second quantum number, $m_l$, can have the values $m_l = -l, -l+1, \ldots, l-1, l$. The spherical harmonics include a class of functions known as associated Legendre polynomials. A few are tabulated in Table 10.1 to give a sense of what they look like.

TABLE 10.1  Spherical harmonic functions

| $l$ | $m_l$ | $Y_l^{m_l}(\theta,\phi)$ |
| --- | --- | --- |
| 0 | 0 | $Y_0^0 = \dfrac{1}{\sqrt{4\pi}}$ |
| 1 | 0 | $Y_1^0 = \sqrt{\dfrac{3}{4\pi}}\cos\theta$ |
| 1 | $\pm 1$ | $Y_1^{\pm 1} = \sqrt{\dfrac{3}{8\pi}}\sin\theta\, e^{\pm i\phi}$ |
| 2 | 0 | $Y_2^0 = \sqrt{\dfrac{5}{16\pi}}(3\cos^2\theta - 1)$ |
| 2 | $\pm 1$ | $Y_2^{\pm 1} = \sqrt{\dfrac{15}{8\pi}}\sin\theta\cos\theta\, e^{\pm i\phi}$ |
| 2 | $\pm 2$ | $Y_2^{\pm 2} = \sqrt{\dfrac{15}{32\pi}}\sin^2\theta\, e^{\pm 2i\phi}$ |

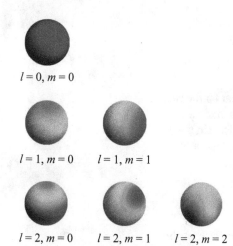

$l = 0, m = 0$

$l = 1, m = 0$     $l = 1, m = 1$

$l = 2, m = 0$     $l = 2, m = 1$     $l = 2, m = 2$

**FIGURE 10.4.** Plots of spherical harmonic functions. Nodes occur where the color is green.

(It would be good practice to verify that these functions are normalized and give the proper energy.) These functions are also orthogonal to each other and form a complete set, as is required for eigenfunctions of the Hamiltonian operator. Figure 10.4 shows plots of these functions. These functions also exhibit nodes on the surface of the sphere. These nodes either run from pole to pole or parallel to the equator; the quantum number $l$ tells how many total nodes we have, and $m_l$ is the number of polar nodes. Another reason the spherical harmonic functions are important is that they will be part of the solution to the hydrogen atom, as we will see in Chapter 11.

The energy eigenvalues are given by

$$E_{rot} = l(l+1)\frac{\hbar^2}{2I} \quad \text{where} \quad l = 0, 1, 2, \dots \quad (10.15)$$

The spherical harmonics are also eigenfunctions of the $\hat{l}^2$ operator, with eigenvalues given by

$$\hat{l}^2 Y_l^{m_l}(\theta,\phi) = l(l+1)\hbar^2 Y_l^{m_l}(\theta,\phi) \quad \text{where} \quad l = 0, 1, 2, \dots \quad (10.16)$$

Because the energy only depends on $l$ and not on $m_l$, each energy level has a degeneracy equal to

$$g_l = 2l + 1 \quad (10.17)$$

Recall that degeneracy is a result of symmetry, in this case due to the equivalence of rotating in any particular direction compared to another. If there is no preference to rotate in one direction or another, the way we define the coordinate system cannot matter, and the energy cannot depend on the orientation of the angular momentum vector.

There are some limitations on our knowledge of the rotation of our system that need to be addressed. For a particle traveling in one dimension, we had an uncertainty relationship between its position and its linear momentum. We likewise have uncertainty in rotational motion. Recall that whenever two quantum-mechanical operators do not commute, we have an uncertainty relationship. It can be shown that the operators for the $x$ and $y$ components of angular momentum do not commute with each other or with $\hat{l}_z$. All three of these, however commute with the $\hat{l}^2$ operator. This means that we can know the total angular momentum and one of its components, however there is uncertainty in our knowledge of the other two components. By convention, the $z$ component is typically the one we choose to know about.

The definition of $\hat{l}_z$ from Eq. 10.7 still applies to the 3-D rotor. The spherical harmonics are also eigenfunctions of this operator, with eigenvalues of $m_l \hbar$.

$$\hat{l}_z Y_l^{m_l}(\theta,\phi) = m_l \hbar Y_l^{m_l}(\theta,\phi) \quad \text{where} \quad m_l = -l, -l+1, \dots, l-1, l \quad (10.18)$$

This means that the $z$-component of the angular momentum vector is also quantized, and the orientation of that vector can only take on certain possibilities. This idea is sometimes referred to as **space quantization**.

To better understand this idea, we need to consider what happens to the rotational states of our system if we break the symmetry by introducing an external electric or magnetic field. You may recall from physics that a charge moving in a circular path gives rise to a magnetic moment. This magnetic moment will therefore interact with an external magnetic field. We will take the field as being along the $z$ direction. In order to fully treat the presence of an external field, we need to add a term into our Hamiltonian operator, which changes both the wavefunctions and the energies we obtain from solving the Schrödinger

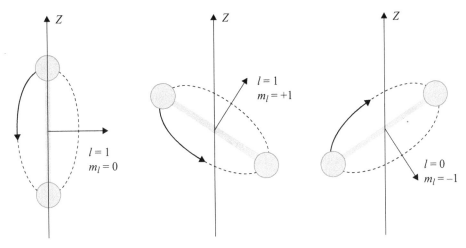

**FIGURE 10.5.** Rigid rotor with $l = 1$ and an external field. The different $m_l$ states are oriented differently with respect to the external field, which breaks the degeneracy of the rotational states.

equation. The full details are beyond the scope of this book, but we can learn a lot by looking at things qualitatively. (The solution to this situation involves an implementation of perturbation theory, which is discussed in Chapter 12.)

Consider a system with $l = 1$. This means that the values of $m_l$ can either be $-1, 0$, or $1$. A value of 0 means that the $z$-component of the angular momentum is perpendicular to the $z$ axis. This also means the magnetic moment of the rotor is aligned perpendicular to the external field, so there is no interaction between them. For $m_l = \pm 1$, the angular momentum vector is either aligned with or against the external field. These geometric relations are shown in Figure 10.5. This interaction with the field will cause these previously degenerate rotational states to **split**, one going to higher energy and one to lower, and the degree of splitting depends on the strength of the field. For this reason, the $m_l$ quantum number is sometimes called the "magnetic quantum number." If the field strength is reduced to zero, all three states once again become degenerate because direction no longer matters.

The splitting of degenerate rotational states due to an external magnetic field was first observed by Otto Stern and Walther Gerlach in 1922. They specifically designed their experiment to test the predictions of the new quantum theories. As predicted, they observed discrete rotational states rather than a continuum of possibilities as classical mechanics predicted. This was just one more piece of evidence that quantum mechanics was a more correct model of the microscopic world than the classical models. The Stern–Gerlach experiment also helped set the stage for a new era of scientific experimentation to test the predictions of theoretical physicists that continues to this day.

## 10.2 Rotational Spectroscopy

In the last chapter, we saw how we could use spectroscopy and the particle-in-a-box model to learn about linear, highly conjugated organic molecules. In this section, we will learn about rotational spectroscopy and what it can tell us about the structure of molecules.

## 10.2.1 The Rotational Constant

One of the important parameters we developed in our discussion of rotational motion was the moment of inertia, $I$. This was originally defined according to Eq. 10.3 as $I \equiv mr^2$, but this definition really only holds for a single particle spinning about a central point. What about a more complicated structure like a molecule, which can be thought of as balls connected by sticks, spinning about some point?

First, we need to be clear that any complicated object will always spin about its **center of mass**. Imagine we want to balance our structure at the tip of a sharp pole. The only way to do this is to ensure that the center of mass is directly above that tip. Mathematically, the center of mass is the point such that

$$\sum_i m_i r_i = 0 \tag{10.19}$$

where the sum is over each particle in the system, $m_i$ is the mass of each particle and $r_i$ is the distance of that particle from the center of mass position. Once the position of the center of mass is properly located, the moment of inertia can be more generally defined as

$$I = \sum_i m_i r_i^2 \tag{10.20}$$

where $r_i$ is now the distance from the axis of rotation. Any three-dimensional object will, in principle, have three axes of rotation, each of which will be orthogonal to the others. There are therefore three values for the moment of inertia. Depending on the symmetry of the molecule, the moments of inertia for different rotational axes could be the same or different. Note that for a linear molecule, one of these axes will be along the bond, so the distance of each atom from that axis of rotation is zero, making that moment of inertia also zero. This is why we only had 2 rotational degrees of freedom for a linear molecule in our equipartition model back in Chapter 7. The moment of inertia for a diatomic molecule is given by Eq. 10.4 as $I \equiv \mu r^2$.

Regardless of the value of $I$, we can see that the rotational energy depends on the moment of inertia by Eq. 10.15.

$$E_{rot} = l(l+1)\frac{\hbar^2}{2I}$$

Because $\hbar$ is a constant, we can define the **rotational constant**, $B$, as

$$B \equiv \frac{\hbar^2}{2I} \tag{10.21}$$

The rotational constant contains the moment of inertia, which in turn contains information about the positions of the atoms in our molecule relative to rotational axes. Thus, if we can determine the rotational constant, we can learn a great deal about bond lengths and bond angles.

## 10.2.2 Rotational Spectrum of a Diatomic Molecule

To keep things simple, we will first consider the rotational energy states of a diatomic molecule. For a diatomic molecule, we only have one moment of inertia, and therefore a single rotational constant $B$. For historical reasons, rotational spectroscopists prefer to use $J$ as the quantum number instead of the $l$ we used previously. Making this switch lets us write the energy of a given rotational level in terms of the rotational constant as

$$E_J = J(J+1)B \quad \text{where} \quad J = 0, 1, 2, \dots \quad (10.22)$$

Rotational states are sometimes referred to as "$J$ states."

Just as we had with the particle in a box, there are selection rules that govern the allowed transitions between these different rotational energy levels. The first rule, sometimes called the "gross selection rule" is that in order to absorb or emit light, the molecule must have a permanent dipole moment. If we evaluate transition dipole moments for our rotational wavefunctions, we also obtain the rule for a linear molecule that

$$\Delta J = \pm 1 \quad (10.23)$$

Thus a photon can be absorbed and cause the rotational level to increase one step, or a molecule can emit a photon to drop down one rotational level. The difference in energy levels between any two states is given by

$$\Delta E = E_{J+1} - E_J = 2(J+1)B \quad (10.24)$$

where $J$ is the label corresponding to the lower state of the transition. The rotational levels, their spacings, and the allowed transitions are shown in Figure 10.6.

We can see now that the energy difference between rotational levels is on the order of magnitude of the rotational constant, $B$. Rotational constants for small linear molecules are easily calculated. For CO, $B = 3.84 \times 10^{-23}$ J, and for HCl, $B = 2.10 \times 10^{-22}$ J. To put these numbers in perspective, let's calculate the wavelength of light associated with the $0 \rightarrow 1$ transition for CO.

$$\Delta E_{0\rightarrow1} = 2B = \frac{hc}{\lambda}$$

Doing so gives us a wavelength of $2.59 \times 10^{-3}$ m, or 2.59 mm. This places us in the microwave region of the electromagnetic spectrum. Thus, rotational spectroscopy is also often referred to as **microwave spectroscopy**. Talking about rotational constants in units of Joules is somewhat inconvenient, because of the order of magnitude of $10^{-23}$ associated with it. It is very common in the field of microwave spectroscopy to use a different unit, the **wavenumber**, defined as

$$\bar{v} \equiv \frac{1}{\lambda} \quad (10.25)$$

This uses the Greek letter nu, and this symbol is sometimes called *nu bar*. The energy of a photon can now be written in terms of wavenumber as

$$E = hc\bar{v} \quad (10.26)$$

Because energy and wavenumber are proportional to each other by fundamental constants, we can effectively use the wavenumber as a unit of energy. Rotational constants are also reported in these units. For reasons of convenience, the wavenumber is typically reported in units of cm$^{-1}$. Thus, for CO, the rotational constant would have a value of 1.93 cm$^{-1}$.

A microwave spectrum is measured by sending microwave radiation through our sample and measuring the intensity of the light that reaches the detector on the other side as the

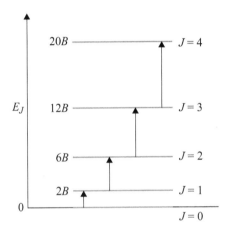

FIGURE 10.6. Rotational energy levels and allowed transitions for a diatomic molecule.

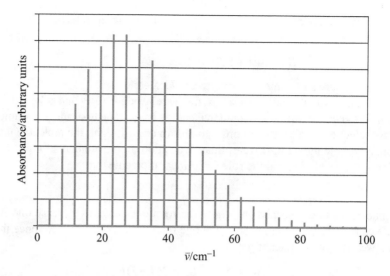

**FIGURE 10.7.** Simulated rotational spectrum of CO at 200 K.

wavelength of the microwave radiation is scanned. When the energy of the incident light is **resonant** with a rotational transition, some of the incident light will be absorbed and not reach the detector. This will show up as a **peak** in the rotational spectrum. A simulated rotational spectrum of CO at 200 K is shown in Figure 10.7. Keep in mind that the peak in a spectrum corresponds to a transition between two rotational states. We never measure the energy of a state directly, just the difference in energy between two states.

The patterns in the rotational spectrum are very informative. The first peak shows up at $\Delta E_{0 \to 1} = 2B$. The second peak will be at $\Delta E_{1 \to 2} = 4B$, the third at $\Delta E_{2 \to 3} = 6B$, and so on. We can also look at the energy difference between any two peaks, which corresponds to the difference of the difference between energy levels. It is straightforward to show that this is

$$\Delta(\Delta E) = 2B \tag{10.27}$$

regardless of which two peaks in the spectrum we choose. Remember that the rotational constant tells us about the moment of inertia, which depends on the bond length. Thus, by taking a microwave spectrum, we can effectively measure the length of a diatomic molecule.

### Sample Problem 10.1

A microwave spectrum of $^{14}N^{16}O$ contains peaks at the following locations: 21.73, 25.08, 28.42, 31.76, 35.11, 38.45 and 41.79 cm$^{-1}$. From these data, determine the bond length of the NO molecule.

### Solution

We begin by recalling that the spacing between peaks in the microwave spectrum corresponds to twice the rotational constant (see Eq. 10.27). Taking the difference between the peak positions and averaging them gives the value $2B = 3.34$ cm$^{-1}$, or a rotational constant of $B = 1.67$ cm$^{-1}$. From this rotational constant—and being careful with our units—we can calculate a moment of inertia of $I = 1.67 \times 10^{-46}$ kg m$^2$. (Yes, moments of inertia for molecules are typically this small.)

To determine the bond length, we could use Eq. 10.20, but that requires us to know the position of the center of mass for the molecule. For a diatomic molecule, we can use the reduced mass and Eq. 10.4 to greatly simplify things. The reduced mass for NO is

$$\mu = \frac{m_N m_O}{m_N + m_O} = \frac{14 \times 16}{14 + 16} \text{amu} = 7.47 \text{ amu} = 1.24 \times 10^{-26} \text{ kg}$$

The bond length is then determined to be <u>1.16 Å</u>.

---

Another way to do spectroscopy is to take an emission measurement. In this case, a molecule in an excited rotational state can emit light and drop down one rotational level. The energy of that transition is the same as for an absorbance, so the peaks will show up in the same place in an emission spectrum as in an absorbance spectrum. The signal tends to be much weaker, however, because nothing causes the emission to happen. You may wonder why anyone would do microwave emission spectroscopy if they could instead do an absorbance measurement. In a laboratory, you would be correct that an absorbance measurement would always be the better choice. But there is one field where that's not an option: astronomy. Molecules in space can and do emit light in the microwave region, and radioastronomers can detect and analyze those signals to determine the composition of nebulae and the interstellar medium. Hundreds of compounds have been detected in space, and more are being found all the time.

There is one other aspect of a microwave spectrum that merits some discussion, and that is the intensity of peaks in the spectrum. The position of the peak tells us the energy of the transition, but the intensity of the peak relates to the probability that the transition takes place. One key component of that probability is the number of molecules in the appropriate state to make the transition. We learned in Chapter 2 that the Boltzmann distribution gives us the relative population in a given energy state. Using the energy and degeneracy of a rotational level in the Boltzmann distribution thus gives us

$$P_J = \frac{(2J + 1)e^{-J(J+1)B/k_B T}}{q} \tag{10.28}$$

Remember that rotational levels have a degeneracy of $2J + 1$. We will formally develop expressions for the rotational partition function in Chapter 14. For now, we can determine the relative probability of any level relative to the $J = 0$ level by dividing one probability by the other.

$$\frac{P_J}{P_0} = (2J + 1)e^{-J(J+1)B/k_B T} \tag{10.29}$$

The intensity pattern in our spectrum will thus vary depending on the $J$ state associated with the transition. At low values of $J$, the probability of transition—which reflects the population that can make the transition—will increase linearly with $J$. At high values of $J$, however, the exponential term will take over and the probability—and populations—will decrease exponentially, eventually dying out because there are no molecules in very high $J$ states. If we know the relative intensities of transitions in the microwave spectrum—either absorbance or emission—we can therefore determine the temperature of the sample, which is again a very useful thing in radioastronomy. (There are other factors that affect peak intensities, but this is a good first approximation.)

There is one more point that needs to be made here, now that we have brought the Boltzmann distribution back into our discussion. That is the relative spacing of rotational energy levels. We made the argument in Chapter 7 that rotational levels are fairly close together relative to $k_B T$. Now we can provide some justification for that argument. As we saw, the rotational constant is around $10^{-23}$ to $10^{-22}$ J. At room temperature, $k_B T$ has a value of about $10^{-21}$ J. Thus, rotational levels are at least 10–100 times closer together than $k_B T$ and our assumption was valid.

### 10.2.3 Rotational Spectra of Polyatomic Molecules

The rotational spectra of polyatomic molecules can be much more complicated than for diatomics. Other than mentioning a few features, we won't go into the details of them here. Recall that any three-dimensional object has three mutually orthogonal axes of rotation. This means that any molecule has, in principle, three different moments of inertia, one for each rotational axis. For a linear molecule, two of them were the same and the third, corresponding to the axis of rotation, is zero. For a nonlinear molecule, it is possible for all three moments of inertia to be the same; we call this a **spherical rotor**. Examples of spherical rotors include $CH_4$ and $SF_6$. A spherical rotor can never have a permanent dipole moment, however, therefore they are microwave invisible. The same is true for homonuclear diatomic molecules.

Another possible arrangement of the atoms in a molecule will have two of the moments of inertia be the same, but different from the third moment. Such a molecule is described as a **symmetric rotor**. Examples include $NH_3$ and $CH_3Cl$. The energy levels for symmetric rotors can be highly degenerate and an external field can give rise to lots of splitting. If all three moments of inertia are different, the molecule is described as an **asymmetric rotor**. Clearly, most molecules fall into this category. Rotational spectra of asymmetric rotors, even something as simple as $H_2O$, can be very complicated and difficult to analyze.

One approach to analyzing rotational spectra is to propose molecular structures and determine the spectrum that would arise from that structure. If the predicted spectrum matches the experimentally measured spectrum, the structure is considered to be valid. If not, the proposed structure must be refined until a better match is obtained. This iterative process is very common in modern physical chemistry; we make a model, predict what a measurement would look like for that system, compare it to actual measurements, and then refine the model to get a better match. Spectroscopists and theorists often work hand in hand to solve difficult problems.

### 10.2.4 Other Aspects of Rotational Spectroscopy

Everything we have done with rotating systems has been based on a key assumption—that of a rigid rotor. By saying the rotor is rigid, we are saying that it cannot change shape. Real molecules, however, are not strictly rigid. As we will see in the next section, molecules can vibrate. It is also possible that the bond lengths of our molecule could change as it spins faster in a higher rotational state. Dealing with all the complexities of rotational spectroscopy is outside the scope of this book, but we do want to point some of these things out.

Imagine you are on a merry-go-round at a playground. If the merry-go-round is going slowly, you can stand in one place without too much trouble. As it spins faster, however, you feel a force pushing you away from the center of the merry-go-round. This type of centrifugal force is felt by a spinning molecule as well and leads to a **centrifugal distortion** in the rotational spectrum. Empirically, the energy of a rotational level experiencing this distortion is written as

$$E_J = J(J+1)B - D_J J^2 (J+1)^2$$

where $D_J$ is the centrifugal distortion constant. This constant depends on the relative stiffness of the various bonds in the molecule. Note that this distortion tends to reduce the energy of the rotational levels, thus the spacing between peaks in a rotational spectrum will decrease as the quantum number $J$ increases.

Rotational spectroscopy is a very powerful technique. This is one method by which scientists measured the bond lengths and angles you learned about in general chemistry. It can also allow us to determine the chemical makeup of interstellar space and inform us about important processes happening in the cosmos. An understanding of rotational energy levels will also improve our understanding of vibrational transitions, as we will see in the next section.

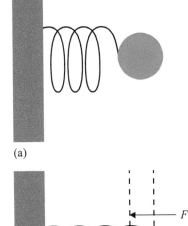
(a)

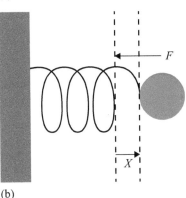
(b)

FIGURE 10.8. Schematic of the harmonic oscillator a) at equilibrium and b) extended. The restoring force, $F$, acts in the opposite direction of the displacement, $x$.

# 10.3 Vibrational Motion

The next type of internal motion we need to consider is vibrational motion. As we did with rotational motion, we will first review the classical model and then present the quantum-mechanical treatment. In both cases, we start with the picture of a mass connected to a wall by a spring, or by two masses connected to each other by a spring. With the concept of reduced mass introduced earlier, both are mathematically equivalent. If there is no friction or other damping in the system, this model is known as the **harmonic oscillator**.

## 10.3.1 Classical Harmonic Oscillator

Figure 10.8 depicts a mechanical model of the harmonic oscillator, which is a mass connected to a wall by a spring. According to Hooke's law, if the mass is displaced from its equilibrium position, there is a restoring force given by

$$F = -kx \tag{10.30}$$

The parameter $k$ here is known as the **force constant** and reflects the stiffness of the spring. Note that $x$ can be either positive or negative; if positive, then the restoring force of the spring will pull it back to the equilibrium position and if negative, the restoring force of the spring will push it back towards the equilibrium position. The motion of the oscillator is analyzed by writing Newton's second law in its mathematical form

$$F = ma = m\frac{dx^2}{dt^2} \tag{10.31}$$

Setting Eqs. 10.30 and 10.31 equal to each other gives the differential equation

$$\frac{dx^2}{dt^2} = \frac{-k}{m}x$$

We've seen this type of differential equation before; it looks very much like the Schrödinger equation for the free particle. In writing our solution this time, we will rewrite the constants on the right-hand side according to the relation

$$\omega = \left(\frac{k}{m}\right)^{1/2} \tag{10.32}$$

For convenience, we will use the trigonometric version of the solution to this differential equation and write

$$x(t) = A \sin \omega t + B \cos \omega t$$

We can see now that $\omega$ can be thought of as the angular frequency of the oscillation. If we take the particle's position at time $t = 0$ to be at the origin, then $x(0) = 0$, which requires that $B = 0$. We can now write the position function as

$$x(t) = A \sin \omega t$$

The velocity of our particle at any time can be determined by taking the derivative of this position function.

$$v(t) = \frac{dx(t)}{dt} = A\omega \cos \omega t$$

We can now use this relation to determine $A$, by requiring that $v(0) = v_0$, the initial velocity.

$$v(0) = v_0 = A\omega$$

Thus, our complete solution, given the boundary conditions we have imposed, can be written as

$$x(t) = \frac{v_0}{\omega} \sin \omega \, t \tag{10.33}$$

Now that we have a general solution for the position of our particle as a function of time, we can talk about the total energy of this system. The kinetic energy depends on the velocity, so we can write

$$E_K = \frac{1}{2}mv^2 = \frac{1}{2}mv_0^2 \cos^2 \omega t$$

This system also has potential energy, the energy stored in the spring. Recall from your physics classes that potential energy, $V$, is related to force by the relation

$$F = \frac{-dV}{dx}$$

$$V = -\int F dx \tag{10.34}$$

If we integrate Eq. 10.34, we obtain an expression for the potential energy

$$V = \frac{1}{2}kx^2 \tag{10.35}$$

The total energy is then given by

$$E = E_K + V = \frac{1}{2}mv_0^2\cos^2\omega t + \frac{1}{2}k\frac{v_0^2}{\omega^2}\sin^2\omega t$$

$$E = \frac{1}{2}mv_0^2$$

where we used Eqs. 10.32 and 10.33 and the trigonometric relation $\sin^2\omega t + \cos^2\omega t = 1$. The total energy of the oscillating system is constant with time, but the energy switches back and forth between potential and kinetic energy as the particle moves. At maximum extension or compression of the spring, all the energy is potential and the particle is instantaneously at rest. At the equilibrium position, all the energy is kinetic and the particle is moving at its maximum velocity. The energy oscillates back and forth sinusoidally.

## 10.3.2 Quantum-Mechanical Harmonic Oscillator

The most important thing to come out of our discussion of the classical harmonic oscillator is the potential energy function, Eq. 10.35. We will use this parabolic function (see Figure 10.9) as the potential energy operator in our Hamiltonian operator for the one-dimensional quantum-mechanical harmonic oscillator.

$$\hat{H} = \frac{-\hbar^2}{2m}\frac{d^2}{dx^2} + \frac{1}{2}kx^2 \qquad (10.36)$$

The Schrödinger equation for the harmonic oscillator is now written as

$$\frac{-\hbar^2}{2m}\frac{d^2\psi}{dx^2} + \frac{1}{2}kx^2\psi = E\psi \qquad (10.37)$$

Things are now getting tricky. We need a function such that, when we take the second derivative, multiply it by some constants, and add the function back again, multiplied by different constants, we get the same original function back, multiplied by a constant.

The solution to this equation is not obvious, but we can get a hint at the solution by again returning to the requirements of a valid wavefunction. Note that the potential function has some similarities to the particle in a box, except now the walls are sloped instead of vertical. (See Figure 10.9.) We can thus expect to find the particle near the center of the potential well, where the potential energy is zero. We also know that we don't expect to find the particle

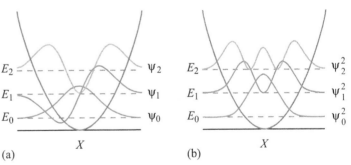

(a)  (b)

FIGURE 10.9. First three states of the quantum-mechanical harmonic oscillator. a) Shows the wavefunctions themselves and b) shows the square of the wavefunction. Notice that there is a classically forbidden region for this system, just as we saw for the particle in a finite well.

at long distances away from this center. A function that meets these physical criteria, and might work mathematically as well, is the Gaussian function.

$$f(x) = Ae^{-\alpha x^2/2}$$

(The factor of 1/2 in the exponential will be helpful later on.) The second derivative of this function is written as

$$f''(x) = -\alpha A e^{-\alpha x^2} + \alpha^2 x^2 A e^{-\alpha x^2} = (\alpha^2 x^2 - \alpha) A e^{-\alpha x^2}$$

If we try this as our wavefunction and put it into the Schrödinger equation, we have

$$\frac{-\hbar^2}{2m}(\alpha^2 x^2 - \alpha) + \frac{1}{2}kx^2 = E$$

If we can require that

$$\alpha^2 = \frac{km}{\hbar^2}$$

then the two quadratic terms would cancel out, and we would be left with

$$\frac{\hbar^2}{2m}\alpha = E$$

We can simplify things a bit by using Eq. 10.32 to write

$$\alpha = \frac{m\omega}{\hbar} \tag{10.38}$$

which gives us an energy of

$$E = \frac{1}{2}\hbar\omega$$

In the other systems we have investigated, we have always obtained a whole series of functions, but our approach so far has just yielded a single function. Once again, the mathematical form of the Schrödinger equation for this problem was already known, so the physicists working on this problem were able to jump straight to the answer. The general solutions to this differential equation involve a series of functions known as the Hermite polynomials, symbolized as $H_n(y)$, the first few of which are written as

$$H_0(y) = 1 \qquad H_1(y) = 2y \qquad H_2(y) = 4y^2 - 2$$

Note that the polynomials only involve either even or odd terms. Additional polynomials in the series can be found by the relation

$$H_{n+1}(y) = 2yH_n(y) - 2nH_{n-1}(y)$$

The general form of the harmonic oscillator wavefunctions is then written as

$$\psi_n(x) = \left(\frac{\alpha}{\pi}\right)^{1/4}\left(\frac{1}{2^n n!}\right)^{1/2} H_n(y)e^{-y^2/2} \tag{10.39}$$

where $\alpha$ is given by Eq. 10.36, $H_n(y)$ is the Hermite polynomial of order $n$, and $y = \alpha^{1/2}x$. The first few harmonic oscillator functions are tabulated in Table 10.2 and shown in Figure 10.9.

## TABLE 10.2 Harmonic oscillator wavefunctions.

| $n$ | $\psi_n$ |
| --- | --- |
| 0 | $$\psi_0(x) = \left(\frac{\alpha}{\pi}\right)^{1/4} e^{-\alpha x^2/2}$$ |
| 1 | $$\psi_1(x) = \left(\frac{4\alpha^3}{\pi}\right)^{1/4} x e^{-\alpha x^2/2}$$ |
| 2 | $$\psi_2(x) = \left(\frac{\alpha}{4\pi}\right)^{1/4} (2\alpha x^2 - 1)e^{-\alpha x^2/2}$$ |

The allowed energies for the harmonic oscillator end up being given by

$$E_n = \left(n + \frac{1}{2}\right)\hbar\omega \quad \text{where } n = 0, 1, 2, \ldots$$

Most of us are not used to thinking in terms of angular frequency. The angular and linear frequencies are related by

$$\omega = 2\pi\nu \tag{10.40}$$

Making this substitution lets us write the more common form of the energy expression

$$E_n = \left(n + \frac{1}{2}\right)h\nu \quad \text{where } n = 0, 1, 2, \ldots \tag{10.41}$$

Unlike the energies for the particle in a box or the rigid rotor, where the energy levels get further apart as we go up, these energy levels are evenly spaced. Notice that even though the bottom of the potential well is taken as the zero of energy, the particle itself can never have zero energy; in its lowest energy state, the energy is $\frac{1}{2}h\nu$. As we did for the particle in a box, we call this lowest allowable energy the **zero-point energy**. Figure 10.9 shows the harmonic oscillator potential and the first few wavefunctions, again shifted vertically by the energy of the state.

It is useful to make some other comparisons between the solution to the harmonic oscillator and the particle-in-a-box and rigid-rotor solutions. Just like those other systems, the harmonic-oscillator wavefunctions exhibit nodes, and the number of nodes increases as the energy increases. And like the particle in a finite well, the harmonic oscillator wavefunctions can penetrate into the classically forbidden region. In fact, many chemical systems are modeled as two displaced harmonic oscillators where the potential wells overlap. If the energy becomes sufficiently high, tunneling between the two wells is possible.

It is also useful to consider the wavefunction in light of the correspondence principle. A classical particle moving on a harmonic potential is most likely to be found at the edges, since that is where the velocity is the slowest. For the quantum system in the $n = 0$ state, however, we have a maximum probability at the bottom of the well. As the quantum number and the number of nodes increase, the likelihood of finding the particle at the edges of the well increases, just as we would expect for the classical system. Once again, correspondence is verified.

# 10.4 Vibrational Spectroscopy

We now come to one of the most powerful spectroscopic techniques available: vibrational spectroscopy. One of the most common uses of vibrational spectroscopy is to identify organic compounds; thus it is widely used to monitor the product stream of a reactor. A basic understanding of the principles of vibrational spectroscopy is essential for anyone working in the chemical or material sciences. More detailed treatments can be found in other sources dedicated to the subject.

## 10.4.1 Vibrational Spectrum of a Diatomic Molecule

As we did with rotational spectroscopy, we will begin our discussion of vibrational spectroscopy with a diatomic molecule. We can think of the two nuclei that make up our molecule as being connected by a spring, representing the chemical bond. The two nuclei can now oscillate, or vibrate, about the equilibrium bond length. The strength of the bond affects the stiffness of the "spring", which in turn affects the frequency of the vibrational motion. As we did with two particles that collide, we can treat the two masses in our molecule as a single particle of the reduced mass, given by $\mu = \dfrac{m_1 m_2}{m_1 + m_2}$. The frequency of the vibrational motion is then given by

$$v = \frac{\omega}{2\pi} = \frac{1}{2\pi}\left(\frac{k}{\mu}\right)^{1/2} \tag{10.42}$$

The energies of the states, if we treat our molecule as a harmonic oscillator, are again given by Eq. 10.41.

As with all other forms of spectroscopy, vibrational spectroscopy is governed by selection rules. The first, gross selection rule is that the vibrational motion must lead to a change in the dipole moment of the molecule. For this reason, a homonuclear diatomic cannot have a vibrational spectrum; there is no dipole moment regardless of the bond length. Second, we find that transitions are only allowed when

$$\Delta n = \pm 1 \tag{10.43}$$

The difference in energy between any two levels is given by

$$\Delta E_{n \to n+1} = \left((n+1)+\frac{1}{2}\right)hv - \left(n+\frac{1}{2}\right)hv = hv \tag{10.44}$$

Notice that the frequency of the light that causes a transition is exactly the same as the frequency of the vibrational motion. It also doesn't matter what level we start in, so a pure vibrational spectrum of a diatomic molecule should only contain a single peak at $hv$.

The real situation is a bit more complex, and to understand why we first need to get a sense of the spacing of the vibrational energy levels. As you learned in organic chemistry, vibrational transitions can be excited by infrared (IR) light. The wavelengths of IR light are in the $\mu m$ region. For convenience, the vibrational spectroscopy community also uses wavenumbers in units of $cm^{-1}$. The IR spectrum covers the range of about 100–5000 $cm^{-1}$. This means that vibrational levels of a given molecule are typically spaced several hundred to a thousand times further apart than the rotational levels. Thus, if we have enough energy to cause a vibrational transition, there is the possibility we can cause a rotational transition as well.

If we treat the energy of our molecule according to both the harmonic-oscillator and rigid-rotor models for vibrational and rotational motion, respectively, we would write

$$E_{n,J} = \left(n + \frac{1}{2}\right)h\nu + J(J+1)B \qquad (10.45)$$

Transitions are now possible only if both selection rules are obeyed; $\Delta n = \pm 1$ for the vibration and $\Delta J = \pm 1$ for the rotation. Let's consider the case of an absorption of an IR photon, therefore $\Delta n = +1$. Note that if the rotational $J$ state didn't change, the energy associated with that transition would be the same regardless of the initial value of $J$ and would simply be $h\nu$. We call this the **fundamental transition**, and the frequency of this transition is sometimes labeled $\nu_0$.

The rotational state does have to change, however; therefore, we will not see a peak at the energy of the fundamental transition. The rotational quantum number $J$ can either increase or decrease by one step. If $J$ increases, then the energy of the transition is given by

$$\Delta E = E_{n+1,J+1} - E_{n,J} = h\nu + 2(J+1)B$$

This peak will appear at a slightly higher energy than the fundamental transition. Notice also that the difference in energy from the fundamental transition will increase as the initial value of $J$ increases. This set of peaks on the higher energy side of the fundamental transition is known as the **R branch**; the $R$ comes from *rich*, since these transitions involve more energy than the fundamental transition. We can also have a transition where the molecule ends up in a lower $J$ state. In this case, the energy of the transition is given by

$$\Delta E = E_{n+1,J} - E_{n,J-1} = h\nu - 2JB$$

These peaks all show up on the lower energy side of the fundamental transition and will get progressively lower in energy as the initial value of $J$ increases. Because these states are somewhat energy "poor," this branch is labeled as the **P branch**. If we could see the fundamental transition, it would be called the **Q branch**. (The letter Q comes between P and R.) The allowed transitions and a simulated spectrum are shown in Figure 10.10. (Note that the R side of the spectrum looks virtually the same as the pure rotational spectrum we saw earlier in Figure 10.7.)

If this were all that were going on, the spacing between the peaks in both the P and R branches would correspond to $2B$. Thus, a vibrational spectroscopy measurement can allow us to determine the rotational constant of our molecule. Because this measurement contains both rotational and vibrational information, such a spectrum is often called a **rovibrational spectrum**. The situation is not always this simple, however. As we saw with the centrifugal distortion of the rotational spectrum, a rovibrational spectrum is also typically distorted from the ideal case. What is typically seen is that the peaks in the P branch tend to spread out, and the peaks in the R branch tend to compress as we move away from the fundamental transition. This is because our model assumed that the value of the rotational constant did not depend on the vibrational state. In reality, each vibrational state has its own value for the rotational constant, and this has to be taken into account in analyzing the spectrum. The rotational constant in the excited vibrational state is typically slightly smaller than that of the ground state, because the bond is slightly extended, which changes the moment of inertia. This phenomenon was included in the simulated spectrum of Figure 10.10.

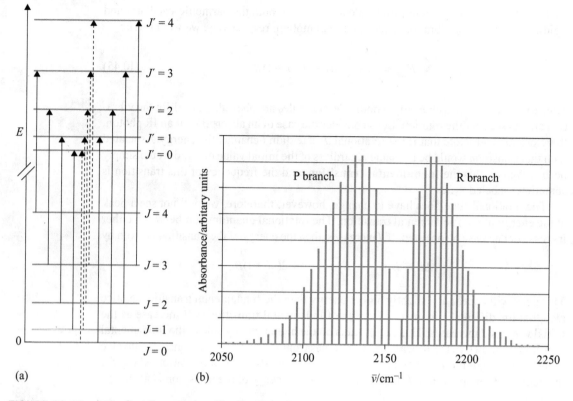

**FIGURE 10.10.** a) The first five rotational levels of the first two vibrational states. $J$ denotes a rotational state of the ground vibrational state, and $J'$ denotes a rotational state of the first excited vibrational state. Allowed transitions are indicated by solid arrows. The dashed arrows show the forbidden transitions that don't involve a change in $J$. b) Simulated rovibrational spectrum of CO at 200 K.

## 10.4.2 Anharmonicity

We have done quite a bit with the harmonic oscillator as our model of molecular vibrations. It has its limitations, however, which we must now acknowledge. The most serious problem with the harmonic oscillator is that it can never break; you can stretch or compress it as much as you want and it will always bounce back. A real molecule, however, can **dissociate**; in other words, the bond can break. You might then ask why we would even use the harmonic oscillator at all, knowing this limitation. To address this, let's consider a more accurate representation of the potential energy for two atoms connected by a covalent bond.

We will call the function that describes the potential energy of our chemical bond as a function of internuclear distance $U(R)$. This function and a corresponding harmonic oscillator potential are shown in Figure 10.11. Let's qualitatively sketch out some of the details of this function. If the two nuclei are very far apart, then there is no bond and in fact there is no interaction at all between them. We could call the potential energy at large distance zero, since there is no interaction, although we will find it more convenient to set the zero of energy somewhere else. Let's set this potential energy as a positive number, to indicate that our nuclei have the potential of forming a bond. As the nuclei come closer together, they begin to interact. If that interaction is favorable, and a bond is forming, the potential energy will decrease. The potential energy will continue to decrease until we reach the equilibrium bond length between the two nuclei. If we try to move them closer to each other, then the two positively charged nuclei begin to experience a repulsive interaction between themselves, which will increase the potential energy. Eventually, as we try to put the two nuclei on top of each other, that repulsive energy will become very large.

So what does this have to do with the harmonic oscillator? Let's go to the minimum energy point on this potential energy curve, at $R = R_e$, the equilibrium bond length. For our convenience, we will take this as the zero of energy. We now perform a Taylor expansion about this point on our function. Recall from your mathematics classes that the general form of a Taylor series is written as

$$f(x) = \sum_n \frac{1}{n!} \left( \frac{d^n f(x)}{dx^n} \right)_{x_0} (x - x_0)^n \tag{10.46}$$

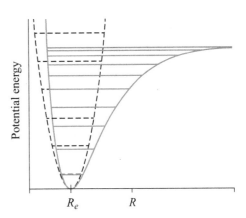

FIGURE 10.11. Comparison of the harmonic (black, dashed) and anharmonic (blue, solid) potentials. Corresponding energy states are also indicated.

Let's consider this in terms of our potential energy function, $U(R)$, expanding about $R_e$ and write the first three terms in the series

$$U(R) \approx U(R_e) + \left( \frac{dU(R)}{dR} \right)_{R_e} (R - R_e) + \frac{1}{2} \left( \frac{d^2 U(R)}{dR^2} \right)_{R_e} (R - R_e)^2$$

The first term we have already said is zero. The second term involves the first derivative of the potential energy function. However, recall that the position $R_e$ is the minimum on this curve, therefore the first derivative is also zero. This leaves us with

$$U(R) \approx \frac{1}{2} \left( \frac{d^2 U(R)}{dR^2} \right)_{R_e} (R - R_e)^2$$

If we call the second derivative of the potential energy function $k$, we have exactly the same potential as we used for the harmonic oscillator. In other words, the harmonic oscillator potential is a good approximation for the true molecular potential energy function in the vicinity of the equilibrium bond distance, $R_e$.

If we want a better representation of the actual function, we need to include the next term in the series.

$$U(R) \approx \frac{1}{2} \left( \frac{d^2 U(R)}{dR^2} \right)_{R_e} (R - R_e)^2 + \frac{1}{6} \left( \frac{d^3 U(R)}{dR^3} \right)_{R_e} (R - R_e)^3$$

We can again call the second derivative $k$. The third derivative we will call $\Upsilon_3$. We now write the potential for an **anharmonic oscillator** as

$$U(R) \approx \frac{1}{2} k (R - R_e)^2 + \frac{1}{6} \Upsilon_3 (R - R_e)^3 \tag{10.47}$$

The energies of an anharmonic oscillator are given, to a first approximation, by the expression

$$E_n = \left( n + \frac{1}{2} \right) h\nu - \left( n + \frac{1}{2} \right)^2 x_e h\nu \tag{10.48}$$

where the new constant $x_e$ reflects the amount of anharmonicity. Notice that the energy levels start to get closer together as the vibrational quantum number increases. This makes sense, because the well becomes wider as we go up and will eventually reach the dissociation limit.

The fact that molecules are not really harmonic oscillators allows for a few interesting effects to be observed. First, as we have already discussed, the anharmonic oscillator model allows the molecule to dissociate, which was not possible for the harmonic oscillator. The selection rules are also different for the anharmonic oscillator, and now jumps of $\Delta n = \pm 2$ are possible. We call these transitions that involve going up two steps **overtones**, and they occur at roughly double the frequency of the fundamental transitions. As we will see in the next section, polyatomic molecules have multiple ways the atoms can vibrate. Anharmonicity allows these different vibrational motions to couple, which gives rise to **combination bands** in a vibrational spectrum. It also allows for **intramolecular vibrational energy redistribution (IVR)** where the energy associated with high-energy vibrational motion can spread out within a molecule and populate lower energy vibrations. Vibrational spectroscopy is a very rich and informative field of study, which we explore some more in the next section.

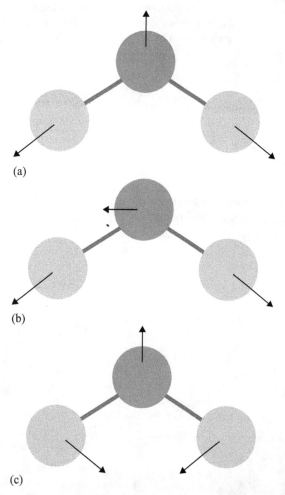

(a)

(b)

(c)

**FIGURE 10.12.** Normal modes of $H_2O$: a) symmetric stretch, b) antisymmetric stretch, and c) bend. Note that the center of mass must not move during any of these vibrations.

### 10.4.3 Vibrational Spectra of Polyatomic Molecules

Up until now, we have focused on the vibrational motion of a diatomic molecule. Polyatomic molecules can also vibrate. Just as we can analyze the rotation of any three-dimensional object in terms of its principle rotational axes, the vibrational motion of a complicated molecule can be analyzed in terms of its **normal modes**. The number of modes is the same as the number of vibrational degrees of freedom we discussed back in Chapter 7; $3n - 5$ for a linear molecule and $3n - 6$ for a nonlinear molecule, where $n$ is the number of atoms in the molecule. The normal modes of $H_2O$ are shown in Figure 10.12.

Even though each of these motions may involve several atoms, or even the entire molecule, they can all be treated by the harmonic oscillator approximation and each has its own characteristic vibrational frequency. Different types of motion have different effective mass and different effective force constants, so the frequencies vary quite a bit, depending on the motion. This is one way that we can identify molecular structures with IR spectroscopy. You have learned about some of these characteristic frequencies in organic chemistry. C–H stretching motion tends to occur around 2900 cm$^{-1}$, whereas the C–H bends are seen around 1500 cm$^{-1}$. C=O stretching motion is seen around 1700–1800 cm$^{-1}$, and so forth.

The vibrational spectra of polyatomic molecules, especially in liquid samples, tend not to show the rich rotational structure that can be seen in gas-phase spectra of smaller molecules. This is because the interactions that take place in the liquid scramble the various energy states, making them indistinguishable and causing the peaks to smear out. Thus the IR spectrum of a liquid tends to have broad peaks that often overlap, rather than the very sharp and distinct peaks of a gas. Figure 10.13 shows the IR spectrum of toluene. Even with the lack of spectral resolution, IR spectroscopy is a very powerful tool for identifying organic

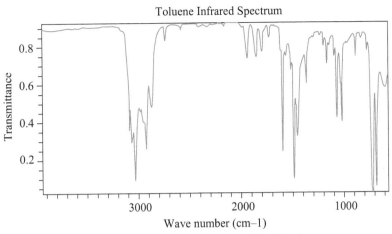

Toluene Infrared Spectrum

NIST Chemistry WebBook (http://webbook.nist.gov/chemistry)

**FIGURE 10.13.** IR transmission spectrum of liquid toluene. Note the range of coverage of the spectrum. Rotational features are not resolvable in this spectrum.

molecules because each spectrum can serve as a molecular "fingerprint." For this reason, it is commonly used to monitor the product stream of a chemical reactor to ensure that the proper compounds are being produced.

## 10.4.4 Raman Spectroscopy

Direct absorption of IR radiation is not the only way to induce a vibrational transition. Before we discuss the other way of causing a vibrational transition, we must first talk about scattering of light. You have all observed that when a speck of dust floats through a sunbeam, you see it sparkle. The light of the sunbeam scatters off the dust particle and travels toward your eyes. Molecules themselves can also scatter light. One way to think of this is that the molecule absorbs the incoming photon, then reemits a photon of the same frequency (energy). But the scattered photon doesn't have to travel in the same direction as the incoming photon. This is known as **Rayleigh scattering** and this phenomenon provides the explanation for why the sky is blue. The probability of scattering is inversely proportional to the fourth power of the wavelength, meaning blue light scatters more readily than red light.

Rayleigh scattering is an **elastic** process, meaning that the photon that is scattered is of the same frequency as the incoming photon. **Inelastic** scattering is also possible and was first observed in 1928 by the Indian physicist C. V. Raman. He observed that the scattered light sometimes had a different energy, generally slightly lower, than the incident light. But according to the law of conservation of energy, that extra energy had to be somewhere. Where it went was to an internal degree of freedom of the molecule. As shown in the Figure 10.14, a photon can scatter inelastically if it deposits a quantum of energy into a vibrational mode. This is known as **Stokes Raman scattering**. The energy of the scattered photon is shifted by the energy of the vibrational transition. If the molecule is already in an excited vibrational state, then the photon can pick up that energy and the molecule drops down to the ground vibrational state. This is known as **anti–Stokes Raman spectroscopy**. By measuring the shift in the frequency, the vibrational energy is determined. (There is also a rotational Raman effect, but we won't go into that here.)

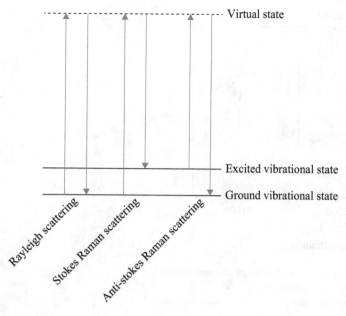

Virtual state

Excited vibrational state

Ground vibrational state

Rayleigh scattering

Stokes Raman scattering

Anti-stokes Raman scattering

**FIGURE 10.14.** Energy diagrams for Rayleigh, Stokes Raman, and anti–Stokes Raman scattering.

Note that the scattering process involves a "virtual state." This means that the molecule doesn't actually have to have a real state that absorbs the photon, although the presence of a real state can enhance the Raman effect; this is known as **resonance Raman**. The Raman effect strongly supported the quantum theory that was still being developed and this effect was immediately recognized as greatly important. C. V. Raman received the Nobel Prize in 1930 for his discovery.

Raman spectroscopy has certain advantages over IR spectroscopy. First of all, it can be done with a visible light source, rather than an IR source. Raman scattering is many orders of magnitude weaker than Rayleigh scattering, but lasers make it quite straightforward to perform. (It's actually amazing that Raman was able to observe the effect, given the limited equipment he had in 1928.) Just as with IR spectroscopy, the frequencies of the transitions can be used to identify molecules and determine their structures. Also, because Raman spectroscopy is done with visible light, it can be combined with a microscope to provide information about chemical composition of a sample with a spatial resolution of better than 10 μm.

Raman spectroscopy will never completely replace IR spectroscopy, however. Some vibrational modes cannot be observed with IR spectroscopy, just as there are certain modes that are not Raman active. For example, if a molecule has a center of symmetry, then all the vibrational modes are either IR active or Raman active, but not both. This is known as the **mutual exclusion principle**. Raman and IR spectroscopy are often both required, together with other techniques such as nuclear magnetic resonance (NMR), for full determination of the structure of an unknown molecule.

As we saw with rotational spectra, the probability of a transition occurring will depend on the number of molecules in the relevant vibrational states. Because more molecules are in the ground vibrational state than the excited vibrational state, the Stokes signal will always be stronger than the anti-Stokes signal. For a sample at elevated temperature, however, the population in an excited vibrational state will be increased, and so will the anti–Stokes Raman signal. Anti–Stokes Raman experiments can therefore be used as a sort of optical thermometer, which can be useful in measuring the temperature of combustion plumes or other environments where more conventional temperature measurements may be difficult to perform.

## 10.5  Summary, and Where We Go Next

In this chapter, we have explored rotational and vibrational motion, making use of two simple quantum-mechanical models, the rigid rotor and the harmonic oscillator. We have also learned about rotational and vibrational spectroscopy and gained a sense for what we can learn about the structure of molecules with these techniques. In the next chapter, we will develop the quantum-mechanical treatment of atoms and molecules.

**10.1** The wavefunctions for a particle on a ring are written as $\psi_{rot} = \dfrac{1}{\sqrt{2\pi}} e^{im_l \phi}$ with $m_l = 0, \pm1, \pm2, \ldots$

   a) For a particle on a ring, what is the probability of finding the particle at any particular position for any value of $m_l$?

   b) What is the expectation value for the position of the particle on a ring? Provide a physical interpretation of your result?

   c) What is the expectation value of the angular momentum? Because this is a two-dimensional system, the angular momentum vector must be along the $z$ direction, so use the $\hat{l}_z$ operator.

**10.2** The benzene molecule can be modeled with the particle on a ring model. Knowing that benzene exhibits a strong absorption at about 180 nm, estimate the radius of the benzene ring.

**10.3** Show that the spherical harmonic functions $Y_0^0$, $Y_1^0$, and $Y_1^1$ are each normalized and that they are all orthogonal to each other.

**10.4** Which of the following molecules can exhibit a pure rotational spectrum? Provide justification for your answers.

   a) $N_2$       b) $H_2O$       c) $CO_2$       d) $CH_4$       e) $NH_3$

**10.5** The bond length of the $O_2$ molecule is 121 pm.

   a) Calculate the energy of the $J = 5$ rotational state at a temperature of 350 K.

   b) Compare this rotational energy to the translational kinetic energy at the same temperature.

   c) What are the relative populations of the $J = 5$ and $J = 0$ levels at this temperature?

**10.6** Radioastronomers measure microwave emission lines to determine the composition of nebulae and other features. During a particular observation, an emission line at 7.71 cm$^{-1}$ was measured. Assuming this corresponds to a transition between the $J = 2$ and $J = 1$ states, determine the following.

   a) The moment of inertia of the molecule.

   b) Assuming a bond length of about 110 pm, identify the molecule.

**10.7** a) Calculate the angular frequency (rotations per second) for the H$^{35}$Cl molecule in each of the first three rotational levels. The bond length is 127.5 pm.

   b) Compare this to the vibrational frequency in Hz, where $n_0 = 2888.7$ cm$^{-1}$.

   c) Use the results of parts a) and b) to provide some justification for the idea of combining the rigid rotor and harmonic oscillator models at the same time.

**10.8** a) Calculate the vibrational frequency for $^{12}C^{16}O$ in s$^{-1}$ and cm$^{-1}$. Treat the molecule as a harmonic oscillator with a force constant of 1903.17 N m$^{-1}$.

   b) The experimentally determined vibrational frequency is 2143.26 cm$^{-1}$. Comment on the differences between your result in part a) and the experimental result.

**10.9** The fundamental vibrational frequency of $H^{35}Cl$ is 2888.7 $cm^{-1}$, and the equilibrium bond length is 127.5 pm.

a) Calculate the force constant for the H–Cl bond.

b) Calculate the rovibrational spectrum for this molecule, including all transitions where the initial rotational level is three or lower.

c) Find a high-resolution spectrum online and compare your results in part b) to the experimental data. Comment on any similarities and differences.

**10.10** Which of the following molecules can exhibit an IR absorbance spectrum? Provide justification for your answers.

a) $N_2$     b) $H_2O$     c) $CO_2$     d) $CH_4$     e) $NH_3$

**10.11** This problem will explore a common model for the potential of a diatomic molecule, known as the Morse potential. The Morse potential is mathematically written as

$$V(x) = D_e\left[1 - e^{-\alpha(x-x_e)}\right]^2$$

The quantity $\alpha$ is related to the harmonic oscillator frequency by $\alpha = \left(\dfrac{\mu\omega^2}{2D_e}\right)^{1/2}$. The parameter $D_e$ is the dissociation energy, and it relates to the depth of the well.

a) Make a plot of a Morse oscillator and the corresponding harmonic oscillator. Describe the differences between the two curves, particularly in the regions of short and long internuclear distance. Choose a value of $D_e$ that is at least a few times $v$.

b) The first several energy levels of the anharmonic Morse oscillator are given by

$$E_n = \left(n+\frac{1}{2}\right)hv - \left(n+\frac{1}{2}\right)^2 x_e hv \quad \text{with} \quad x_e = \frac{v}{4D_e}$$

Compare the energy levels for both the harmonic and anharmonic oscillators. Does this expression for the energy describe all the energy states? If not, what else is needed?

c) Discuss why we use the harmonic oscillator model for molecular vibrations, even though we know it has problems. When does the harmonic approximation work well and when does it break down? In answering this question, include some discussion of the parameters of the bond, such as bond strength.

**10.12** Selective deuteration of organic molecules is a useful tool for determining reaction mechanisms. An organic chemist thinks a particular OH group is the source of hydrogen in a hydrogen transfer reaction and replaces the H with a D atom. If the OH vibrational stretches for this molecule appear at around 3150 $cm^{-1}$, at what frequency will the OD stretch appear, assuming the force constant is unchanged by the substitution? (If changes are observed at this new frequency due to the reaction, this will support the proposed mechanism.)

**10.13** For the molecule NO, the fundamental vibrational frequency occurs at 1878 cm$^{-1}$. The rotational constant has a value of 1.67 cm$^{-1}$.

   a) Using the Boltzmann distribution, determine the fraction of molecules that are in a vibrational state other than the ground state at a temperature of 300 K.

   b) Find the rotational $J$ state of NO that has the largest total population at 300 K.

**10.14** A combustion scientist is using Raman spectroscopy to monitor the plume of an incinerator. One of the purposes of this incinerator is to destroy chlorine containing compounds. Molecules that contain C–Cl bonds tend to have vibrational signatures at around 750 cm$^{-1}$. If the relative intensity of the anti-Stokes to Stokes Raman signals is 0.60, what is the temperature in the incinerator plume?

# The Hydrogen Atom, Atomic Orbitals, and Electronic Structure of Atoms

## 11.1 The Structure of the Atom

The existence of atoms and molecules had long been theorized, but was never rigorously proven until the late 19th and early 20th centuries. Boltzmann, who was a strong proponent of the molecular hypothesis, was criticized for insisting that atoms and molecules were real and not just useful theoretical constructs. Convincing proof of the atomic model came from the discovery of the electron by J. J. Thomson in 1897 and the atomic nucleus by Ernest Rutherford in 1909. The Rutherford model of the atom consisted of a positively charged nucleus surrounded by the negatively charged electrons. The exact behavior of the electrons was not yet understood, but many thought they should orbit the nucleus, similar to how planets orbit the sun. Understanding the structure of the atom was one of the main goals of those who developed quantum mechanics in the early 20th century.

### 11.1.1 Emission Spectra and the Bohr Model of the Atom

Experiments showed quite clearly that when a gas was subjected to an electrostatic discharge, light was emitted. (This is how neon signs work, by the way.) However, this light consisted of a series of discrete frequencies, or colors, which is different from a blackbody. Remember that a heated body emits light over a broad, continuous range of frequencies—not in discrete lines. The emission spectrum of hydrogen is shown in Figure 11.1. The pattern of discrete lines was fit to an equation by Johannes Rydberg in 1888.

$$\frac{1}{\lambda} = R\left(\frac{1}{n_1^2} - \frac{1}{n_2^2}\right) \text{ with } R = 1.097 \times 10^7 \text{ m}^{-1} \tag{11.1}$$

Unfortunately, Rydberg's formula did not provide a physical explanation for the pattern of emission lines. Their source was one more mystery at the end of the 19th century.

Niels Bohr, a Danish physicist, took the Rutherford model of the atom one step further in his attempt to explain the observed atomic emission spectra. To explain these discrete spectra and the Rydberg formula, Bohr developed a model of the atom that had the electrons confined to orbits of particular energies. The only way that an electron could increase its energy was to absorb enough energy to "leap" to a higher energy orbit. When an excited electron released energy to drop down to a lower energy orbit, that extra energy was carried away by the emitted light. This model is depicted in Figure 11.2. These discrete transitions give the emission spectrum its characteristic lines. Bohr's model was developed in 1913, and he received the Nobel Prize in Physics in 1922.

We won't go through the full development of Bohr's model, but we will highlight some of its features. In order for an electron orbit to be stable, there needs to be a balance between the Coulombic attraction of the electron toward the nucleus and the centrifugal force pulling the electron away from the nucleus.

$$\frac{e^2}{4\pi\epsilon_0 r^2} = \frac{mv^2}{r}$$

Hydrogen emission spectrum in the visible region

FIGURE 11.1. Emission spectrum of atomic hydrogen in the visible region. Other lines exist in the UV and IR regions.

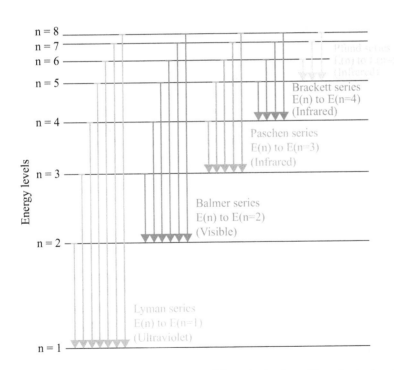

FIGURE 11.2. Energy diagram showing possible emission transitions for hydrogen. Each level corresponds to one of the possible electron orbits.

To fit the experimental data, Bohr needed to quantize the angular momentum of the different orbits in units of Planck's constant (funny how that same number keeps showing up, isn't it?). Let's see why. The length of the path around the orbit is given by $L = 2\pi r$. Because of the wave behavior of the electron, the length of the orbit must be an integer number of de Broglie wavelengths, where $\lambda = \dfrac{h}{p}$. Putting these ideas together gives us

$$L = 2\pi r = n\lambda = n\frac{h}{p} \quad \text{or} \quad r = \frac{n\hbar}{p}$$

If we rearrange things, using $p = mv$, we have

$$mvr = n\hbar$$

Substituting in the force-balance expression above and solving for the radius of the $n = 1$ orbit, we have

$$r = \frac{\epsilon_0 h^2}{\pi m e^2} = a_0 \tag{11.2}$$

This quantity is known as the Bohr radius and has a value of $5.29177 \times 10^{-11}$ m. Going through some more algebra and calculating the total energy of each orbit, we ultimately find

$$E_n = \frac{-m_e e^4}{8\epsilon_0^2 h^2 n^2} \tag{11.3}$$

The difference between energy levels matches the observed lines in the emission spectrum of hydrogen, and the collection of constants in Eq. 11.3—when converted to the same units—exactly matches the constant in Rydberg's formula. (Bohr's work predates de Broglie's hypothesis, so he didn't take this exact approach, but that hypothesis leads to the same result. The details of the original derivation are a bit more complicated, however, which is why we have presented things this way.)

The Bohr model was successful, in that it explained a great deal of experimental observations. However, it had some very fundamental problems. First of all, there was no basis for it in classical physics. Classically, an electron traveling in a circular orbit should be radiating energy, leading to a loss of its own energy. Eventually (actually, very quickly; $\sim 10^{-10}$ s) the electron would lose enough energy that it would crash into the nucleus. The Bohr model is based on the idea of electron orbits, but provides no rationale for why these orbits, or in fact atoms themselves, are stable. This requires quantum mechanics.

## 11.1.2 Schrödinger Equation for the Hydrogen Atom

We have explored several model systems that can be solved analytically, specifically the particle in a box, the rigid rotor, and the harmonic oscillator. Even though real systems are more complicated, these model systems are useful approximations. The hydrogen atom is the first real situation that we can solve exactly (subject to the approximation that the proton and electron are point particles, but that's a minor quibble). A hydrogen atom consists of a single proton surrounded by a single electron. The interaction between the proton and the electron is represented by the Coulomb potential, of the form

$$V(r) = \frac{-Ze^2}{4\pi\epsilon_0 r} \tag{11.4}$$

$Z$ is the nuclear charge, $e$ is the elementary charge of an electron (or proton), and $\epsilon_0$ is the permittivity of free space, which has a value of $8.854187 \times 10^{-12}$ C$^2$ J$^{-1}$ m$^{-1}$. This potential depends on the distance between the particles $r$. Unlike previous potentials, we choose our zero of energy to be at infinite separation of the two particles, meaning our energies will be negative, not positive. This potential actually works for any hydrogen-like atom, meaning all but one of its electrons have been removed, such as Li$^{2+}$; only $Z$ will change for different atoms.

If we take the proton to be at the origin, we can write our Hamiltonian as

$$\hat{H} = \hat{T}_e + \hat{V} = \frac{-\hbar^2}{2\mu_e}\nabla_e^2 - \frac{Ze^2}{4\pi\epsilon_0 r} \tag{11.5}$$

The symbol $\mu_e$ represents the reduced mass of the electron–nucleus system, which is approximately equal to the mass of the electron. The first term accounts for the kinetic energy of the electron and the second term is the Coulombic interaction between the electron and the nucleus. Since we are keeping our coordinate system fixed on the nucleus, we can ignore nuclear motion. The $\nabla^2$ operator, known as the Laplacian, is written in Cartesian coordinates as

$$\nabla^2 = \frac{\partial^2}{\partial x^2} + \frac{\partial^2}{\partial y^2} + \frac{\partial^2}{\partial z^2}$$

In spherical coordinates, which make sense here, this becomes significantly more complicated

$$\nabla^2 = \frac{1}{r^2}\left[\frac{1}{\sin\theta}\frac{\partial}{\partial\theta}\left(\sin\theta\frac{\partial}{\partial\theta}\right) + \frac{1}{\sin^2\theta}\frac{\partial^2}{\partial\phi^2}\right] + \frac{1}{r^2}\frac{\partial}{\partial r}\left(r^2\frac{\partial}{\partial r}\right) \tag{11.6}$$

The portion in the square brackets is exactly the same as the total angular momentum operator $\hat{l}^2$ that we encountered with the rigid rotor (see Eq. 10.14). It only needs the factor of $-\hbar^2$, which is in the Hamiltonian operator above. We now write the Schrödinger equation as

$$\hat{H}\psi = \frac{1}{2\mu_e r^2}\hat{l}^2\psi - \frac{\hbar^2}{2\mu_e r^2}\frac{\partial}{\partial r}\left(r^2\frac{\partial\psi}{\partial r^2}\right) - \frac{Ze^2}{4\pi\epsilon_0 r}\psi = E\psi \tag{11.7}$$

Notice that the only derivatives we have outside the $\hat{l}^2$ operator are derivatives with respect to $r$. This suggests that we can use separation of variables to solve this problem. Because we already know the eigenfunctions of the total angular momentum operator, the spherical harmonics, we write the wavefunction as

$$\psi(r,\theta,\phi) = R(r)Y_l^{m_l}(\theta,\phi) \tag{11.8}$$

We can now write the Schrödinger equation as

$$\frac{1}{2\mu_e r^2}R(r)\hat{l}^2 Y_l^{m_l}(\theta,\phi) - \frac{\hbar^2}{2\mu_e r^2}Y_l^{m_l}(\theta,\phi)\frac{d}{dr}\left[r^2\frac{dR(r)}{dr}\right]$$

$$-Y_l^{m_l}(\theta,\phi)\frac{e^2}{4\pi\epsilon_0 r}R(r) = ER(r)Y_l^{m_l}(\theta,\phi)$$

This looks quite formidable, but we already know that

$$\hat{l}^2 Y_l^{m_l}(\theta,\phi) = \hbar^2 l(l+1)Y_l^{m_l}(\theta,\phi) \tag{11.9}$$

If we make this substitution, we can divide out the spherical harmonics and write

$$\frac{-\hbar^2}{2\mu_e r^2}\frac{d}{dr}\left[r^2\frac{dR(r)}{dr}\right]+\left[\frac{\hbar^2 l(l+1)}{2\mu_e r^2}-\frac{e^2}{4\pi\epsilon_0 r}\right]R(r)=ER(r) \qquad (11.10)$$

We have grouped the terms this way for a reason. The first term, involving derivatives with respect to $r$, relates to the kinetic energy of the electron in the radial direction. The second term is an effective potential with two parts. The first part has to do with the angular momentum of the electron and is a centripetal potential. Notice that if the electron has no angular momentum, i.e. $l = 0$, this term doesn't contribute. The last part is the Coulombic potential describing the attraction between the proton and the electron.

Just like the other differential equations we have encountered, the solution to this radial equation was already known. We already have the spherical harmonics in Chapter 10, which give us the angular dependencies of the wavefunction. The radial function is of the form

$$R_{n,l}(r)=-\left[\frac{4Z^3}{n^4 a_0^3}\frac{(n-l-1)!}{[(n+1)!]^3}\right]^{1/2}\left(\frac{2Zr}{na_0}\right)^l e^{-Zr/na_0}L_{n+l}^{2l+1}\left(\frac{2Zr}{na_0}\right) \qquad (11.11)$$

where $a_0 = \dfrac{4\pi\epsilon_0\hbar^2}{\mu_e e^2}$ is known as the Bohr radius, and matches what Bohr determined in his electron-orbit model. The $L_{n+l}^{2l+1}\left(\dfrac{2Zr}{na_0}\right)$ functions are known as the associated Laguerre polynomials. The first few radial functions are tabulated in Table 11.1 and plotted in Figure 11.3.

TABLE 11.1   Radial wavefunctions for hydrogenic atoms

| $n$ | $l$ | $R_{n,l}(r)$ |
|---|---|---|
| 1 | 0 | $R_{1,0}=2\left(\dfrac{Z}{a_0}\right)^{3/2}e^{-Zr/a_0}$ |
| 2 | 0 | $R_{2,0}=\dfrac{1}{\sqrt{2}}\left(\dfrac{Z}{a_0}\right)^{3/2}\left(1-\dfrac{Zr}{2a_0}\right)e^{-Zr/2a_0}$ |
| 2 | 1 | $R_{2,1}=\dfrac{1}{2\sqrt{6}}\left(\dfrac{Z}{a_0}\right)^{5/2}re^{-Zr/2a_0}$ |
| 3 | 0 | $R_{3,0}=\dfrac{2}{3\sqrt{3}}\left(\dfrac{Z}{a_0}\right)^{3/2}\left(1-\dfrac{2Zr}{3a_0}+\dfrac{2Z^2 r^2}{27a_0^2}\right)e^{-Zr/3a_0}$ |
| 3 | 1 | $R_{3,1}=\dfrac{8}{27\sqrt{6}}\left(\dfrac{Z}{a_0}\right)^{3/2}\left(\dfrac{Zr}{a_0}-\dfrac{Z^2 r^2}{6a_0^2}\right)e^{-Zr/3a_0}$ |
| 3 | 2 | $R_{3,2}=\dfrac{4}{81\sqrt{30}}\left(\dfrac{Z}{a_0}\right)^{7/2}r^2 e^{-Zr/3a_0}$ |

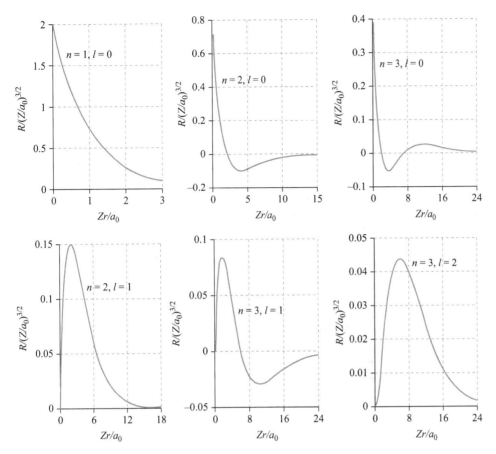

FIGURE 11.3. Radial wavefunctions for the hydrogen atom corresponding to the set of quantum numbers indicated.

Because we have three coordinates in our wavefunction, we have three quantum numbers:

| | |
|---|---|
| principle quantum number | $n = 1, 2, 3, \ldots$ |
| orbital angular momentum | $l = 0, 1, 2, \ldots, n-1$ |
| magnetic quantum number | $m_l = -l, -(l-1), \ldots, 0, \ldots, (l-1), l$ |

The restrictions on the quantum numbers result from the boundary conditions of the problem.

The energy of these states is given by

$$E_n = \frac{-Z^2 \mu_e e^4}{8\epsilon_0^2 h^2 n^2} = \frac{-Z^2 e^2}{8\pi \epsilon_0 a_0 n^2} \tag{11.12}$$

(Compare this energy to Bohr's result above, Eq. 11.3.) Note that the energy only depends on the principle quantum number, $n$. This means that each energy level has some degree of degeneracy for the various values of $l$ and $m_l$. Figure 11.4 shows a plot of the potential energy function and the placement of the allowed energy levels. The total effective potential for $l = 1$ is also included as a dashed curve. Note that the lowest possible energy level for $l = 1$ is the $n = 2$ state; when there is too much angular momentum, it is not possible to reach the lower energy states. This is why the possible values of the $l$ quantum number

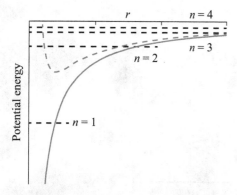

**FIGURE 11.4.** Potential energy curves for the hydrogen atom with (blue solid) $l = 0$ and (blue dashed) $l = 1$. The first four energy levels are also indicated.

depend on the value of the $n$ quantum number. The relationship between $m_l$ and $l$ is the same as we saw before with the rigid rotor, that is $m_l$ can range from $-l$ to $l$ in integer steps. Thus, for a given value of $l$, there are $2l + 1$ degenerate states. If you add up all the states for each allowed value of $l$ and $m_l$, the degeneracy of level $n$ is $n^2$.

### 11.1.3 Stability of Atoms

Now that we have the solutions for the hydrogen atom, we can comment on why atoms are stable. It all has to do with the balance between kinetic and potential energy. The Coulombic potential gets more and more negative as the distance between the electron and the nucleus decreases; being closer to the nucleus decreases the potential energy. However, recall from the particle in a box that confinement leads to higher kinetic energy; being closer to the nucleus increases the kinetic energy. The stable levels balance the kinetic and potential energy.

The angular momentum of the electron enters into this discussion as well. As the angular momentum increases, this effectively adds an extra potential energy term. Note that the angular term in Eq. 11.10 is positive whereas the Coulombic term is negative. Adding these two terms together creates a minimum in the potential energy, and the position of that minimum increases with increasing values of $l$. This means that an electron with a large amount of angular momentum cannot get very close to the nucleus, and therefore can't occupy a lower energy level. As we have already seen, the energy only depends on $n$. It turns out, through some fortuitous mathematics, that the lowest possible energy level for a given value of $l$ is the $n = l + 1$ level.

### 11.1.4 Atomic Orbitals

Each of the solutions for the hydrogen atom $\psi_{n,l,m_l}(r, \theta, \phi) = R_{n,l}(r) Y_l^{m_l}(\theta, \phi)$ is known as an **atomic orbital**. (The term orbital is clearly derived from Bohr's idea of the electrons orbiting the nucleus, although that's not actually how they move.) Illustrations of some atomic orbitals are shown in Figure 11.5. As with the other wavefunctions we have seen,

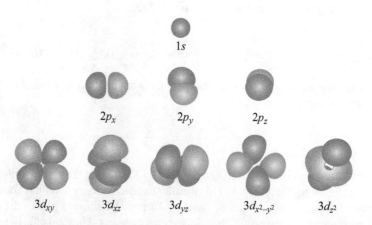

**FIGURE 11.5.** Illustrations of atomic orbitals. The colors represent the positive and negative lobes of the wavefunction. These lobes are separated by nodal surfaces.

these functions have nodes. Because of the spherical symmetry, these nodes can either be radial—as in the radial functions plotted above in Figure 11.3—or angular, as with the spherical harmonics shown in Figure 10.4. The locations of these nodes give characteristic shapes to the different atomic orbitals. Atomic orbitals are typically grouped according to the angular momentum quantum number, $l$, with the following assignments:

$$l = \quad 0 \quad\quad 1 \quad\quad 2 \quad\quad 3$$
$$\quad\quad s \quad\quad p \quad\quad d \quad\quad f$$

(These labels are chosen for historical reasons and stand for *sharp, principle, diffuse,* and *fine*.) $s$-type orbitals have no angular nodes, so they must have spherical symmetry— although they can have radial nodes, as seen in the plots in Figure 11.3. $p$-type orbitals have an angular node that runs through the origin, giving them a characteristic dumbbell shape. $d$-type orbitals have two angular nodes, so they are more complicated. The shapes of the orbitals depict the probability distribution of the position of the electrons. Where we have a node, or the wavefunction is small, we don't expect to find the electrons; whereas in regions where the wavefunction is large, we expect to find them most of the time. The orbital represents a "cloud of probability," not a discrete path the electrons take.

## 11.1.5 Multielectron Atoms, the Pauli Principle, and Electron Spin

We now have a working solution for the hydrogen atom, but there is more to the universe than hydrogen. How can we extend this approach to atoms other than hydrogen? First, we need to consider all the interactions in a multielectron atom and construct the corresponding Hamiltonian operator. Let's begin with the next simplest atom, helium.

For the helium atom, we have one nucleus with a +2 charge, and two electrons. The Hamiltonian is written as

$$\hat{H} = -\frac{\hbar^2}{2\mu_e}\nabla_{e_1}^2 - \frac{\hbar^2}{2\mu_e}\nabla_{e_2}^2 - \frac{2e^2}{4\pi\epsilon_0 r_1} - \frac{2e^2}{4\pi\epsilon_0 r_2} + \frac{e^2}{4\pi\epsilon_0 r_{12}} \tag{11.13}$$

Let's briefly discuss the terms here. The first two terms represent the kinetic energy of electron 1 and electron 2, respectively. The next two terms are the interactions of the two electrons with the nucleus; $r_1$ is the distance of electron 1 from the nucleus and $r_2$ is the distance of electron 2 from the nucleus. If this were all we had to deal with, we could treat this with separation of variables and write the wavefunction as the product of 2 one-electron functions. However, the last term accounts for the interaction between the two electrons, with $r_{12}$ being the distance between them. This term makes it impossible to analytically solve the Schrödinger equation; the wavefunction needs to account for the coordinates of both electrons, and the solution for the first electron depends on the location of the second, and vice versa.

The Schrödinger equation for a multielectron atom can only be solved approximately. We will discuss some approaches for tackling this problem in the next chapter, in Section 12.1.1, but one approach is to describe the solution in terms of the hydrogenic orbitals. Recall that the eigenfunctions of an operator comprise a complete mathematical set, meaning we can describe the solutions of any atom in terms of the hydrogenic orbitals. Mathematically we write the solutions to the Schrödinger equation for the He atom as a product of the hydrogenic atomic orbitals. Note, however, that the real orbitals for helium are not exactly the same as they were in hydrogen. For helium, there really isn't a $1s$ orbital, but the first solution is dominated by the hydrogen $1s$ orbital function; the first He orbital is $1s$-like. It is also important to note that the degeneracy of the different states is broken by the interactions between the electrons; the $2s$-like and $2p$-like orbitals are not at exactly the same energy in helium, as they were in hydrogen.

Lastly, we need to know about one more property of electrons, **spin**. Electron spin is a purely quantum-mechanical property; it has no classical analog. (It arises from relativistic quantum mechanics, which is definitely beyond the scope of this book. That being said, if we allow for the fourth dimension of time in our treatment, we should not be surprised that a fourth quantum number shows up in the solution.) There are two possible spin states for an electron, called **spin-up** and **spin-down**, commonly represented by up and down arrows. The spin quantum number is often labeled $m_s$ and can have values of $+1/2$ or $-1/2$. The **Pauli exclusion principle**, proposed by Wolfgang Pauli in 1924, states that no two electrons in a quantum-mechanical system can have exactly the same set of quantum numbers. For purposes of our discussion, we can take this as a postulate of quantum mechanics. Because there are two spin states, each atomic orbital can contain at most two electrons, a rule you should have learned in general chemistry. (Pauli won the Nobel Prize in 1945, nominated by Einstein, for his fundamental work in developing quantum mechanics, particularly the exclusion principle.)

Using the hydrogenic orbitals and the Pauli principle, we can approximately describe the electronic configuration of multielectron atoms. Going back to He, we describe its electronic configuration as $1s^2$, meaning the $1s$-like orbital contains two electrons. The **Aufbau principle** gives the order in which orbitals are filled as:

$$1s \quad 2s \quad 2p \quad 3s \quad 3p \quad 4s \quad 3d \quad 4p \quad 5s \quad 4d \quad 5p \quad 6s$$

So the configuration of boron is described as $1s^2 2s^2 2p^1$ or $[He]2s^2 2p^1$. A diagram of this configuration is shown in Figure 11.6. (This ordering of the orbitals is somewhat empirical, but it does agree with detailed quantum-mechanical calculations.)

The last thing that is needed to describe electronic configurations is **Hund's rule**, which states that electrons will enter unfilled orbitals before occupying part-filled orbitals. This leads to the maximum total electron spin, because the electrons can line up their spin states. Correlation of spins helps to lower the total energy of the electrons, again a purely quantum-mechanical effect. Thus, when making a diagram for the electrons of oxygen, with configuration $[He]2s^2 2p^4$, we would first put one electron, typically indicated as spin-up, in each of the 3 $2p$ orbitals before putting the fourth electron, spin-down, in an orbital that already has one electron. This is shown in Figure 11.6.

Our description of the atomic orbitals of a multielectron atom in terms of hydrogenic orbitals is an approximation. Because it is an approximation, it is not the only model that can be used to describe these atomic orbitals. Another approach involves mixing hydrogenic orbitals to make new orbitals, which is possible whenever the orbitals are of the same, or very similar energy. This is the mathematical basis behind the idea of hybridized orbitals that you learned about in organic chemistry; examples of hybridized orbitals include such things as $sp^3$ and $sp^2$ orbitals. Ultimately, the atom does what the atom does, and we try to find adequate models to understand that behavior. Quantum mechanics is the best way we have to understand the properties of atoms.

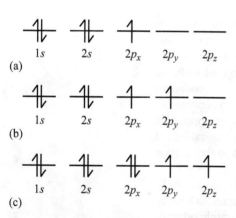

**FIGURE 11.6.** Electron configuration diagrams for a) boron, $1s^2 2s^2 2p^1$, b) carbon, $1s^2 2s^2 2p^2$, and c) oxygen, $1s^2 2s^2 2p^4$.

# 11.2 Lasers

Now that we have learned about the discrete electronic energy states of atoms, we can discuss one of the most useful tools of modern science, the laser. To begin this discussion, we need to briefly go over the basic processes that happen when light and matter interact. When a photon is incident on a material, and the energy of that photon is the same as the energy spacing between two electronic states, the electron can absorb the incident energy and jump up to the excited electronic state. (Of course, as we learned in Section 9.2.2, this transition must be allowed.) We call this process **stimulated absorption**, represented in Figure 11.7a.

Once an electron has been placed in an excited state, it will try to find a way to relax back down to the ground state. We have already seen this with the line spectrum of hydrogen at the beginning of the chapter. When this relaxation happens on its own, without anything directly causing it to happen, we call that process **spontaneous emission**, shown in Figure 11.7b. Another process that can lead to relaxation is **stimulated emission**, shown in Figure 11.7c. In stimulated emission, a photon of the same energy as the one that caused absorption comes and induces the electron to relax and emit a second photon of the same energy. These two photons now travel together, and they are actually in phase with each other. Albert Einstein was the one who worked through the details of all three of these processes. (Incidentally, even though he could correctly describe the process of spontaneous emission, Einstein didn't like it because there is no identifiable proximate cause. He was much more comfortable with stimulated emission, but that process seems odd to most students today.)

In Figure 11.7, we have shown these three processes for a simple system that only has two energy levels. Initially, all the population of this two-level system is in the ground state. As we shine light on the sample, some of that light will be absorbed and move electrons up to the excited state. Once we build up some population in the excited state, however, incident photons can cause either stimulated emission or further absorption. When the two populations become equal, the likelihood of either process becomes the same, and we have the same number of photons leaving as entering the system; such a system will actually be transparent to the incident light.

The word laser is actually an acronym meaning "Light Amplification by Stimulated Emission of Radiation." If we only have two states, though, we can see that there can be no amplification. In order to get more photons out than we put in, we need to have more electrons in the excited state than in the ground state. This situation is called a **population inversion**. Unfortunately, there is no way to get a population inversion with only two levels. As we have just seen, using light to drive electrons to the excited state can at best give us a 50–50 split between the two levels. If we try to populate the excited state thermally, 50–50 is also the best we can do, because of the Boltzmann distribution. So how can we achieve the needed population inversion? We need more energy levels.

Figure 11.8 shows three- and four-level systems. The excitation, or **pump**, light promotes electrons to the excited state, which then quickly relaxes through a **nonradiative transition** (a transition that does not emit light) to a third state. The important thing is that this nonradiative transition needs to happen quickly so we don't build up population in the first excited state. The incident pump light is not of the right energy to cause stimulated emission from this state. We want this second excited state, however, to

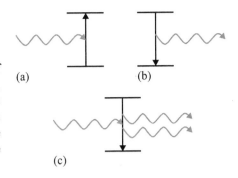

**FIGURE 11.7.** Energy diagrams for a) stimulated absorption, b) spontaneous emission, and c) stimulated emission.

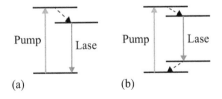

**FIGURE 11.8.** Energy diagrams for a a) three-level and b) four-level laser. Dashed lines indicate nonradiative transitions.

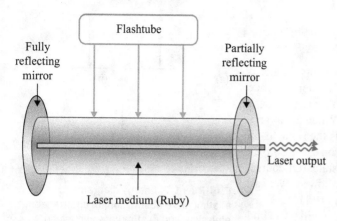

Fully reflecting mirror

Flashtube

Partially reflecting mirror

Laser output

Laser medium (Ruby)

**FIGURE 11.9.** Schematic of the ruby laser, indicating the pump source (flashtube), gain medium, and optical cavity set up by the mirrors on the ends.

be long lived so we can build up population in it. The population will build up here, and eventually one of the electrons will spontaneously emit a photon and relax back to the ground state for a three-level system, or to a fourth state that is slightly above the ground state, which then quickly relaxes back down to the ground state.

The material containing our atoms (or molecules) with these electronic states is known as the **gain medium**. If the gain medium is placed inside an **optical cavity**, then eventually one of those spontaneously emitted photons will travel back along the same optical path, reenter the gain medium, and cause stimulated emission. These two photons will continue along the optical path of the cavity, and each time they come back through the gain medium, they will cause more stimulated emission—thus amplifying the light at this wavelength, known as the **lasing** wavelength. Typically one end of the optical cavity has an **output coupler**, a partially reflecting mirror, that allows some of the laser light to leave the cavity. The first laser was a rod of ruby crystal, which contains chromium ions, wrapped in a flash lamp, with silver mirrors coated on the ends of the rod. A schematic of such a laser is shown in Figure 11.9.

This discussion covers just the basics of lasers. Simply put, you need three components: a pump source, a gain medium, and an optical cavity. There are many design options for lasers, including the choice of gain medium, which determines the wavelength of the output. As we will see in the next chapter, molecules also have discrete energy levels, so molecules with the right types of electronic states can also be used in the gain medium of a laser. Other choices for the gain medium include gases, crystals with selectively chosen atoms or ions, and even semiconductor junctions; the last of these is used to make a diode laser.

Lasers can be built to operate in a pulsed or continuous wave (CW) mode. The advantage of CW lasers is that the linewidth of the output light can be very narrow; thus, a CW laser approximates a monochromatic (one-color) light source. Some lasers can even be tuned to generate one of many colors. Other lasers are pulsed and, because of the time–energy uncertainty principle, these lasers produce light that covers a range of frequencies; the shorter the pulse, the broader the range. The choice of laser to use depends on the type of experiment to be performed.

## 11.3 Summary, and Where We Go Next

In this chapter, we have explored the fundamental nature of atoms, the very heart of chemistry itself. Unfortunately, we can only solve the simplest atomic system, even when making reasonable approximations. In the next chapter, we will discuss some of the ideas and procedures that can be used to analyze more complicated systems than the hydrogen atom and apply those ideas to the structure of molecules.

# PROBLEMS

**11.1** a) Calculate the expectation value of $r$ for an electron in the hydrogen $1s$ orbital. The total wavefunction is a product of the radial function $R_{1,0}$ from Table 11.1 and the spherical harmonic $Y_0^0$ from Table 10.1. (Note: Remember the necessary integral needs to be done in spherical coordinates.)

b) Calculate the most probable value of $r$ for the $1s$ orbital by considering the maximum of $\psi^*\psi$. Interpret your result.

c) Because of the spherical symmetry of the hydrogen atom, a better representation of the radial probability function is actually $\psi^*\psi r^2$. Plot this function and determine the maximum value of this function for the $1s$ orbital. Compare your results to parts a) and b).

**11.2** a) Show that the radial functions for $1s$ ($n = 1, l = 0$) and $2s$ ($n = 2, l = 0$) orbitals are orthogonal to each other. (Hint: Don't forget the factor of $r^2$ from the volume element.)

b) Are the radial functions for $1s$ ($n = 1, l = 0$) and $2p$ ($n = 2, l = 1$) orthogonal to each other? Why or why not?

c) Given that each atomic orbital must be orthogonal to every other atomic orbital, what other consideration should be taken into account to meet this requirement.

**11.3** a) The hydrogen atom is often described as being about 1Å (100 pm) in diameter. For the $1s$ orbital of hydrogen, calculate the probability of finding the electron within a distance of $r = 50$ pm from the nucleus.

b) One measure of the size of an atom is the distance from the nucleus that contains 90% of the probability of finding the electron. By this definition, determine the size of the $1s$ orbital of hydrogen.

c) Repeat the calculation of part b) for the $He^+$ ion and compare the results. Provide a physical explanation for any similarities or differences.

**11.4** The hydrogen atom is the only real, physical system for which we can explicitly write the wavefunctions, which we call atomic orbitals. We construct these functions by taking the spherical harmonics and the radial functions we discussed in the text. You will notice on careful inspection, however, that many of these functions are mathematically complex, meaning they contain the imaginary number $i$. For example, for the $2p$ orbitals, we write the following functions, indexed by their $m_l$ quantum numbers:

$$\psi_{2p_0} = \frac{1}{4\sqrt{2\pi}}\left(\frac{Z}{a_0}\right)^{5/2} re^{-Zr/2a_0}\cos\theta \qquad \psi_{2p_{\pm1}} = \frac{1}{8\sqrt{\pi}}\left(\frac{Z}{a_0}\right)^{5/2} re^{-Zr/2a_0}\sin\theta\; e^{\pm i\phi}$$

Because of the complex exponential, these functions can be a little hard to think about. However, we can make functions that are purely real by taking linear combinations of these complex functions. Recall that all the $2p$ orbitals are degenerate. It will also be helpful to recall our convention for the angular coordinates: $\theta$ is the tilt from the $z$ axis and $\phi$ is the azimuthal angle in the $x$–$y$ plane.

a) To begin, make plots of these three functions in the $x$–$z$ plane (meaning $\phi = 0$). Do this as a function only of $\theta$, taking $r = a_0$. You can ignore all the constants at the front of the function; they are there for normalization. Comment on similarities and differences between the three plots.

b) Now, construct linear combinations of $\Psi_{2p_1}$ and $\Psi_{2p_{-1}}$ to create two real functions. The Euler identities for the complex exponential will be very helpful here. Don't worry about normalizing the functions. Determine which combinations correspond to $\Psi_{2p_x}$ and $\Psi_{2p_y}$. To do that, you may want to take various slices across the functions at different values of $\phi$. What function do we use for $\Psi_{2p_z}$?

**11.5** The electron in a $Li^{2+}$ ion is prepared in the following state:

$$\Psi(r,\theta,\phi) = -\left(\frac{1}{3}\right)^{1/2}\Psi_{4p_x} + \frac{2}{3}i\Psi_{3p_y} - \left(\frac{2}{9}\right)^{1/2}\Psi_{1s}$$

This is a linear combination of the hydrogenic atomic orbitals.

a) If the energy of this system is measured, what value(s) will be found? If more than one value can be found, give the probability of measuring that value.

b) What is the average energy of this system?

**11.6** Different isotopes have slightly different atomic spectra. The ratio of isotopes can be used by astronomers to learn about the processes taking place at the interior of stars. Calculate the wavelengths for the $n = 3 \rightarrow n = 2$ and $n = 2 \rightarrow n = 1$ transitions for the $^3He^+$ and $^4He^+$ ions. (Hint: You cannot approximate the reduced mass as being equivalent to the electron mass in this problem.)

# Approximate Methods for Solving Real Problems, Electronic Structure of Molecules, and Electronic Spectroscopy

## 12.1 Approximation Methods

Thus far, we have worked with a few simple systems for which we could solve the Schrödinger equation exactly: free particle, particle in a box, rigid rotor, harmonic oscillator, and hydrogen atom. Other than a few variations on these systems (particle on a ring, particle on a sphere), these are the only systems that can be solved exactly. Unfortunately, that means that most physical situations that we actually care about are unsolvable. We've already seen this with the helium atom. We kind of waved our hands at the time in talking about atoms with more than one electron, but now we will get more specific on how to deal with this problem, as well as more complicated situations.

Before we begin, let's recall what the main tools of quantum mechanics are. We begin solving the Schrödinger equation by constructing a Hamiltonian operator, which represents the total energy of the system. Solving the Schrödinger equation then gives us the wavefunctions and energy states of the system. In a case that can't be solved analytically, we generally begin with the model system that most closely resembles the real system. We then have two options: we can make successively better approximations to the Hamiltonian and numerically solve for the energies and wavefunctions, or we can use the full Hamiltonian and make successive approximations to the wavefunctions that in turn improve the energies we determine. Both approaches have certain advantages and disadvantages, so the choice of which to use often depends on the specific problem to be solved. We'll use the He atom as our test case.

## 12.1.1 Perturbation Theory

The first approach to solving a problem we can't solve analytically, which involves making approximations to the Hamiltonian, is known as **perturbation theory**. We begin with the simplest Hamiltonian that we can actually solve. In the case of the He atom, that is everything except for the term that accounts for the interaction between the two electrons. We call this simplified Hamiltonian the **zero-order Hamiltonian**. By solving the Schrödinger equation with the simplified Hamiltonian, we can obtain **zero-order wavefunctions**, and their corresponding energies.

For the case of the He atom, the zero-order Hamiltonian is written

$$\hat{H}^{(0)} = -\frac{\hbar^2}{2\mu_e}\nabla_{e_1}^2 - \frac{\hbar^2}{2\mu_e}\nabla_{e_2}^2 - \frac{Ze^2}{4\pi\epsilon_0 r_1} - \frac{Ze^2}{4\pi\epsilon_0 r_2} = \hat{H}^{(0)}(1) + \hat{H}^{(0)}(2) \tag{12.1}$$

The nuclear charge, $Z$, will be 2 for He. Note that the two sets of terms are the same, just referring to electron 1 and electron 2. (If you compare to Eq. 11.13, you will see that one term is missing, the one for the electron–electron repulsion.) Because this Hamiltonian is written as the sum of two 1-electron Hamiltonians, the zero-order wavefunction is simply the product of two hydrogen $1s$ wavefunctions, one for each electron.

$$\psi_1^{(0)} = \psi_{1s}(1)\psi_{1s}(2) \tag{12.2}$$

Some explanation of the notation is in order here. The subscript 1 tells us this is the lowest energy wavefunction, and the superscript (0) tells us this is the zero-order approximation of that wavefunction. The Hamiltonian operator for electron 1 does nothing to the wavefunction for electron 2, and vice-versa. It is therefore fairly easy to show that the zero-order energy is simply the sum of two 1-electron energies. In this case, the nuclear charge is 2, so the total ground-state energy (from Eq. 11.12) is

$$E_1^{(0)} = \frac{-e^2}{\pi\epsilon_0 a_0} \tag{12.3}$$

We know this is not the correct final answer (the energy is much too low) because we have ignored the repulsion between the electrons, but it's a place to start.

Now we have to deal with the source of the difficulty, the electron–electron repulsion. This is termed the **perturbation**, which we write as

$$\hat{H}^{(1)} = \frac{e^2}{4\pi\epsilon_0 r_{12}} \tag{12.4}$$

(This is the missing term from Eq. 11.13.) The superscript (1) tells us this is the first correction to the Hamiltonian. We will skip the full derivation of the next result, but to obtain the first-order correction to the energy, we need to evaluate the following integral

$$E_1^{(1)} = \int \psi_1^{(0)*} \hat{H}^{(1)} \psi_1^{(0)} d\tau \tag{12.5}$$

This is actually a six-dimensional integral, because we have two electrons. Evaluation gives us

$$E_1^{(1)} = 1.25 \frac{e^2}{4\pi\epsilon_0 a_0}$$

Putting this with the zero-order energy gives us a first-order energy of

$$E_1 \approx E_1^{(0)} + E_1^{(1)} = -2.75 \frac{e^2}{4\pi\epsilon_0 a_0}$$

You might be wondering how well this relation does. The experimental value for the ground state energy of He is $-1.264 \times 10^{-17}$ J. The zero-order energy was way off, $-1.7439 \times 10^{-17}$ J, which is too low by 38%. Our first-order corrected energy turns out to be $-1.199 \times 10^{-17}$ J, correct to about 5%.

To go further with this, we need to make adjustments to the wavefunction. We do this by including excited states, which for He would have electronic configurations of $1s^1 2s^1$, $2s^2$ and so forth. The first-order wavefunction correction, which we won't derive here, is written as

$$\psi_1^{(1)} = \sum_{k=2}^{\infty} \frac{\int \psi_k^{(0)*} \hat{H}^{(1)} \psi_k^{(0)} d\tau}{E_1^{(0)} - E_k^{(0)}} \psi_k^{(0)} \tag{12.6}$$

where the sum is over zero-order excited states, like the ones just mentioned. Note that the sum starts with the first excited state ($k = 2$), since starting at the ground state would cause the denominator to be zero. We improve our approximation of the wavefunction by adding this correction to the zero-order wavefunction (Eq. 12.2).

The second-order energy correction is written as

$$E_1^{(2)} = \sum_{k=2}^{\infty} \frac{\left[\int \psi_k^{(0)*} \hat{H}^{(1)} \psi_k^{(0)} d\tau\right]^2}{E_1^{(0)} - E_k^{(0)}} \tag{12.7}$$

Note that the denominator in both Eqs. 12.6 and 12.7 will get larger as $k$ increases, meaning the correction gets smaller as we go to higher and higher excited states. In other words, we probably only need to worry about the first few excited states in the sum, which simplifies things considerably. Including the second-order correction to the energy brings our result to within 3.5% of the experimental value. The first-order wavefunction ends up being about 67% $1s^2$ and 30% $1s^1 2s^1$, with much smaller contributions from a few other states. Remember, we said in the last chapter that the lowest energy atomic orbital of He was not the same as a hydrogen $1s$ orbital. If we so desire, we can go to successively higher corrections to the wavefunctions and the energy.

As you can see, doing a perturbation theory calculation involves lots of integrals and lots of sums. This can make these calculations difficult, but modern computers make them much more practical. One of the advantages of perturbation theory is that it can be used to calculate excited states of atoms and molecules in addition to the ground electronic state. This is particularly useful for calculations of spectroscopic transitions, where we represent the light–matter interaction as a perturbation on the system. (We alluded to this approach back in Section 9.2.2.)

## 12.1.2 Variational Theorem

The second approach is to start with the best Hamiltonian we can but begin with a simple wavefunction. This is called a **trial wavefunction** and needs to include one or more adjustable parameters. This trial wavefunction will not be an eigenfunction of the full Hamiltonian, but we can calculate an expectation value of the energy for this wavefunction by evaluating

$$\langle E \rangle = \frac{\int \psi_{trial}^* \hat{H} \psi_{trial} d\tau}{\int \psi_{trial}^* \psi_{trial} d\tau} \tag{12.8}$$

The variational theorem states that the expectation value of the energy for this trial function is greater than or equal to the correct ground-state energy.

$$\frac{\int \psi_{trial}^* \hat{H} \psi_{trial} d\tau}{\int \psi_{trial}^* \psi_{trial} d\tau} = E_{trial} \geqslant E_1 \tag{12.9}$$

The foundation of the variational approach is the idea that the correct wavefunction will have the lowest possible energy; any wavefunction that is incorrect to any degree will have a higher energy than the correct energy. We then try to minimize the energy by varying the adjustable parameter to get the best possible value—that is, the lowest value—for the energy.

The proof of the variational theorem is one of the most elegant applications of quantum mechanics, so it's worth taking a little time to go through it. The first thing we have to do is assume that the correct Hamiltonian operator has a set of eigenfunctions, even though we don't know what those eigenfunctions are. Recall from our discussion in Section 8.3.3 that we can always express any wavefunction as a superposition, or linear combination, of a set of eigenfunctions. We therefore express our trial function as a linear combination of these (unknown) eigenfunctions of the fully correct Hamiltonian.

$$\psi_{trial} = \sum_i c_i \phi_i \tag{12.10}$$

Recall that the eigenfunctions of the Hamiltonian operator form a complete, orthonormal set of functions. By inserting the sum from Eq. 12.10 into Eq. 12.9, we can write

$$E_{trial} = \frac{\int \sum_i (c_i \phi_i)^* \hat{H} \sum_j c_j \phi_j d\tau}{\int \sum_i (c_i \phi_i)^* \sum_j c_j \phi_j d\tau}$$

Let's first look at the denominator of this expression. Because an integral of a sum is equal to a sum of integrals, we can pull the summations outside the integral and write

$$\int \sum_i (c_i \phi_i)^* \sum_j c_j \phi_j d\tau = \sum_i \sum_j c_i^* c_j \int \phi_i^* \phi_j d\tau$$

Recall that the eigenfunctions of the Hamiltonian operator are orthogonal to each other. We can also assume that they have been properly normalized. Thus each integral in the double sum is either 1 or 0; 1 if the two functions are the same, or $i = j$, and 0 if they are different, or $i \neq j$. (See Eq. 8.37.) This reduces the double sum to a single sum and we can write

$$\int \sum_i (c_i \phi_i)^* \sum_j c_j \phi_j d\tau = \sum_i |c_i|^2 \tag{12.11}$$

If the trial function has been normalized, this sum will equal 1, but we don't actually have to make that assumption.

Now, let's turn our attention to the numerator. We again pull the summations outside the integral, which lets us write

$$\int \sum_i (c_i \phi_i)^* \hat{H} \sum_j c_j \phi_j d\tau = \sum_i \sum_j c_i^* c_j \int \phi_i^* \hat{H} \phi_j d\tau$$

Because we are using the eigenfunctions of the Hamiltonian, for each function we can write

$$\hat{H} \phi_j = E_j \phi_j \tag{12.12}$$

Making this substitution lets us write

$$\int \sum_i (c_i \phi_i)^* \hat{H} \sum_j c_j \phi_j d\tau = \sum_i \sum_j c_i^* c_j E_j \int \phi_i^* \phi_j d\tau$$

Again, the integrals are all either 1 or 0, so we can reduce the double sum to a single sum because the only nonzero terms are the ones where $i = j$.

$$\int \sum_i (c_i \phi_i)^* \hat{H} \sum_j c_j \phi_j d\tau = \sum_i |c_i|^2 E_i \tag{12.13}$$

We can then write the expectation value of the energy for our trial function as Eq. 12.13 over Eq. 12.11, giving us

$$E_{\text{trial}} = \frac{\sum_i |c_i|^2 E_i}{\sum_i |c_i|^2} \tag{12.14}$$

To move to the completion of our proof, we make the very reasonable statement that the energy of every allowed state is greater than or equal to the lowest possible energy.

$$E_i \geq E_1$$

For any term in the sum, $|c_i|^2$ is a real, positive number, so we can multiply both sides of the inequality by this value without changing the direction of the inequality.

$$|c_i|^2 E_i \geq |c_i|^2 E_1$$

Because this is true for all the states, we can sum over all the states and still maintain the same inequality. Doing so lets us write

$$\sum_i |c_i|^2 E_i \geq \sum_i |c_i|^2 E_1 = E_1 \sum_i |c_i|^2$$

We can remove $E_1$ from the sum on the right, since it is the same for all terms in the sum. If we then divide by the sum of coefficients on the right and compare to Eq. 12.14, we have

$$\frac{\sum_i |c_i|^2 E_i}{\sum_i |c_i|^2} = E_{trial} \geq E_1 \tag{12.15}$$

We have now proven the variational theorem. The energy of our trial function can never be less than the true energy of the lowest state of the system. We can therefore judge one trial function against another by comparing these energies; the best trial function is the one with the lowest energy.

Let's demonstrate how this works for the He atom. This time, we use the full Hamiltonian

$$\hat{H} = -\frac{\hbar^2}{2\mu_e}\nabla^2_{e_1} - \frac{\hbar^2}{2\mu_e}\nabla^2_{e_2} - \frac{Ze^2}{4\pi\epsilon_0 r_1} - \frac{Ze^2}{4\pi\epsilon_0 r_2} + \frac{e^2}{4\pi\epsilon_0 r_{12}} \tag{12.16}$$

Note that this Hamiltonian operator is the sum of Eqs. 12.1 and 12.4 (and the same as Eq. 11.13). Now we need to choose a trial wavefunction; let's start with a product of two hydrogenic $1s$ orbitals. One parameter that we could adjust is the nuclear charge, based on the idea that the electrons will partially screen the nucleus from each other. We write the trial wavefunction as

$$\Psi_{trial} = A e^{-Z_{eff}r_1/a_0} e^{-Z_{eff}r_2/a_0} \tag{12.17}$$

where $A$ is the normalization constant. This is a product of two $1s$ wavefunctions, but with the effective nuclear charge as the variable parameter. Evaluating the trial energy gives us

$$E_{trial} = \left( Z^2_{eff} - 2ZZ_{eff} + \frac{5}{8}Z_{eff} \right)\frac{e^2}{a_0} \tag{12.18}$$

where $Z$ is the full nuclear charge, which in the case of He is 2. To determine the best value of $Z_{eff}$, we take the derivative of Eq. 12.18 with respect to $Z_{eff}$, set that equation to zero, and solve for $Z_{eff}$. Doing so gives us $Z_{eff} = 1.69$, which is less than 2. This makes sense due to partial screening of the nucleus by the second electron. After substituting this value for $Z_{eff}$ back in to Eq. 12.18, the determined energy is $-1.242 \times 10^{-17}$ J, which is correct to 1.9%. Not bad for a simple trial function.

Note that the variational approach did much better at determining the energy than perturbation theory on the first try. But this approach has its limitations. Unlike perturbation theory, where we can continue to make higher order corrections, this is as good as we can do with this trial function. We also don't get a better sense of what the actual wavefunction should be, nor do we get the energies of excited electronic states. If all we care about is the ground-state energy, however, these are not serious limitations. One caution in using the variational approach is that the choice of the trial wavefunction is critical; if we choose a poor trial function, we can get an energy that is significantly higher than the true ground state energy with no way to get a better answer other than changing the function.

## 12.1.3 Linear Variational Theory

Remember that any function can be written as a linear combination of a set of basis functions. If we have a system that is similar to one we have already solved, we can use those wavefunctions as our basis set for the real system. The unknown function can be written as

$$\psi_{trial} = c_1\phi_1 + c_2\phi_2 + \ldots = \sum_{i=1}^{n} c_1\phi_1 \qquad (12.19)$$

Note that these functions do not have to be the correct eigenfunctions for the full Hamiltonian operator; if we knew what those were, we would just use the correct ground–state wavefunction and we'd be done. In this approach, the parameters to be varied are the various coefficients, which represent the contributions of the various basis functions to the trial wavefunction. By properly varying these coefficients, we should arrive at a function that closely approximates the true function. Computing the energy of that trial function will be a good measure of the energy of the real system. This is actually the approach we alluded to when we talked about atomic orbitals in the last chapter. Since the atomic system is very similar to a hydrogen atom, we use the hydrogenic orbitals as our set of functions. The trial function is known as a **linear combination of atomic orbitals** (LCAO). (Hybrid orbitals such as $sp^3$ and $sp^2$ are examples of just this type of linear combination.) With modern computers, the optimal values of the various coefficients can be determined fairly quickly.

The linear variational approach is one of the most common methods used in quantum chemistry calculations, so we will quickly go through the basic ideas of how this works. Let's consider a simple case, where we only use two terms in our trial wavefunction.

$$\psi_{trial} = c_1\phi_1 + c_2\phi_2$$

We then write for the trial energy

$$\frac{\int (c_1\phi_1 + c_2\phi_2)^* \hat{H}(c_1\phi_1 + c_2\phi_2)dx}{\int (c_1\phi_1 + c_2\phi_2)^* (c_1\phi_1 + c_2\phi_2)dx} = E_{trial} \geq E_1$$

We need to expand the integrals, which leads to a sum of integrals in both the numerator and the denominator. We can simplify our notation if we define the following quantities:

$$H_{ij} \equiv \int \phi_i^* \hat{H}\phi_j dx$$
$$\qquad (12.20)$$
$$S_{ij} \equiv \int \phi_i^* \phi_j dx$$

The first type of integral is an energy integral. The second type is known as an overlap integral. (Note that if the basis functions are orthonormal, which they don't have to be, then $S_{ij} = \delta_{ij}$, which simplifies things considerably.) We can now write our expanded energy expression as

$$\frac{c_1^2 H_{11} + 2c_1 c_2 H_{12} + c_2^2 H_{22}}{c_1^2 S_{11} + 2c_1 c_2 S_{12} + c_2^2 S_{22}} = E_{trial} \geq E_1$$

where we have used a property of the Hamiltonian that $H_{21} = H_{12}$. (We won't prove this property, so you can just accept it for now.) We have also assumed that the coefficients are real.

Our task now is to vary the coefficients $c_1$ and $c_2$ to minimize the trial energy. We have to work on both coefficients simultaneously to do this. Let's move the denominator to the right-hand side and write

$$c_1^2 H_{11} + 2c_1 c_2 H_{12} + c_2^2 H_{22} = E_{trial}(c_1^2 S_{11} + 2c_1 c_2 S_{12} + c_2^2 S_{22})$$

We now take the derivative of this expression with respect to $c_1$ and $c_2$.

$$2c_1 H_{11} + 2c_2 H_{12} = \frac{\partial E_{trial}}{\partial c_1}(c_1^2 S_{11} + 2c_1 c_2 S_{12} + c_2^2 S_{22}) + E_{trial}(2c_1 S_{11} + 2c_2 S_{12})$$

$$2c_1 H_{12} + 2c_2 H_{22} = \frac{\partial E_{trial}}{\partial c_2}(c_1^2 S_{11} + 2c_1 c_2 S_{12} + c_2^2 S_{22}) + E_{trial}(2c_1 S_{12} + 2c_2 S_{22})$$

The energy will be minimized when $\frac{\partial E_{trial}}{\partial c_1} = 0$ and $\frac{\partial E_{trial}}{\partial c_2} = 0$. This gives us two simultaneous equations to solve:

$$(H_{11} - ES_{11})c_1 + (H_{12} - ES_{12})c_2 = 0$$

$$(H_{21} - ES_{21})c_1 + (H_{22} - ES_{22})c_2 = 0$$

(For simplicity of notation, we are now dropping the "trial" subscript from $E$.)

We have collected terms based on the coefficients, since that is what we can vary. The techniques of linear algebra are applicable to this problem, meaning we need to evaluate the determinant

$$\begin{vmatrix} H_{11} - ES_{11} & H_{12} - ES_{12} \\ H_{12} - ES_{12} & H_{22} - ES_{22} \end{vmatrix} = 0$$

This is known as a **secular determinant**, and evaluating it will give two possible answers for the energy. The one we are interested in is the lower of the two, since we are trying to find the ground-state energy. Once we know the value of the energy, we can determine the values of the coefficients that correspond to our best trial ground-state wavefunction.

We have set up the example case with only two terms in our trial wavefunction. Of course, a better estimate of the ground-state energy will be determined if more terms are used. Instead of a 2 X 2 secular determinant, we will have a $n$ X $n$ determinant of the form

$$\begin{vmatrix} H_{11} - ES_{11} & H_{12} - ES_{12} & \cdots & H_{1n} - ES_{1n} \\ H_{21} - ES_{21} & H_{22} - ES_{22} & \cdots & H_{2n} - ES_{2n} \\ \cdots & \cdots & \cdots & \cdots \\ H_{n1} - ES_{n1} & H_{n2} - ES_{n2} & \cdots & H_{nn} - ES_{nn} \end{vmatrix} = 0 \qquad (12.21)$$

where $n$ is the number of functions in the sum of Eq 12.19. Note that evaluating this determinant will give $n$ possible roots for $E$. Again, we are interested in the lowest value for the energy. The other values of $E$ correspond to excited states, but they become less accurate the higher you go.

To obtain good results, hundreds or thousands of functions need to be used in a linear variational calculation. Computers can handle these types of operations very well and the variational approach is the basis for much of modern computational chemistry.

## 12.2 The Structure of Molecules

Now that we have discussed the structure of atoms, as well as ways to approximate solutions to more complicated problems, let's move on to molecules. In general chemistry, you learned about various models for chemical bonding, such as Lewis dot structures and valence shell electron pair repulsion (VSEPR) theory. We will not fully review these topics, so you should brush up on your own if necessary. These models help us to understand a great deal about bonding in molecules, however they both have certain deficiencies. Here we will develop a quantum-mechanical model of chemical bonding. Before beginning, let's establish some foundational ideals. First, we can (in principle) write down a Hamiltonian operator for our molecule. This operator needs to account for all the motions and interactions of the nuclei and the electrons that make up our molecule. This Hamiltonian operator will then have eigenfunctions, which are molecular wavefunctions. Each of those molecular wavefunctions will have a corresponding energy associated with it. So none of the basic ideas have changed, but how we go after them needs to change for even the simplest molecules. We'll consider the simplest possible molecule next.

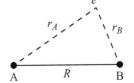

### 12.2.1 The Hydrogen Molecular Ion

The simplest possible molecule is the hydrogen molecular ion, $H_2^+$, shown in Figure 12.1. This molecule consists of two hydrogen nuclei (protons) and a single electron. Let's construct the Hamiltonian for this system.

$$\hat{H} = -\frac{\hbar^2}{2m_p}\nabla_A^2 - \frac{\hbar^2}{2m_p}\nabla_B^2 - \frac{\hbar^2}{2m_e}\nabla_e^2 - \frac{e^2}{4\pi\epsilon_0 r_A} - \frac{e^2}{4\pi\epsilon_0 r_B} + \frac{e^2}{4\pi\epsilon_0 R} \quad (12.22)$$

**FIGURE 12.1.** Schematic of the hydrogen molecular ion with two protons (black circle) and one electron ($e^-$).

We will label the nuclei as $A$ and $B$. The first two terms account for the kinetic energy of the two nuclei and the third term is the kinetic energy of the electron. We then have three Coulombic potential terms, one for the interaction with the electron and nucleus $A$, where $r_A$ is the distance between them. Likewise, $r_B$ is the distance between the electron and nucleus $B$. $R$ is the internuclear distance, so the last term accounts for the repulsion of the two nuclei. Note the signs on the potential terms; the interaction between an electron and a proton is attractive and lowers the potential energy, whereas the interaction between the two protons is repulsive and increases the potential energy. As we did with the hydrogen atom, we will take our zero of energy as the completely dissociated molecule, where the protons and electron are infinitely far apart from each other.

This Hamiltonian looks very similar to the one for the helium atom we considered in Section 11.1.5 and above in Sections 12.1.1 and 12.1.2. Recall that we couldn't solve the Schrödinger equation for that Hamiltonian, and we can't solve it for this situation either. (In physics language, this is a three-body problem, which does not have an analytical solution.) However, we can greatly simplify this new situation by making a well-justified approximation. Consider the masses of the proton and the electron. A proton is about 2,000 times heavier than an electron, so the electron can respond very quickly to any changes in the nuclear positions; electrons move faster than protons. We will therefore fix the internuclear distance and solve for the motion of the electron. To be complete, we have to do this at all values of $R$, but the problem then becomes solvable at each $R$ value. This separation of the nuclear and electronic motion is known as the **Born–Oppenheimer approximation**. Under the Born–Oppenheimer approximation, our Hamiltonian is

$$\hat{H}_R = -\frac{\hbar^2}{2m_e}\nabla_e^2 - \frac{e^2}{4\pi\epsilon_0 r_A} - \frac{e^2}{4\pi\epsilon_0 r_B} + \frac{e^2}{4\pi\epsilon_0 R} \tag{12.23}$$

The subscript $R$ reminds us that the nuclear separation is a parameter of the operator, not a variable.

Now, let's consider the case where the internuclear separation $R$ is large. In this case, the electron will be localized on one nucleus or the other, and we effectively have a hydrogen atom and a bare proton. The electron in its ground state is well described by $\phi_{1s}$, the $1s$ orbital of hydrogen. What happens as the nuclei come closer together? Now the electron can interact with both nuclei. Let's take the atomic orbitals as our basis set for describing this situation. Because of the wave nature of the electron, we have to treat this as a combination of the atomic orbitals, one from each nucleus. In other words, we don't know which nucleus the electron is closest to, so we have to allow for the possibility that it is close to either one. To proceed similar to our variational approach, the trial molecular wavefunction is written as an LCAO.

$$\psi_\pm = N(\phi_{1s_A} \pm \phi_{1s_B}) \tag{11.24}$$

The subscripts indicate nucleus $A$ and nucleus $B$, respectively. The $N$ is a normalization constant.

There are two ways to add these terms, with a + or a − sign, and we need to consider both; we can't really tell the nuclei apart, so we don't know which is $A$ and which is $B$. Each of these two possibilities is called a **molecular orbital**. The wavefunction has to be the same regardless of our assignment, which is why we have equal contributions for the wavefunction centered on nucleus $A$ and on nucleus $B$. Now, we ask the question; what happens to the energy of the molecular orbitals compared to the atomic orbitals? In other words, we want to determine the expectation value of the energy of the molecular orbitals compared to that of a separate atomic $1s$ orbital.

We first consider the + wavefunction (where the orbitals are added together) and determine its energy.

$$E_+ = \frac{\int \psi_+^* \hat{H}_R \psi_+ \, d\tau}{\int \psi_+^* \psi_+ \, d\tau} \tag{12.25}$$

Let's look at the denominator of this expression. When we expand it out, what we have is

$$\int \psi_+^* \psi_+ \, d\tau = \int \phi_{1s_A}^* \phi_{1s_A} \, d\tau + \int \phi_{1s_B}^* \phi_{1s_B} \, d\tau + 2\int \phi_{1s_A}^* \phi_{1s_B} \, d\tau$$

Recall that the atomic orbitals are themselves normalized, so the first two integrals are each 1. The last integral accounts for the **overlap** between the two atomic orbitals, and we'll call it $S_{AB}$. Because the orbitals are on different atoms, they are not orthonormal, and $S_{AB} \neq 0$. This gives us

$$\int \psi_+^* \psi_+ \, d\tau = 2 + 2S_{AB}$$

Note that as $R$ decreases to zero, the two orbitals effectively become the same, so the overlap increases to a maximum value of 1.

In a similar fashion, we can write the numerator as

$$\int \psi_+^* \hat{H}_R \psi_+ d\tau = \int \phi_{1s_A}^* \hat{H}_R \phi_{1s_A} d\tau + \int \phi_{1s_B}^* \hat{H}_R \phi_{1s_B} d\tau + 2 \int \phi_{1s_A}^* \hat{H}_R \phi_{1s_B} d\tau$$

We will symbolically represent each integral by the notation

$$H_{ij} = \int \phi_i^* \hat{H}_R \phi_j d\tau$$

Because the two atomic orbitals are really the same mathematical function, just centered on separate nuclei, $H_{AA} = H_{BB}$, and we can write

$$E_+ = \frac{2H_{AA} + 2H_{AB}}{2 + 2S_{AB}} = \frac{H_{AA} + H_{AB}}{1 + S_{AB}} \tag{12.26}$$

Let's look at $H_{AA}$ and $H_{AB}$. The first two terms of $\hat{H}_R$ are identical to the Hamiltonian for the hydrogen atom. The last term doesn't depend on any electronic coordinates, so we can write

$$H_{AA} = E_{1s} - J + \frac{e^2}{4\pi\epsilon_o R} \tag{12.27}$$

where

$$J = \int \phi_{H1s_A}^* \left( \frac{e^2}{4\pi\epsilon_0 r_B} \right) \phi_{H1s_A} d\tau \tag{12.28}$$

The $J$ integral accounts for interactions between one nucleus and the electron density on the other nucleus. We can think of the quantity $H_{AA}$ as the energy of a hydrogen atom interacting with a bare proton a distance $R$ away. Note that in the limit that $R$ becomes very large, the last two terms in Eq. 12.27 approach zero and the energy approaches that of a hydrogen $1s$ atom. We also write

$$H_{AB} = E_{1s} S_{AB} - K + \frac{e^2}{4\pi\epsilon_o R} S_{AB} \tag{12.29}$$

where

$$K = \int \phi_{H1s_B}^* \left( \frac{e^2}{4\pi\epsilon_0 r_B} \right) \phi_{H1s_A} d\tau \tag{12.30}$$

The $K$ integral accounts for the interference between the two atomic orbitals; you can think of it as the tendency of the electron to exchange position between the two nuclei. As $R$ gets large, the entire quantity $H_{AB}$ approaches zero. In that limit, by Eq. 12.16, $E_+ = H_{AA} = E_{1s}$.

Let's put it all together.

$$E_+ = \left( E_{1s} + \frac{e^2}{4\pi\epsilon_0 R} \right) - \left( \frac{J + K}{1 + S_{AB}} \right) = H_{AA} + J - \left( \frac{J + K}{1 + S_{AB}} \right)$$

What we really care about is the difference in energy between $E_+$ and $H_{AA}$, the energy when the proton is infinitely far away from the hydrogen atom. We will call this difference $\Delta E_+$

$$\Delta E_+ = E_+ - H_{AA} = \frac{-K + S_{AB} J}{1 + S_{AB}} \tag{12.31}$$

Both $J$ and $K$ are positive quantities and $S_{AB}$ is less than 1, so we can see that the tendency is for $\Delta E_+$ to be negative. This means that the energy of the $H_2^+$ ion is less than that of a separate H atom and $H^+$ ion when we add the two wavefunctions together in our trial function.

What about the other orbital? It would be good practice to work through the algebra, but we'll jump to the final answers

$$E_- = \left( E_{1s} + \frac{e^2}{4\pi\epsilon_0 R} \right) - \left( \frac{J - K}{1 - S_{AB}} \right)$$

$$\Delta E_- = E_- - H_{AA} = \frac{K - S_{AB}J}{1 - S_{AB}} \tag{12.32}$$

Again, because $J$ and $K$ are positive quantities and $S_{AB}$ is less than 1, the tendency is for $\Delta E_-$ to be positive. This means that the energy of the $H_2^+$ is greater than that of a separate H atom and $H^+$ ion when we subtract the two wavefunctions in our trial function.

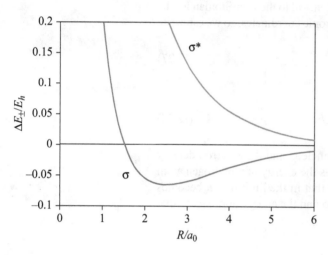

**FIGURE 12.2.** Plots of the energy difference for the bonding and antibonding orbitals with internuclear separation. Distance is in units of $a_0$, the Bohr radius. Energy is in units of hartrees (1 hartree = 27.2 eV = 2625 kJ mol$^{-1}$).

Figure 12.2 shows both $\Delta E_+$ and $\Delta E_-$, which represent the difference in energy of the $H_2^+$ molecule from a separate H atom and bare proton, as functions of $R$. Over a certain region, adding the two atomic orbitals together leads to a lowering of the energy, and subtracting the two leads to an increase of the energy. For this reason, we refer to the first (using the + sign in Eq. 12.24) as a **bonding** orbital and the second (using the − sign in Eq. 12.24) as an **antibonding** orbital. Notice that there is a well in the bonding state, meaning that the molecule is stable. Note also that as the nuclei get closer together, the repulsion term takes over and the energy increases.

This type of bonding orbital is known as a σ orbital because it has similar characteristics to s orbitals. A notation that is often used is to put a * on an antibonding orbital, so the antibonding orbital is symbolized as σ*. It should be noted that the solutions we have shown in Figure 12.2 are only approximations to the correct results for the $H_2^+$ molecule; to get more accurate results would require a more sophisticated trial wavefunction than we have used here. The general features, however, are correct and allow us to move on in our discussion.

This is the only molecule that we can even come close to solving directly, with the caveat of the Born–Oppenheimer approximation, but it does give us a way to discuss the structure and stability of molecules generally. Again, the stability has to do with the balance of kinetic and potential energy. As the nuclei come closer together, the electron can delocalize over two nuclei instead of one. Recall that spreading out where the electron can be lowers the kinetic energy. The potential energy is also lowered because the electron can interact with both nuclei, and the electron shields the two nuclei from each other.

You can also think of this in a wave picture, as shown in Figure 12.3. In the bonding orbital, the two atomic orbitals are added together in phase. Constructive interference leads to increased electron density between the nuclei. What about the antibonding orbital? Note that the atomic orbitals are still added together, but out of phase. This leads to destructive interference and less electron density between the nuclei. In fact, there is a node at the

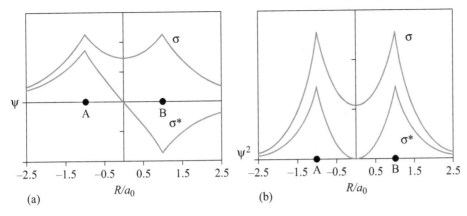

FIGURE 12.3. Plots of a) wavefunctions and b) wavefunctions squared for the bonding and antibonding orbitals of $H_2^+$. Note the node running between the nuclei in the antibonding case.

center of the molecule, just like we had nodes in higher energy wavefunctions for all our other systems. The electron is forced away from the center of the molecule, so its position is somewhat more restricted than in the bonding state and it cannot effectively interact with both nuclei. Also, because the electron is prohibited from being between the two nuclei, the positive charges are not screened from each other.

One other thing to note is that the total number of orbitals is always conserved. We started with two atomic $1s$ orbitals, and we have two molecular orbitals, one bonding and one antibonding ($\sigma$ and $\sigma^*$). This will always be the case; we must always have the same number of molecular orbitals as we have total atomic orbitals in our original trial function.

## 12.2.2 Molecular Orbital Theory

The picture we have developed for the hydrogen molecular ion and its molecular orbitals provides a basis for describing molecules in general. The approximation we are using is to construct a molecular orbital as an LCAO. Remember, however, that this is only a model and involves a certain degree of approximation, but it works quite well. The real molecule has real molecular orbitals, but we don't have the mathematical tools to directly calculate what they are. In the language of perturbation theory, we are treating each electron independently, and handling the interactions between them as a perturbation. In the language of linear variational theory, we are using hydrogenic atomic orbitals as our basis functions to approximate the correct molecular wavefunction.

All the rules of how electrons behave still apply to molecular orbitals. As we did with atomic orbitals, we put the electrons in the molecular orbitals so that they pair up, with a maximum of two electrons (one spin-up, the other spin-down) per molecular orbital. If multiple molecular orbitals are present at the same energy (they are degenerate), we first put each additional electron in a separate orbital until they are all half-filled, and only start pairing them up once all the molecular orbitals are half-filled.

Let's consider diatomic hydrogen, as shown in Figure 12.4a. We have two $1s$ electrons from the two atoms. These two atomic orbitals combine to create a $\sigma$ bonding orbital and a $\sigma^*$ antibonding orbital. The two electrons both go into the $\sigma$ molecular orbital. The bonding orbital is at lower energy than the individual atomic orbitals, so the molecule is stable, more stable in fact that the separated atoms. (If you are worried about why one of

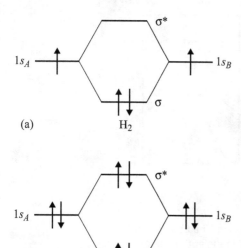

(a)       H₂

(b)       He₂

**FIGURE 12.4.** Molecular orbital diagrams for a) $H_2$ and b) $He_2$.

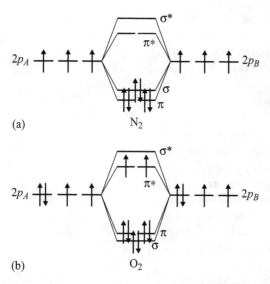

(a)       N₂

(b)       O₂

**FIGURE 12.5.** Molecular orbital diagrams for a) $N_2$ and b) $O_2$. Note that there are three degenerate $p$ orbitals two degenerate $\pi$ and $\pi^*$ orbitals.

the electrons changes its spin from up to down, think of it this way: the separate atoms are independent of each other and it's not until the two electrons are in the same orbital that the Pauli exclusion principle applies and their spins have to be different.)

What about diatomic helium, shown in Figure 12.4b? Now each atomic orbital brings two electrons instead of one, so we have four total electrons. This means we have two bonding electrons and two antibonding electrons. Note that the difference in energy between the antibonding orbital and the atomic orbitals is greater than that between the atomic orbitals and the bonding orbital. Thus, forming the bond leads to a net increase in energy; it is less favorable to form the bond than for the atoms to remain unbonded. This is why we don't see diatomic helium molecules.

Now, let's consider the nitrogen molecule. We have five valence electrons from each N atom (two electrons in the $2s$ and three in the $2p$ orbitals). The $2s$ orbitals are lower in energy, so we mainly concern ourselves with the $2p$ orbitals. The mixture of the six $p$ orbitals leads to six molecular orbitals, as shown in the Figure 12.5a. When two $p$ orbitals overlap end on, that forms a $\sigma$-type orbital. When they overlap above and below the bond axis, this is called a $\pi$-type orbital, and there are two of them, each orthogonal to the other. Placing the six valence $p$ electrons in the molecular orbitals leads to a filled $\sigma$ orbital, and two filled $\pi$ orbitals. The net bond order is 3 (6 bonding minus 0 antibonding, divided by 2). Now what about the oxygen molecule, shown in Figure 12.5b? The addition of two more $p$ electrons leads to two half-filled $\pi^*$ orbitals. Now the net bond order is 2 (6 bonding minus 2 antibonding, divided by 2). This approach also predicts that $O_2$ is paramagnetic because of the unpaired electrons in the $\pi$ antibonding orbitals. Other models, such as VSEPR and Lewis structures, do not make this prediction.

The simple $\sigma$- and $\pi$-type molecular orbitals help us to talk about bonding in molecules with more than two atoms. It must be remembered, however, that polyatomic molecules don't really have $\sigma$ and $\pi$ molecular orbitals. The actual orbitals spread out over the entire molecule. Let's consider a small molecule like $H_2O$. A simple picture would say that there are two $\sigma$ bonds, between the O atom and each H atom, with two lone pairs of electrons. We might even talk about hybridization of the $s$ and $p$ atomic orbitals of oxygen. These approaches are all different types of **localized bonding models**.

A full molecular orbital calculation, however, presents a somewhat different picture. In reality, the molecular orbitals are best treated as being **delocalized** across the whole molecule. The molecular orbitals of $H_2O$ are depicted in Figure 12.6. (The labels $a_1$, $b_1$, and so on reflect the symmetry of the molecule and the orbital. We won't cover the formalism for assigning those labels, which requires a treatment of group theory.) The first two are clearly bonding orbitals. In fact, the first orbital looks somewhat like an $s$ orbital that covers the entire molecule. Note that this first orbital has no nodes. The node of the second orbital does not cut across any of the bonds, so it is still a bonding orbital.

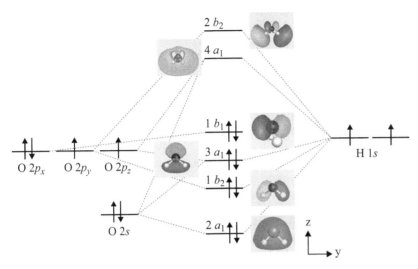

**FIGURE 12.6.** Molecular orbitals of $H_2O$. The labels correspond to the number and types of nodes. The lowest energy orbital, not shown, is the 1s orbital of O. The 2 $a_1$ and 1 $b_2$ orbitals clearly have bonding character. The 3 $a_1$ and 1 $b_1$ orbitals are nonbonding and correspond to the lone pairs. Note that the nodes in the unoccupied 4 $a_1$ and 2 $b_2$ orbitals have nodes that run through the bonds.

The third and fourth orbitals are mostly nonbonding; these are the "lone pairs". Orbital number four, in fact, is mostly the $p$ orbital on the oxygen that is out of plane of the molecule. The fifth orbital is the first unoccupied antibonding orbital. The sixth orbital is also antibonding. Notice that there tend to be more nodes, or regions of zero electron density, as the energy of the orbital increases.

The shapes of these orbitals look very different from the standard Lewis dot model of $H_2O$. In particular, the idea of a "lone pair" of electrons doesn't exactly fit with the delocalized molecular orbital picture. For larger molecules, the molecular orbitals will look even more complicated, and they are often located in certain parts of the molecule. For example, in $CO_2$, two of the "lone pair" orbitals are localized on the oxygen atoms and are actually lower in energy than the bonding orbitals that do spread out more across the whole molecule.

Our treatment of molecular orbital theory has been largely qualitative, but it has revealed some important ideas. Molecular orbitals are important for a variety of reasons. First, they give us a sense of where the electron density is located in a molecule. In molecules with many electrons, the highest occupied molecular orbital (HOMO) may have significant density in one or a few particular regions of the molecule. This may dramatically affect the reactivity of the molecule and give us some sense of the detailed mechanisms of a particular reaction. In general, the HOMO is the most important molecular orbital. The next most important is the lowest unoccupied molecular orbital (LUMO). These two orbitals are commonly called the **frontier orbitals**. The difference in energy between the HOMO and LUMO tells us the lowest energy transition that can take place in that molecule. If the LUMO has significant antibonding character along a particular bond, that can help us predict which bond will be broken photochemically. Also, when a molecule with a high-energy HOMO approaches one with a low-energy LUMO, a chemical reaction is likely.

### 12.2.3 Stability of Molecules

We have now arrived at an important aspect of quantum mechanics: the discussion of the structure and stability of molecules. As with atoms, the formation of a chemical bond involves a complex interplay between kinetic and potential energy. Interaction of electrons with multiple nuclei lowers their potential energy but tends to localize the electrons between the nuclei—that is, in the bonds. Formation of a molecule, however, allows the electrons to delocalize over a larger region in space, which in turn lowers the kinetic energy. A stable molecule balances these tendencies.

All of chemistry involves molecules, their structure, and how they interact with each other. The most sophisticated models of chemical reactions consider the frontier orbitals of the reactant molecules and their relative energies. The Woodward–Hoffmann rules, for example, help predict the stereochemistry of certain reactions in organic chemistry based on molecular orbitals. Reactivity, thermodynamics, and kinetics—often thought of as bulk phenomena—ultimately depend on the detailed molecular structure of matter.

# 12.3 Electronic Spectroscopy

The last type of spectroscopy we need to discuss is electronic spectroscopy. This involves transitions of electrons between different atomic or molecular orbitals, caused by absorption or emission of light. Electronic spectra can be fairly complicated, and we won't treat all the details here. Rather, we will focus on some of the most significant principles of electronic transitions and spectra.

### 12.3.1 Atomic Spectroscopy

When light of the proper wavelength interacts with an atom, and the transition is allowed, an electron can be promoted from one energy level to a higher energy level. Likewise, an electron in an excited energy level can fall down to a lower level, provided there is room for it; don't forget the exclusion principle. Either type of electronic transition in an atom falls under the field of **atomic spectroscopy**. The first case we call atomic absorption and the second is atomic emission. Recall that Bohr based his model for the atom on the measured emission spectrum of hydrogen. The prediction of the $He^+$ emission spectrum by Bohr's model was an early triumph of quantum theory.

There are selection rules for atomic spectroscopy, but we won't go into them here. One important fact is that the exact energies of the various levels are unique to each type of atom; thus the emission or absorption spectrum serves as an atomic fingerprint. This is how we know the composition of the sun and other stars—by characteristic lines in the spectra of those stars. Atomic spectroscopy is also a powerful analytical technique for determining the elemental composition of an unknown sample.

### 12.3.2 Molecular Electronic Spectroscopy

It is simplest to begin our discussion of molecular electronic spectroscopy with diatomic molecules. We saw above that for the hydrogen molecular ion we had two molecular orbitals, the bonding and antibonding orbitals. The energy of the molecule depends on the distance between the nuclei, as shown in Figure 12.7 for a model diatomic molecule. We refer to these curves as **potential energy curves**; they tell us about the potential energy as a function of bond length. If the potential energy curve has a minimum, it is a **bound** state, and the chemical bond is stable. If there is no minimum, this is an **unbound** state and the molecule will fall apart. In our hypothetical molecule, the ground state and the second and third excited states are bound states, but the first excited state is unbound.

At room temperature, most molecules exist in their ground electronic state. If that is a bound state, we have a stable molecule. The nuclei don't just sit at their equilibrium bond distance, however. They vibrate back and forth with a characteristic frequency, as we discussed in Chapter 10. This means that each electronic state has a manifold of vibrational states, which in turn have a manifold of rotational states.

Electronic states are spaced fairly far apart and can be excited by visible or UV light. So, what happens when a photon hits a molecule? If the photon has enough energy

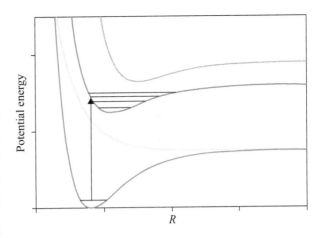

FIGURE 12.7. Potential energy curves for the ground and first three excited states of a hypothetical diatomic molecule. The arrow indicates a transition from the ground vibrational state on the ground electronic state to an excited vibrational state on an excited electronic state.

to promote the molecule to an excited electronic state, and the transition is allowed, that photon is absorbed. But the electronic state isn't all we need to worry about. The photon energy must also be equal to the difference in energy between the ground vibrational state on the ground electronic state and a vibrational state on the excited electronic state. Often, an excited electronic state has a different equilibrium bond length and different vibrational frequency than the ground state. Within the Born–Oppenheimer approximation, we assume that the electronic transition occurs much more quickly than rearrangement of the nuclei. As shown in Figure 12.7, when the molecule absorbs the light, it typically does not end up at the equilibrium position for the excited electronic state and is in an excited vibrational state.

An absorption spectrum will have structure depending on the vibrational states of the molecule. Recall that each vibrational state has its own wavefunction, showing the probability of finding the molecule with a certain internuclear distance. Recall also that as the vibrational quantum number increases, the molecule is more likely to be found at the turning points of the potential than at the center. The absorption intensity will be the greatest when there is good overlap between the ground state and excited vibrational state wavefunctions. This is known as the **Franck–Condon** principle. Note that if the photon provides too much energy, it can lead to dissociation of the molecule. Note also that when we are transitioning between electronic states, the selection rule that the vibrational level only changes by ±1 no longer holds.

For a polyatomic molecule, we don't have a simple potential energy curve that depends only on one internuclear distance. Rather, the potential energy depends on all the distances and angles between all the nuclei, as well as the electronic interactions. This is a rather complicated **potential energy surface** that exists in a multidimensional hyperspace. Needless to say, depicting a full potential energy surface is not possible because we are limited in the number of dimensions we can represent. Mathematics and computers, however, have no such limitations. A bound state represents a minimum on this potential energy surface, and the bottom of this potential well is often modeled with a harmonic function in all relevant dimensions. Excitation to an excited potential energy surface will generally put the molecule at a location that is not a minimum on the new surface. Following excitation, the molecule will rearrange until a minimum is reached, which could lead to the breaking of one of the bonds in the molecule. Probing the details of this type of dynamics is an area of current physical chemistry research.

### 12.3.3 Fluorescence and Phosphorescence

You might ask what happens to the energy in the molecule following photoexcitation? There are several processes that can take place. First of all, the molecule can relax through collisions with other molecules; the energy of the photon basically becomes random heat. Collisions may not lead to complete relaxation, but they generally do lead to relaxation to the ground vibrational state on the excited electronic state. These are known as **nonradiative** transitions, because they do not involve any emission of light. They also typically involve a change in the geometry of the molecule and can lead to isomerization or even dissociation of the molecule.

It is also possible that the molecule can radiate a photon to drop back down to the ground electronic state. This process is known as **fluorescence**. The downward transitions will involve multiple vibrational states on the ground electronic state, again through the Franck–Condon principle. Electronic spectroscopy has selection rules—just like the other forms of spectroscopy we have seen—but we won't go into all the details. The most significant rule is that the **spin state** of the molecule cannot change in an allowed transition.

If all the electrons in a molecule are paired up, we call this a **singlet** state; there is only one way to have all the spins paired. If there is one unpaired electron, such as in a radical molecule, we call this a **doublet**; the spin of that unpaired electron can either be up or down. If we have two unpaired electrons, that is known as a **triplet** state; the three possibilities are up–up, down–down, and up–down. For an allowed spectroscopic transition, the spin state cannot change.

The left side of Figure 12.8 shows possible transitions between the ground singlet state, labeled $S_0$, and the first excited singlet state, labeled $S_1$. This type of diagram is known as a **Jablonski diagram** and is a useful way of indicating the various vibronic (vibration + electronic) transitions. Absorption originates in the ground vibrational state of the $S_0$ electronic state but can end in a variety of vibrational states of the $S_1$ electronic state. The vibrational excitation is quickly lost, placing the molecule in the ground vibrational state of the $S_1$ electronic state. Fluorescence relaxes the molecule down to a variety of vibrational states on the ground $S_0$ electronic state.

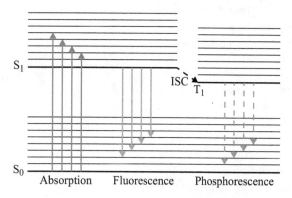

**FIGURE 12.8.** Jablonski diagram showing absorption (blue), fluorescence (green), and phosphorescence (dashed orange). The intersystem crossing (ISC) between $S_1$ and $T_1$ is indicated by the dashed black arrow.

It is possible that the molecule has other excited electronic states, some of which have different spin states. In many molecules, there is a triplet state that lies close in energy to an excited singlet state. This is indicated as state $T_1$ in Figure 12.8. A nonradiative process known as **intersystem crossing** can allow the molecule to move over to that triplet state as one of the electrons flips its spin. Once the molecule is in an excited triplet state, it needs to find a way back down to the ground singlet state. But if the molecule is in an excited state that has different spin from the ground state, transitions between them are forbidden. *Forbidden* really means, though, that the process is just much less likely than an allowed transition. The relaxation from a triplet state to a singlet state by emission of a photon does happen, and this process is known as **phosphorescence**, shown on the right of Figure 12.8. Because phosphorescence is spin forbidden, it occurs over a much longer time scale than fluorescence. (Glow-in-the-dark stickers operate on this principle, and they can last for hours.)

# 12.4 Computational Chemistry Methods

As you have seen throughout the last few chapters, even solving the simplest quantum-mechanical problems involves some fairly complicated mathematics. In this chapter, we have explored some of the tools we can use to approach a solution to the He atom, which is a fairly simple system as far as chemistry is concerned. We also extended those ideas to a treatment of simple diatomic molecules. How can we possibly contemplate solving something more complicated, such as the possible states of a molecule like butane, much less a large molecule like a protein? Fortunately, modern computers have made such attempts not only possible but commonplace. In fact, a good portion of the time of any supercomputer facility is dedicated to solving quantum-chemistry problems. The field of using computational methods to determine the quantum-mechanical states of molecules is known as **computational chemistry**. The 1998 Nobel Prize in chemistry was awarded to two pioneers in the field of computational chemistry, J. A. Pople and W. Kohn, continuing the long tradition of Nobel Prizes for quantum mechanics and related fields. We will now discuss some of the foundational ideas of computational chemistry to give you a sense of how this is done.

## 12.4.1 Hartree–Fock Self-Consistent Field Approach

The most significant factors that prevents us from solving the Schrödinger equation for anything more complicated than the hydrogen atom are the many-body interactions that take place when there are multiple nuclei and multiple electrons. As we saw in Section 12.2, we can deal with the nuclear problem by invoking the Born–Oppenheimer approximation that the electrons move very quickly compared to the nuclei. Thus, we can "freeze" the nuclei at a given position, solve for the electrons, move the nuclei a little bit, and keep going until we have all the results we need. But how can we deal with the repulsions between the various electrons?

The simplest approach for dealing with the electron-electron repulsions is known as the **self-consistent field (SCF)** approach. The central ideas at work here were developed by D. R. Hartree in 1927 and further refined with V. A. Fock in the 1930s. First, the wavefunction is approximated as the product of one-electron wavefunctions, similar to our zero-order wavefunction for He in Section 12.1.1. We then compute the average field each other electron sets up and modify the wavefunction for the first electron in the presence of the fields from those other electrons. Once we have adjusted the wavefunction for the first electron, we compute the average field from it and adjust the wavefunction of the second electron in the presence of the field of the first and all other electrons. We continue adjusting each wavefunction one at a time until we have adjusted all of them. We then start the process over again and repeat until the wavefunctions no longer change. Thus, the final solution is consistent with itself.

The Hartree–Fock (HF) level of theory can generally only serve as a first approximation to the correct solution. Energies calculated by the HF approach will often be off by several percent, which is unfortunately comparable to the change in energy for most chemical reactions. One of the main limitations of the SCF approach is that it cannot account for any of the **correlations** that take place between electrons due to their spins; the motion of one electron can influence the motion of other electrons. Another factor that is missing has to do with the **exchange** of electrons; because electrons are indistinguishable, we don't know which is which and the correct total energy of the system needs to account for this. HF calculations are a good place to start, but generally should not be taken as the final answer.

## 12.4.2 Ab Initio Methods

Recall that we can represent any wavefunction as a linear combination of a set of **basis functions**. This idea forms the foundation of the variational approach. We can get better and better answers if we use more and more functions in our linear combination. Thus, one way to get a better result with the Hartree–Fock self-consistent field (HF-SCF) approach is to use a larger set of basis functions, or **basis set**. We already discussed the LCAO approach and, while this is very useful conceptually, it is not actually the most efficient computationally. In fact, atomic orbitals are themselves typically represented by a series of Gaussian functions. The integrals of Gaussian functions can be evaluated quite easily, and this greatly streamlines the calculations. We won't go through all the details of basis sets here, but they involve using multiple mathematical functions to represent each atomic orbital. Basis sets are given labels like 3-21G and 6-311G, which tell us the number and type of functions being used for each atomic orbital. Those atomic orbitals are in turn combined to form the molecular orbitals. Basis sets of thousands of functions are commonly used, which again shows the need for large computers to handle all the data and perform all the various calculations.

The HF-SCF approach is one of the lowest **levels of theory** that can be used in calculating molecular properties. Clearly, more-sophisticated approaches are needed to take all the relevant effects, such as electron exchange and correlation, into account. One way to do this, similar to our inclusion of more functions in the basis set, is to include the effect of electronic excited states in our calculation, similar to what we saw with the perturbation approach to the He atom. This is known as **configuration interaction (CI)**. The highest level of theory, then, is known as a full CI calculation. A full CI calculation is very impractical, however, because there are so many excited states. For this reason, often only the first few excited states are included, known as CI-SD (single and double excitations) and CI-SDT (single, double, and triple excitations).

All these approaches, beginning with HF-SCF and going through full CI, are known as **ab initio** methods. The phrase *ab initio* comes from the Latin and means "from first principles." The idea is that we start with the correct Hamiltonian operator (or the most correct one we can write) and do not influence the results by any experimental data. While the ab initio approach should, in principle, give us the correct answer, it involves infinite sums. We therefore have to make some approximations in implementing it that limit the accuracy of the final outcomes. There is also the problem of scaling. Most ab initio methods are based on linear variational theory, so the basis sets can involve thousands of functions. The number of basis functions often scales as $N^4$ or even $N^6$, where $N$ is the number of atoms in the molecule under study. This means that doubling the number of atoms in the system can increase the number of functions we need by 16 or 64. Clearly, the more functions we have to deal with, the longer the calculation will take. While high-level quantum calculations can be done for small molecules, we are still a long way away from applying these approaches to large systems like polymers and proteins.

### 12.4.3 Semiempirical Methods

Because of the limitations in applying ab initio methods to large systems, and because of the long times involved even in working with small systems, other approaches have been developed. Approaches that incorporate experimental results as shortcuts for some of the necessary calculations fall under the class of **semiempirical methods**. These methods are widely used in calculating the geometries of organic molecules and proteins. For structures that occur frequently, such as methyl groups or aromatic rings, average properties are tabulated and used as the basis for the calculation. In some approaches, entire functional groups are represented as a single object. Semiempirical methods are much faster to perform than ab initio calculations, but the results are often far from accurate. Often, however, a quick semiempirical calculation can be used to refine the geometry to be used to start a more accurate ab initio calculation. On the other hand, if all that is needed are qualitative trends, these methods may be adequate.

### 12.4.4 Density Functional Theory

In both ab initio and semiempirical methods, attempts are made to determine the wavefunctions and energies by solving the Schrödinger equation. Recall, however, that the wavefunction itself has very limited physical meaning; it is $\psi^*\psi$ that tells us the probability of finding the electron. An alternative approach to solving computational chemistry problems focuses on the electron density rather than the wavefunction itself. This approach is known as **density functional theory (DFT)**. A **functional** is a function of a function. In this case, the energy of the system depends on the electron density, which is in turn a function of position. The central equation of DFT was developed by P. Hohenberg and W. Kohn in 1965 and is written as

$$E[\rho] = E_{classical}[\rho] + E_{XC}[\rho]$$

where $\rho$ represents the electron density, $E_{classical}$ accounts for the kinetic and potential energy of the system, and $E_{XC}$ accounts for electron exchange and correlation, the purely quantum-mechanical interactions.

The problem in applying DFT is that the exact form of the exchange–correlation functional is not known. If it were, we could calculate the correct energy of our system. Instead, there are various approximations that can be made, and the quality of the answer depends on these approximations. (As you may have noticed, approximations have to be made somewhere.) New functionals are being developed all the time and compared to experimental results to check their validity. Even though DFT results may only be as accurate as HF-SCF calculations, they can generally be performed much more quickly; DFT calculations typically scale as $N^3$ rather than $N^4$. Because of its relative speed, DFT is one of the more popular methods in use today.

### 12.4.5 Uses of Computational Chemistry

Regardless of the methods used, computational chemistry can calculate a wide range of molecular properties. A brief overview of what can be done is in order, to give you a sense of how these methods can be used. Clearly, one of the most commonly calculated properties is the geometry of a molecule, including bond lengths and bond angles, as well as charge distribution and dipole moment. For larger molecules, there are multiple conformations of a given molecule, and each of those, including their relative energies, can be calculated. Once we have a molecular geometry, we can also calculate the vibrational frequencies of our molecule, which can be compared to IR or Raman measurements. We can also calculate the shapes of the molecular orbitals which, as we discussed previously, can give us significant insight into the reactivity of a molecule.

In more sophisticated calculations, we can determine the dissociation energies of molecules following reaction or photoexcitation. We can also determine the shapes of the potential energy surfaces and the details of how chemical bonds form and are broken as a reaction takes place. We can also investigate the interactions between molecules—for example; in identifying a potential drug target. The development of new catalysts, both homogeneous and heterogeneous, also involves the use of computational chemistry. Computational chemistry is a rich and very active field, and many scientists and engineers use it to complement their experimental efforts.

Most of the applications we have discussed in this section center on the properties of single molecules that are not too large. For collections of molecules, or for very large molecules such as proteins or polymers, other approaches need to be used because full ab initio calculations are simply too time- and resource intensive. Such methods typically involve dynamic simulations where the molecules are moved according to the strengths of the interactions between them, but the fine level of detail we have seen in this section is typically lost. We will discuss some of these techniques in Chapter 14.

## 12.5 Summary, and Where We Go Next

In this chapter we have briefly gone over perturbation theory and the variational theorem, two approaches for solving quantum-mechanical problems that can't be solved analytically. We have seen how we can use these approaches to develop solutions for the helium atom and the simplest molecules. We also explored some of the ideas associated with electronic spectroscopy. We have also had an overview of the methods of computational chemistry to give you a sense of what can be done with it. This chapter concludes our journey through quantum mechanics. In the next chapter, we will build on what we have learned and use statistical mechanics to build a bridge from the microscopic, quantum-mechanical world to the macroscopic world.

## PROBLEMS

**12.1** a) Write a full Hamiltonian for the Li atom and describe each term.

b) Identify the terms in the Hamiltonian from part a) that would be part of the zero-order Hamiltonian and which other terms would be part of the perturbation Hamiltonian.

c) If you were to use the variational theorem, similar to what we did in Section 12.1.2, and recalling the rules for putting electrons into atomic orbitals, what atomic orbital functions would you include in your trial wavefunction? Also, how many different values for the effective nuclear charge would you use and why?

**12.2** This problem will slightly modify the particle-in-a-box potential to include a flat bump in the middle of the box. This bump is of height $V_0$ and extends from $L/3$ to $2L/3$; in other words, the bump covers the central third of the box.

a) Sketch a graph of this potential.

b) Write the zero-order and perturbation Hamiltonians.

c) Using the particle in a box wavefunction as the zero-order wavefunction, calculate the first order correction to the energy.

**12.3** Consider a particle confined to a V-shaped well, with a potential given by

$$V = k|x|$$

a) Sketch a graph of this potential.

b) Since this shape is somewhat similar to the quadratic potential we used for the harmonic oscillator, let's use the lowest harmonic oscillator wavefunction as our trial function.

$$\psi_0(x) = \left(\frac{\alpha}{\pi}\right)^{1/4} e^{-\alpha x^2/2}$$

Determine the optimal value of the parameter $\alpha$ and the best estimation of the ground-state energy for this system.

**12.4** a) Write a full Hamiltonian for the $H_2$ molecule. Clearly identify the physical meaning behind each term.

b) Identify the term(s) that can be handled with the Born–Oppenheimer approximation.

c) With the remaining terms, once the Born–Oppenheimer approximation has been applied, identify the zero-order Hamiltonian and perturbation term(s).

**12.5** For each of the following molecules, draw a molecular orbital diagram, describe the occupancy of the molecular orbitals, give the bond order of the molecule, and state whether the molecule is diamagnetic or paramagnetic: NO, $NO^-$, $NO^+$, $F_2$, and HF.

**12.6** The following results were obtained for a sample of anthracene vapor. The emission spectrum has peaks of increasing intensity at 440, 410, 390, and 370 nm with a sharp cutoff at shorter wavelength. The absorption spectrum rises sharply at 360 nm, with a trail of weaker peaks at 345, 330, and 305 nm. What do these results tell you about anthracene?

**12.7** Absorption spectroscopy can be used to measure the concentration of chemicals with a high degree of precision. For solutions of low concentration, the Beer–Lambert law is used to relate the observed absorbance to the concentration.

a) The Beer–Lambert law can be derived from on a simple collisional model. The light travels through a sample of thickness $d$. Assume the concentration of absorbing species is uniform throughout the sample. Given this information, derive the Beer–Lambert law, written $A = \varepsilon d[J]$ ($A$ is the absorbance, defined as $A = -\log(I/I_0)$; $\varepsilon$ is the molar absorption coefficient, with units of L $mol^{-1}$ $cm^{-1}$; and $[J]$ is the concentration of the absorbing species.)

b) You are given a solution of tryptophan and told that its molar absorption coefficient has a value of $5.4 \times 10^3$ L mol$^{-1}$ cm$^{-1}$ for 280 nm light. You have a standard 1 cm cuvette and measure the absorbance at 280 nm to be 0.27. What is the concentration of tryptophan?

c) If you can reliably measure absorbances as low as 0.01, what is the lowest concentration of tryptophan you can measure with this instrument?

**12.8** Quenching is a process whereby a fluorescent or phosphorescent molecule in an excited electronic state interacts with another molecule—termed a *quencher*—and relaxes to its ground state without emitting a photon. Basically, the quencher removes the excitation from the fluorescent or phosphorescent molecule before the photon can be emitted. Benzophenone is a phosphorescent molecule but can be quenched by the presence of triethylamine. A time-resolved laser spectroscopy experiment has shown that the half-life of the phosphorescence with no quencher present is 29 µs. The following data were obtained for the phosphorescence intensity with varying amounts of triethylamine

| $[Q]$/(mol L$^{-1}$) | 0.0010 | 0.0050 | 0.0100 |
|---|---|---|---|
| $I_{ph}$/(arbitrary units) | 0.41 | 0.25 | 0.16 |

Construct a kinetic model of this process and determine the rate constant for the quenching.

# RETURN
## TO
# STATISTICAL
# MECHANICS

Predicting Bulk
Properties

# The Molecular Partition Function and Connections to Thermodynamics

## 13.1 Return to Statistical Mechanics

We began our journey through the realm of quantum mechanics partly because our simple molecular models were unable to correctly predict the bulk property of heat capacity. Recall from Chapter 7 that the classical equipartition theorem broke down for even a diatomic gas. Ultimately, we want to understand matter at the molecular level, but our everyday experience is at the macroscopic scale, not the microscopic. How can we make these connections? We take advantage of the fact that even a moderately sized sample contains trillions of trillions of molecules, which means we can benefit from the statistics of large numbers. This method of bridging the microscopic and macroscopic realms is known as **statistical mechanics**. The power player in this approach will be our old friend, the Boltzmann distribution. Ultimately, statistical mechanics allow us to use our knowledge of quantum mechanics to make predictions about thermodynamic properties of matter.

### 13.1.1 Boltzmann Distribution Revisited

Now that we have completed our survey of quantum mechanics, we have a much better sense of the allowed energy states of atoms and molecules. These states are needed to fully utilize the Boltzmann distribution and understand how energy is spread around. Let's begin by recalling the Boltzmann distribution:

$$P_i = \frac{n_i}{N} = \frac{g_i e^{-\epsilon_i/k_B T}}{q} \quad \text{where} \quad q = \sum_i g_i e^{-\epsilon_i/k_B T}$$

The quantity $q$ is known as the **molecular partition function** and gives us a rough idea of the number of states that are important. The quantity $g_i$ is the degeneracy of the level with energy $\epsilon_i$. Recall that the Boltzmann distribution tells us the probability of finding a molecule with a particular energy; $n_i$ is the number with that energy, and $N$ is the total number of molecules.

We now need to be more careful in what we mean by *zero energy*. For some types of energy, such as translational and vibrational motion, the lowest energy state is not a state of zero energy; recall that there is a zero-point energy associated with these types of motion. We also have the case of atoms and molecules where we defined the zero of energy to correspond to an infinite separation of all the nuclei and electrons; thus all bound states were of negative energy. What does that do to our partition function? To address this problem, let's look at the population of the lowest possible energy level.

Let's consider the lowest possible energy level to have an energy of $\epsilon_0 = 0$. The population of that level is then written as

$$P_0 = \frac{g_0 e^{-\epsilon_0/k_B T}}{q} = \frac{g_0}{q} \tag{13.1}$$

Now, our choice of the zero of energy cannot affect the population of the state; the system doesn't care what we call zero. Let's consider the relative population of any other level compared to the lowest possible level, where the lowest level is not necessarily at zero energy.

$$\frac{P_i}{P_0} = \frac{g_i e^{-\epsilon_i/k_B T}}{g_0 e^{-\epsilon_0/k_B T}} \tag{13.2}$$

We can rewrite this expression slightly by combining the exponential terms

$$P_i = P_0 \frac{g_i}{g_0} e^{-(\epsilon_i - \epsilon_0)/k_B T}$$

The sum of the population of each level still needs to equal 1, which we can write as

$$\sum_i P_i = 1 = \frac{P_0}{g_0} \sum_i g_i e^{-(\epsilon_i - \epsilon_0)/k_B T}$$

We can solve this expression for the population in the lowest level by writing

$$P_0 = \frac{g_0}{\sum_i g_i e^{-(\epsilon_i - \epsilon_0)/k_B T}}$$

If we compare this to Eq. 13.1, we see that we should now slightly redefine the molecular partition function as

$$q = \sum_i g_i e^{-(\epsilon_i - \epsilon_0)/k_B T} \tag{13.3}$$

The population in any particular level can now be written as

$$P_i = \frac{g_i e^{-(\epsilon_i - \epsilon_0)/k_B T}}{q} \qquad (13.4)$$

With this slight redefinition of probability and the molecular partition function, we no longer have to worry about what convention we used in setting the absolute zero of energy. Because a molecule or atom can never be in an energy level lower than the lowest level, all we really need to be concerned with is the difference of energy of a given level from the lowest possible level. From this point on, we should assume that we are always talking about the difference in energy from the lowest possible energy when talking about the energy of a state.

## 13.1.2 Separation of the Partition Function

The partition function is a very powerful idea. As we will soon see, it tells us all we need to know about the system. In many ways, it is similar to the wavefunction in quantum mechanics. The details of the partition function depend on the system under study, in particular the possible energy levels. For any molecule, its total energy can be broken up into various parts that represent the translational, rotational, vibrational, and electronic states of the molecule.

$$\epsilon_i = \epsilon_{tr,j} + \epsilon_{rot,k} + \epsilon_{vib,l} + \epsilon_{el,m} \qquad (13.5)$$

The different subscripts $j$, $k$, $l$, and $m$ refer to the particular energy levels for each individual type of motion. (These expressions assume no coupling between the different types of motion. In fact, vibrations and rotations are coupled to some degree, which must be taken into account in very accurate calculations.)

When evaluating the partition function, we need to sum over all the possible energy levels in all the different types of motion. Let's substitute Eq. 13.5 into Eq. 13.3. Doing so lets us write

$$q = \sum_i g_i e^{-(\epsilon_{tr,j} + \epsilon_{rot,k} + \epsilon_{vib,l} + \epsilon_{el,m} - \epsilon_0)/k_B T}$$

When multiple terms are written inside an exponential, we can rewrite it as products of exponentials, or

$$q = \sum_i g_i e^{-(\epsilon_{tr,j} - \epsilon_{tr,0})/k_B T} e^{-(\epsilon_{rot,k} - \epsilon_{rot,0})/k_B T} e^{-(\epsilon_{vib,l} - \epsilon_{vib,0})/k_B T} e^{-(\epsilon_{el,m} - \epsilon_{el,0})/k_B T}$$

The total degeneracy of a given level is the product of the degeneracies of each type of motion

$$g_i = g_{tr,j} g_{rot,k} g_{vib,l} g_{el,m}$$

It is helpful now to collect terms for each type of motion.

$$q = \sum_i g_{tr,j} e^{-(\epsilon_{tr,j} - \epsilon_{tr,0})/k_B T} g_{rot,k} e^{-(\epsilon_{rot,k} - \epsilon_{rot,0})/k_B T} g_{vib,l} e^{-(\epsilon_{vib,l} - \epsilon_{vib,0})/k_B T} g_{el,m} e^{-(\epsilon_{el,m} - \epsilon_{el,0})/k_B T}$$

$$q = \left( \sum_j g_{tr,j} e^{-(\epsilon_{tr,j} - \epsilon_{tr,0})/k_B T} \right) \left( \sum_k g_{rot,k} e^{-(\epsilon_{rot,k} - \epsilon_{rot,0})/k_B T} \right)$$

$$\left( \sum_l g_{vib,l} e^{-(\epsilon_{vib,l} - \epsilon_{vib,0})/k_B T} \right) \left( \sum_m g_{el,m} e^{-(\epsilon_{el,m} - \epsilon_{el,0})/k_B T} \right)$$

We can now define a partition function for each type of motion and write

$$q = q_{tr} q_{rot} q_{vib} q_{el} \tag{13.6}$$

You may notice some similarities to how we dealt with multidimensional wavefunctions, by separating them into products of one- or two-dimensional functions. For wavefunctions, whenever the potential energy can be written as a sum of independent terms, we can write the overall wavefunction as a product. The same holds for partition functions; whenever we can write the energy as a sum of independent terms, we can write the overall partition function as a product of individual partition functions. We will now consider the separate partition functions for each type of energy a molecule can have.

### 13.1.3 Translational Partition Function

Let's first consider only the translations of molecules, where we will treat the molecules as rigid particles of their molecular mass. The quantum-mechanical model that fits this situation is the particle in a three-dimensional box. Recall that the energy for this situation is (see Eq. 9.20):

$$E = \frac{h^2}{8m} \left( \frac{n_x^2}{L_x^2} + \frac{n_y^2}{L_y^2} + \frac{n_z^2}{L_z^2} \right)$$

The total translational energy is a sum of terms, one for each dimension,

$$E_{tr} = E_x + E_y + E_z$$

where

$$E_x = \frac{h^2 n_x^2}{8mL_x^2} \qquad E_y = \frac{h^2 n_y^2}{8mL_y^2} \qquad E_z = \frac{h^2 n_z^2}{8mL_z^2}$$

Because the energy is a sum, we can write the translational partition function as a product.

$$q_{tr} = q_{tr(x)} q_{tr(y)} q_{tr(z)} \tag{13.7}$$

Let's write an expression for the one-dimensional translational partition function.

$$q_{tr(x)} = \sum_{n_x=1}^{\infty} e^{-h^2 n_x^2 / 8mL_x^2 k_B T} \tag{13.8}$$

Since we are talking about a macroscopic box where $L_x$ is much larger than the size of the gas atoms, the levels will be spaced very close together. (Mathematically, we need the condition $h^2/8mL_x^2 \ll k_B T$ to be true.) In this case, we can approximate the sum as an integral.

$$q_{tr(x)} \approx \int_{n_x=1}^{\infty} e^{-h^2 n_x^2/8mL_x^2 k_B T} \, dn_x$$

We are now assuming the energy levels are continuous, which is a good approximation for a molecule in a large box. The difference between the lowest level and zero energy is very small, so it is not a bad approximation to simply write

$$q_{tr(x)} = \int_0^{\infty} e^{-h^2 n_x^2/8mL_x^2 k_B T} \, dn_x \tag{13.9}$$

This integral is in a standard form

$$\int_0^{\infty} e^{-bx^2} \, dx = \frac{1}{2}\sqrt{\frac{\pi}{b}}$$

which lets us write

$$q_{tr(x)} = \left(\frac{2\pi m k_B T}{h^2}\right)^{1/2} L_x \tag{13.10}$$

The form of the partition function for the $y$ and $z$ directions will be exactly the same as Eq. 13.10. Since $V = L_x L_y L_z$, we can write the total translational partition function as

$$q_{tr} = \left(\frac{2\pi m k_B T}{h^2}\right)^{3/2} V \tag{13.11}$$

If we consider a monatomic ideal gas, this is the only part of the partition function we need to worry about; there are no rotations or vibrations.

## 13.1.4 Rotational Partition Functions

Now, let's consider a heteronuclear diatomic molecule, such as CO. We used the quantum-mechanical rigid rotor to determine the energy states of this system. (See Eq. 10.15, where we have replaced $l$ with $J$ to follow the spectroscopic convention.)

$$E_J = J(J+1)\frac{h^2}{2I}$$

Each state has a degeneracy of $g_J = 2J+1$ (Eq. 10.17). We write the rotational partition function as

$$q_{rot} = \sum_{J=0}^{\infty} (2J+1)e^{-J(J+1)h^2/2Ik_B T} \tag{13.12}$$

We treat this as we did for translations; in the high temperature limit, $\hbar^2/2I \ll k_B T$, and we can treat the sum as an integral and evaluate it. The result is

$$q_{rot} = \frac{2 I k_B T}{\hbar^2} \quad \text{or} \quad q_{rot} = \frac{T}{\Theta_{rot}} \tag{13.13}$$

where $\Theta_{rot} = \dfrac{\hbar^2}{2 I k_B}$ is the **rotational temperature**.

The rotational temperature is a convenient shorthand that merits some attention. Recall that the moment of inertia, $I$, depends on the reduced mass and equilibrium bond length of the molecule. (See Eq. 10.4.) These parameters are readily determined from microwave spectroscopy. As we discussed back in Chapter 10, the rotational constant $B$, which includes the moment of inertia, is often reported in various units. The rotational temperature is basically just another way of reporting the rotational constant for a molecule, now in units of Kelvin.

The idea of a rotational temperature also allows us to readily determine when we can make the approximation that the rotational energy levels are close together compared to $k_B T$. The value of $\Theta_{rot}$ for the molecule CO is 2.77 K, thus at room temperature, $q_{rot} = 108$. This means we have significant population in about the first 108 rotational states, so assuming the levels are continuous is a reasonable approximation. On the other hand, the rotational temperature of $H_2$ is 87.6 K, and $T/\Theta_{rot} = 3.4$. Now, we are not as justified in assuming that the rotational levels form a continuum, and in fact we should not even make the approximation that treats the partition function as an integral. Comparing the rotational temperature to the ambient temperature is a good check for the validity of the integral assumption. So long as the ambient temperature is much greater than the rotational temperature, we can make the approximation that the levels are continuous.

The partition function in Eq. 13.13 is only strictly correct for a heteronuclear diatomic molecule. For a homonuclear diatomic molecule, we have to modify the partition function because of the symmetry of the molecule. Consider a heteronuclear diatomic, such as CO, rotated by 180°; it looks different. Now, rotate the homonuclear molecule, such as $O_2$, by 180°; it looks the same. In effect, the two states are the same for the homonuclear diatomic, so we are overcounting our states by a factor of two. To correct for this, we divide the partition function by 2. We add this in by including a **symmetry number**, symbolized by $\sigma$, in the partition function.

$$q_{rot,\, linear} = \frac{T}{\sigma \Theta_{rot}} \tag{13.14}$$

This expression works for any linear molecule. If the molecule can be rotated 180° and it looks the same, such as for a homonuclear diatomic or a linear molecule like $CO_2$, then $\sigma = 2$. For heteronuclear diatomics, or asymmetric linear molecules like HCN, $\sigma = 1$.

For a nonlinear polyatomic molecule, we have to consider rotations about the three separate rotational axes of the molecule. Each rotational axis can have its own moment of inertia, and hence it will have its own rotational temperature. We write the rotational partition function for a nonlinear polyatomic molecule as

$$q_{rot,\, nonlinear} = \frac{1}{\sigma} \left( \frac{\pi T^3}{\Theta_{rot,x}\, \Theta_{rot,y}\, \Theta_{rot,z}} \right)^{1/2} \tag{13.15}$$

Polyatomic molecules also have a symmetry number, but these numbers can be higher than 2, depending on the symmetry of the molecule. Consider the ammonia molecule, $NH_3$. We can rotate the molecule by 120°, and it still looks the same. The symmetry number here is 360°/120° = 3. The symmetry number for methane is 12, because of the tetrahedral symmetry of that molecule. Rotational temperatures and symmetry numbers for several molecules are tabulated in Tables 13.2 and 13.3 at the end of the chapter.

## 13.1.5 Vibrational Partition Function

For vibrations of a diatomic molecule, we used the harmonic oscillator as our quantum-mechanical model. The energy levels for this system are given by (Eq. 10.41)

$$E_n = \left( n + \frac{1}{2} \right) h\nu \qquad \text{where } n = 0, 1, 2, \ldots$$

Making the shift in energy by ½ $h\nu$, the energy of the lowest vibrational level, we can write the vibrational partition function as

$$q_{vib} = \sum_{n=0}^{\infty} e^{-nh\nu/k_B T} \tag{13.16}$$

As we discussed before, the vibrational levels are fairly far apart compared to $k_B T$, thus we cannot convert this sum to an integral. We can, however, use the infinite series

$$\sum_{n=0}^{\infty} e^{-nx} = \frac{1}{1 - e^{-x}}$$

to give us

$$q_{vib} = \frac{1}{1 - e^{-h\nu/k_B T}} = \frac{1}{1 - e^{-\Theta_{vib}/T}} \qquad \text{where } \Theta_{vib} = \frac{h\nu}{k_B} \tag{13.17}$$

Note that we didn't make any approximations here as we did for translations and rotations. The parameter $\Theta_{vib}$ is the **vibrational temperature** and—like the rotational temperature—basically takes the molecular parameter of the fundamental vibrational frequency and converts it into units of Kelvin. As we did with the rotational temperature, we can compare the vibrational temperature to the ambient temperature to estimate how close the levels are compared to $k_B T$. For CO, the fundamental vibrational frequency is 2157 cm$^{-1}$, which translates to a vibrational temperature of 3103 K. So, at room temperature, the separation between vibrational levels is about 10 times $k_B T$; no wonder the classical equipartition theorem failed for describing the heat capacity due to vibrations. The situation is even worse for $H_2$; the vibrational temperature is 6332 K. For most molecules, except those that involve fairly heavy atoms, the vibrational partition function will have a value close to 1; only the ground vibrational level is populated at room temperature.

Recall that the number of vibrational degrees of freedom is equal to $3N - 6$ for a nonlinear molecule and $3N - 5$ for a linear molecule. Each of these vibrations has its own fundamental frequency, and hence its own vibrational temperature. For a polyatomic molecule, there is one of these partition functions for each vibrational degree of freedom. The total vibrational partition function of a polyatomic molecule is the product of these partition functions for each individual vibrational mode. Vibrational temperatures are also tabulated at the end of the chapter, in Tables 13.2 and 13.3.

### 13.1.6 Electronic Partition Function

We typically deal with molecules in the ground electronic state. The electronic partition function is therefore just the degeneracy of the ground electronic state. For a molecule with all its electrons paired up, the electronic partition function has a value of 1. If there are unpaired electrons, such as for NO or $O_2$, the electronic partition function has the value of that degeneracy. This is related to the total spin state we talked about in Section 12.3.3. One unpaired electron can be either spin-up or spin-down, so there is a degeneracy, and value of $q_{el}$, of 2. For two unpaired electrons, the degeneracy is 3 (up–up, down–down, and up–down). Only when a molecule has a low-lying excited electronic state, or when we are working at sufficiently high temperatures, such as in a flame or plasma, will we have to worry about including excited states in the electronic partition function. Information on electronic states is tabulated at the end of the chapter in Tables 13.1, 13.2, and 13.3.

### 13.1.7 Total Molecular Partition Function

We now have all the parts of the molecular partition function. Putting it all together for a diatomic molecule (assuming no low-lying electronic excited states) gives us

$$q = \left( \frac{2\pi m k_B T}{h^2} \right)^{3/2} V \frac{T}{\sigma \Theta_{rot}} \frac{1}{1 - e^{-\Theta_{vib}/T}} g_{el,0} \tag{13.18}$$

For a nonlinear polyatomic molecule, we write

$$q = \left( \frac{2\pi m k_B T}{h^2} \right)^{3/2} V \frac{1}{\sigma} \left( \frac{\pi T^3}{\Theta_{rot,x} \Theta_{rot,y} \Theta_{rot,z}} \right)^{1/2} \frac{1}{\displaystyle\prod_{j=1}^{N_{vib}} \left( 1 - e^{-\Theta_{vib}/T} \right)} g_{el,0} \tag{13.19}$$

Note that the vibrational portion of the partition function has one term for each vibrational degree of freedom, which is $N_{vib} = 3N - 6$, where $N$ is the number of atoms in the molecule. For linear polyatomic molecules, we write

$$q = \left( \frac{2\pi m k_B T}{h^2} \right)^{3/2} V \frac{T}{\sigma \Theta_{rot}} \frac{1}{\displaystyle\prod_{j=1}^{N_{vib}} \left( 1 - e^{-\Theta_{vib}/T} \right)} g_{el,0} \tag{13.20}$$

In this case, $N_{vib} = 3N - 5$.

# 13.2 Statistical Thermodynamics

In the formalism of quantum mechanics, we learn about the properties of a system by using the wavefunction and the appropriate operator, and taking expectation values. In this section, we will develop a formalism for using the partition function to learn about the thermodynamic properties of our system. Because we are using statistical mechanics to calculate thermodynamic properties, this methodology is sometimes called **statistical thermodynamics**.

## 13.2.1 Total Energy of a Collection of Molecules

Let's imagine that we have a collection of $N$ molecules in a container of fixed volume $V$. Not all of the molecules have the same amount of energy; energy is spread around according to the Boltzmann distribution, and the temperature $T$ tells us how the energy is distributed. We will, however, fix the total amount of energy in the system, which is given by

$$E = \sum_i n_i \epsilon_i = \frac{N}{q} \sum_i \epsilon_i g_i e^{-\epsilon_i / k_B T} \tag{13.21}$$

Now, let's play with this expression mathematically. First, we note that we have an exponential function with part of the argument of the exponential in front of it. Let's consider the derivative of the Boltzmann exponential function with respect to temperature:

$$\frac{\partial}{\partial T} e^{-\epsilon_i / k_B T} = \frac{\epsilon_i}{k_B T^2} e^{-\epsilon_i / k_B T}$$

We need to recall that the energy states of the molecules may depend on the volume of the container and other variables, which is why we write the partial derivative.

Let's rearrange this expression

$$\epsilon_i e^{-\epsilon_i / k_B T} = k_B T^2 \frac{\partial}{\partial T} e^{-\epsilon_i / k_B T}$$

We can substitute this in to Eq. 13.21, our expression for the total energy, and write

$$E = \frac{N}{q} \sum_i g_i k_B T^2 \frac{\partial}{\partial T} e^{-\epsilon_i / k_B T} = \frac{N k_B T^2}{q} \frac{\partial}{\partial T} \left( \sum_i g_i e^{-\epsilon_i / k_B T} \right)$$

Recall that a sum of derivatives is the same as the derivative of a sum. The quantity in parentheses is simply the partition function, $q$, so we can simplify the expression even further

$$E = \frac{N k_B T^2}{q} \left( \frac{\partial q}{\partial T} \right)_V = N k_B T^2 \left( \frac{\partial \ln q}{\partial T} \right)_V \tag{13.22}$$

Now we have an expression for the total energy of our system in terms of the partition function. If we replace the number of molecules with $n N_A$, where $N_A$ is Avogadro's number, then the molar internal energy is given by

$$U_m = R T^2 \left( \frac{\partial \ln q}{\partial T} \right)_V \tag{13.23}$$

Let's return to our consideration of a monatomic ideal gas, where the partition function only includes a translational part (Eq. 13.11). What is the energy of this gas? We simply insert that partition function into Eq. 13.23 and evaluate it.

$$U_m = RT^2 \left( \frac{\partial \ln q}{\partial T} \right)_V = RT^2 \frac{\partial}{\partial T} \ln \left[ \left( \frac{2\pi m k_B T}{h^2} \right)^{3/2} V \right]$$

$$= RT^2 \frac{\partial}{\partial T} \left[ \frac{3}{2} \ln \left( \frac{2\pi m k_B}{h^2} \right) + \frac{3}{2} \ln T + \ln V \right] = RT^2 \frac{3}{2} \frac{1}{T}$$

$$U_m = \frac{3}{2} RT \tag{13.24}$$

We have obtained the classical result through our use of the molecular partition function. Notice that when we use the partition function for an ideal gas, we get an expression for the energy that only depends on the temperature. In fact, having an energy that only depends on $T$ is another way to define an ideal gas.

## 13.2.2 Constant-Volume Heat Capacity

The constant-volume heat capacity is formally defined as

$$C_V \equiv \left( \frac{\partial U}{\partial T} \right)_V \tag{13.25}$$

We can use Eq. 13.22 to develop a general expression for the constant-volume heat capacity in terms of the partition function. After we take the necessary derivative, we have

$$C_V = 2 N k_B T \left( \frac{\partial \ln q}{\partial T} \right)_V + N k_B T^2 \left( \frac{\partial^2 \ln q}{\partial T^2} \right)_V \tag{13.26}$$

In molar terms, we write

$$C_{V,m} = 2 RT \left( \frac{\partial \ln q}{\partial T} \right)_V + RT^2 \left( \frac{\partial^2 \ln q}{\partial T^2} \right)_V \tag{13.27}$$

For the monatomic ideal gas, we can simply take the temperature derivative of Eq. 13.24 to obtain the constant-volume heat capacity.

$$C_{V,m} = \left( \frac{\partial U_m}{\partial T} \right)_V = \frac{3}{2} R \tag{13.28}$$

Again, this is the classical result, arrived at with a quantum-mechanical model and the partition function.

We can also revisit the energy and heat capacity of a monatomic crystal that we considered back in Chapter 7. If the only energy the particles have is vibrational energy, and we only allow multiples of a fundamental frequency, the total partition function would be given by

$$q_{vib} = \left( \frac{1}{1 - e^{-hv/k_B T}} \right)^3$$

The factor of 3 is needed for each of the $N$ atoms moving in the three spatial directions. When we calculate the total energy and heat capacity from this partition function, we actually get the Einstein formula we used earlier (Eq. 7.42), but in a much more elegant derivation.

Now is also a good time to talk about the heat capacity in a slightly different way. First, we need to introduce the idea of the **variance**. This is a parameter that statisticians use to talk about the width of a probability distribution. (The square root of the variance is the standard deviation, symbolized as $\sigma$.) The variance of a parameter $x$ is defined as

$$\sigma_x^2 = \langle x^2 \rangle - \langle x \rangle^2 \qquad (13.29)$$

To apply this to heat capacity, we need to find the averages of $E$ and $E^2$. We can get the average of $E$ by simply dividing Eq. 13.22 by the number of particles, $N$.

$$\langle E \rangle = k_B T^2 \left( \frac{\partial \ln q}{\partial T} \right)_V$$

We could try to derive a similar expression for $E^2$, however that gets pretty messy. Instead, let's take a step back and write the simplest expression we can

$$\langle E^2 \rangle = \frac{1}{N} \sum_i n_i \epsilon_i^2$$

We also want to go back to Eq. 13.21 and take the temperature derivative of it to obtain

$$C_V = \left( \frac{\partial E}{\partial T} \right)_V = \sum_i \epsilon_i \left( \frac{\partial n_i}{\partial T} \right)_V$$

We have made a slight notational switch from $U$ to $E$ here. Note that we are also asserting that the energy states are unaffected by a change in temperature at constant volume. (The translational energy states depend on the size of the container, but we are keeping that size fixed.) The populations of the various states, however, do change when the temperature changes. To evaluate the derivative, we take the temperature derivative of the Boltzmann distribution

$$\left( \frac{\partial n_i}{\partial T} \right)_V = \frac{\partial}{\partial T} \left( \frac{N e^{-\epsilon_i/k_B T}}{q} \right) = N \left( \frac{\epsilon_i}{k_B T^2} \frac{e^{-\epsilon_i/k_B T}}{q} - \frac{1}{q^2} \left( \frac{\partial q}{\partial T} \right)_V e^{-\epsilon_i/k_B T} \right)$$

If we look carefully at the last term, we see the average energy hiding there. This lets us rewrite the derivative of the occupation number as

$$\left( \frac{\partial n_i}{\partial T} \right)_V = N \left( \frac{\epsilon_i}{k_B T^2} \frac{e^{-\epsilon_i/k_B T}}{q} - \frac{1}{q} \frac{\langle E \rangle}{k_B T^2} e^{-\epsilon_i/k_B T} \right)$$

Substituting this into our expression for $C_V$ above, and again using the Boltzmann distribution, gives us

$$C_V = \frac{1}{k_B T^2} \left( \sum_i \frac{N\epsilon_i^2}{q} e^{-\epsilon_i/k_B T} - \langle E \rangle \sum_i \frac{N\epsilon_i}{q} e^{-\epsilon_i/k_B T} \right)$$

$$C_V = \frac{1}{k_B T^2} \left( \sum_i n_i \epsilon_i^2 - \langle E \rangle \sum_i n_i \epsilon_i \right)$$

The first sum is simply $N\langle E^2 \rangle$ and the second sum is $N\langle E \rangle$, so we can write

$$C_V = \frac{N}{k_B T^2} (\langle E^2 \rangle - \langle E \rangle^2) = \frac{N\sigma_E^2}{k_B T^2} \tag{13.30}$$

where we have inserted the variance of the energy via Eq. 13.29.

This relation gives us yet another way to think about the heat capacity. Somewhat akin to our bucket analogy from Chapter 7, we can see that the heat capacity increases the more we can spread the energy around. If we have many accessible energy states, the variance of the energy is large and so is the heat capacity. However, if there are only one or a few accessible energy states, then there will be very little variance in the energy and the heat capacity will decrease. So, in a sense, heat capacity has to do with the fluctuation of energy among the available states. As more states become available with an increase in temperature, the heat capacity can also increase. Note that if the variance of the energy increases as $T^2$, then the heat capacity will be a constant, as it is for the ideal gas.

These results illustrate the general pattern we can use to connect quantum mechanics with thermodynamics. We start with the molecular energy states derived from appropriate quantum-mechanical models and determine the corresponding partition function. The partition function can then be used to calculate bulk thermodynamic quantities.

### 13.2.3 Pressure

Now that we know how to determine the molar internal energy and the constant volume heat capacity from a partition function, let's briefly develop methods for determining other thermodynamic properties. We'll begin with the pressure. We will learn more about the thermodynamic pressure in Chapter 16 but, for now, we can consider the pressure to be the change in the energy of our system with a change in volume. (We will get more precise on this, but this formulation will work for now.)

$$P = -\frac{\partial E}{\partial V} \tag{13.31}$$

The reason for the negative sign has to do with mechanical compression. When we compress something by increasing the pressure, the volume decreases, but the energy increases. Pressure can never be negative; therefore, we include a minus sign in this definition. (A more traditional, classical definition of pressure will be presented in Chapter 16.)

To evaluate the pressure due to a collection of molecules, we again assert that the mechanical property we will measure is due to each individual molecule. Mathematically, we write

$$P = \sum_i n_i \left( -\frac{\partial \epsilon_i}{\partial V} \right) = \frac{N}{q} \sum_i \left( -\frac{\partial \epsilon_i}{\partial V} \right) g_i e^{-\epsilon_i/k_B T} \tag{13.32}$$

As we saw in developing our expression for the energy, we again have what looks like the derivative of an exponential, this time with respect to $V$ rather than $T$. Let's write this derivative.

$$\frac{\partial}{\partial V} e^{-\epsilon_i/k_B T} = \frac{-1}{k_B T} \frac{\partial \epsilon_i}{\partial V} e^{-\epsilon_i/k_B T}$$

which we can rewrite as

$$-\frac{\partial \epsilon_i}{\partial V} e^{-\epsilon_i/k_B T} = k_B T \frac{\partial}{\partial V} e^{-\epsilon_i/k_B T}$$

Substituting this back in to Eq. 13.32, we have

$$P = \frac{N}{q} \sum_i g_i k_B T \frac{\partial}{\partial V} e^{-\epsilon_i/k_B T} = \frac{N k_B T}{q} \frac{\partial}{\partial V} \sum_i g_i e^{-\epsilon_i/k_B T} = \frac{N k_B T}{q} \frac{\partial q}{\partial V}$$

$$P = N k_B T \left( \frac{\partial \ln q}{\partial V} \right)_T \tag{13.33}$$

As we did in with Eq. 13.22, we can rewrite this in molar terms by using $N = n N_A$.

$$P = nRT \left( \frac{\partial \ln q}{\partial V} \right)_T \tag{13.34}$$

Let's use this expression with our partition function for a monatomic gas, which again only contains the translational partition function.

$$P = nRT \frac{\partial \ln q}{\partial V} = nRT \frac{\partial}{\partial V} \ln \left[ \left( \frac{2\pi m k_B T}{h^2} \right)^{3/2} V \right]$$

$$P = nRT \frac{1}{V} \quad \text{or} \quad PV = nRT$$

Once again, we have obtained the ideal gas law. In fact, we should have expected this, since our molecular partition function does not include any way to deal with interactions between the gas molecules. It is left to the student to show that the ideal gas law will still be obtained even for a polyatomic molecule with rotations and vibrations. (See Problem 13.3.)

### 13.2.4 Statistical Entropy

The next thermodynamic property we want to consider is the entropy of the system. We begin with Boltzmann's relation

$$S = k_B \ln W$$

where $W$ is the statistical weight of the most probable arrangement of the system. It is worth providing some brief justification for the use of the natural logarithm in this expression. Imagine that we have two systems, each with their own statistical weight. If we combine those two systems, then we need to multiply the statistical weights.

$$W_{total} = W_1 \cdot W_2$$

Entropy is a physical property, so it should scale linearly with the size of the system. Boltzmann's expression, and the rules of logarithms, make this work

$$S_{total} = k_B \ln W_{total} = k_B \ln(W_1 \cdot W_2) = k_B \ln W_1 + k_B \ln W_2 = S_1 + S_2$$

If we double the size of the system, the statistical weight is squared, but the entropy doubles.

Now, let's start developing a general expression for the total entropy of a collection of independent molecules. The development of the entropy in terms of the partition function is a bit complicated, so bear with the following derivation. We start again with Boltzmann's expression

$$S = k_B \ln W$$

We will write the statistical weight again in terms of the number of particles and the occupation numbers of the various possible energy states (Eq. 2.11).

$$W = \frac{N!}{\prod_i n_i!}$$

Combining these expressions gives us

$$S = k_B \left[ \ln N! - \sum_i \ln n_i! \right] = k_B \left[ N \ln N - N - \sum_i (n_i \ln n_i - n_i) \right]$$

$$S = k_B \left[ N \ln N - \sum_i n_i \ln n_i \right]$$

where we have used Stirling's approximation $\ln x! = x \ln x - x$ and the fact that $N = \sum_i n_i$.

We can now express the number in a given state in terms of the probability of being in that state; $n_i = N P_i$. This lets us write

$$S = k_B \left[ N \ln N - \sum_i N P_i \ln(N P_i) \right] = N k_B \left[ \ln N - \sum_i P_i \ln P_i - \ln N \sum_i P_i \right]$$

$$S = -N k_B \sum_i P_i \ln P_i \qquad (13.35)$$

We used the fact that $\sum_i P_i = 1$ to simplify our expression. Eq. 13.35 is known as the Gibbs entropy, and is often more useful than the Boltzmann expression, since it is generally easier to determine a probability (population) than a statistical weight.

With the Gibbs entropy expression, we can now use the Boltzmann distribution to develop an expression for entropy in terms of the molecular partition function. It will actually be simpler in this case to use the form of the Boltzmann distribution and partition function where we consider each degenerate state individually, so we recall Eq. 2.18:

$$P_i = \frac{e^{-\epsilon_i/k_BT}}{q} \quad \text{where} \quad q = \sum_i e^{-\epsilon_i/k_BT}$$

Let's put this into the Gibbs entropy expression, Eq. 13.35.

$$S = -Nk_B \sum_i \frac{e^{-\epsilon_i/k_BT}}{q} \ln \frac{e^{-\epsilon_i/k_BT}}{q}$$

$$= -\frac{Nk_B}{q} \left[ \sum_i e^{-\epsilon_i/k_BT} \left( \frac{-\epsilon_i}{k_BT} - \ln q \right) \right]$$

$$S = \frac{Nk_B}{q} \left[ \frac{1}{k_BT} \sum_i \epsilon_i e^{-\epsilon_i/k_BT} + \ln q \sum_i e^{-\epsilon_i/k_BT} \right]$$

Let's look at the two terms we have here. The first term looks a lot like Eq. 13.21; using that equation, we can write

$$\sum_i \epsilon_i e^{-\epsilon_i/k_BT} = \frac{Eq}{N}$$

The sum in the second term is simply the partition function, $q$, so we can write our expression for the entropy (after cancelling many terms) as

$$S = \frac{E}{T} + Nk_B \ln q \tag{13.36}$$

We can also write this strictly in terms of the partition function as

$$S = Nk_BT \left( \frac{\partial \ln q}{\partial T} \right)_V + Nk_B \ln q \tag{13.37}$$

We need to be a little bit careful with using Eq. 13.37 to calculate the entropy of a system. Note that our expressions for energy and pressure don't depend on the value of the partition function itself, but rather on how $q$ changes with either temperature or volume. With entropy, however, the actual value of $q$ matters. This makes some sense when we think about entropy in terms of probabilities. Eq. 13.37 can strictly only be used for evaluating the entropy of a system where the particles are *distinguishable* in some manner. An example of this would be a solid where each molecule can be identified by its spatial position. We should not use this expression for a gas, where the molecules are moving around and are *indistinguishable*.

To obtain an expression for the entropy of a system of noninteracting, indistinguishable particles, we need to make a simple adjustment to Eq. 13.37. Using the rules of logarithms, we can rewrite the last term as

$$Nk_B \ln q = k_B \ln q^N$$

Each molecule has its own partition function, and the overall probability can be thought of as the product of each partition function of each molecule, or $q^N$. This vastly over-counts the possible states, however, when the particles are indistinguishable. To fix this problem, we need to divide the partition function by $N!$. We now write our expression for the entropy as

$$S = Nk_B T \left( \frac{\partial \ln q}{\partial T} \right)_V + k_B \ln \frac{q^N}{N!}$$

$$= Nk_B T \left( \frac{\partial \ln q}{\partial T} \right)_V + k_B \ln q^N - k_B \ln N!$$

$$= Nk_B T \left( \frac{\partial \ln q}{\partial T} \right)_V + Nk_R \ln q - k_B (N \ln N - N)$$

$$S = Nk_B T \left( \frac{\partial \ln q}{\partial T} \right)_V + Nk_B \ln \frac{q}{N} + Nk_B \tag{13.38}$$

Eq. 13.38 is the expression we should use to calculate the entropy of an ideal gas, where the particles are independent and indistinguishable. In molar terms, we write these expressions as

$$S_m = RT \left( \frac{\partial \ln q}{\partial T} \right)_V + R \ln q \qquad \text{Distinguishable}$$

$$S_m = RT \left( \frac{\partial \ln q}{\partial T} \right)_V + R \ln \frac{q}{N} + R \qquad \text{Indistinguishable} \tag{13.39}$$

## Sample Problem 13.1

Using the complete partition function, calculate the total molar entropy for CO at 1 bar pressure and 298 K. Compare your result to thermodynamic tables.

Solution

For the molecule CO, we can write the total molecular partition function as

$$q = \left( \frac{2\pi m k_B T}{h^2} \right)^{3/2} V \frac{T}{\sigma \Theta_{rot}} \frac{1}{1 - e^{-\Theta_{vib}/T}} g_{el,0}$$

Because the CO molecules are indistinguishable, we use the bottom line of Eq. 13.39 to develop a general expression for the molar entropy of CO.

$$S_m = RT\left(\frac{\partial \ln q}{\partial T}\right)_V + R\ln\frac{q}{N} + R$$

Let's write the natural logarithm of the partition function.

$$\ln q = \frac{3}{2}\ln\left(\frac{2\pi m k_B T}{h^2}\right) + \ln V + \ln\frac{T}{\sigma\Theta_{rot}} - \ln(1 - e^{-\Theta_{vib}/T}) + \ln g_{el,0}$$

In the second term of Eq. 13.39, we need $\ln q/N$. Let's include the number with the volume (since we are doing a molar entropy, $N$ is equal to Avogadro's number.) That lets us write

$$\ln q = \frac{3}{2}\ln\left(\frac{2\pi m k_B T}{h^2}\right) + \ln\frac{V}{N_A} + \ln\frac{T}{\sigma\Theta_{rot}} - \ln(1 - e^{-\Theta_{vib}/T}) + \ln g_{el,0}$$

Taking the temperature derivative of the natural logarithm of our partition function gives us

$$\left(\frac{\partial \ln q}{\partial T}\right)_V = \frac{3}{2}\frac{1}{T} + \frac{1}{T} + \left(\frac{\Theta_{vib}}{T^2}\frac{e^{-\Theta_{vib}/T}}{1 - e^{-\Theta_{vib}/T}}\right)$$

The mass of one CO molecule is $5.31365 \times 10^{-26}$ kg. We can find the rotational and vibrational temperatures in Table 13.2; they are 2.77 K and 3103 K, respectively. The ground state electronic degeneracy is found there to be 1. The symmetry number is also 1. For the volume, we can use the ideal gas law to determine the volume of 1 mol at 298 K and 1 bar to be 0.02445 $m^3$.

Putting all this together, we calculate $S_m$ = 199.17 J/mol K for CO. The literature value is 197.67 J/mol K. This is working quite well.

---

If desired, we can calculate the molar entropy from the various types of motion, for example from rotations or vibrations. If we are doing this, we should use the top line of Eq. 13.39 for each contribution, except one. This is not because the molecules are now distinguishable, but because we only need one factor of $R$ in the molar entropy to account for indistinguishability; including a factor of $R$ for each contribution would cause the molar entropy to be much too high. Somewhat by convention, the factor of $R$ for indistinguishability is typically included with the translational molar entropy.

## 13.2.5 Other Thermodynamic Quantities

Table 13.4 summarizes how to calculate thermodynamic variables from the molecular partition function. This table includes two variables we haven't formally seen yet, the Helmholtz energy, $A$, and the Gibbs energy, $G$. (The Gibbs energy should be familiar to you from your general chemistry courses.) Because we have not formally introduced them yet, we will not discuss them further at this point. They are included in the table for sake of completeness and for ease of reference later on.

# 13.3  Summary, and Where We Go Next

In this chapter, we have developed the formalism for calculating thermodynamic properties from the molecular partition function. We've done some pretty heavy lifting in terms of the mathematics, and you may be wondering what good all this is. First of all, we now have a way to calculate the thermodynamic properties of a material from measured spectroscopic results; we saw this in Sample Problem 13.1. This can be very powerful in cases where more conventional measurements are difficult to do. We can also use computational chemistry to calculate the properties of molecules that haven't actually been made yet, and then use statistical mechanics to determine the thermodynamic properties of those new molecules. In Chapter 20, we will learn how to calculate equilibrium constants from partition functions, which means we can determine equilibrium constants from quantum chemistry calculations or spectroscopic measurements, again for reactions that have never been performed in the lab. This is a very powerful use of these ideas.

It is important to note again that we have not yet allowed the molecules to interact in any way, thus these expressions only work for noninteracting particles. Generally speaking, we can only use the approaches we've developed here for gases at low pressures, although that does cover a lot of useful ground. Including interactions adds a whole new dimension of complexity but also allows us to model real gases much better, as well as liquids and solids. We'll tackle that problem in the next chapter.

TABLE 13.1  Parameters of atomic energy levels.

| Atom | Energy level | $g_{el}$ | $\Theta_{el}$ (K) |
|---|---|---|---|
| H | 0 | 2 | 0 |
| He | 0 | 1 | 0 |
| Li | 0 | 2 | 0 |
| O | 0 | 5 | 0 |
|  | 1 | 3 | 228.05 |
|  | 2 | 1 | 325.88 |
| F | 0 | 4 | 0 |
|  | 1 | 2 | 581.27 |

*Source:* McQuarrie, D. A. (1976). *Statistical mechanics.* New York: HarperCollins.

## TABLE 13.2  Parameters of selected diatomic molecules

| Molecule | $g_{el}$ | $\Theta_{vib}$ (K) | $\Theta_{rot}$ (K) | $D_0 = -E_{0,m}$ (kJ mol$^{-1}$) |
|---|---|---|---|---|
| $H_2$ | 1 | 6332 | 85.3 | 432.1 |
| $D_2$ | 1 | 4394 | 42.7 | 435.6 |
| $Cl_2$ | 1 | 805 | 0.351 | 239.2 |
| $Br_2$ | 1 | 463 | 0.116 | 190.1 |
| $I_2$ | 1 | 308 | 0.0537 | 148.8 |
| $O_2$ | 3 | 2256 | 2.07 | 493.6 |
| $N_2$ | 1 | 3374 | 2.88 | 941.6 |
| HCl | 1 | 4227 | 15.02 | 427.8 |
| HBr | 1 | 3787 | 12.02 | 362.6 |
| HI | 1 | 3266 | 9.25 | 294.7 |
| CO | 1 | 3103 | 2.77 | 1070 |

*Source:* McQuarrie, D. A. (1976). *Statistical mechanics*. New York: HarperCollins.

## TABLE 13.3  Parameters of selected polyatomic molecules.

| Molecule | $\sigma$ | $\Theta_{vib, j}$ (K) | $\Theta_{rot, j}$ (K) | $D_0 = -E_{0,m}$ (kJ mol$^{-1}$) |
|---|---|---|---|---|
| $CO_2$ | 2 | 954(2), 1890, 3360 | 0.561 | 1596 |
| $H_2O$ | 2 | 2290, 5160, 5360 | 40.1, 20.9, 13.4 | 917.6 |
| $NH_3$ | 3 | 1360, 2330(2), 4800, 4880(2) | 13.6(2), 8.92 | 1158 |
| $ClO_2$ | 2 | 640, 1360, 1600 | 2.50, 0.478, 0.40 | 378 |
| $SO_2$ | 2 | 750, 1660, 1960 | 2.92, 0.478, 0.422 | 1063 |
| $N_2O$ | 1 | 850(2), 1840, 3200 | 0.603 | 1104 |
| $NO_2$ | 2 | 1080, 1900, 2330 | 11.5, 0.624, 0.59 | 928 |
| $CH_4$ | 12 | 1870(3), 2180(2), 4170, 4320(3) | 7.54(3) | 1642 |
| $CH_3Cl$ | 3 | 1050, 1460(2), 1950, 2140(2), 4270, 4380(2) | 7.32, 0.637(2) | 1551 |
| $CCl_4$ | 12 | 310(2), 450(3), 660, 1120(3) | 0.0823(3) | 1292 |

*Source:* McQuarrie, D. A. (1976). *Statistical mechanics*. New York: HarperCollins.
*Note:* The numbers in parentheses are the relevant degeneracies.

TABLE 13.4 Formulas for calculating thermodynamic properties for indistinguishable, noninteracting molecules from the molecular partition function.

$$U = Nk_BT^2 \left( \frac{\partial \ln q}{\partial T} \right)_V$$

$$C_V = 2Nk_BT \left( \frac{\partial \ln q}{\partial T} \right)_V + Nk_BT^2 \left( \frac{\partial^2 \ln q}{\partial T^2} \right)_V$$

$$P = Nk_BT \left( \frac{\partial \ln q}{\partial V} \right)_T$$

$$S = Nk_BT \left( \frac{\partial \ln q}{\partial T} \right)_V + Nk_B \ln \frac{q}{N} + Nk_B$$

$$A = -Nk_BT \left( \ln \frac{q}{N} + 1 \right)$$

$$G = -Nk_BT \ln \frac{q}{N}$$

# PROBLEMS

**13.1** a) Determine the molar heat capacity at constant volume due to rotations in the classical, or high temperature, limit for both a linear and nonlinear molecule.

    b) For $O_2$, evaluate the rotational partition function by summing over states at a temperature of 300 K and compare this to what you calculate using the high-temperature expression (Eq. 13.14).

**13.2** a) Determine the heat capacity at constant volume due to vibrations in the classical, or high temperature, limit for a nonlinear triatomic molecule.

    b) Choose a molecule from Table 13.3 that is a nonlinear triatomic and calculate the vibrational partition function at 298 K with no approximations. Estimate a temperature that will be high enough for the classical limit to apply in determining the vibrational heat capacity.

**13.3** a) Calculate the pressure, molar internal energy, and constant volume heat capacity of a monatomic ideal gas and a diatomic ideal gas at room temperature.

    b) Using data from the tables, calculate the pressure, molar internal energy, and constant volume heat capacity for $CO_2$ at 300 K. Compare your results to the ideal gas law and classical equipartition theorem.

**13.4** A spectroscopist is able to measure the populations of the first four vibrational states for a sample of CO gas. The data are: $P_0 = 0.8625$, $P_1 = 0.1186$, $P_2 = 0.0163$, $P_3 = 0.0022$.

    a) Determine the vibrational temperature of the sample. (This means the temperature used to describe the distribution between vibrational states, not the parameter of the molecule.)

    b) Is the translational temperature necessarily the same as this vibrational temperature? Why or why not?

**13.5** NO has a doubly degenerate ground electronic state and a doubly degenerate excited state only 121.1 cm$^{-1}$ higher in energy. Make a plot that shows how the electronic partition function changes with temperature from 0 to 1500 K.

**13.6** a) For the system described in Problem 13.4, determine the contribution to the entropy from the electronic states using the expression for the Gibbs entropy.

b) What is the electronic contribution to the entropy if all molecules are in the ground electronic state?

**13.7** a) Consider a monatomic ideal gas. Using an explicit expression of the partition function, derive an expression for the entropy of this gas in terms of state variables. (This is known as the Sackur–Tetrode equation.)

b) Derive another expression for the change in entropy of a monatomic ideal gas that changes its volume at constant temperature.

**13.8** a) Calculate the translational contribution to the entropy for $O_2$ and $Cl_2$ at 298 K and 1 bar, using the second line of Eq. 13.39.

b) Calculate the rotational, vibrational, and electronic contributions to the entropy for $O_2$ and $Cl_2$ at 298 K and 1 bar using the first line of Eq. 13.39.

c) Combine your results and compare to literature values for the entropy of $O_2$ and $Cl_2$.

d) In general chemistry, you may have learned that entropy tends to increase with molecular mass. Do your results to parts a) and b) confirm or contradict this idea? Provide a justification in terms of the energies of the relevant molecular states.

# The Canonical Ensemble and Molecular Interactions

## 14.1 The Canonical Ensemble

Everything we have done with statistical mechanics to this point has been for collections of independent, noninteracting molecules. This would be sufficient if everything were an ideal gas, but that would be a very uninteresting world. We need a way to allow molecules to interact, but we need to develop those interactions in a systematic way. In order to set the stage for molecular interactions, we are first going to develop a new conceptual framework, that of an ensemble.

### 14.1.1 The Concept of an Ensemble

To start us thinking about a statistical-mechanical ensemble, let's consider a bulk sample of gas or liquid. Clearly, we can't possibly keep track of what all the individual molecules are doing in such a large sample. Imagine instead that we take that large sample and divide it up into smaller parts. To be systematic, we want each small part, or **microsystem**, to be of the same size (volume) and to contain the same number of molecules. We also keep the individual microsystems in thermal contact with each other, so they are all at the same temperature. A collection of individual microsystems, each in a slightly different arrangement, is called an **ensemble**. If we make the microsystems small enough, we can conceptually keep track of all the molecules in one of them, and we can allow those molecules to interact with each other. In the last chapter, we showed how we can average over the possible states of a single molecule to gain an understanding of a collection of noninteracting molecules. By performing appropriate operations on the molecular partition function, we were able to determine such thermodynamic properties as energy, pressure, and entropy. In this chapter we will learn how to use the properties of the microsystem that contains molecules that can interact, to gain insight into bulk properties.

The concept of an ensemble is due to J. W. Gibbs, an American physical chemist and one of the pioneers of statistical mechanics. The key part of Gibbs's ensemble hypothesis is that the average over the entire ensemble will give us the macroscopic thermodynamic property. The particular ensemble that we have discussed, where all the microsystems have the same number of molecules, are of the same volume and are at the same temperature, is known as the **canonical ensemble**. The word *canonical* means "according to a rule," and the rule we have chosen is to have the same number ($N$), volume ($V$), and temperature ($T$), for each microsystem in the ensemble.

### 14.1.2 The Canonical Partition Function

The formal description of the canonical ensemble is slightly different from the conceptual picture we have just painted. Let's first begin with a single microsystem. This microsystem is of a particular volume $V$, and contains a fixed number of molecules $N$; the density is fixed. Each of these molecules will be in a particular quantum state involving translational, rotational, vibrational, and electronic energy states. The molecules can also interact with each other, which adds another aspect to the total energy of our microsystem. Because of the many possible arrangements of the different molecules among the various states, and because of the interactions between them, there are many, many ways we could configure our microsystem.

Let's imagine now that we form $M$ copies of our microsystem, one for each possible arrangement. (There will be a lot of copies; in fact, $M$ will approach infinity.) All of these copies are now surrounded by a constant temperature bath; they are all at the same $T$.

This is an important difference from what we did before, where we fixed the energy of our system. By fixing the temperature, the energy of each microsystem can in principle be different, but whatever amount of energy it has must be distributed among the available internal states according to a Boltzmann distribution described by the same $T$ as every other microsystem. This is the full picture of a canonical ensemble; near-infinite copies of our microsystem all in slightly different arrangements and all in thermal contact with each other. This is depicted in Figure 14.1.

The total energy of any given microsystem depends on the energy of each individual molecule and the interaction energy between all the molecules in that microsystem. As you can imagine, there are going to be many microsystems that are degenerate, because of the many different ways we can arrange the molecules but keep the energy the same. As we did in developing the Boltzmann distribution,

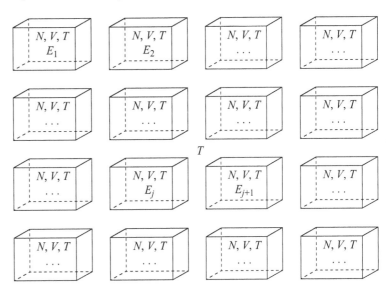

FIGURE 14.1. Depiction of the canonical ensemble. Each microsystem (box) contains the same number of molecules, is of the same volume, and is at the same temperature. The energy of each microsystem can in principle be different. The number of microsystems is of course much greater than those depicted.

we are first interested in the likelihood that a microsystem is in a state with a particular energy, but we will approach this problem from a slightly different direction than we did before.

Let's consider two states of our microsystem with energies $E_1$ and $E_2$. Before going further, it is important to clarify what we mean by the "state" of the microsystem. Recall that each molecule can have its own set of quantum numbers to describe its translational, rotational, vibrational, and electronic states. The state of the microsystem is then described by the complete set of these quantum numbers of all the molecules, plus whatever is needed to describe the interactions. Because the molecules are indistinguishable, if we switch the set of quantum numbers for any two molecules, we have two microsystems that are in the same state; the two microsystems are equivalent. The probability of finding a microsystem in either of two different energy states we would write as

$$P(E = E_1) = \frac{m_1}{M} \quad \text{and} \quad P(E = E_2) = \frac{m_2}{M} \tag{14.1}$$

where $m_1$ and $m_2$ are the number of equivalent microsystems in the ensemble with energies $E_1$ and $E_2$, respectively. $M$ is the total number of microsystems in the ensemble, which will approach infinity.

We don't really care about the absolute probabilities of either case, but the relative probability is of some interest. We can write this relative probability as the ratio of the two absolute probabilities, which has the advantage of eliminating $M$. We write this relative probability as

$$\frac{P(E = E_2)}{P(E = E_1)} = \frac{m_2}{m_1} = f(E_2 - E_1) \tag{14.2}$$

If two states have the same energy, the chance of finding one of them is basically the same as finding the other, and the relative probability approaches 1. If two states have very different energy, then one may be more likely than the other, so the relative probability departs from 1. The relative probability of finding a microsystem in either of the two states will depend in some way on the difference in the energies of those two states, although we don't yet know what that dependence is. We represent this unknown dependence by the function $f(E_2 - E_1)$. (We can write this in terms of the difference in energy because, as we discussed in the last chapter, it is only differences in energy that matter. The absolute energy is always relative to an arbitrary reference.) We can likewise write for the relative probability of finding our microsystem in state 3 or state 2

$$\frac{P(E = E_3)}{P(E = E_2)} = \frac{m_3}{m_2} = f(E_3 - E_2)$$

We can write a similar expression for states 3 and 1

$$\frac{P(E = E_3)}{P(E = E_1)} = \frac{m_3}{m_1} = f(E_3 - E_1)$$

Here is where we use some mathematical reasoning to guess at the form of our function $f$. Let's take the last expression we just wrote and rewrite the middle part slightly

$$\frac{m_3}{m_1} = \frac{m_3}{m_2}\frac{m_2}{m_1}$$

All we've done is multiply and divide by $m_2$; remember, in algebra you can always multiply or divide by 1. This means we could rewrite the right-hand side as

$$f(E_3 - E_1) = f(E_3 - E_2)f(E_2 - E_1)$$

The fact that we can write the function as a product of terms that each depend on a difference of energy suggests that the energy needs to be in an exponent. Recall the rules of multiplying exponentials

$$e^x e^y = e^{x+y}$$

Guided by what we saw with the Boltzmann distribution, we propose a function of the form

$$f(\Delta E) = Ce^{-\Delta E/k_B T}$$

to describe the relative probability of finding two microsystems in states whose energies differ by $\Delta E$, where $C$ is a constant that we will determine soon.

We now propose that the probability of finding a microsystem in a particular state is

$$P_j = \frac{m_j}{M} = Ce^{-E_j/k_B T}$$

where $E_j$ is the energy of that state. (The reference energy is now taken to be the lowest possible energy for the entire microsystem.) To determine the value of the constant $C$, we recall that all the probabilities need to add up to 1.

$$\sum_j P_j = \sum_j \frac{m_j}{M} = 1 = C\sum_j e^{-E_j/k_B T}$$

The constant $C$ is clearly equal to the reciprocal of the sum on the right-hand side of this expression. Thus we can write the probability as

$$P_j = \frac{e^{-E_j/k_B T}}{\sum_j e^{-E_j/k_B T}} \tag{14.3}$$

This looks very much like the Boltzmann distribution we developed back in Chapter 2, and the sum in the denominator looks very similar to the partition function we used before. The key difference here is that the sum is now over the possible states of the entire microsystem, not just the possible states of an individual molecule. The sum in the denominator is called the **canonical partition function** and is symbolized by $Q$. This lets us write the **canonical distribution function** as

$$P_j = \frac{e^{-E_j/k_B T}}{Q} \qquad \text{where} \qquad Q = \sum_j e^{-E_j/k_B T} \tag{14.4}$$

(The approach we used here is clearly different from what was done in Chapter 2; we could actually have used this approach before. We can also arrive at the canonical distribution function in a similar fashion to what we did in Chapter 2 by recognizing that the total energy of our ensemble and the number of microsystems in the ensemble are both fixed. These are basically the same constraints we had before; therefore, we obtain basically the same distribution. The alternate approach we took here was done to give you another way to think about these ideas.)

### 14.1.3 Connections to Thermodynamics

In setting up the canonical ensemble, we have fixed the thermodynamic variables of $N$, $V$, and $T$. The total energy of a single microsystem will depend on these parameters. We are now prepared to formally present the **ensemble postulate** of Gibbs, that the value of the observed thermodynamic property will correspond to the average over the entire ensemble. Mathematically, we write this as

$$\langle M \rangle = \sum_j M_j P_j = \frac{1}{Q} \sum_j M_j e^{-E_j/k_B T} \tag{14.5}$$

where $M$ is a thermodynamic variable—such as energy, pressure, or entropy—and $P_j$ is the probability that a microsystem has the value $M_j$ of the property $M$. (We can't use this to determine $N$, $V$, or $T$, because those parameters are fixed in the canonical ensemble, but we can use it for all other thermodynamic variables.) This average value is what we would measure for the equivalent macroscopic system under the same conditions (temperature and density) as our ensemble.

The average energy for the microsystems in our ensemble is given by

$$E = \sum_j E_j P_j = \frac{1}{Q} \sum_j E_j e^{-E_j/k_B T}$$

Following the same mathematical procedures we used to derive Eq. 13.22, we obtain an expression for the average energy of a microsystem in a canonical ensemble

$$U = \langle E \rangle = k_B T^2 \left( \frac{\partial \ln Q}{\partial T} \right)_{N,V} \tag{14.6}$$

The constant volume heat capacity is readily determined from

$$C_V = \left( \frac{\partial U}{\partial T} \right)_V$$

We then write the constant-volume heat capacity in terms of the canonical partition function as

$$C_V = 2 k_B T \left( \frac{\partial \ln Q}{\partial T} \right)_{N,V} + k_B T^2 \left( \frac{\partial^2 \ln Q}{\partial T^2} \right)_{N,V} \tag{14.7}$$

We can determine an expression for the pressure by following the same procedure we used to derive Eq. 13.33. Doing this gives us

$$P = k_B T \left( \frac{\partial \ln Q}{\partial V} \right)_{N,T} \tag{14.8}$$

Getting an expression for the entropy takes a bit more work, since we don't have a ready relation between entropy and energy to use in Eq. 14.5. We will instead follow a similar procedure to what we used in Chapter 13 and return to the fundamental Boltzmann definition

$$S = k_B \ln W$$

In this case, we are considering the number of ways to arrange the entire ensemble—meaning we are counting the microsystems, not the individual molecules in a microsystem. We write the statistical weight in this case as

$$W = \frac{M!}{\prod_j m_j!}$$

where $M$ is the total number of microsystems in the ensemble and $m_j$ is the number of microsystems in the ensemble in a state with energy $E_j$. Combining these expressions gives us

$$S = k_B \left[ M \ln M - \sum_j m_j \ln m_j \right]$$

where we again used Stirling's approximation and the fact that $\sum_j m_j = M$. We can express the number of microsystems at each energy as a probability, $m_j = MP_j$. Since we did a similar thing in the last chapter, we'll skip some of the intervening steps and jump to the result

$$S_{\text{ensemble}} = - Mk_B \sum_j P_j \ln P_j$$

Note that this is the total entropy of the entire ensemble, which will necessarily approach infinity. It is more useful to consider the typical entropy of a single member of the ensemble, which we obtain by dividing the above expression by $M$.

$$\frac{S_{\text{ensemble}}}{M} = S_{\text{system}} = -k_B \sum_j P_j \ln P_j \tag{14.9}$$

This looks very similar to Eq. 13.35 and gives us the average Gibbs entropy for a microsystem in the canonical ensemble. We can now insert the canonical distribution into Eq. 14.9, which (again skipping a few steps here, because they are basically the same as what we did to derive Eq. 13.37) gives us

$$S = k_B T \left( \frac{\partial \ln Q}{\partial T} \right)_{N,V} + k_B \ln Q \tag{14.10}$$

When we derived Eq. 13.37, we made a modification for situations where the molecules were indistinguishable. That is not needed here, however. Remember that this is the average entropy of a single microsystem. The properties of the molecules in the microsystem, including whether they are indistinguishable or not, are accounted for in the canonical partition function $Q$. So Eq. 14.10 can be used for both the distinguishable and indistinguishable cases, so long as $Q$ is properly defined.

Table 14.1 at the end of the chapter summarizes how to calculate various thermodynamic properties from the canonical partition function. As in Table 13.1, there are two variables we haven't formally introduced yet. The first is the Helmholtz energy, $A$, which we will encounter in Chapter 18. The second is known as the chemical potential, $\mu$, which we will formally introduce in Chapter 19. They are included here for completeness and ease of reference.

### 14.1.4 Fluctuations From the Average Energy

We now have expressions for determining the average energy, heat capacity, pressure, and entropy of the microsystems in our canonical ensemble. As we will now show, not only do these expressions give us the average of these quantities, but they also give us the most likely values of these quantities. One thing about Eq. 14.4 that is not readily obvious is that we are summing over the possible states of the microsystem. We have not explicitly accounted for the degeneracy of these states. For example, imagine that one of our microsystems has a molecule in an excited vibrational state. We could find another microsystem where that molecule is in the ground vibrational state and the difference in vibrational energy is redistributed as rotational and translational energy. The total energy is the same, but the states are different. Thus, the probability of a microsystem having a certain energy—rather than being in a particular state—will need to account for this degeneracy. As the energy of the microsystem increases, the number of ways to spread that energy around among the molecules in the microsystem also increases. The exponential decay of Eq. 14.4 must be multiplied by a sharply rising function to describe the degeneracy, giving rise to a peaked function that will be centered about the average energy we determine from Eq. 14.6. This is similar to what we saw with the populations of rotational levels back in Chapter 10, where the population first rises and then falls away, although this distribution will be much more sharply peaked. In fact, the most probable energy for a microsystem to have will be the average energy given by Eq. 14.6.

Here's another way to think about this. We have described our ensemble as a collection of microsystems, all in thermal contact with each other. The entire ensemble is isolated; therefore, the total energy inside that ensemble is fixed. That total energy now must be spread around among all the separate microsystems. What is the most probable way to do that? Since all the microsystems all have the same volume and contain the same number of molecules, they are to a first approximation all the same. As we saw back in Chapter 2, when the available states are all the same, the most probable way to distribute the energy is to do it uniformly. In other words, even though they differ in the details of how the energy within the microsystem is spread around among the various translational, rotational, vibrational, electronic, and interaction states, the total energy in each microsystem is basically the same as all the others.

Let's present this idea of a narrow distribution of the energies of the microsystems in a more quantitative fashion. In Chapter 13, we developed an expression for the heat capacity in terms of the variance of the energy (Eq. 13.30). Deriving a similar expression for the canonical ensemble gives us

$$\sigma_E^2 = k_B T^2 C_V$$

Recall that the standard deviation (the square root of the variance) relates to the width of the distribution. We can write a relative width of the distribution by dividing the standard deviation by the average energy, which gives us

$$\frac{\sigma_E}{\langle E \rangle} = \frac{(k_B T^2 C_V)^{1/2}}{\langle E \rangle} \tag{14.11}$$

As we saw in Chapter 13 for an ideal gas, the average energy is proportional to $Nk_BT$ and the heat capacity is proportional to $Nk_B$. This means the relative width of the distribution is proportional to $N^{-1/2}$; the more molecules in each microsystem, the narrower the distribution will be. This is one more manifestation of the central limit theorem. In the thermodynamic limit of a very large number of molecules, the standard deviation will approach zero, and each microsystem will have the same energy as every other microsystem, which will be the same as the average energy for the entire ensemble.

# 14.2 Molecular Interactions

## 14.2.1 Canonical Ensemble of Noninteracting Molecules

Now that we have the formalism of the canonical ensemble, and mechanisms to determine thermodynamic properties of that ensemble, we are prepared to deal with interacting molecules. Before doing this, however, we need to be sure that this new formalism matches what we previously did for a system where the molecules cannot interact. This is an important consideration in developing a complicated model; we need to be sure that the more complicated model still describes the simpler case we started with. After we are confident that we can still do what we did before, we can extend our approach to more complicated systems.

The canonical partition function is written as the sum of all the possible states of our microsystem.

$$Q = \sum_j e^{-E_j/k_BT}$$

For a system of noninteracting particles, the total energy of the microsystem is simply the sum of the energies of the individual molecules.

$$E_j = \epsilon_1 + \epsilon_2 + \epsilon_3 + \ldots = \sum_{i=1}^{N} \epsilon_i$$

Now, we put this relation into our expression for the canonical partition function above. But first, let's think about what we have to do. In summing over all the possible states of the microsystem, we need to sum over all possible energy states. This means we need to allow each molecule to be in each of its possible energy states. In other words, we need to do a summation for each molecule

$$Q = \sum_j e^{-E_j/k_BT} = \sum_{i1}\sum_{i2}\cdots\sum_{iN} e^{-(\epsilon_{i1}+\epsilon_{i2}+\cdots+\epsilon_{iN})/k_BT}$$

Using the rules of exponentials, this can be written as a product of sums.

$$Q = \left(\sum_{i1} e^{-\epsilon_{i1}/k_BT}\right)\left(\sum_{i2} e^{-\epsilon_{i2}/k_BT}\right)\cdots\left(\sum_{iN} e^{-\epsilon_{iN}/k_BT}\right)$$

Because all the molecules are the same, the energy states of all the molecules are all the same. This means that each of the summation terms is the same as all the others.

In fact, each of the summation terms is simply the molecular partition function. This lets us write

$$Q = \left( \sum_i e^{-\epsilon_i / k_B T} \right)^N = q^N$$

We need to note that there is generally no way to distinguish any one molecule from another; if we switch the states of two molecules, the total energy of the microsystem remains unchanged. So, to prevent this overcounting, we need to divide by $N!$. This lets us write the canonical partition function for indistinguishable, noninteracting molecules as

$$Q = \frac{q^N}{N!} \tag{14.12}$$

where $N$ is the number of molecules in each microsystem. So, if we know what $q$ is, we know the canonical partition function, and we can determine all thermodynamic properties of our system, **assuming there are no interactions between the molecules**.

Let's revisit the case of indistinguishable, noninteracting monatomic particles—in other words, a monatomic ideal gas. In this case, the atoms only have translational states and the molecular partition function is written as

$$q = \left( \frac{2\pi m k_B T}{h^2} \right)^{3/2} V$$

The canonical partition function would then be written as

$$Q = \frac{1}{N!} \left( \frac{2\pi m k_B T}{h^2} \right)^{3N/2} V^N \tag{14.13}$$

We plug this partition function into Eq. 14.8 to determine the pressure

$$P = k_B T \left( \frac{\partial \ln Q}{\partial V} \right)_{N,T} = k_B T \left( \frac{\partial}{\partial V} \ln \left( \frac{2\pi m k_B T}{h^2} \right)^{3N/2} + N \frac{\partial \ln V}{\partial V} \right) = k_B T \frac{N}{V}$$

Once again, we get the ideal gas law, as expected. Showing that this works for noninteracting polyatomic molecules is left to the student. The energy for the monatomic ideal gas is readily found as

$$U = k_B T^2 \left( \frac{\partial \ln Q}{\partial T} \right)_{N,V} = k_B T^2 \left( \frac{3N}{2} \frac{\partial}{\partial T} \ln T + \frac{\partial}{\partial T} \left( \frac{2\pi m k_B}{h^2} \right)^{3N/2} V^N \right) = \frac{3}{2} N k_B T$$

just as we saw before. (Hopefully you can see why we like taking derivatives of $\ln Q$.)

## 14.2.2 Interacting Molecules and the Configuration Integral

To develop a partition function for interacting molecules, we will again begin with a monatomic gas, where the only motion is translational. The total energy of a collection of interacting atoms can now be written as

$$E_{tot} = \sum_{i=1}^{N} \frac{p_{i,x}^2 + p_{i,y}^2 + p_{i,z}^2}{2m} + V(\vec{r}_1, \vec{r}_2, ..., \vec{r}_N) \qquad (14.14)$$

where $p_{i,x}$ is the $x$-component of the momentum of molecule $i$, with similar terms for the $y$ and $z$ components of momentum. We thus have $3N$ momentum terms; each of the three spatial directions for each of the $N$ molecules. The sum is therefore the total kinetic energy of the gas atoms. The last term is the potential energy, which depends on the position of each atom, represented by the spatial position vector $\vec{r}_i$. The potential energy function also depends on $3N$ variables, the three spatial coordinates of the $N$ atoms. The total energy depends on $6N$ variables, $p_x$, $p_y$, $p_z$, and $x$, $y$, and $z$ for each particle.

The canonical partition function is written as

$$Q = \sum e^{-E_{tot}/k_B T}$$

As we saw in the last chapter, the translational states are effectively continuous and we can treat them classically. We'll take a purely classical view of the canonical partition function to begin evaluating it. Doing so allows us to replace the summation with an integral over each of the coordinates.

$$Q = \int ... \int e^{-\sum_{i=1}^{N} \frac{p_{i,x}^2 + p_{i,y}^2 + p_{i,z}^2}{2mk_B T}} e^{-V(\vec{r}_1, \vec{r}_2, ..., \vec{r}_N)/k_B T} dp_{1,x} ... dp_{N,z} d\vec{r}_1 ... d\vec{r}_N$$

which is a $6N$ dimensional integral. This looks quite intimidating, but we can evaluate much of it quite readily. For the integrals over momentum, this is a standard integral. For each momentum coordinate ($3N$ of them), we have

$$\int_{-\infty}^{\infty} e^{\frac{-p^2}{2mk_B T}} dp = (2\pi m k_B T)^{1/2}$$

To deal with the position integrals, we define a quantity called the **configuration integral**, $Z$.

$$Z = \int ... \int e^{-V(\vec{r}_1, \vec{r}_2, ..., \vec{r}_N)/k_B T} d\vec{r}_1 ... \vec{r}_N \qquad (14.15)$$

This is a $3N$-dimensional integral.

Now we have the total canonical partition function in the general form

$$Q = (2\pi m k_B T)^{3N/2} Z$$

Looking at the first term, we see that it looks very similar to what we had before for our translational partition function in Eq. 13.11. What's missing is the factor of $h^2$ in the denominator of the quantity in parentheses. Note also that the partition function should be unitless, which this isn't.

We conjecture that the proper partition function should have a factor of $h$ for each momentum variable. It is worth spending a little time to justify this conjecture. First, we started with a classical expression for the total energy, and we wouldn't expect the quantum-mechanical factor of $h$ to arise from a classical expression. Also, there must be some degree of uncertainty between the position and momentum variables, which is proportional to $h$ for each pair. Finally, we already did the quantum-mechanical solution for the translational partition function and this is all that's missing, so we know it needs to be there.

The last thing we need to do is account for the indistinguishability of the atoms. This is done by dividing by a factor of $N!$. Now we can write our canonical partition function for indistinguishable, interacting atoms as

$$Q = \frac{1}{N!}\left(\frac{2\pi m k_B T}{h^2}\right)^{3N/2} Z \tag{14.16}$$

For polyatomic molecules, it is actually a good approximation to assume that the configuration integral is independent of rotations and vibrations. In this case, we can write

$$Q = \frac{1}{N!}\left(\frac{2\pi m k_B T}{h^2}\right)^{3N/2} q_{rot}^N q_{vib}^N q_{el}^N Z \tag{14.17}$$

Now, the difficulty comes in evaluating the configuration integral.

As we have done before, we need to make sure that this more complicated depiction of the partition function reduces to the simpler case if there are no interactions. In the case of no interactions, the potential energy is zero. This makes the argument of the exponential in Eq. 14.15 equal to zero and, since $e^0 = 1$, the configuration integral becomes

$$Z = \int ... \int d\vec{r}_1 ... d\vec{r}_N = V^N$$

This brings us right back to Eq. 14.13, the same canonical partition function we had before for a noninteracting monatomic gas. Thus, if we "turn off" the interactions, we go right back to the partition function of an ideal gas.

### 14.2.3 Pairwise Interaction Potentials

Evaluating the configuration integral for fully interacting systems is obviously a difficult undertaking. Following the pattern we have used all along, we will increase the level of complexity in small steps. The simplest way we can allow our particles to interact is through a pairwise interaction potential. This means that the interaction between particle 1 and particle 2 is independent of the position of particles 3 through $N$. Because the particles are all the same, and indistinguishable, the interactions between any two of them will be the same as any other two. We can thus pick two of the particles to be representative of all the particles and write the potential in terms of only their positions.

$$V_{\text{pairwise}} = V(\vec{r}_1, \vec{r}_2) \tag{14.18}$$

When we evaluate the configuration integral for this type of potential, we can readily integrate out the spatial coordinates of the remaining particles and write

$$Z = V^{N-2} \int\int e^{-V(\vec{r}_1, \vec{r}_2)/k_B T} d\vec{r}_1 d\vec{r}_2 = V^{N-2} Z_2$$

The integral that we are denoting $Z_2$ now only depends on the three spatial coordinates of the three particles, so it is a six-dimensional integral. The location of the particles inside the box doesn't matter, so we can switch to a center of mass frame of reference. The potential energy depends on the relative positions of the particles, not their absolute placement in the system. This reduces the six dimensional integral to a three-dimensional integral; the other three dimensions integrate out and give another factor of the volume. If the interaction is isotropic, meaning it doesn't depend on direction, we can convert to spherical coordinates and integrate over the angular components, leaving only the relative distance between the molecules, which we will denote as $r$. (Integrating over the angular coordinates introduces a factor of $4\pi$.) Thus for molecules that only interact through an isotropic pairwise interaction, the configuration integral reduces from $3N$ dimensions to one dimension, $r$.

In your general chemistry courses, you probably encountered an equation of state known as the virial equation. (We will formally present the virial equation in Chapter 16.) The virial equation is written as a series expansion in terms of the molar volume of a gas.

$$\frac{PV_m}{RT} = 1 + \frac{B}{V_m} + \frac{C}{V_m^2} + \dots \tag{14.19}$$

where the virial coefficients $B$, $C$, and so on are determined empirically. For a gas that is behaving ideally, $B$, $C$, and all higher terms go to zero. We won't formally go through the derivation here, but if we have an isotropic pairwise interaction potential of the type we have been describing, the second virial coefficient $B$ can be determined from that potential according to the relation

$$B(T) = -2\pi N_A \int_0^\infty (e^{-V(r)/k_B T} - 1)r^2 \, dr \tag{14.20}$$

Note that if there are no interactions, the argument of the exponential goes to zero, which makes the entire integral go to zero and returns the ideal gas law. The higher virial coefficients depend on three- and four-body interactions, which we will not formally explore here.

There are many ways to describe the interactions between molecules, depending on their shape and whether they are polar or not. These functions can become quite complicated, depending on the particular molecules under study. The simplest possible function is the so-called **hard sphere potential**, which simply treats the molecules as hard spheres that can't overlap with each other. Beyond a distance $d$ between the molecular centers of mass, the interaction potential is zero. At distances less than $d$ the potential is infinite, to prevent the particles from overlapping.

$$V_{\text{hard sphere}} = \begin{array}{l} \infty \text{ for } r < d \\ 0 \text{ for } r \geq d \end{array} \tag{14.21}$$

Another interaction potential that is commonly used is the Lennard-Jones potential, developed by J. E. Lennard-Jones in 1924.

$$V_{LJ} = 4\epsilon \left[ \left( \frac{\sigma}{r} \right)^{12} - \left( \frac{\sigma}{r} \right)^6 \right] \tag{14.22}$$

This is sometimes called the 6–12 potential because of the exponents in the two terms. The first term shows the repulsive interaction that only becomes important as the molecules get close to each other. The second term is the attractive interaction that extends over a larger distance. The parameters $\sigma$ and $\epsilon$ are the contact distance and strength of the

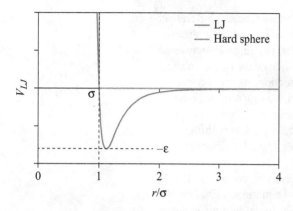

**FIGURE 14.2.** Plots of the Lennard-Jones and hard-sphere potentials where $d = \sigma$.

interaction, respectively. Figure 14.2 shows the Lennard-Jones and hard-sphere potentials. The Lennard-Jones potential is most applicable to quasi-spherical molecules with no permanent dipole moment, such as $CH_4$. More complicated potentials are necessary for polar molecules and other types of interactions.

# 14.3 Other Types of Ensembles

This section is given for a sense of completeness. We won't do too much more with it, but you should be aware that there are different ways to build an ensemble. We have already discussed the canonical ensemble, which has fixed $N$, $V$, and $T$ for each microsystem. Another approach is not to fix the $T$ of the microsystem, but the energy $E$. This is known as the **microcanonical ensemble**. (No energy can be exchanged between microsystems, rather each microsystem is isolated from all the others.) Another approach fixes $N$, $T$, and $P$, and is known as the **isothermal–isobaric ensemble**. In this ensemble, the different "boxes" can be of different size (volume) to keep the pressure constant. The last type of ensemble that is commonly used is known as the **grand canonical ensemble**. In this ensemble, the number of particles in each microsystem is allowed to change; the fixed variable is the chemical potential, $\mu$, which we will introduce in Chapter 19. The choice of ensemble depends on the problem being solved. Note also that the form of the partition function changes depending on the choice of ensemble, as do the mathematical operations that are used to extract thermodynamic variables from that partition function.

# 14.4 Molecular Simulations

As we have seen, once we allow molecules to interact with each other, it can be very difficult to describe the system analytically. One alternative approach is to conduct numerical simulations of the system of interest. In Chapter 12, we explored quantum chemistry calculations and what we can learn about the structure and energy states of molecules. Those methods, however, generally only treat a single molecule, or a small group of molecules. For large groups of molecules that are interacting in complicated ways, we need different computational tools. Two of the most common methods, which we will describe here, are **molecular dynamics** and **Monte Carlo** simulations. Each has its own strengths and weaknesses, but both are powerful ways to investigate complicated systems at the molecular level.

## 14.4.1 Molecular Dynamics Simulations

The basic principles of a molecular dynamics (MD) simulation are fairly straightforward and are based on classical (rather than quantum) mechanics. We can get away with using classical physics because the translational states of molecules are so close together at room temperature. The heart of an MD simulation is the use of Newtonian mechanics to modify the trajectories of each particle due to the interactions between the various particles. The interactions are modeled by an interaction potential, sometimes called a *force field*. Potentials such as the Lennard-Jones are often used, although the force fields can be much more complicated, depending on the system.

To start an MD simulation, the simulation space is populated with molecules. Each molecule is given an initial position and an initial velocity; the distribution of velocities is determined by the temperature of the simulation and the Boltzmann distribution. MD simulations are performed in an iterative fashion. The steps are as follows:

- For each molecule, calculate all the forces acting on that molecule from neighboring molecules. The forces are calculated according to $\vec{F} = -\nabla V$, where $V$ is the total potential experienced by each molecule.
- Once the total force acting on each particle has been determined, the velocity is modified according to Newton's second law $\vec{F} = m\dfrac{d\vec{v}}{dt}$.
- Each particle is allowed to move a short distance during a time interval $\Delta t$, after which the forces are recalculated and the cycle starts again.

Because the molecules all move about deterministically, and we can track the position of each particle over time, an MD single simulation is sometimes referred to as a **trajectory**. It is very common to make movies of these trajectories to visualize how the molecules move over time.

The simulation space of an MD simulation needs to be large enough to contain a statistically significant number of molecules, but yet not be too large. Remember, we have to keep track of the position and velocity (and possibly the orientation) of every molecule in the system, as well as calculate changes in the trajectory of each molecule. The size of the simulation is thus ultimately limited by the speed and memory capacity of the computer on which it is to be run. Another consideration of the simulation is the time step, $\Delta t$. This time interval needs to be shorter than any relevant physical process taking place in the simulation. Recall that for a gas, the average time between collisions was on the order of 1 ns ($10^{-9}$ s). Thus, MD simulations of gases need to have time steps of maybe a few 10s of ps ($10^{-11}$ s). For liquid simulations, where the molecules are in almost perpetual contact, the time step often needs to be less than 1 fs ($10^{-15}$ s). Therefore, a complete simulation may only be able to cover a few ns of real time; storage of all the data is a real problem.

Thermodynamic properties can be extracted from an MD simulation because of the **ergodic hypothesis**. Simply put, the ergodic hypothesis states that the time average of a small system (our simulation space) represents the ensemble average of a large system. Therefore, to determine a thermodynamic property such as the pressure or the energy, we can calculate that property at each step of the simulation, and then average that result over many (often thousands) of simulation steps. So long as the simulation has equilibrated, meaning that this average value is not changing over time, this calculated average represents what we would measure for the actual physical system. Allowing the system to equilibrate may take up to half or more of the run time of the simulation, but if that is neglected, the simulation will give nonphysical results.

The idea of the ergodic hypothesis gives us another way to think of an ensemble. We originally thought of the ensemble as replicates of our system such that we have one representation of every possible situation that meets the specified values of $N$, $V$, and $T$. Well, our simulation space in an MD simulation is just such a representation; it has a fixed number of molecules in a fixed volume at a fixed temperature. Therefore, each time step of the simulation represents one of the possible elements of our ensemble. As the simulation runs, we are in effect switching which microsystem of the ensemble we are looking at. This is what is meant by *sampling the configuration space*. By taking the time average of the simulation, we are also averaging over the elements of our ensemble. Now you may be saying to yourself that there are some configurations in the ensemble that we won't see in our simulation, and you are right. But, the configurations we won't see are the ones that are least likely to occur, so they don't significantly affect the average anyway. Once the simulation has equilibrated, we are only going to see configurations that have properties close to what the ensemble average would be if we were to calculate it directly. So taking the time average of the simulation gives us the same results.

MD simulations are typically run in one of two modes: *NVT* or *NPT*. (You should recognize the first as the same variables we control in the canonical ensemble.) In a *NVT* simulation, a fixed number of particles are modeled in a simulation space of a fixed volume. Often, **periodic boundary conditions** are used, which means that if a particle leaves through one wall of the simulation space, it will reenter through the opposite side. The simulation space thus needs to be large enough that a molecule can't interact with itself through the walls, which can be in issue when simulating large molecules like polymer strands or proteins. Temperature is controlled by adding or subtracting small amounts of energy to keep the temperature constant, through a part of the simulation program known as the thermostat. In a *NPT* simulation, the pressure needs to be kept constant, which means the volume of the simulation space is constantly changing.

Another aspect of an MD simulation we need to discuss is the level of detail in the simulation. You may think that we would always want to include every atom in the simulation (known as an **all-atom simulation**), but that can become computationally prohibitive for large systems. In some cases, particularly when modeling proteins or polymers, entire functional groups are represented by a single simulation particle. For example, each residue in a protein could be condensed to a single simulation object. The protein then resembles beads on a chain, with flexibility in the bonding between beads. This allows for the modeling of larger molecules but sacrifices some of the finer details.

Another consideration is the solvent. Even at moderate concentrations, we will have thousands or millions of solvent molecules for each solute molecule. Again, we have to make a choice as to the level of detail we want in our results and the available resources to run the simulation. When we include each solvent molecule in the simulation, this is known as **explicit solvent**. Another option is to represent the solvent by collective properties, such as its dielectric constant, meaning the solute molecules move about in a continuous medium; this is known as **implicit solvent**. A hybrid approach, often used in modeling proteins, is to include enough explicit solvent molecules to fully solvate the protein, but beyond the second solvation shell to represent the solvent implicitly. Making choices of this type is part of the "art" of MD.

MD simulations are a very powerful way to perform molecular simulations. In cases where quantum effects are important, those can be added to perform so-called **quantum MD**. Quantum-MD simulations, however, are very computationally expensive, and so are only done when absolutely necessary. Hybrid approaches are again possible. For example, the active site of an enzyme can be treated quantum mechanically, while the rest of the protein is treated with classical MD. Again, there is an art to doing this well and efficiently.

## 14.4.2 Monte Carlo Simulations

The other significant method used to investigate molecular systems computationally is known as Monte Carlo. The city of Monte Carlo, which is located in Monaco on the coast of the Mediterranean, is best known for its casinos. In a Monte Carlo simulation, we quite literally roll dice to determine the outcome. The key here is that the probabilities of outcomes are weighted by a Boltzmann distribution.

A Monte Carlo (MC) simulation begins similar to an MD simulation; molecules are randomly placed in the simulation space. Once the simulation begins, however, things look very different from MD. Whereas an MD simulation proceeds deterministically from the initial conditions, there are no trajectories in the conventional sense in an MC simulation. Rather, a random new configuration—which could be very different from the initial configuration—is generated. The simulation then has to decide whether to accept this new configuration or not. The steps proceed as follows:

- Randomly generate a possible new configuration of the simulation space.
- Determine the energy of the new configuration and compare that value to the energy of the current configuration.
- If the energy of the new configuration is lower than that of the old configuration, accept the new configuration and start the process over.
- If the energy of the new configuration is higher than that of the old, calculate a Boltzmann factor, $e^{-\Delta E/k_B T}$, where $\Delta E$ is the energy difference between the new and old configurations. Because the energy difference must be positive, the Boltzmann factor will always be less than 1.
- Generate a random number between 0 and 1 and compare it to the Boltzmann factor. If the random number is greater than the Boltzmann factor, reject the new configuration and restart the process. If the random number is less than the Boltzmann factor, accept the new configuration and restart the process.

Because an MC simulation allows for random changes to the configuration, it can more quickly sample the "configuration space" of the simulation. This may allow the simulation to converge more quickly than an equivalent MD simulation. Care must be taken, however, in conducting the simulation that reasonable new configurations are proposed. To maintain efficiency, there should be a limit to the number of rejected configurations; it would not be an effective use of computational resources if 90% of the new configurations are rejected. The rules for these "moves" can vary depending on the type of system under study, and designing the process for proposing reasonable moves is part of the art of using the MC method. Once we have found many energetically equivalent (degenerate) configurations, we can average over any other property, such as pressure, to determine the bulk quantity. Data storage can again be an issue, because we have to record enough information about each acceptable configuration "snapshot" to perform this averaging.

## 14.4.3 Comparison of Methods

The choice of whether to use MD or MC depends to a great extent on the nature of the system you want to study. Each has its own advantages and disadvantages. MD is a deterministic simulation, so it can depend greatly on the starting conditions. For this reason, multiple simulations, each referred to as a trajectory, are often run to make sure the answers are independent of the starting conditions. This may take more time than running an MC simulation, where you randomly sample multiple configurations during the course of the simulation; MC simulations are, in principle, less sensitive to starting conditions. One advantage of MD, though, is that you can watch how the system evolves from those initial conditions. That's not possible in MC, because the system is randomly changing. There are multiple packages that animate the results of an MD simulation to make molecular "movies," but you would only get "still shots" from MC results.

One disadvantage of MD is the possibility of the system getting trapped in a local energy minimum. This is particularly problematic in problems like protein folding, where there are many stable configurations. If an MD simulation finds itself in a local energy minimum, it may not be able to work its way out, hence the need again for multiple starting conditions to make sure you find the true minimum energy configuration. MC is much less susceptible to this, since it can sample configurations that are different from any local minimum. Thus, MC is more likely to find the true minimum energy configuration more quickly than MD, however an MC simulation won't give as much insight into how the protein can dynamically achieve that configuration. For some problems, it may make sense to use both MD and MC to more fully understand the system.

Both MD and MC methods are valuable in investigating the molecular behavior of systems with a great deal of interactions. MD is a deterministic approach, based on classical mechanics, whereas MC is a stochastic process that uses probability and random numbers to change the configuration of the system. Both approaches have value, and some inherent limitations, but they can provide very valuable insight into how molecular interactions drive a wide variety of processes.

## 14.5 Summary, and Where We Go Next

In this chapter, we have developed our understanding of the canonical ensemble and learned how to deal with molecules that can interact with each other. This isn't too bad for fairly simple cases of pairwise interactions, but we can see how it can get quite difficult for more complicated systems. Developing interaction potentials and ways to evaluate the configuration integral for more complex systems is an area of active research in statistical mechanics. This is pretty much as far as we are going to go in our treatment of statistical mechanics. We also learned about molecular dynamics and Monte Carlo simulations and how they can help us explore interacting molecules.

In the next chapter, we move into the development of thermodynamics. Throughout our discussion of thermodynamics, we will "look under the hood" and explore the molecular-level phenomena that drive macroscopic behavior. One way we will do this is by connecting the partition function to the new thermodynamic variables that will be introduced, such as the Gibbs energy. As we mentioned back in Chapter 1, thermodynamics does not require any underlying theory on the structure of matter, but our understanding of thermodynamics is significantly enriched by taking a molecular perspective.

**TABLE 14.1.** Formulas for calculating thermodynamic properties from the canonical partition function.

$$U = k_B T^2 \left( \frac{\partial \ln Q}{\partial T} \right)_{N,V} \qquad C_V = 2k_B T \left( \frac{\partial \ln Q}{\partial T} \right)_{N,V} + k_B T^2 \left( \frac{\partial^2 \ln Q}{\partial T^2} \right)_{N,V}$$

$$P = k_B T \left( \frac{\partial \ln Q}{\partial V} \right)_{N,T} \qquad S = k_B T \left( \frac{\partial \ln Q}{\partial T} \right)_{N,V} + k_B \ln Q$$

$$A = -k_B T \ln Q \qquad \mu_i = -k_B T \left( \frac{\partial \ln Q}{\partial N_i} \right)_{T,V,N_{j \neq i}}$$

# PROBLEMS

**14.1** This problem will simulate some of the ideas of an ensemble. Consider a large container of gas at 1 bar and 300 K that we subdivide into small boxes all of the same size.

a) Neglecting gravity or any other effects, the most probable way to distribute the gas molecules throughout the various boxes is to do so uniformly. Write an expression for the statistical weight of this uniform distribution of the molecules.

b) Imagine now that we take a small number of molecules from one box and put them in another box. Write an expression for the statistical weight of this new distribution.

c) We can think of the relative probability of the two situations by taking the ratio of the respective statistical weights. Derive such an expression.

d) If the boxes are 1 cm³ in size, what is the probability that we have a change in number of 0.1% between two neighboring boxes? What does this mean physically for our sample of gas?

e) Repeat the calculation for boxes of 100 Å on a side and interpret the results.

**14.2** a) Write an expression for the canonical partition function for a diatomic ideal gas.

b) Show that you obtain the ideal gas law from this partition function.

**14.3** a) Derive an expression for the virial $B$ coefficient for a gas that is well modeled by the hard sphere potential.

b) Show that the virial equation of state for this gas becomes the ideal gas law in the limit that the diameter of the hard spheres goes to zero.

**14.4** a) For the Lennard-Jones interaction potential, derive the distance at which the energy is a minimum.

b) Recall that the force acting between two particles is found by evaluating $F = \dfrac{-dV}{dr}$. Derive an expression for the maximum attractive force between two particles that interact through a Lennard-Jones potential.

c) The $\epsilon$ parameters for He and $CH_4$ are 10 and 148, respectively, given in units of K. The $\sigma$ parameters have values of 2.58 and 3.73 Å, respectively. Compare the maximum attractive forces between two He atoms and two $CH_4$ molecules using the results to part b).

**14.5** a) Consider an MD simulation of water vapor. The time step of the simulation is $10^{-14}$ s and the simulation space contains 2,500 molecules. We need to calculate changes in motion for all translational and rotational coordinates of each molecule. If we want to run the simulation for 1 ns ($10^{-9}$ s), how many calculations need to take place over the duration of the simulation?

b) Notice that we did not ask for calculations of vibrational motion. Why is it justified to neglect the vibrational motion in this simulation?

**14.6** The results from the last 10 steps of an MC simulation are given below, including proposed configurations that were rejected by the simulation code. From these results, what value should be reported for the average pressure of the system? The temperature of the simulation was 300 K.

| Step | Pressure/bar | Energy/J mol$^{-1}$ | Random number |
|------|------|------|------|
| 0 | 1.04 | 6500 | |
| 1 | 0.993 | 6190 | 0.785 |
| 2 | 1.08 | 6720 | 0.087 |
| 3 | 1.02 | 6330 | 0.589 |
| 4 | 1.13 | 7035 | 0.930 |
| 5 | 1.12 | 7007 | 0.096 |
| 6 | 1.33 | 8320 | 0.804 |
| 7 | 1.15 | 7200 | 0.301 |
| 8 | 0.99 | 6230 | 0.349 |
| 9 | 1.06 | 6700 | 0.858 |
| 10 | 1.04 | 6478 | 0.421 |

# CHEMICAL THERMO-DYNAMICS

Why Things Happen

# State Variables and Equations of State Revisited

## Molecular Structure of Matter

## 15.1 Mathematics of State Variables

Back in Chapter 1, we introduced the concept of **state variables**, which are mathematical variables that describe the physical state of our system. The variables we first discussed were temperature ($T$), pressure ($P$), volume ($V$), and amount ($n$). Since then, we have also encountered internal energy ($E$ or $U$), heat capacity ($C_v$), and entropy ($S$), which are also state variables. As we continue our study of thermodynamics, we will develop some additional state variables for our convenience in describing physical systems. Before going much further, it is important that we go over some of the important mathematical characteristics of state variables and how we can use these properties in solving problems.

### 15.1.1 Extensive and Intensive Variables

First, recall that there are two types of state variables, **extensive** and **intensive**. An extensive variable depends on the size of the system, so if we double the size of the system, the numerical value of that property will also double. Examples of extensive variables include volume, amount, mass, energy, heat capacity, and entropy. An intensive variable, on the other hand, is independent of the size of the system. Temperature and pressure are both intensive variables. If we double the size of the system, the temperature does not double, but instead remains the same.

If we divide an extensive variable by another extensive variable, we obtain an intensive variable. For example, density is the ratio of the extensive variables mass and volume, so density is intensive. It is very common to divide an extensive variable by the amount to obtain a molar quantity, such as the molar volume or molar heat capacity. Such molar quantities are all intensive. One advantage of working with intensive variables is that they depend on the type of system under study, not any particular sample. Whether I have 10 g or 10 tons of material does not affect its intensive properties. We will primarily work with intensive variables in the main text for these reasons, but many problems will deal with systems of a specific size, so pay attention.

## 15.1.2 Equations of State

The state variables describe the physical state of the system, and the mathematical relationships between them need to correspond to those physical properties. A mathematical expression that describes the relation between the state variables is known as an **equation of state**. The equation of state, or EOS, we have dealt with almost exclusively is the ideal gas law

$$PV = Nk_BT \qquad \text{or} \qquad PV = nRT$$

This simple mathematical expression describes how the quantities of pressure, volume, amount (or number), and temperature are related to each other for an ideal gas.

Notice that we cannot independently vary all four of our state variables; for example, if we choose the amount, temperature, and volume of our gas, the pressure is defined by the equation of state. Mathematically, the EOS acts as a constraint on the possible values of the state variables. Any three of the four can be chosen as our **independent variables**, and the fourth one becomes the **dependent variable**. Another way to represent this mathematically is to write

$$P(n,V,T) \tag{15.1}$$

which shows that the pressure is a function of amount, volume, and temperature. If we fix the amount, or if we prefer to talk about molar volume instead of absolute volume, we can write

$$P(V_m,T) \tag{15.2}$$

Using this approach, we would write the ideal gas law as

$$P = \frac{RT}{V_m} \tag{15.3}$$

Now, we only have two independent variables, molar volume and temperature. The pressure is fixed by the EOS.

The choice of which variables are independent and dependent is really up to us. Perhaps it is easier to measure one quantity than another. Or, perhaps the mathematical relationship is more convenient to write in a particular way. The system under study doesn't care how we describe it, as long as our description is true to the physical reality. It is nice that we can do what is most convenient for us. We will see examples of other equations of state later in the chapter.

Before moving on, it is good to put the equation of state into context with what we have done before. It is really quite remarkable that we can describe all the motion and interactions of all the molecules in a sample of gas at relatively low pressure and high temperature by just four variables. This is because of probability, the central limit theorem, and the very large number of molecules in a macroscopic sample. All the different positions, momenta, and quantum states of all the molecules average out to these four state variables and a simple relation between them. Even for more complicated systems, where the molecules can interact, the equation of state will be much simpler than the full quantum mechanical description of that system, again because of the statistics of very large numbers. As we work at the macroscopic scale, we won't have to deal directly with the molecular complexity, but we can gain some insight into what is happening at the molecular level from the relations between the state variables.

## 15.1.3 Total Differentials and Partial Derivatives

Equations of state are quite clearly functions of more than one variable. To discuss changes in the state variables, therefore, we need to use the tools of multivariable calculus. Let's define a function $f(x, y, z)$. The total change in $f$, which we call $df$, can be written in terms of the changes in the variables $dx$, $dy$, and $dz$, in this fashion:

$$df = \left( \frac{\partial f}{\partial x} \right)_{y,z} dx + \left( \frac{\partial f}{\partial y} \right)_{x,z} dy + \left( \frac{\partial f}{\partial z} \right)_{x,y} dz \qquad (15.4)$$

$dx$, $dy$, and $dz$ are **differentials**, and the coefficients in front of them are called **partial derivatives**. The overall change, $df$, is the **total differential**. Each partial derivative tells us how $f$ changes with changes in one of the variables while keeping all the other variables constant. For any function of any number of independent variables, we can always write the total differential in the same fashion with one term for each independent variable.

We now need to talk about partial derivatives and some of the notation we are using. Notice that we use a script d ($\partial$) for a partial derivative, but a print $d$ for differentials and total differentials. (Note that if the function has only one independent variable, there is no distinction between a partial and total derivative, so we use the print $d$.) The subscripts next to the partial derivative tell us the variables that are kept constant; only one variable is changed at a time in a partial derivative.

Recall that the EOS describes a surface in $(P, V, T)$ space for some value of $n$. (See Figure 1.6 for the ideal gas.) We can evaluate the shape of this surface along particular directions through the use of partial derivatives. Let's first write the total derivative for $P$. (For simplicity, we'll use molar volume, so $P$ is described by Eq. 15.2.)

$$dP = \left( \frac{\partial P}{\partial V_m} \right)_T dV_m + \left( \frac{\partial P}{\partial T} \right)_{V_m} dT \qquad (15.5)$$

Let's now use the ideal gas law for some practice in working with partial derivatives. Since we know the relation between $P$, $V_m$, and $T$ from Eq. 15.3, we can solve for the partial derivatives explicitly.

$$\left( \frac{\partial P}{\partial V_m} \right)_T = \frac{-RT}{V_m^2} \qquad \left( \frac{\partial P}{\partial T} \right)_{V_m} = \frac{R}{V_m} \qquad (15.6)$$

Since the EOS describes a surface, we can think of the partial derivatives as the slope of that surface along one of the coordinate axes. For example, $\left( \frac{\partial P}{\partial V_m} \right)_T$ describes the slope of the surface perpendicular to the temperature axis at a chosen value of $T$ and $V_m$. Complete description of the surface requires the slope in both directions at any given point on the surface.

As another example, let's define the internal energy as $U(n,V,T)$. (You might ask yourself why we don't have to write $U(n,V,T,P)$.) We write the total differential as

$$dU = \left(\frac{\partial U}{\partial n}\right)_{V,T} dn + \left(\frac{\partial U}{\partial V}\right)_{n,T} dV + \left(\frac{\partial U}{\partial T}\right)_{n,V} dT$$

If we are using the molar internal energy, then $n$ is no longer a variable and we can write

$$U_m(V_m,T)$$

$$dU_m = \left(\frac{\partial U_m}{\partial V_m}\right)_T dV_m + \left(\frac{\partial U_m}{\partial T}\right)_{V_m} dT$$

(This is another reason why molar quantities are convenient; they remove one more variable, $n$, from our total differential.) The first partial derivative tells us how the molar internal energy changes with a change in molar volume, keeping the temperature constant. The second partial derivative tells us how the molar internal energy changes with a change in temperature, keeping the molar volume constant. (You should recognize this last partial derivative as the constant volume molar heat capacity.)

Because the choice of which variables are independent is up to us, we could also write the molar internal energy and it total differential as

$$U_m(P,V_m)$$

$$dU_m = \left(\frac{\partial U_m}{\partial P}\right)_{V_m} dP + \left(\frac{\partial U_m}{\partial V_m}\right)_P dV_m$$

The choice is ours. (Later on, we will see that this particular choice of independent variables will not actually be very convenient in describing the internal energy.) In answer to our earlier question, the reason we only need to specify two of the three variables $P$, $V_m$, and $T$, is that the equation of state constrains the value of the third one, so it's not actually variable.

### 15.1.4 Properties of Partial Derivatives

Now back to math for a little while. There are several properties of partial derivatives that will prove useful as we pursue our development of thermodynamics.

*Reciprocal Rule* – It can be shown that

$$\left(\frac{\partial f}{\partial x}\right)_y = \frac{1}{\left(\dfrac{\partial x}{\partial f}\right)_y} \tag{15.7}$$

Let's demonstrate this with the ideal gas law. Let's first write this as

$$P = \frac{nRT}{V}$$

If we evaluate the change in pressure with temperature, keeping volume and amount constant, we have

$$\left(\frac{\partial P}{\partial T}\right)_{V,n} = \frac{nR}{V}$$

We can also solve the ideal gas law for temperature, which we write as

$$T = \frac{PV}{nR}$$

We can now write the change in temperature with respect to pressure, keeping volume and amount constant, as

$$\left(\frac{\partial T}{\partial P}\right)_{V,n} = \frac{V}{nR}$$

If we substitute these both into the reciprocal rule, we have

$$\left(\frac{\partial P}{\partial T}\right)_{V,n} = \frac{nR}{V} = \frac{1}{\left(\frac{\partial T}{\partial P}\right)_{V,n}} = \frac{1}{\left(\frac{V}{nR}\right)} = \frac{nR}{V}$$

(For the mathematicians out there, this is a demonstration, not a proof.) Always make sure you are keeping the same variables constant in your partial derivatives when using the reciprocal rule.

*Chain Rule* – Let's start with the total differential of $f(x, y)$

$$df = \left(\frac{\partial f}{\partial x}\right)_y dx + \left(\frac{\partial f}{\partial y}\right)_x dy$$

Let's first consider the case where $y$ is kept constant. This means $dy = 0$, so we can write

$$df_y = \left(\frac{\partial f}{\partial x}\right)_y dx_y$$

The subscript $y$ means that $y$ is kept constant. If we divide both sides by $dx_y$, then we have

$$\frac{df_y}{dx_y} = \left(\frac{\partial f}{\partial x}\right)_y \tag{15.8}$$

So, we can write the ratio of differentials where all but one variable is being kept constant as a partial derivative.

We'll also allow for a variable $z$ on which $x$ and $y$ both depend: $x(z)$, $y(z)$. Let's divide the first expression by $dx$ at constant $z$. That gives

$$\left(\frac{\partial f}{\partial x}\right)_z = \left(\frac{\partial f}{\partial x}\right)_y \left(\frac{\partial x}{\partial x}\right)_z + \left(\frac{\partial f}{\partial y}\right)_x \left(\frac{\partial y}{\partial x}\right)_z$$

$$\left(\frac{\partial f}{\partial x}\right)_z = \left(\frac{\partial f}{\partial x}\right)_y + \left(\frac{\partial f}{\partial y}\right)_x \left(\frac{\partial y}{\partial x}\right)_z \tag{15.9}$$

Eq. 15.9 is known as the chain rule. (Note that $\left(\dfrac{\partial x}{\partial x}\right)_z = 1$.)

If instead we divide by $dz$ at constant $y$, we have

$$\left(\frac{\partial f}{\partial z}\right)_y = \left(\frac{\partial f}{\partial x}\right)_y \left(\frac{\partial x}{\partial z}\right)_y \tag{15.10}$$

because $\left(\dfrac{\partial y}{\partial z}\right)_y = 0$. This is a special case of the chain rule, and it can be quite useful. This is similar to splitting up a fraction by multiplying top and bottom by the same number; remember, you can always multiply by 1. Note that the same variable is kept constant in all three partial derivatives in Eq. 15.10.

*Cyclic Rule* – Let's take the general chain rule (Eq. 15.9) and replace $f$ with $z$. Doing so gives

$$\left(\frac{\partial z}{\partial x}\right)_z = 0 = \left(\frac{\partial z}{\partial x}\right)_y + \left(\frac{\partial z}{\partial y}\right)_x \left(\frac{\partial y}{\partial x}\right)_z \quad \text{or} \quad \left(\frac{\partial z}{\partial x}\right)_y = -\left(\frac{\partial z}{\partial y}\right)_x \left(\frac{\partial y}{\partial x}\right)_z$$

This can be rewritten, through use of the reciprocal rule, as

$$\left(\frac{\partial z}{\partial y}\right)_x \left(\frac{\partial y}{\partial x}\right)_z \left(\frac{\partial x}{\partial z}\right)_y = -1 \tag{15.11}$$

Notice that each variable appears once in each of the three locations. Because the three variables are written in a cyclic permutation, this is known as the cyclic rule.

Using these relations, you can effectively switch your dependent and independent variables. For example, as we will see in section 15.2.2, the van der Waals equation of state can't be solved as $V_m(P,T)$. So if you want $\left(\dfrac{\partial V_m}{\partial P}\right)_T$, you can express the van der Waals equation as $T(P,V_m)$ and determine $\left(\dfrac{\partial T}{\partial P}\right)_{V_m}$ and $\left(\dfrac{\partial T}{\partial V_m}\right)_P$, then use these rules to get what you want.

### 15.1.5 Integrals with Partial Derivatives

We often want to describe changes in a property over a certain set of conditions—say, the expansion of a gas from some initial temperature, pressure, and volume to a final temperature, pressure, and volume. Such calculations involve integrating these differentials over the limits of the change. Let's write again our expression for the molar internal energy in terms of molar volume and temperature.

$$U_m(V_m, T)$$

$$dU_m = \left(\frac{\partial U_m}{\partial V_m}\right)_T dV_m + \left(\frac{\partial U_m}{\partial T}\right)_{V_m} dT$$

For example, if we are doing an isothermal (constant $T$) expansion of a gas and want to know the change in molar internal energy, we would write

$$\Delta U_m = \int_{U_{m,1}}^{U_{m,2}} dU = \int_{V_{m,1}}^{V_{m,2}} \left( \frac{\partial U_m}{\partial V_m} \right)_T dV_m$$

Remember $dT = 0$ for an isothermal process, so the second term in the total differential drops out. The delta ($\Delta$) denotes a large change; $d$ denotes an infinitesimally small change. Depending on the functional relation between $U$ and $V$, this integral may be easy or difficult to evaluate.

Throughout our development of thermodynamics, you will notice that most of the expressions we present will be in a differential form. This is useful because it minimizes the number of assumptions that we need to make. The limitation is that a differential only describes the instantaneous change at a particular set of conditions. If we want to know the total change from some initial condition to some final condition, we will need to integrate these differential expressions. Depending on the system under study, we may need to make some approximations in evaluating such an integral.

## 15.1.6 Commonly Used Partial Derivatives

Let's write the total derivative for $V(P,T)$ ($n$ is being kept constant)

$$dV = \left( \frac{\partial V}{\partial T} \right)_P dT + \left( \frac{\partial V}{\partial P} \right)_T dP$$

The two partial derivatives, $\left( \dfrac{\partial V}{\partial T} \right)_P$ and $\left( \dfrac{\partial V}{\partial P} \right)_T$, are important quantities, particularly in developing equations of state for condensed phases. They are so important, in fact, that they have been given their own names.

*Coefficient of Thermal Expansion* – The quantity $\left( \dfrac{\partial V}{\partial T} \right)_P$ tells us how the volume of an object changes with a change in temperature, with the pressure being held constant. Thus, it is known as the coefficient of thermal expansion (or thermal expansion coefficient), symbolized as $\alpha$. This can be a very important quantity in the design of materials subjected to significant temperature changes. For example, if a part in an engine has a large coefficient of thermal expansion, it will swell as the temperature increases, possibly causing seizure of parts and failure of the engine. The coefficient of thermal expansion is mathematically defined as

$$\alpha = \frac{1}{V} \left( \frac{\partial V}{\partial T} \right)_P \tag{15.12}$$

Thermal expansion coefficients have units of $K^{-1}$, or $°C^{-1}$ since the two temperature scales have steps of the same size and are generally on the order of $10^{-4}$. Numerically, heating an object one degree will cause its volume to change by about 0.01%. Most materials have positive thermal expansion coefficients, meaning they expand when they are heated, but there are some materials with negative thermal expansion coefficients.

*Isothermal Compressibility* – The other volume derivative that is tabulated for many materials is the pressure derivative at constant temperature. This is known as the isothermal compressibility, symbolized as $\kappa_T$ (or simply $\kappa$) and mathematically defined as

$$\kappa_T = -\frac{1}{V}\left(\frac{\partial V}{\partial P}\right)_T \tag{15.13}$$

This quantity tells us how much the volume changes with an increase in pressure at constant temperature. The minus sign is included in this definition because $\left(\frac{\partial V}{\partial P}\right)_T < 0$ for all materials, and editors of books decided it was easier to tabulate positive numbers than negative ones. The isothermal compressibility is also a small number, typically $10^{-6}$ atm$^{-1}$.

Notice that in the definitions of both the thermal expansion coefficient and isothermal compressibility, we divide by the volume. There are some good reasons for doing this. The actual pressure and temperature derivatives can be pressure or volume dependent, respectively. For example, the value of the partial derivative with respect to temperature may change depending on the actual value of the constant pressure. Dividing by the absolute volume, however, gives a quantity that is essentially constant over larger ranges of temperature or pressure. Dividing by the volume also makes these quantities intensive rather than extensive, meaning they are independent of the size of the system and thus reflect general properties of the material and are not specific to any given sample. By doing this, they give us the fractional change in volume with a change in either temperature or pressure.

## Sample Problem 15.1

The thermal expansion coefficients for diamond and lead have values of $0.030 \times 10^{-4}$ and $0.861 \times 10^{-4}$ K$^{-1}$, respectively. If the temperature of lead and diamond are each increased by 250°C at constant pressure, what is the percent change in the volume of each sample?

Solution

The mathematical definition of the thermal expansion coefficient is given by Eq. 15.12. Because the pressure is constant, we can write this slightly differently as

$$\alpha \, dT = \frac{1}{V} dV$$

We now need to integrate this expression. To do so, we need to make the reasonable assumption that the thermal expansion coefficient is itself constant with temperature. (Without this assumption, we would have to know how it varies with $T$.)

$$\int_{T_1}^{T_2} \alpha \, dT = \int_{V_1}^{V_2} \frac{1}{V} dV$$

$$\alpha(T_2 - T_1) = \alpha \Delta T = \ln\frac{V_2}{V_1} = \ln\frac{V_1 + \Delta V}{V_1}$$

We want to know the fractional increase, which mathematically is $\Delta V / V_1$. If we look at the value of $\alpha$, we can see that we expect the change to be fairly small, on the order of $10^{-2}$.

So, we are justified in making an approximation in working with the logarithm on the right-hand side. If we recall that $\ln(1 + x) \approx x$ for small $x$, we can write

$$\ln \frac{V_1 + \Delta V}{V_1} = \ln\left(1 + \frac{\Delta V}{V_1}\right) \approx \frac{\Delta V}{V_1}$$

$$\alpha \Delta T = \frac{\Delta V}{V_1}$$

Since Kelvin and centigrade scales step in the same size, we have $\Delta T = 250°C = 250$ K. We can thus readily see that the sample of diamond will increase in size by 0.075%, and the sample of lead will increase in size by 2.2%.

# 15.2 Equations of State for Real Gases

Now that we have gone over more details about state variables and how they behave, we are prepared to discuss equations of state other than the ideal gas law. The ideal gas law only applies under conditions of low (close-to-zero) pressure and high temperature. At the molecular level, there are no interactions between the gas molecules because the average distance between molecules is significantly greater than their size. Under other conditions, particularly high pressure and/or low temperature, significant deviations from ideal behavior are observed, due to interactions; and the ideal gas law no longer holds true. In order to account for the behavior of a real gas, we need to use a different equation of state.

## 15.2.1 Deviations From the Ideal Gas Law

It should not come as a surprise that under most conditions, the ideal gas law is not a good fit to the actual data. Figure 15.1 contains real data for $CO_2$. For each curve, the temperature is fixed; we saw these in Chapter 1, and they are called isotherms. The curve for 50°C looks very similar to Boyle's law, but as the temperature drops, the curves deviate from the hyperbolic shape of Boyle's law. Along the 31.04°C isotherm, the curve goes through an inflection point. This temperature is known as the **critical temperature** $T_C$, and the inflection point is the **critical point**. (In addition to a critical temperature, the critical point is also defined by a critical pressure $P_C$ and critical volume $V_C$. These critical constants often show up in equations of state for real gases.)

The shaded region, which occurs at temperatures below the critical temperature, is the gas–liquid coexistence region. If a gas is compressed at a temperature below $T_C$, it will eventually condense and form a liquid. The ideal gas law does not predict condensation; with no interactions between molecules, condensation can never occur. In order to deal with critical phenomena and other behaviors of real gases, the equations of state must be much more complex than the simple ideal gas law.

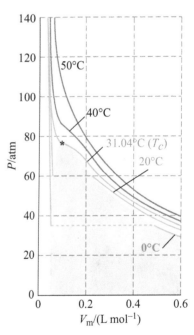

**FIGURE 15.1.** Isotherms for $CO_2$. At a temperature above $T_C$, condensation does not occur. The shaded blue region is the two-phase region where liquid $CO_2$ exists in equilibrium with the vapor.

## 15.2.2 Van der Waals Equation of State

Historically, the first attempt at a real gas EOS was made by J. D. van der Waals in 1873. (He received the 1910 Nobel Prize for his work on equations of state.)

He modified the ideal gas law to account for two of its basic limitations. These are the molecules do not have zero volume, and the molecules interact with each other. The van der Waals equations is written as

$$P = \frac{nRT}{V - nb} - a\left(\frac{n}{V}\right)^2 \quad \text{or} \quad P = \frac{RT}{V_m - b} - \frac{a}{V_m^2} \tag{15.14}$$

The parameter $b$ accounts for the finite volume of the gas molecules and the parameter $a$ accounts for attractions between molecules. This equation is based on a physical understanding, but the parameters $a$ and $b$ have to be determined for each individual gas. The vdW equation is an improvement over the ideal gas law, but it still has its limitations. For example, it does not contain a repulsive term, so it breaks down at low temperature and high density. This EOS also has problems below the critical temperature but does correctly predict condensation. In the limit of a very diffuse gas, however, this EOS goes right back to the ideal gas law. At low density (low pressure), the molar volume will be large, so the last term approaches zero, and $V_m \gg b$, meaning $V_m - b \approx V_m$.

We can extend the molecular interpretation of the van der Waals $b$ term if we assume the molecules are spherically shaped. Similar to how we defined a collision cross section back in Chapter 3, we can determine the excluded volume between two hard spheres of diameter $d$. Using some simple geometric arguments, we can show that the volume per molecule is given by

$$b = \frac{2}{3}\pi d^3 N_A \tag{15.15}$$

Thus, we can use measured van der Waals coefficients to estimate molecular size.

## 15.2.3 Virial Equation of State

A purely empirical model of the behavior of gases can be developed based on the ideal gas law as follows. Let's first define a quantity $Z$, the **compression factor**, as follows:

$$Z = \frac{V_m}{V_m^\circ} = \frac{PV_m}{RT} \tag{15.16}$$

the superscript $^\circ$ denotes "ideal gas molar volume" at the given $T$ and $P$. The volume in the numerator is the real molar volume, or what is actually measured. Thus $Z$ is a measure of the deviations from ideality, and $Z$ can be either greater or less than 1. If $Z > 1$, this means that the real gas volume is greater than an equivalent ideal gas would be. This is due to a predominance of repulsions between the gas molecules. If the compression factor is less than 1, however, this means that attractive interactions are dominating the behavior, thus reducing the volume of the gas. The closer $Z$ is to 1, the more ideally the gas is behaving.

In principle, $Z$ can change with the conditions. We can take the ideal gas law as the first approximation of a more complicated expression and expand $Z$ as a series with additional terms that depend on the pressure:

$$PV_m = RT(1 + B'P + C'P^2 + \dots) \tag{15.17}$$

or the volume

$$PV_m = RT\left(1 + \frac{B}{V_m} + \frac{C}{V_m^2} + \dots\right) \tag{15.18}$$

These are two versions of the **virial equation of state**; the second form is generally the most convenient. The terms $B$, $C$, and so on are known as the virial coefficients. These coefficients must be determined experimentally and in fact depend on $T$. Because the virial coefficients are based on experimental data, they generally reproduce the observed behavior quite well. Molecular interpretations of the virial coefficients, however, are not quite as straightforward as the van der Waals $b$ coefficient. Recall though, as we discussed in Chapter 14, that $B$ relates to binary collisions, $C$ relates to three-body collisions, and so on.

## 15.2.4 Other Real Gas Equations of State

Other attempts have been made to find good EOSs for real gases. They all have their advantages and shortcomings, depending on the assumptions made in their derivations or the conditions they attempt to model. All these equations are the result of our desire to describe the behavior of a gas in mathematical terms. Remember, though, that nature doesn't do math. So the problems with an EOS are really ours, not nature's. Be certain that you are aware of any limitations of the range of applicability of a given equation of state. Some other common EOSs are given below.

Berthelot EOS
$$P = \frac{RT}{V_m - b} - \frac{a}{TV_m^2} \tag{15.19}$$

Dieterici EOS
$$P = \frac{RTe^{-a/RTV_m}}{V_m - b} \tag{15.20}$$

Redlich–Kwong EOS
$$P = \frac{RT}{V_m - B} - \frac{A}{T^{1/2}V_m(V_m + B)} \tag{15.21}$$

where
$$A = \frac{0.42748R^2T_c^{2.5}}{P_c} \quad \text{and} \quad B = \frac{0.08664RT_c}{P_c}$$

It should be noted that these EOSs are still quite simple compared to those required for liquids and solids. For example, there are equations of state for water that have 58 coefficients.

# 15.3 Condensed Phases

It is worth spending a little time talking about the structure of condensed phases, meaning solids and liquids. First, we need to establish the criteria that define a solid, liquid, and gas. The practical definition of a gas, as a state of matter, is that it completely fills the available volume. In general, the gas molecules are fairly far apart and are constantly moving around, thus any interactions are generally short lived. A solid differs from a gas in that the substance has a definite volume and shape and the molecules are more or less in fixed positions. A liquid is an in-between state; the substance has a definite volume but not a definite shape and the molecules are able to move around quite a bit. In this section, we will first discuss how we can use thermodynamic data to develop approximate equations of state for solids. Then we will discuss some of the important aspects of the molecular structure of solids and liquids.

### 15.3.1 Developing an EOS for a Solid From Thermodynamic Data

Consider the following example. The molar volume of copper at 298.15 K and 1 atm is 7.09 cm$^3$ mol$^{-1}$. The coefficient of thermal expansion at room temperature is $0.501 \times 10^{-4}$ K$^{-1}$. What is the volume of copper at 400 K and 1 atm, assuming $\alpha$ is constant over this temperature range?

This would be easy if we had an EOS for copper, but we don't. We do, however, have the definition of $\alpha$. As long as we impose the condition of constant pressure, we can treat the partial derivative as a ratio of differentials. This allows us to write

$$\alpha dT = \frac{1}{V} dV$$

We then integrate this expression over our limits

$$\int_{T_1}^{T_2} \alpha \, dT = \int_{V_1}^{V_2} \frac{1}{V} dV$$

Remember, we assumed $\alpha$ is constant. This lets us write

$$\alpha(T_2 - T_1) = \ln\left(\frac{V_2}{V_1}\right)$$

We take the exponential of both sides and rearrange

$$V_2 = V_1 \exp\left(\alpha\left(T_2 - T_1\right)\right)$$

Now we can plug in our numbers to get $V_2 = 7.13$ cm$^3$ mol$^{-1}$. Notice that this is not very different from the value at 298.15 K, which is to be expected because of the small value of $\alpha$. (This also validates the assumptions we made back in Sample Problem 15.1.)

This approach is often taken for condensed systems. Note that the volume didn't change very much, which is expected for a solid. Remember also that we kept the pressure constant. If we were interested in changes with pressure at constant temperature, we would use the isothermal compressibility instead. If both temperature and pressure are changed, we have to account for both effects, which may involve making more approximations.

### 15.3.2 Molecular Structure of Solids

The atoms and molecules in a solid are generally in fixed positions; they can vibrate about their equilibrium positions but can't really move far away from them. They are also very close to their neighbors. If these positions occur in a regular pattern, the material is termed **crystalline**. Every crystal is described by a **unit cell** and the entire sample is just a repeating pattern of this unit cell. The regular patterns of position can be measured by X-ray or electron diffraction. Other solids are **amorphous**, like glass, where the molecules do not occur in repeating positions, but they still can't move freely.

We can describe the electronic properties of solids by extending molecular orbital theory. When two atoms come together, we need to have the same number of molecular orbitals as we had atomic orbitals; if each atom has $n$ atomic orbitals, we have $2n$ molecular orbitals. Now, if we bring together $N$ atoms to form a solid, we will have $Nn$ orbitals to describe the solid. The splitting between levels gets smaller each time we add another atom, and the molecular orbitals effectively form a continuous **band** of states; this model is known as **band theory**. Depending on the atoms, some of the atomic orbitals are full and some are empty. Likewise, the bands will either be full, empty, or partially filled. The important parameter here is the **band gap**, or the difference in energy between the filled and empty states. If the band

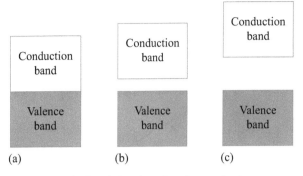

FIGURE 15.2. Band structure for a) a conductor, b) a semiconductor, and c) an insulator.

gap is small or nonexistent, then electrons can readily move from the full band (called the **valence band**) to the empty band (called the **conduction band**). Such a material is termed a **conductor**; metals are all conductors. If there is a large band gap, then electrons can't move into the empty states, and we have an **insulator**. If the band gap is small enough that thermal energy can provide some excitation, we have a **semiconductor**. These bands are shown in Figure 15.2.

Let's look at these ideas more quantitatively. Recall that the Pauli exclusion principle (Sec. 11.1.5) tells us that only two electrons can occupy a given atomic or molecular orbital. When we apply the Pauli principle to band theory, we find that the probability of an energy state being filled is described by the Fermi–Dirac distribution:

$$P(E) = \frac{1}{e^{(E-E_F)/k_B T} + 1} \tag{15.22}$$

The energy $E_F$ is known as the **Fermi level** and is the energy at which the probability of occupation drops to 50%. For a conductor at any temperature above $T = 0$, the tail of the Fermi–Dirac distribution extends into the conduction band, meaning there are some electrons in that band that can easily move about in the material. The states that were previously occupied but are now empty are often referred to as **holes**. Conductivity can be modeled both in terms of the electrons in the conduction band and the holes in the valence band. For insulators, the band gap is so large that the Fermi–Dirac distribution has effectively died off at the next available energy states. For semiconductors, the band gap is small enough that there is a significant amount of electrons in the conduction band. This model also helps understand why the conductivity of semiconductors is highly temperature dependent.

Solids also differ from liquids and gases in their mechanical properties. Gases tend to be fairly compressible with liquids and solids much less so, but solids are the only state of matter that can support **shear**. Shear stress occurs when the force is applied laterally to the surface. Solids also exhibit **elasticity**, which is the ability to "bounce back" to the original shape, provided the stress is not too strong. If too much stress is applied, mechanical failure results and the material will crack or break. There are actually some connections between electrical and mechanical properties. Metals are malleable and tend not to break, whereas semiconductors and insulators tend to be fairly brittle.

Development of equations of state for solids is not trivial. A proper EOS must account for all the properties of the solid, which can involve many different length scales. There is no such thing as a perfect crystal; rather, crystalline materials often

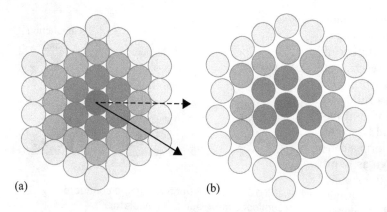

(a)  (b)

**FIGURE 15.3.** Schematic structure of a) a crystalline solid and b) a liquid. The arrows in a) correspond to the curves in Figure 15.4a.

have grains of various sizes and orientations. The grain structure can affect the mechanical properties and therefore needs to be included in any mathematical model of the material. Different models are used depending on the level of detail that is needed for a given application.

### 15.3.3 Molecular Structure of Liquids

Liquids are probably the most difficult state of matter to work with at the molecular level. The atoms are fairly close together and strongly interact, however they are not organized in a regular fashion and move around a lot. One way that we can quantify the structure in a liquid is with something known as the **pair-correlation function**. We start with a given atom and look at the probability another atom is located a distance $r$ away. (The mathematical form of the probability is actually $G(r)r^2dr$, because of the spherical symmetry of the system.)

How will this function look for a crystalline solid, depicted in Figure 15.3a? The function should have regular peaks, corresponding to the lattice positions in the crystal, as shown in Figure 15.4a. This is why we say that crystals have long-range order. What about for a gas? It should level off very quickly, since there is really no preference for another gas molecule to be located any particular distance from our starting point, as shown in Figure 15.4b. The structure of liquids is in between that of a gas and a solid, as shown in Figure 15.3b. At short distances, we expect to see oscillations in the pair-correlation function, reflecting the short-range order. However, this dampens out as we move away, reflecting the lack of long-range order, as shown in Figure 15.4c.

The molecules in liquids experience a lot of different interactions. This and the relative disorder in their arrangement makes them difficult to model. In principle, we can develop an interaction potential, but it will have a lot of parameters that depend on distance and orientation. Proper modeling of liquids is an area of current research in statistical mechanics, and molecular dynamic simulations are also very useful in understanding the structure of liquids. One fact that helps is that even though the atoms are moving around a lot, the pair-correlation function actually stays more or less the same over time. Pair-correlation functions can be measured in a variety of ways, which allows us to check the validity of our models.

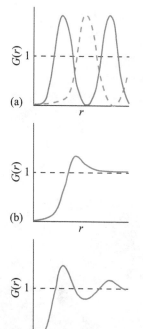

(a)

(b)

(c)

**FIGURE 15.4.** Pair-correlation functions for a) a crystalline solid, b) a gas, and c) a liquid.

## 15.4 Summary, and Where We Go Next

In this chapter, we have gone over some of the mathematical characteristics of state variables, as well as total and partial differentials. We have also discussed equations of state for real gases and the molecular structure of solids and liquids. In the next chapter, we formally begin our development of thermodynamics by a further study of energy and the First Law of Thermodynamics.

# PROBLEMS

**15.1** a) Write the total differential of the molar volume in terms of pressure and temperature.

b) In terms of $\alpha$ and $\kappa$, the coefficient of thermal expansion and the isothermal compressibility, respectively, derive an expression for $\left(\dfrac{\partial P}{\partial T}\right)_V$.

c) For an ideal gas, show that the expression obtained in part b) gives the same result as direct differentiation of the equation of state.

d) A drum at 1 bar and 293 K is filled with $CCl_4$. Heating the drum will cause the pressure to rise. At what temperature will the pressure be 75 bar, assuming the drum is rigid? For this material, $\alpha = 1.236 \times 10^{-3}$ K$^{-1}$ and $\kappa = 90.4 \times 10^{-6}$ bar.

**15.2** You have probably had your body temperature taken using a mercury thermometer. You may have also seen cheap outdoor thermometers that you can attach to your windowsill that use alcohol (plus a red dye) as the thermometric fluid. The temperature dependence of mercury and of alcohol as a function of temperature($t$, °C) can be given as

$$V_{mercury}(t) = V_{0,mercury}(1+0.18182 \times 10^{-3}t + 0.0078 \times 10^{-6}t^2)$$

$$V_{alcohol}(t) = V_{0,alcohol}(1+1.012 \times 10^{-3}t + 2.20 \times 10^{-6}t^2)$$

where $V_{0,mercury} = 14.758$ cm$^3$ mol$^{-1}$ (the molar volume of mercury at 0°C) and $V_{0,alcohol} = 56.782$ cm$^3$ mol$^{-1}$ (the molar volume of alcohol at 0°C).

a) Evaluate $V$ and $(\partial V/\partial T)_P$ for both liquids at 5-degree intervals from 0°C to 70°C. (Note, $T$ is in K; $t$ is in °Celsius. What effect if any does this have on the calculations you are to make?)

b) Calculate $\alpha$ for both liquids at these temperatures. Express the change in $\alpha$ as a percent change: $\dfrac{(\alpha_{70} - \alpha_0)}{\alpha_0} \times 100$. Describe the behavior of $\alpha$ as a function of temperature.

c) An important consideration in liquid-in-glass thermometry is the sensitivity of the working fluid—that is, how large a change in volume one would get for a given temperature change. Discuss which of these two liquids is the better working fluid if sensitivity over the temperature range from 0 °C to 70 °C is the only criterion.

**15.3** Sometimes, it is more convenient to take a partial derivative with respect to a function of a state variable rather than the state variable itself.

a) For the ideal gas EOS, take the partial derivate $\left(\dfrac{\partial P}{\partial 1/V}\right)_{n,T}$.

b) What is the advantage of this expression compared to $\left(\dfrac{\partial P}{\partial V}\right)_{n,T}$?

**15.4** The van der Waals parameters for $CO_2$ are $a = 3.610$ atm $L^2$ mol$^{-2}$ and $b = 0.0429$ L mol$^{-1}$.

a) Calculate the pressure for 7.6 g of $CO_2$ in a 2.0 L container at 298 K using both the van der Waals equation and the ideal gas law.

b) Calculate the compression factor for $CO_2$ under the conditions given in part a).

c) From your results in part b), estimate the second virial coefficient, $B$, for $CO_2$ at 298 K.

d) From the van der Waals parameters, estimate the size of a $CO_2$ molecule.

e) Under the conditions given in part a), estimate the average distance between $CO_2$ molecules and compare that value to your answer in part b). Comment on your results.

**15.5** Given the following data for Ar (R. B. Stewart & R. T. Jacobsen, *J. Phys. Chem. Ref. Data* **18**, 639, (1989)) taken at 300 K:

| P/MPa | $V_m$ /L mol$^{-1}$ | P/MPa | $V_m$ /L mol$^{-1}$ |
|---|---|---|---|
| 0.4000 | 6.2208 | 1.500 | 1.6483 |
| 0.5000 | 4.9736 | 2.000 | 1.2328 |
| 0.6000 | 4.1423 | 2.500 | 0.98357 |
| 0.8000 | 3.1031 | 3.000 | 0.81746 |
| 1.000 | 2.4795 | 4.000 | 0.60998 |

a) Compute the second virial coefficient, $B$, at 300 K with a linear fit.

b) Use a nonlinear curve fit to determine the second and third virial coefficients, $B$ and $C$. Comment on the change in $B$ between the linear and nonlinear fits.

**15.6** a) $TiO_2$ has semiconducting properties and can absorb light at wavelengths shorter than 350 nm. Calculate the band gap for $TiO_2$ in eV.

b) The band gap of Si is 1.12 eV. At what wavelength will Si become transparent?

**15.7** This problem will explore aspects of the Fermi–Dirac distribution (Eq. 15.22) used to model the electronic states of solids.

a) At a temperature of 0 K, what is the occupation probability for a level below and a level above the Fermi level?

b) Derive an expression for the Fermi–Dirac distribution for energy levels much greater than the Fermi level at a finite temperature. (Hint: It should look familiar.)

c) Make plots of the Fermi–Dirac distribution as a function of the energy of the levels for $E_F/k_BT = 0.1$, 1, and 10.

# First Law of Thermodynamics

## Work, Heat, and Energy

## 16.1 Introduction to Thermodynamics

The laws of thermodynamics are based on experimental observation. They can be considered postulates, just like the postulates of quantum mechanics and statistical mechanics that we have already encountered. Before diving into the formalism of thermodynamics, we need to do a little more to set the stage for this rich and vibrant branch of physical chemistry.

### 16.1.1 Historical Development of Thermodynamics

Thermodynamics as a scientific theory was developed in the middle of the 19th century—it predates the rest of physical chemistry. You might be wondering, then, why we have chosen to present it last in this text. There are some very good reasons for this. Because it was developed well before the molecular theory of matter, thermodynamics is a **continuum theory**. This means that it does not depend on any underlying theory about the structure of matter. All we need to agree upon is that we have matter, but we don't have to worry about what it is made of. As long as we can describe a sample in terms of the state variables we discussed in the last chapter, we're good to go. (You might be asking, though, what about moles, which are based on the molecular model? In the early days, everything was in terms of mass; the molar units we use now are a more modern version, but they are much more convenient for chemistry.)

Because the development of thermodynamics does not require any understanding of the structure of matter, it falls under the "top-down" category of approaches. Pure classical thermodynamics need not give any insight into molecular behavior. We have spent practically the whole book, however, in the molecular realm, so we will be able to make connections from what thermodynamics tells us back to the molecular world. In this way, our coverage of thermodynamics will be even richer than if we had started here.

### 16.1.2 Zeroth Law of Thermodynamics

The Zeroth Law of thermodynamics, which provides the basis for temperature in classical thermodynamics, was presented back in Chapter 1, so we will only briefly review it here. If two objects, A and B, are in thermal equilibrium with each other—meaning they are at the same temperature—and a third body, C, is in thermal equilibrium with B, then we can say that A and C are also in thermal equilibrium with each other, even though they may not be in physical contact. Historically, the Zeroth Law was defined after the other three, but rather than renumber the other laws—and because the idea of temperature is foundational to thermodynamics—it was given the zero position.

The Zeroth Law is all about temperature, a property that you hopefully have a much deeper appreciation of now that we have covered statistical mechanics. The First Law, which we will examine in this chapter, is all about internal energy. We have gained some familiarity with this quantity in our study of quantum mechanics and statistical mechanics, and your appreciation of it will grow even deeper as we move into thermodynamics. As we will see, the First Law sets one of the ground rules for what types of processes are even possible in our universe.

### 16.1.3 Systems and Surroundings

As we begin our study of thermodynamics, it is important to define some new terminology. First is the concept of a thermodynamic system. Simply put, the **system** is the thing we care about. This could be a container of gas, a block of metal, or a vessel containing many reacting species in an aqueous environment. Everything that is not a part of the system is considered to be the **surroundings**. The system and surroundings taken together form the **universe**.

Thermodynamic systems come in three different types: open, closed, and isolated; each of these is depicted in Figure 16.1. An **open system** is open to the surroundings and can exchange both mass and energy with the surroundings. A **closed system** cannot exchange mass with the surroundings but can exchange energy. An **isolated system** is completely cut off from the surroundings; it can exchange neither mass nor energy because it is both closed and thermally insulated.

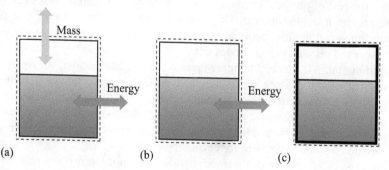

**FIGURE 16.1.** Depictions of a) open, b) closed, and c) isolated systems.

## 16.1.4 State and Path Functions

In the last chapter, we reviewed some of the mathematical properties of state variables. Here, we will present another aspect of these variables. One of the important things about a state variable (or state function) is that a change in that variable only depends on the initial and final conditions, not the actual process of the change. As an example, consider hiking to the top of a mountain. You start at the trailhead and find that you have two choices of trails to take. One is the "easy" trail, which is not very steep and, as a result, covers a distance of 12 miles. The "expert" trail has many steep sections, but only covers a distance of 8 miles. Before starting on your hike, you note your altitude on your GPS. After reaching the top, you find that you have climbed a total of 3000 ft. Mathematically, we could write

$$\Delta h = h_{final} - h_{initial} = 3000 \text{ ft}$$

Now, what if you had some friends that took the other trail. What is their change in elevation? Because you both started and ended at the same place, they have also climbed 3000 ft. But what about the distance traveled? Those distances, because you each took different paths, are different. So even though your GPS says you have the same change in elevation as your friends, it will show a different distance traveled.

Now, you both go back down on the same trails you came up. What is the total elevation change for both you and your friends? Because you have ended where you started, the total elevation change for the round trip is zero. The distance traveled, however is not zero (just ask your feet). If you took the easy trail, you hiked a total of 24 miles, whereas your friends only hiked 16.

Both properties that we have discussed apply to state functions, such as the internal energy. For any change in conditions described by a state function, we can write the total change as

$$\Delta U = U_{final} - U_{initial} \qquad (16.1)$$

If the final and initial conditions are the same, we can see that the total change will be zero. Recall in the last chapter that we also wrote the change in internal energy in terms of an integral

$$\Delta U = \int_{U_{initial}}^{U_{final}} dU$$

As we discussed, the internal energy and its changes will depend on state variables such as temperature and volume. Mathematically, the integral above is a line integral in the space of those variables. If the integral follows a closed path, meaning we begin and start at the same point, then the result of that integration will be zero. Mathematically, we write a line integral around a closed path as

$$\oint dU = 0 \qquad (16.2)$$

A similar expression can be written for any state variable.

We will very soon encounter some functions that are not state functions. This means that their numerical value will depend on the specific process that gets us from initial to final conditions. Likewise, the result of integrating around a closed path for such a function will not be zero. Somewhat akin to our hiking example, such functions are known as **path functions**. The two path functions we will spend the most time with are work and heat, which will be at the heart of our treatment of the First Law of thermodynamics.

# 16.2 The First Law of Thermodynamics

## 16.2.1 Work, Heat, and Internal Energy

You should be familiar with the law of conservation of energy from classical physics. This law was based on experimental observations that energy cannot be created or destroyed. We have talked about the energy involved in the different types of motion of molecules, such as translations, rotations, and vibrations. These different types of energy can be exchanged through molecular collisions. Recall, though, that thermodynamics is a continuum theory, so all these types of molecular motion—as well as any interaction energy between the molecules—simply contribute to the internal energy, symbolized by $U$.

In thermodynamics, there are two forms of energy change that we are generally concerned with: **work** and **heat**. Work has to do with motion against an opposing force. For example, lifting a weight against the force of gravity involves work, as does compressing the gas in a piston. Heat is a flow of energy across the barrier between system and surroundings. If we bring a hot body or a flame in contact with the system, that will increase the internal energy of the system by the addition of heat flowing in. Symbolically, work is represented as $w$ and heat as $q$. Describing the change of internal energy in terms of heat and work gives us the mathematical description of the First Law of thermodynamics.

$$\Delta U = q + w \tag{16.3}$$

This form is used for large-scale changes, such as describing an entire thermodynamic process. As we will see, however, assumptions must often be made to use this version of the First Law. These assumptions can be reduced by using the differential form of the First Law. If we change the internal energy of our system by some small amount, that change is given by $dU$, and the First Law is written as

$$dU = \delta q + \delta w \tag{16.4}$$

We should take a minute to clarify some of the notation in Eq. 16.4. Internal energy is a state function, but work and heat are path functions. To maintain this distinction, we use $d$ for infinitesimal changes in internal energy (and other state functions) and $\delta$ for infinitesimal amounts of heat and work. Likewise, for larger changes in state functions we use the capital $\Delta$. Larger changes in heat and work are simply given by $q$ and $w$, respectively. Unless explicitly stated otherwise, we are concerned with the change in internal energy of the system.

For an isolated system, there can be no exchange of energy with the surroundings, either in the form of heat or work. Stated in nonmathematical terms, the First Law states:

The energy of an isolated system is constant.

If we take the universe as a whole to be an isolated system, then we may also say

The energy of the universe is constant.

In this case, we would write

$$\Delta U_{univ} = 0 \tag{16.5}$$

Eq. 16.5 also holds for any isolated system.

It is important to discuss our sign convention for changes of internal energy. Chemists are generally concerned with the state of the system, so that drives our sign conventions. If we put a burner under a sample, then we are adding energy in the form of heat. Thus, we consider this to be positive heat flow. If the system is providing energy to the surroundings in the form of heat, then the sign is negative because the internal energy of the system has decreased. For work, if we do work on the system (for example by compressing a sample of gas), then we are increasing the internal energy and we give this type of work a positive sign. If the system is doing work on the surroundings, then the work (and the change in internal energy) has a negative sign. Another way to think about this is to ask, has the capacity of the sample to do work increased or decreased? If it has increased, then the sign of that change is positive. If it decreased, the sign of that change is negative. Other disciplines may follow other conventions. For example, mechanical engineers typically consider the system doing work on the surroundings as positive work, not negative. They would therefore write the First Law expressions of Eqs. 16.3 and 16.4 with a minus sign instead of a plus sign.

Recall that we defined the surroundings as that part of the universe that is not the system. Yet another way to state the First Law is that the change in energy of the system and the surroundings must perfectly balance. Mathematically,

$$\Delta U_{univ} = \Delta U_{system} + \Delta U_{surroundings} = 0$$

$$\Delta U_{system} = -\Delta U_{surroundings} \qquad (16.6)$$

## 16.2.2 Mathematical Description of Internal Energy

The internal energy of a system depends on the state variables of that system. Because the equation of state serves as a constraint on the state variables, we only have to specify three of the four state variables $P$, $V$, $T$, and $n$. (If we use molar quantities, we only have to specify two of the three variables $P$, $V_m$, $T$.) Our choice of the variables to use is somewhat arbitrary, but let's take $V_m$ and $T$ as the independent variables.

$$U_m(V_m, T) \qquad (16.7)$$

As we saw in the last chapter, we write the total differential of the internal energy as

$$dU_m = \left(\frac{\partial U_m}{\partial V_m}\right)_T dV_m + \left(\frac{\partial U_m}{\partial T}\right)_{V_m} dT \qquad (16.8)$$

The second term, as we have seen, contains the constant volume heat capacity. The first term is a bit subtler and will be explored later on. We will return to this expression later in this chapter.

## 16.2.3 Expansion Work

We started this course by talking about gases, and we will continue to do so for a while. Gases can do work by expanding and driving back the surrounding atmosphere. Conversely, we can do work on the gas by compressing the gas with an external force. This type of work is referred to as **expansion work**, or pressure–volume work. In classical

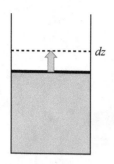

FIGURE 16.2. Expansion of a gas.

physics, work is defined as the energy required to move a mass over a distance $dz$ against an opposing force. Mathematically

$$\delta w = -F_{ex} dz \tag{16.9}$$

The negative sign tells us that the motion is in the direction opposite the applied force.

Consider a cylinder of gas with a movable piston on one end, as shown in Figure 16.2. We take the walls of the cylinder to be perfectly rigid and frictionless; thus the piston slides without any resistance. The piston has area $A$ and we apply an external pressure $P_{ex}$. The force can be written as $F_{ex} = P_{ex} A$, so we can write the work as

$$\delta w = -F_{ex} dz = -P_{ex} A dz$$

The volume swept out by the piston as it moves through a distance $dz$ is $dV = A dz$, letting us write

$$\boxed{\delta w = -P_{ex} dV} \tag{16.10}$$

Eq. 16.10 is the mathematical definition of expansion work. To obtain the total work throughout an entire process, we have to evaluate the integral

$$w = -\int_{V_i}^{V_f} P_{ex} dV \tag{16.11}$$

Integration is required because the external pressure could be changing during the process.

This expression is very important, and we will spend some more time with it for specific processes. But first, let's look at it briefly. If the system is compressed, the change in volume is negative, thus giving us positive work. (The system can do more work in the future if it were to reexpand.) If the gas expands against the external pressure, then the change in volume is positive and the work is negative. (After the gas has expanded, its ability to do additional work has decreased.)

It is important to remember that work is defined in terms of the external pressure, not the pressure inside the cylinder. For an expansion process, this is quite easy to see. We are expanding against an external pressure, so that is what is used in the calculations. But why do we use the external pressure in a compression process? Shouldn't we use the internal pressure, since that is what we are pushing against? In fact, no, we again use the external pressure. Here is why.

Let's consider the process in terms of the motion of the piston. If the piston moves up against gravity a distance $dz$, then the work done is $mg\, dz$. (The force is equal to $mg$, which is equal to $P_{ex}A$, so the work is again $P_{ex}dV$.) This gives us the change in the potential energy of the weight, or the ability of the surroundings to do work on the system. We then compress the gas and return the piston to its original position. Because the piston is where it started, the total energy of the cyclic process must be zero; the piston has lost energy of $mg\, dz = P_{ex}dV$. By compressing the gas, the surroundings have lost energy equal to $P_{ex}dV$, and that is equivalent to the energy gained by the system; the internal energy change of the gas depends on the external pressure. Now, where the type of gas we are compressing comes into play is how much pressure we have to apply to achieve the desired degree of compression. Different materials with different compressibility require a different external pressure to achieve the same change in volume. The expansion work, though, is always written in terms of the external pressure.

There is one other thing about our definition of work that we need to point out. Notice that the definition of work involves the state variables $P$ and $V$. Pressure is an intensive variable, and volume is an extensive variable. These two together form a pair of **conjugate variables**. We will see this pattern followed many times. These variables also allow us to define the condition of **mechanical equilibrium**. Let's imagine we have two containers of gas separated by a movable wall. If the pressure is the same on both sides of the wall, then the total system is at equilibrium and nothing needs to happen. However, if the pressure is greater on one side than the other, what will happen? Because of that pressure difference, the wall will move, meaning the volume on each side will change until the pressures are the same. Therefore, the pressure can tell us whether a system is in mechanical equilibrium with its surroundings. If the system is not at equilibrium with the surroundings, the system volume will change until equilibrium is reached.

### 16.2.4 Other Types of Work

Expansion work is not the only process that you will encounter. There are other types of work, all of which involve a force and a type of displacement. Some examples are:

| | | |
|---|---|---|
| surface expansion: | $\gamma \, d\sigma$ | $\gamma$ is surface tension, $\sigma$ is surface area |
| linear extension: | $f \, dl$ | $\tau$ is linear tension, $l$ is length |
| electrical: | $\phi \, dQ$ | $\phi$ is electric potential, $Q$ is charge |

Note that there is no negative sign in any of these forms of work. This has to do with the natural tendency of a system in response to a change in conditions. Gases want to expand, so the change in volume is positive. As the gas expands, the internal energy decreases. Since pressure can never be negative, we need to include a negative sign in the definition of expansion work to maintain our sign convention for changes in internal energy. For surface and linear extension, however, the opposite is true. Under tension, the tendency is to decrease the length (or area), thus $dl$ or $d\sigma$ being negative corresponds to a negative change in internal energy. Likewise, stretching a rope, or a surface, requires us to put energy into the system. For electrical work we also don't need to include a negative sign because of the conventions used in electrostatics.

All these definitions of various types of work follow the same pattern we saw for expansion work; we have an intensive variable multiplied by the change of an extensive variable. Each form of work gives us another conjugate pair of variables. Each of these definitions also establishes the criteria for the appropriate type of equilibrium.

# 16.3 Work for Specialized P–V Processes

### 16.3.1 Work Calculations for Simple Processes

We have defined work in a differential form (Eq. 16.10); however, to evaluate the work involved in any given process, we need to evaluate the integral in Eq. 16.11. This requires that we know something about the relationship between $P_{ext}$ and $V$ which will depend on the nature of the exact process under consideration. We can readily evaluate the amount of work for certain simple cases, which we will now go through.

*Free Expansion* – Let's first consider the case of free expansion, meaning that the external pressure is zero. It is very straightforward to show that there is no work involved in free expansion. This is because the expanding gas has nothing to push against.

$$\delta w = -P_{ex} dV = -0 \, dV = 0 \tag{16.12}$$

This is true regardless of the volume change, since integrating over zero yields zero.

*Constant Volume Process* – The next simplest case is that of a process where the volume is constant. If the volume doesn't change, then mathematically $dV = 0$, again giving no work.

$$\delta w = -P_{ex} \, dV = -P_{ex} \times 0 = 0 \tag{16.13}$$

In the integral form, we can see that the initial and final volumes are the same, which again gives us no work for a constant volume process.

*Constant External Pressure* – The next simplest case we can consider is where the external pressure is constant throughout the process. Mathematically, we can pull the constant external pressure outside the integral, which lets us write

$$w = -\int_{V_i}^{V_f} P_{ex} dV = -P_{ex} \int_{V_i}^{V_f} dV = -P_{ex} \Delta V \tag{16.14}$$

If the sample is expanding, then the volume increases. This means the sample is doing work on the surroundings, and the sign of the work is negative. Doing work on the system involves compressing the system, so the sign of $\Delta V$ is negative, and the work is positive.

## 16.3.2 Indicator Diagrams

Let's go back to our cylinder of gas with a piston, which we will immerse in a constant temperature bath. We start with a weight on the piston. If the pressure inside the gas is the same as that outside, then the system is in mechanical equilibrium with the surroundings, and the piston does not move. Let's place mechanical stops on the piston to prevent it from moving and then remove the weight from the piston. This reduces the external pressure, and the system is no longer in mechanical equilibrium; $P > P_{ex}$. What happens if we then remove the mechanical stops? Clearly, the gas will expand, meaning the volume of the gas will increase, until the internal and external pressure are again the same.

We can graphically represent the amount of work involved in this process by plotting the pressure vs. the volume, as in Figure 16.3. In the case of a constant pressure expansion, the work is shown as the area of a rectangle. Note that because of our sign convention, if the volume increases, the work is actually negative, so the area under the line indicates the absolute value of the work. Plots of this type are known as **indicator diagrams**. The work of the expansion process is shown by the blue-hashed rectangle.

Let's now put the weight back on the piston. What does this do to the external pressure? It returns it to its initial value, and now the external pressure is greater than the internal pressure. The system is out of mechanical equilibrium with its surroundings, and the volume of the gas needs to decrease. The volume will decrease until the internal pressure is the same as the external pressure. If we put the same weight back on, we will return to our initial point on the diagram. The overall total change in volume for this cycle is zero, since we have returned to the initial volume.

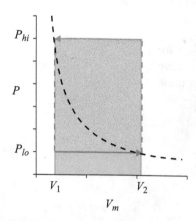

**FIGURE 16.3.** Expansion (blue) and compression (orange) of ideal gas at constant temperature. The dashed line indicates the isotherm.

But what about the total work of this process? The indicator diagram shows us this as well. Let's take $P_{hi}$ as the initial pressure with the weight on the piston and $P_{lo}$ as the pressure without the weight; $P_{hi} > P_{lo}$. The work of the expansion process is given by

$$w_{exp} = -P_{lo}\Delta V$$

When writing an expression for the work of the compression process, we want to be careful in notation. Let's take $\Delta V$ to be the difference between the largest and smallest volumes; thus this quantity will be positive.

$$\Delta V = V_2 - V_1$$

For the compression process, where the direction has been reversed, we can write

$$V_f - V_i = V_1 - V_2 = -\Delta V$$

Thus, we write the work for the compression process as

$$w_{comp} = P_{hi}\Delta V$$

Because we defined $\Delta V$ in such a way that it is positive, we can see that the work of the compression process is also positive, which matches our sign convention. The magnitude of the work of the compression process is the total area under the orange arrow down to the axis.

The total (or net) work for this cyclic process is then given by

$$w_{total} = w_{exp} + w_{comp} = -P_{lo}\Delta V + P_{hi}\Delta V = \left(P_{hi} - P_{lo}\right)\Delta V$$

Because the high pressure is greater than the low pressure, the total work for this cyclic process is positive, meaning we have done net work on the system. Graphically, the net work is shown by just the gray shaded region in Figure 16.3. When both processes are done in one step, it takes more work to recompress a gas that has expanded than we got out as the gas expanded. The fact that the work for a cyclic process is not zero also shows that work is not a state function but is actually path dependent.

### 16.3.3 Reversible Isothermal Expansion of Ideal Gas

In all the cases we've discussed to this point, we have been able to determine simple expressions for the work because the external pressure or the volume were held constant. What if that is not the case? Now we have to go back to our general expression for the work, Eq. 16.11.

$$w = -\int_{V_i}^{V_f} P_{ex}\,dV$$

Until we know some things about the exact nature of the process, we can't go any further.

Let's now specify some conditions of our sample. First, we will state that our piston is filled with an ideal gas. We will also immerse our piston in a constant temperature bath, meaning the temperature will be fixed throughout any process we perform. This also means that the only allowable states our system can be in are given by the ideal gas law, which we can represent as an isotherm on a $P$–$V$ diagram (the black dashed line in Figure 16.3). Let's go back to our example of a piston with a weight on it. Now, however, the weight has been cut in half, so we can remove just half the mass of the weight. If we

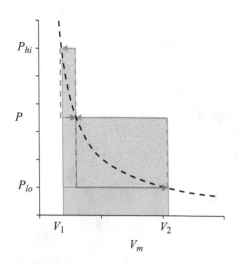

**FIGURE 16.4.** Expansion (blue) and compression (orange) of ideal gas at constant temperature in two steps rather than one.

do this, we will reduce the external pressure to half its initial value, and the gas will expand until the volume matches that given by the ideal gas law at the new pressure and fixed temperature. We can then take off the second half of the weight and expand the gas to its final volume. The indicator diagram for this two-step process is shown in Figure 16.4. Notice that we obtain more work from this expansion if we do it in two steps rather than one.

What about compressing the gas as a two-step process? We first put half the weight on the piston, raising the external pressure halfway to its maximum value, and the gas will compress again to the volume given by the ideal gas law. Putting the second half back on returns us to the initial high pressure. Note, though, that the amount of work required to compress the gas is now less than it was for the one-step process. The net work is also reduced from the one-step process; we obtain more work on the expansion side and perform less work on the compression side. We have still put more work into the system than we got out of it, however.

Now, let's replace our weights by a pile of sand. If we remove one grain of sand, the external pressure will be reduced by a very small amount, and the gas will likewise expand by a very small amount. After we have removed many grains, we will find that we are still on the isotherm, but the pressure is less than it was initially. We can continue doing this grain by grain until all the sand has been removed and we have reached the final conditions. Because of the many steps and the very small expansion that happens with each step, we will basically trace out the curve of the isotherm. What about putting the grains back on one at a time? Again, we will trace out the isotherm and the amount of work we have to put in will perfectly balance the amount of work we got out; the net work will be zero.

This qualitative picture allows us to define a **reversible process**. In a reversible process, the change is infinitesimal and we can return back to the initial condition with no net work being expended. The mathematical definition of a reversible expansion or compression is given in terms of the internal and external pressure of our system. During a reversible process, the pressure of the system and the surroundings are the same throughout the entire process.

$$P_{ex} = P \tag{16.15}$$

(More precisely, the difference between internal and external pressure is infinitesimally small.) This definition is of course an idealized condition. Even when removing a grain of sand, there is a very slight difference in the internal and external pressure. However, there will always be a limit to the size of the change we can measure. If the difference between system and surroundings is too small to measure, even though a change is happening, then we approach the reversible limit.

Let's now apply this to the evaluation of the work for a reversible process. By requiring the process to be reversible, we can write the work as

$$w = -\int_{V_i}^{V_f} P dV$$

We now state the next condition, which is that our system consists of an ideal gas. We can therefore use the ideal gas law to describe the system pressure

$$w = -\int_{V_i}^{V_f} \frac{nRT}{V} dV$$

The next conditions we apply are that the system is closed and the temperature is constant. These requirements let us pull $nRT$ outside the integral, and we can readily evaluate the work for a reversible, isothermal process involving a closed system of ideal gas.

$$w = -nRT \int_{V_i}^{V_f} \frac{1}{V} dV$$

$$w = -nRT \ \ln \frac{V_f}{V_i} \tag{16.16}$$

This expression for the work only applies if all the conditions we have imposed have been met. If any one of them is not correct for our system, we cannot use this expression.

Hopefully you now have a better sense of why we like to work in differential form as long as possible. Keeping our expressions in differential form minimizes the assumptions we need to make. When working problems, start with the general expression and systematically apply the specific conditions of the problem at hand. If you simply try to memorize expressions, you also have to memorize the conditions that must apply for that equation to be used. It's much easier to just know the fundamental definitions and derive what you need when you need it. For ease of reference, however, these expressions for work are collected in Table 16.1 at the end of the chapter.

## Sample Problem 16.1

You have a sample of 2.00 mol of He in a 20.0 L container at 298 K. The container is immersed in a constant temperature bath, and the He can be treated as an ideal gas. The container is allowed to change volume. The ambient pressure outside the container is 1.00 atm. How much work is performed if the gas expands against the constant ambient pressure? How much work is performed is the expansion occurs reversibly?

Solution

To confirm that the gas does, in fact, need to expand, we can determine the initial pressure in the container. Using the ideal gas law, we obtain an initial pressure of 2.45 atm, clearly greater than the external pressure; the system is not in mechanical equilibrium with the surroundings. In order to determine the work, we need to know the final volume of the gas following the expansion. The temperature is fixed, and the final pressure is 1 atm so, by the ideal gas law, we determine the final volume to be 48.9 L.

If the gas expands from 20.0 to 48.9 L against a constant external pressure, the work is

$$w = -P_{ex}\Delta V = -1 \text{ atm} \times (48.9 - 20.0 \text{ L}) = -28.9 \text{ L atm}$$

$$w = -2.93 \text{ kJ}$$

(Note: The L atm is a unit of energy, but that is not an SI unit. You can use the two values of the gas constant $R$ to convert L atm to J. $R = 8.3145$ J mol$^{-1}$ K$^{-1}$ = 0.08206 L atm mol$^{-1}$ K$^{-1}$, thus 1 L atm = 101.32 J.)

If the expansion occurs reversibly, however, the work is

$$w = -nRT \ \ln\frac{V_f}{V_i} = (2 \text{ mol}) \times (8.3145 \text{ J mol}^{-1}\text{K}^{-1}) \times (298 \text{ K}) \ln\frac{48.9 \text{ L}}{20.0 \text{ L}}$$

$$w = -4.43 \text{ kJ}$$

Clearly, more work is performed by the reversible expansion.

# 16.4  Heat Calculations

To this point we have focused on work. Now we will discuss how to calculate the change of energy as heat for various processes. In general, the change in internal energy can be written as

$$dU = \delta q + \delta w_{\text{exp}} + \delta w_{\text{other}} = \delta q - P_{ex}dV + \delta w_{\text{other}}$$

By other types of work, we mean surface tension, electrical work, or some other type. If there is no other work, we simply write

$$dU = \delta q - P_{ex}dV$$

## 16.4.1  Constant Volume Process, No Other Work

As we've done before, let's write a mathematical expression for the energy as a total differential, where $U(T,V)$ (keeping $n$ fixed).

$$dU = \left(\frac{\partial U}{\partial T}\right)_V dT + \left(\frac{\partial U}{\partial V}\right)_T dV = \delta q + \delta w$$

The first partial derivative tells us how the internal energy changes with changes in temperature while holding the volume constant—the **constant volume heat capacity**.

$$\boxed{C_V \equiv \left(\frac{\partial U}{\partial T}\right)_V}$$

(16.17)

Recall that for a monatomic ideal gas, $C_{V,m} = 3/2 \ R$. For a real gas, however, the heat capacity will change with temperature. Over small temperature changes, it is a reasonable approximation to use a constant value for the heat capacity.

If we are performing a constant volume process, we have already shown that the work is zero. Thus, the only way to change the internal energy for a constant volume process, with no other work, is by heating or cooling the sample. We write the energy change as

$$dU_V = C_V dT = \delta q_V \tag{16.18}$$

(The subscript $V$ tells us volume is constant.) For a complete process, we write the integral

$$\Delta U_V = q_V = \int_{T_i}^{T_f} C_V dT \tag{16.19}$$

If we are able to assume the heat capacity is constant, we can write

$$\Delta U_V = q_V = C_V \Delta T$$

## 16.4.2 Constant Pressure Process

The calculation of the heat flow is straightforward for a constant-volume process. However, many chemical processes take place at constant pressure rather than constant volume. It is convenient to define a new thermodynamic quantity for which the change at constant pressure is equal to the heat. We do this by defining a new quantity called **enthalpy**, symbolized as $H$ and defined by

$$\boxed{H \equiv U + PV} \tag{16.20}$$

Enthalpy is both a state function and an extensive variable.

The enthalpy can be thought of in this way: $H$ is the internal energy plus the energy associated with keeping a system at some $P$ and $V$, where $PV$ is the energy associated with keeping the atmosphere from collapsing the system to zero volume. Note that the $P$ is the system pressure, not the external pressure. Often, especially for condensed phases, the $PV$ term is much smaller than the internal energy, so no distinction is made between energy and enthalpy, and we just talk about energy.

Given our definition in Eq. 16.20, we can write the differential of the enthalpy as

$$dH = d(U + PV) = dU + PdV + VdP = (\delta q + \delta w) + PdV + VdP$$

If expansion work is the only type of work we allow, we can write

$$dH = \delta q - P_{ex} dV + PdV + VdP$$

Now, we impose the condition of mechanical equilibrium (or of a reversible process), which is expressed as $P = P_{ex}$. This lets us write

$$dH = \delta q - PdV + PdV + VdP = \delta q + VdP$$

Under the condition of constant pressure, $dP = 0$, so we can write

$$dH_P = \delta q_P \quad \text{or} \quad \Delta H_P = q_P \tag{16.21}$$

Thus, the enthalpy serves as a function for which a change at constant pressure is equal to the heat. This is probably a more useful way to think about enthalpy than the description above.

As we have done before, we write the total differential of enthalpy, with $H(T,P)$, as

$$dH = \left(\frac{\partial H}{\partial T}\right)_P dT + \left(\frac{\partial H}{\partial P}\right)_T dP$$

For a constant pressure process, and using Eq. 16.21, we can write

$$dH_P = \left(\frac{\partial H}{\partial T}\right)_P dT = \delta q_P$$

Similar to $C_V$, we define this partial derivative as the **constant pressure heat capacity**, $C_P$.

$$\boxed{C_P \equiv \left(\frac{\partial H}{\partial T}\right)_P} \tag{16.22}$$

For a complete process, we determine the enthalpy change by evaluating the integral

$$\Delta H_P = q_P = \int_{T_i}^{T_f} C_P \, dT \tag{16.23}$$

If we are able to assume the heat capacity is constant, we can write

$$\Delta H_P = q_P = C_P \Delta T$$

Later, we will be able to show that, for an ideal gas, the two heat capacities are related by

$$C_{P,m} - C_{V,m} = R \tag{16.24}$$

(You should think about why the constant pressure heat capacity can never be less than the constant volume heat capacity. Drawing relevant indicator diagrams may help.)

### Sample Problem 16.2

A resistive heater is wrapped around a solid sample. The power of the heater is 40 W, and the heater is allowed to run for 2 min. The temperature of the sample was measured before and after the heater was used, and the sample temperature increased by 6.3°C. What is the heat capacity of the sample? Is the quantity you measured $C_V$ or $C_P$?

Solution

The amount of heat delivered to the sample is calculated as

$$40 \text{ W} \times 2 \text{ min} \times \frac{60s}{1 \text{ min}} = 4.8 \text{ kJ}$$

Because we are performing this measurement at constant pressure, we are actually measuring $C_P$, not $C_V$. The heat capacity is the ratio of the heat to the temperature change, so we can calculate

$$C_P = \frac{4.8 \text{ kJ}}{6.3 \text{ K}} = 760 \text{ JK}^{-1}$$

(Note: Because we are dealing with a solid sample, and the magnitude of the coefficient of thermal expansion is so small, we can probably ignore any change in volume of the sample. In practice, the difference between $C_V$ and $C_P$ for a solid sample is very small.)

## 16.4.3 Reversible Isothermal Expansion of Ideal Gas

We learned through statistical mechanics, and also through empirical observation, that the internal energy of a monatomic ideal gas is given by

$$U_m = \frac{3}{2} RT$$

Note that the internal energy only depends on the temperature and no other variables; this is an alternative way to define ideal gas behavior. Thus, for an isothermal process involving an ideal gas,

$$\delta U_m = \delta q + \delta w = 0$$

or, solving for the heat

$$\delta q = -\delta w$$

Integration along the path of a process doesn't change this, so for an isothermal process with an ideal gas we can write

$$\Delta U_m = 0 \quad \text{and} \quad q = -w$$

If we now state that the process is reversible, we can write the heat for a reversible, isothermal process of ideal gas as

$$q = nRT \ \ln \frac{V_f}{V_i} \tag{16.25}$$

As with the work expression in Eq. 16.16, this expression can only be used to calculate the heat for a reversible, isothermal process involving an ideal gas. If any of those conditions are not met, this expression should not be used.

## 16.4.4 Adiabatic Processes

We have talked about processes at constant volume, where there is no work, and processes at constant pressure, where the enthalpy change is equal to the heat. Now, we want to talk about processes where there is no energy change as heat. Such a process is termed **adiabatic**.

We can write for this type of process that

$$dU = \delta w = -P_{ex} dV \quad \text{because} \quad \delta q = 0$$

To determine the work (which, in this case, is the same as the internal energy change) during the expansion, we evaluate, as before

$$\Delta U = w = -\int P_{ex} dV$$

We now require that this be a reversible process with ideal gas, therefore we can substitute in the ideal gas law for the external pressure. However, we still can't evaluate the integral without a relationship between $T$ and $V$.

$$w = -nR\int_{V_1}^{V_2} \frac{T}{V} dV$$

We can, however, use the fact that internal energy is a state function to deal with this situation.

The direct process is equivalent to a two-step process:

First, an isothermal expansion from $V_1$ to $V_2$.

Second, a constant volume cooling from $T_1$ to $T_2$.

We can write the total energy as

$$\Delta U = \Delta U_1 + \Delta U_2$$

Because the first step is isothermal, and we are working with an ideal gas, the energy change is zero. Therefore, the total energy change all happens in the second, constant-volume step, and we can write

$$\Delta U = \Delta U_2 = C_V \Delta T = w$$

We have here assumed the heat capacity to be constant, which is reasonable for the ideal gas. Note also that we can use the same expression for the energy change for a constant volume process to describe an overall change where the volume is not constant. Remember, internal energy is a state function, and how we get from the initial to the final conditions cannot change the final answer.

Now, we will determine the exact functional relationship between $T$ and $V$ for the reversible adiabatic expansion of an ideal gas. This will also serve as another good example of how to work thermodynamic problems and derive important relations.

We start with our First Law expression for an adiabatic process ($\delta q = 0$)

$$dU = \delta w = -P_{ex} dV$$

By making the process reversible, $P_{ex} = P$, and, using the ideal gas law and what we know for energy of an ideal gas (see Eq. 16.18), we write

$$dU = C_V dT = -\frac{nRT}{V} dV$$

Let's bring the same variables to the same side of the equation

$$\frac{C_V}{T} dT = -\frac{nR}{V} dV$$

Now, we integrate from initial to final conditions

$$\int_{T_1}^{T_2} \frac{C_V}{T} dT = -\int_{V_1}^{V_2} \frac{nR}{V} dV$$

This integral is pretty straightforward, and we have (assuming constant $C_V$)

$$C_V \ln\left(\frac{T_2}{T_1}\right) = -nR \ln\left(\frac{V_2}{V_1}\right) = nR \ln\left(\frac{V_1}{V_2}\right)$$

Let's switch to molar quantities to get rid of $n$

$$\frac{C_{V,m}}{R} \ln\left(\frac{T_2}{T_1}\right) = \ln\left(\frac{V_{m,1}}{V_{m,2}}\right)$$

Recall that $a \ln(x) = \ln(x^a)$, so we have

$$\ln\left(\frac{T_2}{T_1}\right)^{\frac{C_{V,m}}{R}} = \ln\left(\frac{V_{m,1}}{V_{m,2}}\right)$$

Taking the exponential of both sides gives us

$$\left(\frac{T_2}{T_1}\right)^{\frac{C_{V,m}}{R}} = \frac{V_{m,1}}{V_{m,2}}$$

We can rearrange this to give us

$$V_2 T_2^{\frac{C_{V,m}}{R}} = V_1 T_1^{\frac{C_{V,m}}{R}} \tag{16.26}$$

This lets us relate the initial and final $T$ and $V$ for the reversible, adiabatic expansion or compression of an ideal gas. In addition to the relationship between $T$ and $V$, we can derive a relationship between $P$ and $V$.

$$P_2 V_2^{\gamma} = P_1 V_1^{\gamma} \quad \text{where} \quad \gamma = \frac{C_P}{C_V} \tag{16.27}$$

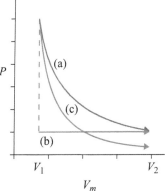

Eqs. 16.26 and 16.27 are forms of the **adiabatic equation of state** for an ideal gas. They should only be used, however, for a reversible adiabatic process involving ideal gas.

In Figure 16.5, we have plotted three curves for expansion processes that start at the same conditions and proceed along different paths to the same final volume. Along path a, we keep $T$ constant and perform the expansion reversibly. Path b is also an isothermal expansion, but done in a single, irreversible step. Path c starts at the same condition as the other two, but represents a reversible, adiabatic expansion to the same final volume; this curve is called an **adiabat**. Note that this curve changes all three variables, because the temperature drops as the gas expands. If we plot the $PV$ behavior of the adiabat, we will find that its slope is always steeper than for an isotherm with the same initial conditions. We can also clearly see that the reversible isothermal process produces the most

**FIGURE 16.5.** a) Reversible isothermal, b) irreversible isothermal, and c) reversible adiabatic expansion of an ideal gas to the same final volume.

work of these three processes; the area under the black curve is greater than the area under the red curve or the blue line.

A sample of Ar gas expands reversibly and adiabatically such that the volume doubles. If the initial temperature of the gas was 300 K, what is the final temperature?

Solution

In order to use the adiabatic equation of state, we need to know the molar constant volume heat capacity. Since Ar is a monatomic ideal gas, we will take the heat capacity to be $^3/_2 R$, based on an equipartition analysis. We can rewrite Eq. 16.26 slightly as

$$\frac{T_2}{T_1} = \left(\frac{V_1}{V_2}\right)^{\frac{R}{C_{V,m}}}$$

Solving for the final temperature gives us

$$T_2 = T_1 \left(\frac{V_1}{V_2}\right)^{\frac{R}{C_{V,m}}} = 300\text{K}\left(\frac{1}{2}\right)^{2/3} = 189\text{K}$$

As the gas expands, it must cool, so our answer makes physical sense.

---

The results of the work and heat calculations we have considered are summarized in Table 16.1 at the end of the chapter.

## 16.4.5 Molecular Perspective of Work and Heat

Even though thermodynamics is a continuum theory, it is useful to keep a molecular perspective in mind. This can also be done with work and heat. As we know, molecules are always in motion; they all have some amount of internal energy. Work refers to this energy being used in an organized fashion. For example, in the case of water pouring over a paddle wheel, all the molecules are generally moving in the same direction. The same is true for an expanding gas; there is some net motion in the direction of the expansion. Heat, however, refers to the random thermal motion of the molecules. A pond can be hot, with all the water molecules moving in random directions; but in this case no work is being done, and there is no order to the motion.

We can also explore work and heat a bit more from a statistical mechanical perspective. Let's return to the canonical ensemble, for which we can write the average energy as

$$U = \sum_j P_j E_j \tag{16.28}$$

where $P_j$ is given by the canonical distribution function, Eq. 14.4. If we make a change in the energy of our system, we can write that change as

$$dU = \sum_j P_j dE_j + \sum_j E_j dP_j \tag{16.29}$$

Now, let's think a little bit about how we can change the energy states and the population of the energy states. If we think back to our quantum-mechanical models of molecular energy states, the only thermodynamic variable that showed up there was the volume. Thus, a change in the energy states will require a change in volume, and we can identify the first sum with the thermodynamic work. Note that for an infinitesimal change in the energy of the state, the population in each state does not change. In the second sum, the energy states don't change, but the populations in each level do. Populations in energy states should make us think of temperature, so we can identify the second sum with the thermodynamic heat. Of course, we can both change the energy of the states and the populations of the states, which would suggest that the process involves both work and heat.

# 16.5 Applications of the First Law

To complete this chapter, we will briefly explore some applications of the ideas contained in the First Law. Specifically, we will go over calorimetry and thermochemistry.

## 16.5.1 Calorimetry

We have seen how certain types of processes allow us to determine the change in internal energy, enthalpy, work, and heat. But how do we actually make those measurements? Measurements of the transfer of heat during a physical or chemical process fall under the field known as **calorimetry**.

*Bomb Calorimetry* – Suppose we want to know the amount of heat generated by a chemical reaction—such as combustion—that produces or consumes gas. Since we want to contain all the reactants and products, it is useful to do this in a confined vessel. This vessel is known as a bomb, and we call this *bomb calorimetry*, shown in Figure 16.6. The vessel is of fixed volume, so no expansion work can take place. This means that the change in energy is equivalent to the heat flow for the reaction. The entire calorimeter is contained in a jacket of water, or some other thermal bath, so none of the heat is lost.

By measuring the temperature change of the surrounding water during the process, we can calculate the heat flow, and thus the energy, by the relation $q = C\Delta T$. This looks very similar to our definition of the constant volume heat capacity; however, we need to make an important distinction. The $C$ here is the heat capacity of the entire system, including the calorimeter, sometimes called the **calorimeter constant**. This must be calibrated prior to the experiment.

*Isobaric Calorimetry* – For reactions that take place in aqueous environments, and don't evolve gaseous products, it is often useful to keep the pressure rather than the volume constant. In this case, the reaction vessel is open to the atmosphere but still contained in a thermal bath. Now, changes in temperature due to the heat flow are related to the enthalpy, rather than the energy. Once the reaction is initiated, the temperature will change, and this can be converted to the enthalpy change, again through $q = C\Delta T$.

If one desires to convert between enthalpy and energy, it is a reasonable approximation to do so in terms of the number of moles of gas that are produced or consumed. Recall that, by definition, $H = U + PV$. Thus, for a chemical reaction, we can write $\Delta H = \Delta U + \Delta(PV)$. If we treat all the gases as ideal, we can write

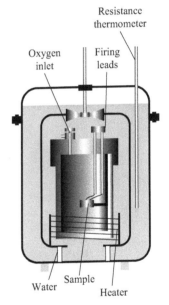

**FIGURE 16.6.** Schematic of a bomb calorimeter. Heat generated by the reaction raises the temperature of the water. The heater can be used for calibration by supplying a known amount of heat.

$\Delta H = \Delta U + \Delta(nRT)$. We generally tabulate a heat (enthalpy) of reaction at a given temperature, meaning that the products have been allowed to return back to the initial temperature. Doing so lets us write

$$\Delta H = \Delta U + RT\Delta n \qquad (16.30)$$

where $\Delta n$ is the change in moles of gas for the reaction. (This raises an interesting idea; how can we treat the process as isothermal when we measured a temperature change? The key experimental detail is that the temperature change needs to be fairly small, but still measurable.)

Calorimeters can, of course, be much more sophisticated, and there are several other techniques that we will not discuss here. It is sufficient to know that we can measure how much heat is produced or consumed during the course of chemical reactions and other processes.

### Sample Problem 16.4

A bomb calorimeter has a calorimeter constant equal to 10.3 kJ $K^{-1}$. A 1.23 g sample of sucrose ($C_{12}H_{22}O_{11}$) is burned in excess oxygen and the temperature increases by 1.97°C. Calculate the heat of combustion of sucrose.

Solution

We can quickly calculate the amount of heat released by the reaction as

$$q = C\Delta T = (10.3 \text{ kJ K}^{-1}) \times (1.97 \text{ K}) = 20.3 \text{ kJ}$$

The molar mass of sucrose is 342.3 g $mol^{-1}$, meaning we have 3.59 mmol of sucrose in this experiment. (Since the combustion happens at constant volume, we are measuring $\Delta U$, not $\Delta H$.) The energy of combustion, $\Delta_c U^\circ$ is found to be −5645 kJ $mol^{-1}$. (We include the negative sign because the reaction liberated energy.) To convert between energy and enthalpy of combustion, we look at Eq. 16.30. The balanced reaction for the combustion of sucrose is written as

$$C_{12}H_{22}O_{11}(s) + 12 \text{ O}_2(g) \rightarrow 12 \text{ CO}_2(g) + 11 \text{ H}_2O \ (l)$$

Because there are the same number of moles of gas on both sides of the reaction, according to Eq. 16.30 the enthalpy and energy are equal. Thus, the heat of combustion for sucrose is $\Delta_c H^\circ = -5645$ kJ $mol^{-1}$.

## 16.5.2 Thermochemistry

Now that we know how to measure changes in energy and enthalpy, we will discuss what we can do with that information. This leads us to a topic known as **thermochemistry**, which involves the relationships between heat and chemical reactions. If we want to know the heat released or required in a particular reaction, we can of course measure it in a calorimetry experiment. However, because energy and enthalpy are state functions, and a lot of these measurements have already been done, we can use tabulated data to determine the heat involved in virtually any reaction.

Before we go much further, we need to define the **standard state** of a material. We will define the standard state of a material as the state of a substance in its pure form at

1 bar ambient pressure and at a temperature of our choice. For example, the standard state of water at 25°C is a pure liquid. The standard state of iron at 500 K is a pure solid.

When we write a chemical reaction and include the enthalpy of reaction, we call this a **thermochemical equation**. For example, the combustion of 1 mol of methane at 298 K evolves 890 kJ of heat when performed under standard conditions. This includes cooling all the reaction products back down to 298 K. We write the thermochemical equation as

$$CH_4(g) + 2\ O_2(g) \rightarrow CO_2(g) + 2\ H_2O\ (l) \qquad \Delta_r H^\circ = -890\ \text{kJ mol}^{-1}$$

The **standard reaction enthalpy** $\Delta_r H^\circ$ is given with the reactants and products all in their standard states. If the reaction is the combustion of one mole of some compound, this is called the **standard enthalpy of combustion**, symbolized $\Delta_r H^\circ$. Standard enthalpies of reaction are tabulated for many reactions, usually specified at 25°C.

The **standard enthalpy of formation** of a substance is the standard-reaction enthalpy for the formation of one mole of that compound from its elements in their standard states, which are the stable forms at the given temperature. Standard enthalpies are expressed as enthalpy per mole of the compound being formed. For example, the thermochemical equation for formation of liquid benzene at 25°C is

$$6\ C(s,\ \text{graphite}) + 3\ H_2(g) \rightarrow C_6H_6(l) \qquad \Delta_f H^\circ = 49.0\ \text{kJ mol}^{-1}$$

By convention, the standard enthalpy of formation of an element in its standard form is exactly 0. Standard enthalpies of formation can be used to develop standard enthalpies of reaction by

$$\Delta_r H^\circ = \sum_{products} v\Delta_f H^\circ - \sum_{reactants} v\Delta_f H^\circ \qquad (16.31)$$

where $v$ is the stoichiometric ratio for each reactant or product.

For a phase change of a material, we write can write a **standard heat of transition**. Let's take as an example of a standard enthalpy change the vaporization of water at 100°C. In this case, both the liquid and the vapor count as the standard state, since they both exist in equilibrium at this temperature. We can write the vaporization process at 373 K as

$$H_2O\ (l)\ [373\ K] \rightarrow H_2O\ (g)\ [373\ K]$$

The measured enthalpy change is 40.66 kJ mol$^{-1}$. This is known as the **standard enthalpy of vaporization** and is written as $\Delta_{vap} H^\circ$ (373 K) = 40.66 kJ mol$^{-1}$. Note that the specific process, in this case vaporization, is written in the subscript. Another example is the **standard enthalpy of fusion** (remember, fusion is melting, not freezing) for water, written as

$$H_2O\ (s)\ [273\ K] \rightarrow H_2O\ (l)\ [273\ K] \qquad \Delta_{fus} H^\circ(273\ K) = 6.01\ \text{kJ mol}^{-1}$$

Now, because enthalpy is a state function, it doesn't matter how we get from the initial to the final states. For example, what if we want to determine the enthalpy to go directly from solid to vapor at a particular temperature? (The process of going from solid to vapor is called **sublimation**.) Suppose that we have the standard enthalpies of fusion and of vaporization for water at a given temperature, $T$.

$$H_2O\ (s) \rightarrow H_2O\ (l) \qquad \Delta_{fus}H^\circ\ (T)$$

$$H_2O\ (l) \rightarrow H_2O\ (g) \qquad \Delta_{vap}H^\circ\ (T)$$

$$\text{Overall:}\quad H_2O\ (s) \rightarrow H_2O\ (g) \qquad \Delta_{sub}H^\circ\ (T) = \Delta_{fus}H^\circ\ (T) + \Delta_{vap}H^\circ\ (T)$$

Because enthalpy is a state function, the enthalpy change for the direct path must equal the change for the two-step path. One conclusion of this is that the enthalpy of sublimation is always greater than the enthalpies of fusion and vaporization at a given temperature.

Doubling the amount of a reaction doubles the heat produced or consumed. When we reverse a process, we also reverse the sign of the enthalpy change. For example, the enthalpy of vaporization of $H_2O$ at 298 K is 44.016 kJ mol$^{-1}$, so the enthalpy of condensation is −44.016 kJ mol$^{-1}$ at 298 K.

## 16.5.3 Hess's Law

One consequence of the path independence of the enthalpy is that we can get the standard enthalpy of reaction for a new reaction by combining reactions for which these values are known. This idea is known as **Hess's law**, and it is incredibly powerful. This means that we can calculate the heat of reaction for any reaction from tabulated standard heats of formation. Thus, we can determine what to expect for a reaction we haven't actually performed yet. The use of Eq. 16.31 is actually a manifestation of Hess's law.

Standard enthalpies of reaction or formation are often given at particular temperatures, typically 298 K. What if you want to compute the enthalpy change at a different temperature? From the definition of the constant pressure heat capacity, we can write

$$H(T_2) = H(T_1) + \int_{T_1}^{T_2} C_P\ dT$$

This assumes no phase transition between $T_1$ and $T_2$. If there are phase transitions, we have to go to the phase transition, evaluate the heat of transition, then continue in the new phase. Because this equation applies to each reactant or product, we can write a similar expression for the entire reaction.

$$\Delta_r H^\circ(T_2) = \Delta_r H^\circ(T_1) + \int_{T_1}^{T_2} \Delta_r C_P^\circ\ dT \tag{16.32}$$

This is known as **Kirchoff's law**. The standard change in heat capacity is given by

$$\Delta_r C_P^\circ = \sum_{products} \nu C_{P,m}^\circ - \sum_{reactants} \nu C_{P,m}^\circ \tag{16.33}$$

where again $\nu$ is the stoichiometric ratio for each reactant or product.

### Sample Problem 16.5

The standard enthalpy of formation for HCl $(g)$ is −92.31 kJ mol$^{-1}$ and that of $H_2O$ $(g)$ is −241.82 kJ mol$^{-1}$, both at 298 K. Making appropriate assumptions about the heat capacity of the gases, estimate the enthalpy of reaction for the formation of $Cl_2$ and $H_2O$ from the reaction of HCl and $O_2$ at 400 K.

Solution

The first thing we should do is write the balanced reaction for which we want to calculate the enthalpy of reaction.

$$4 \text{ HCl } (g) + O_2(g) \rightarrow 2 \text{ Cl}_2(g) + 2 \text{ H}_2\text{O } (g)$$

The formation reactions for HCl and $H_2O$ are written as

$$\tfrac{1}{2} \text{ H}_2 (g) + \tfrac{1}{2} \text{ Cl}_2(g) \rightarrow \text{HCl } (g) \qquad \Delta_r H^\circ = -92.31 \text{ kJ mol}^{-1}$$

$$\text{H}_2 (g) + \tfrac{1}{2} O_2(g) \rightarrow \text{H}_2\text{O } (g) \qquad \Delta_r H^\circ = -241.82 \text{ kJ mol}^{-1}$$

(Recall, that a formation reaction always produces 1 mol of the desired compound.) We can construct the desired reaction by doubling the second reaction and adding the reverse of the first reaction multiplied by 4. Thus, the enthalpy of reaction for the overall reaction at 298 K is

$$\Delta_r H^\circ = 4 \times \left( 92.31 \text{ kJ mol}^{-1} \right) + 2 \times \left( -241.82 \text{ kJ mol}^{-1} \right) = -114.4 \text{ kJ mol}^{-1}$$

In order to determine the enthalpy of reaction as 400 K, we need to use Kirchoff's law (Eq. 16.32), making reasonable assumptions about the heat capacities of the reactants and products. For a diatomic ideal gas, we can use an equipartition analysis (neglecting the vibrational contribution) to have $C_{V,m} = 2.5R$, and therefore $C_{P,m} = 3.5R$. (See Eq. 16.24.) $H_2O$ vapor will have one additional rotational degree of freedom, so the heat capacities will be $C_{V,m} = 3R$ and $C_{P,m} = 4R$. The change in heat capacity for the reaction (Eq. 16.33) is

$$\Delta_r C_P^\circ = [2 \times (3.5R) + 2 \times (4R)] - [4 \times (3.5R) + (3.5R)] = -2.5R$$
$$= -20.79 \text{ J mol}^{-1}\text{K}^{-1}$$

Using Eq. 16.32, and assuming the heat capacities are constant, we have

$$\Delta_r H^\circ(400 \text{ K}) = -114.4 \text{ kJ mol}^{-1} + \int_{298}^{400} -20.79 \text{ J mol}^{-1}\text{K}^{-1} \, dT$$
$$= -114.4 \text{ kJ mol}^{-1} - 20.79 \text{ J mol}^{-1}\text{K}^{-1} \cdot (400 \text{ K} - 298 \text{ K})$$
$$\Delta_r H^\circ(400 \text{ K}) = -116.5 \text{ kJ mol}^{-1}$$

We can see that the enthalpy of reaction didn't change by much (~2%), so our assumptions about the heat capacities are probably reasonable.

# 16.6 Summary, and Where We Go Next

In this chapter, we have explored the fundamental aspects and some applications of the First Law of thermodynamics. Hopefully you now have a better sense of how powerful this rather simple idea can be. There is still more to do, however. While the First Law tells us a great deal about what *can* happen in the universe in terms of energy exchange, it really gives us very little intuition into what *will* happen. For that, we need the second law of thermodynamics, which we explore in the next chapter.

TABLE 16.1. Summary of Thermodynamic Results for various Processes.

| Process | $w$ | $q$ | $\Delta U$ | $\Delta H$ |
|---|---|---|---|---|
| constant volume | 0 | $\int C_V dT$ | $\int C_V dT$ | $\int C_P dT$ |
| constant pressure | $-P_{ex}\Delta V$ | $\int C_P dT$ | $\int C_P dT - P_{ex}\Delta V$ | $\int C_P dT$ |
| isothermal, reversible, IG | $-nRT\ \ln\dfrac{V_2}{V_1}$ | $nRT\ \ln\dfrac{V_2}{V_1}$ | 0 | 0 |
| reversible, adiabatic, ideal gas | $\int C_V dT$ | 0 | $\int C_V dT$ | $\int C_P dT$ |

# PROBLEMS

**16.1** 10 L of a fluid is compressed by a piston from an initial pressure of 1 bar to a final pressure of 50 bar at 300 K. Consider the process to be reversible and isothermal.

a) Calculate the work for this process if the cylinder is filled with ideal gas.

b) Calculate the final volume of the cylinder for the process with ideal gas.

c) Calculate the work if the cylinder is filled with liquid water. The isothermal compressibility of water is $\kappa = 4.46 \times 10^{-10}$ m$^2$ N$^{-1}$.

d) Calculate the final volume of the process with water. Liquid water density is 0.996 g mL$^{-1}$.

**16.2** a) Derive an expression for the work for a reversible isothermal process where the working fluid is a van der Waals gas.

b) The van der Waals parameters for $CO_2$ are $a = 3.610$ atm L$^2$ mol$^{-2}$ and $b = 0.0429$ L mol$^{-1}$. Calculate the work for a reversible isothermal expansion of 0.20 mol of $CO_2$ at 298 K from a volume of 0.50 L to 2.0 L.

c) Calculate the work for the same expansion as in part b) but treating the $CO_2$ ideally. Compare your results and provide a molecular level justification for their difference.

d) Plot the indicator diagrams for the processes in parts b) and c).

**16.3** You have probably seen a baking soda "volcano," formed by the reaction of vinegar, which is about 5% by volume acetic acid, and sodium bicarbonate. An apparatus is set up to allow for the combination of 15 g baking soda and excess vinegar in a sealed vessel. The vessel includes a piston that can change the volume of the vessel. The initial volume of the vessel is 2.0 L. The ambient pressure is 740 torr, and the temperature is 25°C.

a) If the piston is fixed in place until the reaction has finished, and then the piston is released and allowed to expand, calculate the work from this process.

b) If the piston is not fixed in place but allowed to move during the reaction, calculate the work from this process. State any assumptions you make in your calculation.

**16.4** The partial derivative $\left(\dfrac{\partial U}{\partial V}\right)_T$ is sometimes called the internal pressure and can tell us about the intermolecular interactions in a substance. The internal pressure can be related to other state variables by the relation

$$\left(\frac{\partial U}{\partial V}\right)_T = T\left(\frac{\partial P}{\partial T}\right)_V - P$$

(This will be formally derived in Section 18.1.5).

a) Show that the internal pressure is identically zero for an ideal gas. (This is yet another definition of ideal gas behavior).

b) Derive an expression for the internal pressure for a van der Waals gas.

c) Knowing that the $a$ parameter in the van der Waals equation describes the intermolecular attractions, what does the sign of the internal pressure tell us about molecular interactions?

**16.5** A 4.0 mol sample of $O_2$ gas starts off with a volume of 20.0 L at 270 K. It is allowed to undergo an adiabatic expansion against a constant pressure of 600 torr until the volume has increased by a factor of 3. Calculate $q$, $w$, $\Delta T$, $\Delta U$, and $\Delta H$ for this process. Treat the gas as ideal. (Note: Consider this process carefully. Is it reversible? Is the final pressure 600 torr?)

**16.6** 5.0 moles of ideal gas are heated at constant volume from 400 K to 750 K. The initial pressure is 1.2 bar and the molar heat capacity is $C_{V,m} = {}^5/_2 R$. Calculate:

a) the final pressure.

b) the change in internal energy $\Delta U$.

**16.7** This problem will explore the properties of state functions and path functions. We will start with 1 mol of monatomic ideal gas in a 10 L container at 300 K.

a) Heat the gas at constant pressure to 400 K. Calculate the work, heat, and change in internal energy for this process.

b) Heat the gas to 400 K at constant volume, followed by a reversible isothermal expansion to the same final volume as in part b). Calculate the work, heat, and change in internal energy for this two-step process.

c) Compare the values from parts a) and b) and discuss why they are the same or different.

d) Draw the indicator diagrams for both processes on the same graph.

**16.8** The standard enthalpy of combustion of cyclopropane is −2091 kJ mol⁻¹ at 298 K. The standard enthalpy of combustion of propene is −2058 kJ mol⁻¹, also at 298 K. Using these data, calculate the standard enthalpy for the isomerization of cyclopropane to propene at 298 K.

**16.9** Consider a "standard engineer" that weighs 75 kg and takes in food with a caloric content of 500 Cal = $2.09 \times 10^6$ J.

a) If this food were completely converted to heat, estimate the rise in the body temperature of the engineer. Assume the specific heat of the engineer is equivalent to that of liquid water, 4.18 J g$^{-1}$ K$^{-1}$.

b) If the heat were used to vaporize water from body tissue, what would be the mass loss of the engineer? The heat of vaporization of water is 44.0 kJ mol$^{-1}$.

**16.10** 2.00 mL of liquid octane ($C_8H_{18}$) is placed in a bomb calorimeter with excess oxygen. The density of octane is 0.708 g mL$^{-1}$. The system is initially at 300 K. The calorimeter constant of this instrument is 25.0 kJ K$^{-1}$. Upon combustion of the octane, the temperature of the calorimeter increased by 2.68°C. Calculate the standard enthalpy of combustion for octane.

**16.11** The standard enthalpy of combustion of propane is −2220 kJ mol$^{-1}$ at 298 K. Using heat capacity data you can find online, estimate the enthalpy of combustion of propane at 1500°C.

**16.12** The Redlich–Kwong (R–K) equation of state is given in Eq. 15.21.

a) Derive an expression for the work associated with an isothermal reversible volume change of a R–K gas between two volumes $V_1$ and $V_2$. You may find it helpful to know that

$$\int \frac{1}{x(a + bx)} dx = -\frac{1}{a} \ln\left( \frac{a + bx}{x} \right)$$

b) The critical constants for argon are $T_c = 150.72$ K, $P_c = 48.00$ bar, $V_c = 0.07525$ L mol$^{-1}$. Use the relationship you derived in part a) to calculate the work in expanding the gas from $6V_c$ to $7V_c$ at a temperature that is twice the critical temperature.

c) We showed in Problem 16.4 that $\left( \dfrac{\partial U}{\partial V} \right)_T = 0$ for an ideal gas. Evaluate this partial differential for a R–K gas.

d) Knowing that $A$ and $B$ are positive constants for a given R–K gas, does the internal energy increase or decrease for an isothermal expansion? What does this tell you about the intermolecular interactions for the R–K gas?

e) Calculate the change in internal energy for the same process for which you calculated the work.

f) Calculate the heat for this same process.

# Second and Third Laws of Thermodynamics

## Entropy

## 17.1 Spontaneity and the Second Law

### 17.1.1 Spontaneity

We are all familiar with the concept of spontaneity. We observe that some things happen on their own, while others require some outside work or effort to make them happen. For example, a certain amount of gas will spontaneously expand to fill the volume of its container. Likewise, a drop of ink will spontaneously spread out in a glass of water. From a First-Law standpoint, nothing prevents either of these processes from happening in reverse so long as energy is conserved; but no one has ever observed them. The question remains, then, as to why certain things happen on their own and others don't. To start answering these questions, concepts of energy and the First Law are insufficient. To understand spontaneity, we need to explore entropy and the Second Law of thermodynamics.

The Second Law found its original formulation in the context of designing engines to do work with a given input of heat. We have already seen that heat and work both involve a change in the internal energy of the system. The ideal engine is one with which we could convert heat completely to work. Work can be converted completely into heat (rub your hands together to feel this); however, no one was able to perform the reverse process—heat cannot be completely converted into work. There is always some heat that is "wasted."

It was also observed that heat flow is always a directional process; heat flows spontaneously from a hot body to a cold body, but not the other way around. If we want to remove heat from a cold object and make it colder, we must transfer that heat to a warm object, making it warmer. (This is the basic idea behind a refrigerator.) Such a process requires that we perform work on the system; it doesn't happen on its own. The Second Law was formulated to account for the spontaneous flow of heat and the inefficiency of converting heat into work. As we will see, it is one of the most powerful ideas in thermodynamics.

## 17.1.2 Thermodynamic Definition of Entropy

We now want to quantify these ideas, but we need a state function to describe these empirical observations. We have already shown that heat is a path function, so that won't work for us. But if we divide the heat by the temperature, then it becomes a state function, as we will demonstrate a little later. We will call this new function the **entropy**, given the symbol $S$. Mathematically, we write the definition of entropy in a differential form

$$dS \equiv \frac{\delta q_{rev}}{T} \tag{17.1}$$

For a process that involves a change in the state of the system, we write the total entropy change

$$\Delta S = \int_i^f \frac{\delta q_{rev}}{T} \tag{17.2}$$

Note that the entropy is defined for the reversible path between the initial and final states. This is important, again because heat is a path function, but entropy is a state function.

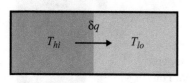

**FIGURE 17.1.** Isolated system consisting of two parts at different temperatures.

Let's demonstrate how the spontaneous flow of heat and the Second Law are related with a simple example. Imagine we have an isolated system (which in effect is its own thermodynamic universe) that consists of two parts, as shown in Figure 17.1. The left part is at a high temperature, and the right part is at a low temperature. Because of the temperature difference between the two sides, this system is not in thermal equilibrium (remember the Zeroth Law). In order to establish thermal equilibrium between the two sides, heat must flow between them until the temperatures are the same.

Let's allow a small amount of heat, $\delta q$, to flow from the hot side to the cold side. We need the amount of heat to be small in order to approximate the process as being reversible. The heat flow for the hot side is then written as

$$\delta q_{hi} = -\delta q$$

The negative sign indicates that the heat is leaving the hot body, with a temperature of $T_{hi}$. The heat flow for the cold body, with a temperature of $T_{lo}$, is written as

$$\delta q_{lo} = \delta q$$

The positive sign here indicates that the heat is flowing into the cold body. Note that the magnitude of the heat is the same on both sides, reflecting the First Law and conservation of energy.

Now, what about the entropy change for the hot body? According to Eq. 17.1,

$$dS_{hi} = \frac{\delta q_{hi}}{T_{hi}} = \frac{-\delta q}{T_{hi}}$$

The entropy change for the cold body is written as

$$dS_{lo} = \frac{\delta q_{lo}}{T_{lo}} = \frac{\delta q}{T_{lo}}$$

We can write an expression for the total entropy change of our entire system that results from moving this small amount of heat from the hot body to the cold body.

$$dS_{tot} = dS_{hi} + dS_{lo} = \delta q \left( \frac{1}{T_{lo}} - \frac{1}{T_{hi}} \right) > 0 \qquad (17.3)$$

For this small flow of heat, the entropy change of the entire isolated system, which again is basically its own thermodynamic universe, is positive. We know from experience that this process is spontaneous. Thus, we can identify an increase in the entropy of an isolated system (or the universe) with a spontaneous process. This leads to the formal statement of the Second Law of thermodynamics:

The entropy of an isolated system (or the universe) never decreases.

$$\Delta S_{univ} \geq 0 \qquad (17.4)$$

In our example, heat will continue to flow until the two bodies come into thermal equilibrium, meaning they are at the same temperature. Note that when this happens, Eq. 17.3 would give us $dS_{tot} = 0$, because the two temperatures will be the same.

What would be the entropy change for the reverse process, such as heat flowing from a cold body to a hot body, or two bodies at the same temperature spontaneously changing temperature? In that case, $dS_{tot}$ would be negative, and that process would not be spontaneous. The fact no one has ever seen heat flow spontaneously in this opposite direction supports our assertion that the Second Law is a fundamental law of the universe.

There is one more aspect of the thermodynamic definition of entropy we need to point out. Recall in our discussion of expansion work that we found a special relationship between the variables of pressure and volume. We called $P$ and $V$ conjugate variables. We now have a conjugate variable to the temperature, and that is entropy. We can see this more clearly if we slightly rewrite Eq. 17.1 as

$$\delta q_{rev} = TdS \qquad (17.5)$$

Notice that, just as with pressure and volume, this conjugate pair consists of an intensive variable (temperature) and an extensive variable (entropy). This also gives us another way to look at thermal equilibrium. If the temperature between two bodies is different, entropy will change (heat will flow) until the temperatures are the same and thermal equilibrium is established.

### 17.1.3 Molecular Interpretation of the Second Law

You have probably heard that entropy relates to the disorder of the system. While this is in some sense true, we need to be careful with this interpretation. Entropy really has to do with the usefulness of the energy, or more properly the lack of usefulness. Processes that dissipate energy, such as friction, lead to "lost" heat and increased entropy. Let's briefly explore the idea of entropy at the molecular level.

The First Law tells us that the energy of an isolated system is constant. The Second Law gives us some idea of the distribution of energy within the system. In Section 16.4.5, we discussed how work is related to the organized motion of molecules and heat relates to the random chaotic motion of molecules. The Second Law then tells us that organized motion can be converted to chaotic motion, but going the other direction requires outside work.

This also agrees with the Boltzmann perspective that entropy relates to the statistical probability of achieving a given arrangement; a random arrangement will have more possible configurations than an ordered configuration. The probability that a random system spontaneously orders itself is vanishingly small. An ordered system, however, can spontaneously rearrange into a more random arrangement.

We can get much more specific in our discussion of entropy at the molecular level. Recall in Section 14.1.3 that we went from the Boltzmann expression $S = k_B \ln W$ to the more convenient Gibbs entropy expression (Eq. 14.9)

$$S_{\text{system}} = -k_B \sum_j P_j \ln P_j$$

where $P_j$ is the probability of a microsystem in the canonical ensemble being in a given state.

$$P_j = \frac{e^{-E_j/k_B T}}{Q} \quad \text{where} \quad Q = \sum_j e^{-E_j/k_B T}$$

Let's now take the differential of the Gibbs entropy expression

$$dS = -k_B \sum_j dP_j - k_B \sum_j \ln P_j dP_j$$

(Recall that $d \ln x = x^{-1} dx$.) Because the sum of the probabilities must always add up to 1, it must be true that the sum of all the changes in the probabilities add up to zero.

$$\sum_j dP_j = 0$$

This leaves us with

$$dS = -k_B \sum_j \ln P_j dP_j$$

We can now substitute in the canonical distribution function into the ln term and write

$$dS = -k_B \sum_j \left( \frac{-E_j}{k_B T} - \ln Q \right) dP_j = \frac{1}{T} \sum_j E_j dP_j + \ln Q \sum_j dP_j$$

Again, the last term drops out, and we are left with

$$dS = \frac{1}{T}\sum_j E_j dP_j$$

In Section 16.4.5, we saw exactly this same sum in our discussion of the molecular nature of heat and work. We identified the heat as

$$\delta q_{rev} = \sum_j E_j dP_j$$

Comparison to our expression for $dS$ clearly gives us

$$dS = \frac{\delta q_{rev}}{T}$$

which is equivalent to the thermodynamic definition of entropy, Eq. 17.1. (As we have seen before, it is always good when two versions of the same ideas give the same result.)

Entropy has to do with probabilities. As energy flows in the form of heat, it changes the probability distribution among the available states. The spontaneous flow of heat always results in a more probable arrangement than what was there before the heat flowed. This is accomplished by the energy exchange resulting from molecular collisions.

There is another way to think about energy, entropy, and temperature that can help us understand these concepts. At the beginning of the course, you probably felt you had a good understanding of temperature and a reasonable understanding of entropy. Hopefully, you now have a very good understanding of entropy in terms of probabilities, but the real meaning of temperature may be a bit less clear.

Let's fix the volume of our system, which lets us write the change in internal energy as

$$dU_V = \delta q + \delta w = \delta q$$

where the subscript $V$ reminds us that the volume is being kept constant. The work term goes to zero, because the volume is not changing (and we are not allowing for other forms of work). We can now slightly rewrite Eq. 17.1 as

$$dS = \frac{dU_V}{T}$$

Solving for the temperature gives us

$$T = \left(\frac{\partial U}{\partial S}\right)_V \qquad (17.6)$$

We have now defined the temperature as a partial derivative of energy with respect to entropy, but what does that mean?

Let's imagine that we have a system with very little energy. We then add some small amount of energy to that system and ask what happens to the entropy. If there was not much energy present, then putting a bit more in will significantly increase the ways we can spread that energy around, and the entropy will increase. If we plot energy vs. entropy on a graph, as in Figure 17.2, we would have a fairly small slope if the entropy change is much larger than

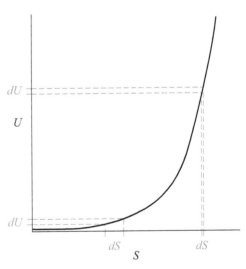

FIGURE 17.2. Energy as a function of entropy. At low temperature (blue), the slope of $U$ vs. $S$ is small. At high temperature, (orange) the slope is large.

the energy change. This corresponds to a low temperature. If, however, we have a system that already has a great deal of energy, the addition of a little bit more doesn't change the probabilities much. Thus, the same change in energy corresponds to a small change in entropy, and we have a very steep slope. This corresponds to a high temperature. The ideas of temperature and entropy both have to do with how energy is spread around within the system.

## 17.2 Entropy Calculations

### 17.2.1 Entropy Change for Specific Processes

As we did with heat, work, and energy, we now evaluate the entropy change for certain processes.

*Isothermal Reversible Expansion of Ideal Gas* – For the reversible isothermal expansion or compression of an ideal gas, the change in energy is zero. Thus the change in heat is equal to the negative change in work. The entropy change is therefore determined by evaluating

$$\Delta S = \int \frac{P_{ex}dV}{T} = \int_{V_i}^{V_f} \frac{1}{T} \frac{nRT}{V} dV = nR \int_{V_i}^{V_f} \frac{1}{V} dV$$

$$\Delta S = nR \ln \frac{V_f}{V_i} \tag{17.7}$$

*Reversible Adiabatic Expansion* – For a reversible adiabatic process, $q_{rev} = 0$, therefore it follows that $\Delta S = 0$. For this reason, a reversible adiabatic process can also be called **isentropic**.

*Reversible Heating* – For an expansion or compression process to be reversible, we require that the pressure inside and outside the system be the same throughout the process. We can define reversible heating in a similar way—this time in terms of the temperature of the system and surroundings. If these temperatures are the same throughout the process (meaning they change at the same rate), we have reversible heating or cooling.

For a constant volume reversible process, the heat is given by

$$\delta q_{rev} = C_V dT$$

The entropy for constant volume heating is then given by

$$\Delta S = \int_{T_1}^{T_2} \frac{C_V}{T} dT \tag{17.8}$$

If $C_V$ is constant, that gives us

$$\Delta S = C_V \ln \frac{T_2}{T_1}$$

For a constant pressure reversible process, the heat is given by

$$\delta q_{rev} = C_p dT$$

The entropy for constant pressure heating is given by

$$\Delta S = \int_{T_1}^{T_2} \frac{C_p}{T} dT \tag{17.9}$$

If $C_p$ is constant, that gives us

$$\Delta S = C_p \ln \frac{T_2}{T_1}$$

Sample Problem 17.1

You have a sample of 2.00 mol of Ar in a 10.0 L container at 300 K. We are going to reversibly and isothermally triple the volume and then reversibly double the temperature. Calculate the total heat and entropy change of the system for this process.

Solution

To calculate the heat for this two-step process, we go back to Eqs. 16.25 and 16.19. (We will assume the heat capacity of Ar is constant and use the integrated form of Eq. 16.19.) The total heat is therefore the sum of the two terms

$$q = nRT_1 \ln \frac{V_2}{V_1} + C_V (T_2 - T_1) = (2.00 \text{ mol}) R(300 \text{ K}) \ln 3 + \frac{3}{2} R(2 \text{ mol})(300 \text{ K})$$

$$q = 13.0 \text{ kJ}$$

Note that if we did the heating step first followed by the isothermal expansion, the temperature in the first term would be replaced by the final temperature, meaning the total heat would be different. Remember, heat is a path function.

To calculate the entropy, we can use Eq. 17.7 and the integrated form of Eq. 17.8.

$$\Delta S = nR \ln \frac{V_2}{V_1} + C_V \ln \frac{T_2}{T_1} = (2 \text{ mol}) R \ln 3 + \frac{3}{2} R(2 \text{ mol}) \ln 2$$

$$\Delta S = 35.6 \ JK^{-1}$$

Note that here there is no temperature in the first term, so changing the order of the steps will not change the value of $\Delta S$. This is a strong hint that entropy is a state function, as we want it to be. Also, the positive values of both the heat and the entropy make physical sense; the molecules are on average moving faster and they have more space in which to move, both of which increase the number of ways to arrange them.

*Phase Transition* – The transformations that accompany a physical change of state require energy to either be added to or removed from the system. At the normal transition temperature, we can define the entropy of the transition as

$$\Delta_{trs} S = \frac{\Delta_{trs} H}{T_{trs}} \tag{17.10}$$

At the normal transition temperature, the phase transition is a reversible process, because the two phases exist in equilibrium with each other. (We will discuss this further in Chapter 19.) For an endothermic transition, such as fusion or vaporization, $\Delta H$ is positive, so there is an increase in the entropy. Likewise, for an exothermic phase transition, such as freezing and condensation, $\Delta H$ is negative and the entropy of the system decreases. You might wonder how the entropy can spontaneously decrease. Keep in mind that the Second Law requires the entropy of the universe (system and surroundings) to never decrease. We'll talk about the surroundings in Section 17.2.4.

### Sample Problem 17.2

The heat of standard enthalpy of fusion of water is 6.008 kJ mol$^{-1}$. Calculate the entropy of freezing of water at 0°C.

### Solution

Fusion is melting, so for the freezing process, the enthalpy change is the reverse of that for fusion; $\Delta_{freezing}H° = -6.008$ kJ mol$^{-1}$. Using Eq. 17.10, we can calculate the entropy change for freezing to be

$$\Delta_{trs}S = \frac{\Delta_{trs}H}{T_{trs}} = \frac{-6008 \text{ J mol}^{-1}}{273.15 \text{ K}} = -22.00 \text{ J mol}^{-1}\text{K}^{-1}$$

The decrease of entropy reflects the change in structure to go from liquid to solid.

---

It has been observed that the entropy of vaporization for many liquids is about 85 J mol$^{-1}$ K$^{-1}$. This observation is known as Trouton's rule. If the boiling point of a liquid is known, the enthalpy of vaporization can be estimated by using this value in Eq. 17.10. Note that liquids with very strong intermolecular interactions, such as water, do not follow this pattern.

## 17.2.2 Entropy as a State Function: The Carnot Cycle

We will now demonstrate that entropy is a state function, as are internal energy and enthalpy. Bear in mind that this is a demonstration, not a proof. We'll take a cycle of the following steps:

1. Reversible isothermal expansion of ideal gas from A to B, at $T_{hi}$.
2. Reversible adiabatic expansion from B to C.
3. Reversible isothermal compression from C to D at $T_{lo}$.
4. Reversible adiabatic compression from D to A.

The corresponding indicator diagram for this cycle is shown in Figure 17.3. This cycle is known as the Carnot cycle, after the French scientist and engineer Sadi Carnot. Because all the steps are reversible, this is an idealized cycle, but it does serve a useful purpose for us.

In the last section, we learned how to evaluate the entropy for these types of processes, and Table 17.1 summarizes the results for the full cycle. Note that we have defined the quantity $\Delta T$ as the difference between the high and low temperature ($\Delta T = T_{hi} - T_{lo}$), thus it is always a positive quantity.

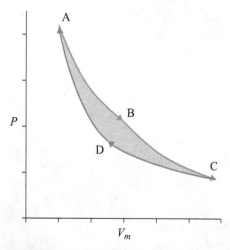

**FIGURE 17.3.** Indicator diagram for the Carnot cycle. Expansion steps are in orange; compression are steps in blue. The shaded region shows the magnitude of the work performed by the cycle.

TABLE 17.1.  The Carnot Cycle.

| Step | $q$ | $w$ | $\Delta U$ | $\Delta S$ |
|---|---|---|---|---|
| 1-Isothermal | $RT_{hi}\ln(V_B/V_A)$ | $-RT_{hi}\ln(V_B/V_A)$ | 0 | $R\ln(V_B/V_A)$ |
| 2-Adiabatic | 0 | $-C_V\Delta T$ | $-C_V\Delta T$ | 0 |
| 3-Isothermal | $RT_{lo}\ln(V_D/V_C)$ | $-RT_{lo}\ln(V_D/V_C)$ | 0 | $R\ln(V_D/V_C)$ |
| 4-Adiabatic | 0 | $C_V\Delta T$ | $C_V\Delta T$ | 0 |
| Total | $\dfrac{RT_{hi}\ln(V_B/V_A)+RT_{lo}\ln(V_D/V_C)}{R\Delta T_{hi}\ln(V_B/V_A)}$ | $\dfrac{-RT_{hi}\ln(V_B/V_A)-RT_{lo}\ln(V_D/V_C)}{-R\Delta T_{hi}\ln(V_B/V_A)}$ | 0 | $\dfrac{R\ln(V_B/V_A)+R\ln(V_D/V_C)}{0}$ |

We can quite easily see that the total energy change for this cyclic process is zero. Showing that the entropy change of the system is also zero requires a little bit more work. Recall our relation between temperature and volume for a reversible adiabatic process (Eq. 16.26):

$$V_A T_{hi}^{\frac{C_{V,m}}{R}} = V_D T_{lo}^{\frac{C_{V,m}}{R}} \quad \text{and} \quad V_B T_{hi}^{\frac{C_{V,m}}{R}} = V_C T_{lo}^{\frac{C_{V,m}}{R}}$$

Dividing these two equations by each other gives us a relationship between the volumes:

$$V_A/V_B = V_D/V_C$$

Substitution into the expression for total entropy in the table gives us the result that the total entropy change is in fact zero. While this has only be strictly demonstrated for the cycle we have defined, it is possible to represent any cyclic process as a sum of different Carnot cycles. You may have done something like this in evaluating line integrals along irregular paths. For our purposes, the Carnot cycle is adequate demonstration that entropy is in fact a state function, and we should always treat it as such.

The Carnot cycle describes an idealized heat engine, where heat is used to produce work. Unfortunately, all the heat supplied cannot be converted into work; this is a consequence of the Second Law. Some heat is lost during the cycle, specifically on step 3. Let's see how much work we can get from a Carnot cycle. We have an expression for the total work in Table 17.1. This is also shown by the shaded area on the indicator diagram in Figure 17.3. The heat we have to supply is from the first step of the process, the isothermal expansion at $T_{hi}$. We can define an efficiency, symbolized $\epsilon$, for our engine as the work performed divided by the heat absorbed.

$$\epsilon = \frac{|w|}{q_{hi}} \tag{17.11}$$

We can also write an expression for the efficiency in terms of the temperatures of the hot and cold reservoirs. We start by expressing the work in terms of the heat, since $\Delta U = 0$ for the cycle.

$$\epsilon = \frac{q_{hi} + q_{lo}}{q_{hi}} = 1 + \frac{q_{lo}}{q_{hi}}$$

Using appropriate lines from Table 17.1, we can end up with a fairly simple expression

$$\frac{q_{lo}}{q_{hi}} = \frac{RT_{lo} \ln (V_D / V_C)}{RT_{hi} \ln (V_B / V_A)} = -\frac{T_{lo} \ln (V_B / V_A)}{T_{hi} \ln (V_B / V_A)} = -\frac{T_{lo}}{T_{hi}}$$

$$\epsilon = 1 - \frac{T_{lo}}{T_{hi}} \qquad (17.12)$$

Let's interpret Eq. 17.12. If the two temperatures are the same, no work can be obtained. We also see that to maximize the efficiency of a heat engine, we need a large temperature difference between the hot and cold parts of the engine. It turns out that no other reversible engine will have a higher efficiency than a Carnot engine, and Eq. 17.12 represents the best that can be done with the two temperatures. A real engine, of course, cannot have the efficiency of a Carnot engine. How close the efficiency approaches the ideal is a measure of how good the engineer is.

### Sample Problem 17.3

A heat engine is constructed that operates between the temperatures of 20°C and 550°C. If 500 J of heat is supplied to the engine, what is the maximum amount of work that can be performed?

### Solution

To begin, we need to convert our high and low temperatures to the Kelvin scale; $T_{hi} = 823.15$ K, $T_{lo} = 293.15$ K. We use Eq. 17.12 to calculate the efficiency of the engine.

$$\epsilon = 1 - \frac{T_{lo}}{T_{hi}} = 1 - \frac{293.15}{823.15} = 0.644$$

The ideal engine is 64.4% efficient. Thus, a heat input of 500 J can produce work of at most 322 J. The remaining 178 J is "lost" as heat that dumps to the cold side of the engine. Remember that this is the ideal limit; any real engine will be less efficient than this ideal case.

---

## 17.2.3 Clausius Inequality

Since entropy is a state function, it doesn't matter what path we use to calculate it; we just need to know the initial and final states of the system. Remember, though, that Eq. 17.1 defines entropy in connection with the heat along a reversible path. A reversible process is an idealized situation that is useful for us in theory, but not realizable in practice. Can we make a connection between entropy and the heat of a process along the path it actually takes?

Let's write an equality for the internal energy change for two expansion processes—one reversible, and one irreversible.

$$dU = \delta q + \delta w = \delta q_{rev} + \delta w_{rev}$$

Since the initial and final states are the same, the internal energy change is also the same, but the amounts of heat and work may be different for the two paths. From our indicator diagrams, we know the reversible path gives the greatest amount of work,

$$-\delta w_{rev} \geq -\delta w \quad \text{or} \quad \delta w - \delta w_{rev} \geq 0$$

(Remember that for an expansion process, $\delta w$ is negative.) It then follows that

$$\delta q_{rev} - \delta q = \delta w - \delta w_{rev} \geq 0 \quad \text{or} \quad \delta q_{rev} \geq \delta q$$

We can divide both sides by $T$ to write

$$\frac{\delta q_{rev}}{T} \geq \frac{\delta q}{T}$$

Recalling our thermodynamic definition of entropy, we can write

$$\boxed{dS \geq \frac{\delta q}{T}}$$ (17.13)

The equality only holds for a reversible process. For any irreversible process, the entropy is greater than the heat divided by the temperature. This is known as the **Clausius inequality** and serves as another statement of the Second Law of thermodynamics. One case where this is particularly important is for an irreversible, adiabatic process. The fact that it is adiabatic means there is no heat, but the entropy can still be positive; $\Delta S > 0$.

## 17.2.4 System Versus Surroundings

At this point we need to more fully develop the Second Law in terms of both the system and the surroundings. Recall that one statement of the First Law is that the energy of the universe is constant. Since the universe is considered to be an isolated system, we can always divide the universe into two parts: the system we are interested in, and everything else—the surroundings. We have seen that for certain processes the entropy change of the system is zero or even negative (see Sample Problem 17.2). To get the full picture, we must also pay attention to the entropy change of the surroundings. A complete statement of the Second Law of thermodynamics is:

The entropy of the universe never decreases.

Or, as originally stated by Clausius:

Die entropie der universe strebt ein maximum zu.
(The entropy of the universe tends to the maximum value.)

Mathematically we write this as

$$\boxed{\Delta S_{universe} = \Delta S_{system} + \Delta S_{surroundings} \geq 0}$$ (17.14)

This leads us back to the notion of spontaneity. A spontaneous process is one for which the entropy of the universe increases. If the entropy of the system is zero or negative for a spontaneous process, then the entropy of the surroundings must increase by enough to offset that amount.

Let's illustrate the entropy of the system and surroundings with a phase transition at a temperature other than the normal transition temperature, for example the freezing of supercooled water.

$$H_2O \, (l) \, [253.15 \text{ K}, 1 \text{ atm}] \rightarrow H_2O \, (s) \, [253.15 \text{ K}, 1 \text{ atm}]$$

We want to calculate $\Delta S$ for the system and the surroundings. To do so, we need the following information:

$C_{P,m}$ (liquid water) = 75.29 J mol$^{-1}$ K$^{-1}$ (constant over this temperature range)

$C_{P,m}$ (ice) = 0.133 $T$ + 1.52 J mol$^{-1}$ K$^{-1}$ (not constant!)

$\Delta_{fus}H°$ (ice) = 6.008 kJ mol$^{-1}$ at 273.15 K

Remember that phase transitions are reversible at the normal transition temperature. Because we are talking about the freezing of supercooled water, this is not a reversible process. We can determine the entropy change of the system by defining a reversible path that makes use of the data we have. We can do this in three steps:

1. Heat the water from 253.15 K to 273.15 K
2. Let the water freeze at 273.15 K
3. Cool the ice from 273.15 K back down to 253.15 K

Since entropy is a state function, we'll get the same result as the process we want, freezing at 253.15 K. Now, let's evaluate the three steps individually.

For the first step, we want to heat the water from 253.15 K to 273.15 K at constant pressure. The entropy change for this process is written as

$$\Delta S_1 = \int_{253.15}^{273.15} \frac{C_P}{T} dT = 5.725 \text{ J mol}^{-1}\text{K}^{-1}$$

The entropy change for the second step is just that of the freezing of water to ice at 273.15 K. Remember fusion is melting, so we need to change the sign.

$$\Delta_{freeze}S = \frac{-\Delta_{fus}H}{T_{fus}} = -21.995 \text{ J mol}^{-1}\text{K}^{-1}$$

The entropy change for the final step is evaluated in a similar manner to the first step.

$$\Delta S_3 = \int_{273.15}^{253.15} \frac{0.133T + 1.52}{T} dT = -2.776 \text{ J mol}^{-1}\text{K}^{-1}$$

The total entropy change for the process can now be calculated.

$$\Delta_{sys}S = 5.725 - 21.995 - 2.776 = -19.047 \text{ J mol}^{-1}\text{ K}^{-1}$$

The entropy change is found to be negative. We should first ask ourselves if this result makes sense. It does, because we are going from liquid to solid. In molecular terms, the water molecules have much less freedom in their possible states than in ice, so a decrease of entropy makes sense. Also note that the entropy change is slightly less than when the process happens at 273.15 K, which makes sense because the whole process happens at a lower temperature.

Now, we need to evaluate the entropy change for the surroundings. To do this, we need to know the actual amount of heat involved in the exact process we are considering. To do this calculation, we first need to make some assumptions:

1. The surroundings are much more massive than the system, so any heat flowing in or out of the surroundings will cause a negligible temperature change in the surroundings.
2. All processes are reversible from the perspective of the surroundings, again because the surroundings are massive compared to the system.

There must be an equivalence in the heat exchanged between the system and the surroundings:

$$q_{sys} = -q_{sur}$$

Since the process we are considering takes place at constant pressure, we can equate the heat with the enthalpy. Therefore,

$$q_{sur} = -q_{sys} = -\Delta H_{sys}$$

We determine $\Delta H$ for the system in the same fashion in which we evaluated $\Delta S$, with slightly different integrals. To determine the enthalpy for heating the water in the first step, we evaluate

$$\Delta H_1 = \int_{253.15}^{273.15} C_p \, dT = 1.506 \text{ kJ mol}^{-1}$$

The enthalpy for the freezing process is readily evaluated as

$$\Delta_{freeze} H = -\Delta_{fus} H = -6.008 \text{ kJ mol}^{-1}$$

The enthalpy change for cooling the ice is also straightforward to calculate.

$$\Delta H_3 = \int_{273.15}^{253.15} 0.133T + 1.52 \, dT = -0.730 \text{ kJ mol}^{-1}$$

We can now put all this together to calculate the enthalpy change of the surroundings.

$$\Delta H_{surr} = -\Delta H_{sys} = -(1.506 - 6.008 - 0.730) = 5.232 \text{ kJ mol}^{-1}$$

Note that the enthalpy change of the surroundings is positive. This is because freezing is an exothermic process; heat leaves the system and flows into the surroundings.

Now, what is the entropy change in the surroundings? We are assuming that the temperature of the surroundings does not change due to the heat flowing into the surroundings.

$$\Delta_{sur} S = \frac{\Delta_{sur} H}{T} = \frac{5232 \text{ J mol}^{-1}}{253.15 \text{ K}} = 20.66 \text{ J mol}^{-1} \text{K}^{-1}$$

The entropy of the surroundings has increased due to the flow of heat to the surroundings. Now, for the total entropy change, we add the changes for the system and the surroundings. The total entropy change of the universe is

$$\Delta_{univ} S = \Delta_{sur} S + \Delta_{sys} S = (20.66 - 19.05) \text{J mol}^{-1} \text{K}^{-1} = 1.61 \text{ J mol}^{-1} \text{K}^{-1}$$

We find that $\Delta S_{univ} > 0$, which tells us that the process is spontaneous. Note that the entropy of the system can spontaneously decrease, so long as the entropy of the surroundings increases by more. What about the reverse process, melting of ice at 253.15 K? $\Delta S_{univ}$ would be negative, so that would not be a spontaneous process.

## 17.2.5 Irreversible Expansion of Ideal Gas

Let's reconsider the expansion of an ideal gas in terms of system and surroundings. For a reversible isothermal expansion, we have already shown that we can write the entropy of the *system* as

$$\Delta S = nR \ln \frac{V_f}{V_i}$$

Entropy is a state function; therefore, as long as we know the initial and final states, this is the entropy of this process for the system—it doesn't depend on the path. The total entropy change, system, and surroundings, however, does depend on the path, as we will now demonstrate.

For any process, $\delta q_{sys} = -\delta q_{sur}$. For the reversible isothermal process with ideal gas, what is $\Delta S_{sur}$?

$$\Delta S_{sur} = \frac{q_{sur}}{T} = -\frac{q_{rev}}{T} = -nR \ln \frac{V_f}{V_i}$$

The entropy change of the surroundings perfectly balances that of the system, and we have

$$\Delta S_{tot} = 0$$

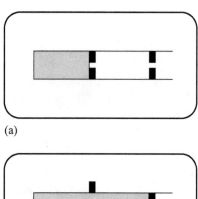

(a)

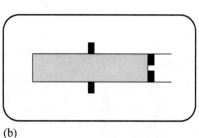

(b)

**FIGURE 17.4.** a) A container of ideal gas inside a larger container of vacuum. Mechanical stops prevent the gas from expanding. b) The first set of mechanical stops have been removed, so the gas expands until the piston reaches the second set of mechanical stops.

This gives us another way to think about a reversible process; for a reversible process, the entropy change of the universe is zero. That's why we can go back and forth with no net change. (That's also why we can't realize a reversible process in practice.)

Now, let's consider a different case. Take a thermally insulated container of ideal gas and provide two sets of mechanical stops, as shown in Figure 17.4. The second set allows the volume to double from that of the first set. Let's place that container in a vacuum chamber and release the first set of stops. Because the pressure inside the container is greater than that outside (the container is in a vacuum), the gas will expand. The external pressure is zero, which means there is no work involved with this expansion; the expanding gas has nothing to push against. What about the heat for this process? Because of the insulation, no heat can flow to the surroundings; therefore the heat is also zero. If we have no work and no heat, then by the First Law $\Delta U$ also equals zero. Likewise, because the energy of our system has not changed, and the energy of an ideal gas only depends on temperature, the temperature of the system has not changed either. All that has changed is the volume and the pressure.

Now, what about the entropy change for this system? We have an ideal gas that has undergone an isothermal expansion. Taking a reversible path between initial and final states, we write the entropy of the system as before.

$$\Delta S_{sys} = nR \ln \frac{V_f}{V_i}$$

To determine the total entropy, we also need the entropy of the surroundings. In this case, there has been no heat flow, so as far as the surroundings are concerned, nothing has happened. Thus

$$\Delta S_{surr} = 0$$

The total entropy change of the universe is just that of the system.

$$\Delta S_{univ} = nR \ln \frac{V_f}{V_i} > 0$$

In setting up this situation, you expected the gas to expand once the stops were removed. We can see that our common sense of what will happen spontaneously is really a common sense about entropy; spontaneous processes involve an increase in the entropy of the universe.

### Sample Problem 17.4

Let's return to the situation of Sample Problem 17.1 You have a sample of 2.00 mol of Ar in a 10.0 L container at 300 K. We are going to expand the volume to 30.0 L and double the temperature by putting the container in an oven that is pressurized at the final pressure. Calculate the total heat and entropy change for this process.

Solution

We have already calculated the entropy change of the system; the initial and final conditions are the same as in Sample Problem 17.1. $\Delta S_{sys} = 35.6$ J K$^{-1}$. To calculate the entropy change of the surroundings, we need to determine the actual amount of heat involved in the process. Since both the pressure and the volume of the gas are changing, we can't just use an expression of the form $q = C_{V\mathrm{or}P}\Delta T$. We'll have to take a different approach.

First, we recall that the energy is a state function and, since we are working with ideal gas, the energy change is always $\Delta U = C_V \Delta T$. This holds true whether the process is at constant volume or not. Thus, we can calculate

$$\Delta U = C_V \Delta T = \frac{3}{2}R(2.00 \text{ mol})(300 \text{ K}) = 7.48 \text{ kJ}$$

Because the process is being done at constant external pressure, the work is also straightforward to calculate. The external pressure is equal to the final pressure of the system, which is calculated from the ideal gas law

$$P_2 = \frac{nRT_2}{V_2} = \frac{(2.00 \text{ mol}) \times R \times (600 \text{ K})}{(30.0 \text{ L})} = 3.28 \text{ atm}$$

The work is therefore

$$w = -P_{ex}\Delta V = -(3.28 \text{ atm}) \times (20.0 \text{ L}) = -65.6\text{L atm} = -6.65 \text{ kJ}$$

By the First Law, we can calculate the heat for the processes

$$q = \Delta U - w = 7.48 \text{ kJ} - (-6.65 \text{ kJ}) = 14.13 \text{ kJ}$$

The entropy of the surroundings, assuming the surroundings are at a constant temperature of 600 K, is

$$\Delta S_{surr} = \frac{\delta q_{surr}}{T_{surr}} = \frac{-\delta q_{sys}}{T_{surr}} = \frac{-14.13 \text{ kJ}}{600 \text{ K}} = -23.5 \text{ J K}^{-1}$$

The total entropy is the sum of the two terms for system and surroundings.

$$\Delta S_{tot} = \Delta S_{sys} + \Delta S_{surr} = 35.6 \text{ J K}^{-1} - 23.5 \text{ J K}^{-1} = 12.1 \text{ J K}^{-1}$$

$\Delta S_{tot}$ is positive, telling us that the process is spontaneous; the gas will expand and heat up without any action on our part.

# 17.3 Third Law of Thermodynamics

## 17.3.1 The Third Law

The molecular interpretation of entropy allows us to develop the Third Law of thermodynamics. To do so, let's go back to the Boltzmann distribution. As we reduce the temperature, the population in any excited state will decrease. As we reach absolute zero, the system must be in its lowest possible energy state. Since there is only one way to arrange the system in this lowest energy state, this configuration has a statistical weight of $1^N$, which is exactly 1. Using the Boltzmann expression $S = k_B \ln W$, the entropy of a system for which $W = 1$ will necessarily be zero.

One formulation of the Third Law of thermodynamics states:

The entropy of all perfect crystalline systems is zero at $T = 0$.

$$S_{m, 0}^{\circ} = 0 \qquad\qquad (17.15)$$

(The subscript 0 denotes $T = 0$; the superscript $^\circ$ denotes a perfect crystal)

## 17.3.2 Residual Entropy

It's important that we clarify why we said the sample must be a perfect crystal. Let's take the case of sample of diatomic molecules and cool it to zero temperature. The two atoms are different, and as the temperature decreases, the material forms a crystal. Now, there is still some possibility of disorder in the system depending on how the molecules are arranged. For example, AB AB AB BA AB AB BA AB AB...

Thus we have some difference in the arrangements, even though there is almost no energy difference between the arrangements. In other words, even though $T = 0$, $W \neq 1$ and there is some *residual entropy*. For example, ice has been measured to have residual entropy of 3.4 J mol$^{-1}$ K$^{-1}$ because of differing arrangements of the hydrogen bonds. This means that, unlike internal energy and enthalpy, we can actually determine absolute values of entropy, not just values relative to some standard state of our choosing. This is the reason thermodynamic tables report absolute standard entropies, $S_m^{\circ}$, rather than entropies of formation, as is done for enthalpy.

Carbon monoxide has an experimental residual entropy of 4.2 J mol$^{-1}$ K$^{-1}$. a) Estimate the residual entropy per mole if each CO molecule has an equal chance of being in either of two orientations. b) From the experimental value, estimate the actual probability of a CO molecule being misaligned.

Solution

a. If each molecule can be in either of two arrangements, then there are $2^N$ different possible arrangements. The residual entropy per mole is then

$$S = k_B \ln W = k_B \ln 2^{N_A} = R \ln 2 = 5.76 \text{ J mol}^{-1}\text{K}^{-1}$$

This is larger than the experimental value, suggesting that there is not equal likelihood of the two arrangements of the CO molecules.

b. Estimating the probability of misalignment will be difficult using the Boltzmann entropy, so let's switch to the Gibbs entropy (Eq. 13.35)

$$S = -Nk_B \sum_i P_i \ln P_i$$

Note, if the probability of being in each state is ½, we go right back to the expression we used in part a). Using a spreadsheet, we can quickly adjust the value of the probabilities (remember, they must add up to 1) until we obtain the experimental value. Doing so gives a misalignment probability of ~20.5%.

## 17.3.3 Measurement of Entropy

You may have wondered, how do we measure entropy? We certainly don't have an entropy-meter. The first clue comes from knowing that entropy is related to heat. If we can measure the heat capacity as a function of temperature, we can also measure the entropy. So in principle, to measure the entropy of a substance, you start at $T = 0$, where you have only the residual entropy, which may be zero (or close to zero) for some materials. Then you raise the temperature. The entropy will rise as $C_p/T$. The entropy at a given temperature can then be evaluated by the integral

$$S(T) = S(0) + \int_0^T \frac{C_P}{T} dT \tag{17.16}$$

You must be careful whenever you encounter a phase transition. At a phase transition, additional heat doesn't raise the temperature but drives the transition. So here you would use the relation $\Delta_{trs} S = \dfrac{\Delta_{trs} H}{T_{trs}}$. Now, you can continue to increase the temperature using the heat capacity of the new phase and continue in the same way to the temperature of your choice. The total entropy would be the sum of all these contributions. Figure 17.5 graphically represents this procedure.

For very low temperatures, recall the Debye heat capacity law (Eq. 7.43) that shows that the heat capacity goes as the temperature cubed. In practice, the heat capacity is measured to as low a temperature as possible, and then is fit down to $T = 0$. Note that these types of

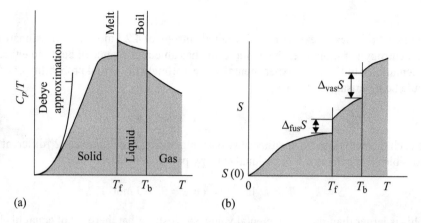

**FIGURE 17.5.** Graphical representation of a) variation of $C_p/T$ with temperature and b) entropy with temperature. The entropy is found by integrating the $C_p/T$ curve from $T = 0$ to the temperature of interest.

experiments can't directly measure the residual entropy. Spectroscopic measurements and computational methods that give us more detail into the partition function of the material are needed for that.

### 17.3.4 Entropy of Reaction

We can use tabulated standard entropies in the same way we use standard enthalpies of formation. If we want the standard entropy of a reaction, we use the tabulated values as we did with Hess's law for enthalpies.

$$\Delta_r S^\circ = \sum_{products} v S_m^\circ - \sum_{reactants} v S_m^\circ \tag{17.17}$$

This gives the entropy for reaction of the system. If we want the entropy change for the surroundings, we first need to determine the heat of reaction using standard enthalpies. We then calculate the entropy of the surroundings similar to what we did in Sample Problem 17.4.

## 17.4 Summary, and Where We Go Next

In this chapter, we have explored the fundamental aspects and some applications of the Second and Third Laws of thermodynamics. We now understand not just the flow of energy, but the direction of that flow. You may feel, however, that having to do two sets of calculations—one for the system and one for the surroundings—is rather cumbersome. You're right, and in the next chapter we will develop some better tools for describing thermodynamic processes.

# PROBLEMS

**17.1** a) Derive general expressions for the change in entropy with temperature at constant pressure and at constant volume (two expressions).

b) Is it ever possible for the entropy to decrease with an increase in temperature at either constant pressure or constant volume? Justify your answer.

**17.2** A 250.0 g block of copper ($C_{P,m} = 24.4$ J mol$^{-1}$ K$^{-1}$) heated to 85°C is placed in water ($C_{P,m} = 75.291$ J mol$^{-1}$ K$^{-1}$) at 25°C in an insulated container. Calculate the final temperature and the total entropy change for the process when the volume of water is:

a) 10.0 mL

b) 100.0 mL

c) 1.00 L

d) Comment on the trends you observe in the values of the final temperature and entropy change, and provide a molecular explanation for them.

**17.3** Eq. 17.7 is only true for a reversible isothermal process involving an ideal gas.

a) Derive an expression for the entropy change for a reversible isothermal process where the gas is described by the van der Waals equation of state. (The results of problems 16.2 a) will be helpful in completing this derivation.)

b) Compare the entropy change for a reversible isothermal doubling of the volume of an ideal gas and a van der Waals gas. Comment on the molecular basis for the difference, if any. (See Problem 16.4 b) for added insight.)

**17.4** Consider the following process. Take 1 mol of monatomic ideal gas at 1 L and 300 K and heat it to 600 K while expanding the volume to 2 L. Calculate the entropy for the system, surroundings, and the universe. (Assume the simplest nonreversible path for this process.)

**17.5** $NH_3$ (g), initially at 25°C and 1 bar, is heated at constant pressure until the volume increases to 4 times the initial volume. The heat capacity of $NH_3$ can be modeled by the expression

$$C_{P,m}(NH_3(g))/\text{J mol}^{-1}\text{K}^{-1} = 25.9 + (33 \times 10^{-3}\,\text{K}^{-1})T$$

a) Determine the final temperature and pressure of the system.

b) Calculate the heat per mole, work per mole, $\Delta H_m$, and $\Delta U_m$ for this process.

c) Calculate $\Delta S_m$ for the system.

d) Calculate $\Delta S_{tot}$ for the process and comment on the spontaneity of this process. Clearly state any assumptions.

**17.6** Eq. 17.10 gives the entropy change for a phase transition at the normal transition temperature. In 1884, Frederick Trouton published a paper showing that for many liquids, the entropy of vaporization is approximately $10.5R$. For the following liquids, use Trouton's rule to predict the standard enthalpy of vaporization using the given boiling point. Compare each result to a literature value and comment on the molecular basis of any differences.

a) benzene, $T_b = 80.1°C$

b) carbon tetrachloride, $T_b = 76.7°C$

c) water, $T_b = 100.0°C$

d) methane, $T_b = -161.5°C$

e) hydrogen sulfide, $T_b = -60.4°C$

f) decane, $T_b = 174°C$

**17.7** When the Carnot cycle is run in reverse, work is done on the system to cause heat to flow from the cold side to the hot side. In other words, the cold side gets colder and the hot side gets hotter; we have a refrigerator. Instead of rating a refrigerator by efficiency, we define a coefficient of performance, taken as the ratio of the energy transferred as heat from the cold side to the work performed.

$$c = \frac{|q_{low}|}{w}$$

a) A given freezer has a coefficient of performance of 12. The heat of fusion of water is 6.008 kJ/mol at 0°C. The heat capacity of liquid water is 75.291 J/mol K. How much work is required to freeze 1 kg of water initially at 25°C in a freezer set at 0°C?

b) Derive a general expression for the coefficient of performance in terms of the two temperatures, $T_{low}$ and $T_{hi}$. Note that $c$ should be positive. (This is the upper limit for an ideal refrigerator. Real refrigerators will have a lower coefficient of performance.)

**17.8** Consider the process described in Problem 16.5.

a) Calculate $\Delta S_{sys}$, $\Delta S_{surr}$, and $\Delta S_{univ}$ for this process.

b) If the gas were expanded reversibly and adiabatically to the same final volume, calculate the final temperature and pressure.

c) Is the final temperature for the irreversible process higher or lower than for the reversible process? Provide a justification for your answer.

**17.9** The standard enthalpy of formation of $NH_3$ (g) is $-46.11$ kJ $mol^{-1}$ at 298 K. The standard molar entropy of $NH_3$ (g) is 192.45 J $mol^{-1}$ $K^{-1}$ at 298 K. Given the heat capacity data below and the data in Problem 17.5, calculate the standard enthalpy of formation and standard molar entropy of $NH_3$ (g) at 1200 K.

$$C_{P,m}(H_2(g))/J\ mol^{-1}K^{-1} = 29.1 - (0.84 \times 10^{-3}\ K^{-1})T$$

$$C_{P,m}(N_2(g))/J\ mol^{-1}K^{-1} = 26.98 + (5.9 \times 10^{-3}\ K^{-1})T$$

**17.10** For the case where a molecule has $M$ equivalent arrangements in a crystal at 0 K, show that the Gibbs entropy expression (Eq. 13.35) can be easily reexpressed as the Boltzmann entropy expression, where $W$ is equivalent to $M$.

**17.11** At very low temperatures (a few K), the heat capacity generally follows the Debye $T^3$ law,

$$C_P(T) = aT^3$$

where $a$ is a constant that depends on the material. Derive a general expression for the standard molar entropy at a temperature where the Debye $T^3$ law holds true. Be sure to include the possibility of residual entropy in your expression.

# Gibbs Energy

## 18.1 Combining the First and Second Laws

In the last chapter, we found that in order to fully determine whether or not a process was spontaneous we had to consider the entropy of both the system and the surroundings. While this wasn't overly difficult, it did require two separate sets of calculations for a single process. In this chapter, we will develop some new tools that can let us handle such situations with a single calculation. To do so, we will introduce two new thermodynamic variables, the Helmholtz and Gibbs energies.

### 18.1.1 Fundamental Equation of Thermodynamics

Let's go back to our statement of the First Law as a differential of the internal energy.

$$dU = \delta q + \delta w$$

From the definition of work, for a system in mechanical equilibrium, we write

$$dU = \delta q - PdV$$

From our statement of the Second Law that defines entropy, $dS = \dfrac{\delta q}{T}$, we have

$$\delta q = TdS$$

(We are technically assuming a reversible process here.) This lets us write

$$\boxed{dU = TdS - PdV} \tag{18.1}$$

This is known as the **fundamental equation of thermodynamics**, because it combines both the First and Second Laws into a single mathematical relation. Because internal energy is a state function, this relation holds true for all processes. Also keep in mind that we are considering the variables of the system here.

This relation also shows us that there are "natural variables" for the internal energy. If we write $U(S,V)$, then the total differential will be

$$dU = \left(\frac{\partial U}{\partial S}\right)_V dS + \left(\frac{\partial U}{\partial V}\right)_S dV \tag{18.2}$$

Comparing to the fundamental equation, we can readily see that

$$\left(\frac{\partial U}{\partial S}\right)_V = T \qquad \left(\frac{\partial U}{\partial V}\right)_S = -P \tag{18.3}$$

These two equations actually serve as thermodynamic definitions of temperature and pressure, respectively.

### 18.1.2 Legendre Transforms

As we discussed in the last two chapters, thermodynamic variables come in pairs that we call conjugate variables. The two pairs we have seen so far are $P$–$V$ and $T$–$S$. The fundamental equation clearly shows these connections; changes in internal energy (for a one-component system, no other work is possible) depend on two products of conjugate variables, an intensive variable multiplied by a change in an extensive variable.

Now, let's briefly return to some mathematics. Let's take an extensive function $f$ that depends on the extensive variables $x_1$, $x_2$, and so on. The conjugate intensive variables are $A_1$, $A_2$, and so on. Mathematically, $f(x_1, x_2, ...)$ We can write the total differential as

$$df = \left(\frac{\partial f}{\partial x_1}\right)_{x_2,...} dx_1 + \left(\frac{\partial f}{\partial x_2}\right)_{x_1,...} dx_2 + ... = A_1 dx_1 + A_2 dx_2 + ...$$

In this expression, the lowercase variables are the independent extensive variables and the capital variables are the intensive conjugate dependent variables. Each intensive variable is now identifiable as a partial derivative of our function $f$ with the conjugate extensive variable—similar to what we just did with temperature and pressure.

If we want to change things so that a conjugate variable, for example $A_1$, becomes independent (making the extensive variable $x_1$ dependent), we can do so by defining a quantity

$$g = f - x_1 A_1$$

The differential of $g$ is then written as

$$dg = df - x_1 dA_1 - A_1 dx_1$$

We can substitute in our expression for $df$ to get

$$dg = A_1 dx_1 + A_2 dx_2 + ... - x_1 dA_1 - A_1 dx_1 = -x_1 dA_1 + A_2 dx_2 + ...$$

Now we have switched one of our variables from being dependent to being independent. Instead of depending on $x_1$, $x_2$, and so on, our new function $g$ depends on $A_1$, $x_2$, $x_3$, and so on. Mathematically, $g(A_1, x_2, ...)$. This process of switching dependent and independent variables is known as a **Legendre transform**.

This is exactly what we did in defining enthalpy. Internal energy is a natural function of $S$ and $V$, but those are not always the most convenient variables for us to use. We've already seen how we can switch to a function that has pressure as a natural variable. This is enthalpy, which we defined as

$$H = U + PV$$

(We add instead of subtract because the minus sign is already in the fundamental equation.) Using the fundamental equation, we have

$$dH = dU + PdV + VdP = TdS - PdV + PdV + VdP$$

$$dH = TdS + VdP \tag{18.4}$$

This is just a restatement of the fundamental equation, only now in terms of enthalpy rather than internal energy. We can also see that the natural variables of the enthalpy are entropy and pressure. Mathematically, $H(S,P)$. As we did for the internal energy, we can write

$$\left(\frac{\partial H}{\partial S}\right)_P = T \qquad\qquad \left(\frac{\partial H}{\partial P}\right)_S = V \tag{18.5}$$

The enthalpy is more convenient when we have control over the pressure rather than the volume; as we saw before–and can see again—at constant pressure, the enthalpy equals the heat.

## 18.1.3 Maxwell Relations

Back to pure mathematics for a minute. We won't prove this, but it is known that for a differential of the form $df = gdx + hdy$, where $g$ and $h$ are both functions of $x$ and $y$, if $f$ is a state function, we can write

$$\left(\frac{\partial g}{\partial y}\right)_x = \left(\frac{\partial h}{\partial x}\right)_y \tag{18.6}$$

Eq. 18.6 is known as the test for exactness. If it holds true for the differential $df$, such a differential is called an **exact differential**, and the function $f$ is a state function. For path functions, their differentials are known as inexact differentials, and the equality of Eq. 18.6 will not hold.

### Sample Problem 18.1

Determine whether the following differentials are exact or inexact:

a)   $df = 2xy\, dx + x^2 dy$ 　　　 b)   $df = \dfrac{ax}{y} dx + b\, y\, dy$

Solution

a)   For the first differential, we have $g = 2xy$ and $h = x^2$. Applying the test for exactness (Eq. 18.6), we have

$$\left(\frac{\partial g}{\partial y}\right)_x = 2x = \left(\frac{\partial h}{\partial x}\right)_y = 2x$$

The equality is satisfied; therefore the differential is exact and $f$ is a state function.

b)  In this case, we have $g = \dfrac{ax}{y}$ and $h = by$. Applying the test gives

$$\left(\frac{\partial g}{\partial y}\right)_x = \frac{-ax}{y^2} \neq \left(\frac{\partial h}{\partial x}\right)_y = 0$$

The equality is not satisfied; therefore the differential is inexact and $f$ is not a state function.

When we know that we are working with a state function—such as the energy—we don't need to test for exactness. Instead, we can use Eq. 18.6 to generate new relations between our thermodynamic variables. Let's apply this to the fundamental equation, Eq. 18.1, which we include here again for convenience.

$$dU = T\,dS - P\,dV$$

Comparing to the relation for an exact differential, we will take $S$ to be $x$ and $V$ to be $y$. Likewise, we take $g$ to be $T$ and $h$ to be $-P$. Inserting these into Eq. 18.6 gives us

$$\left(\frac{\partial T}{\partial V}\right)_S = -\left(\frac{\partial P}{\partial S}\right)_V \tag{18.7}$$

This is the first of the so-called **Maxwell relations**. This expression relates particular partial derivatives of the state variables $P$, $V$, $T$, and $S$. There are three others. We can derive the next Maxwell relation from Eq. 18.4, which is based on the enthalpy.

$$\left(\frac{\partial T}{\partial P}\right)_S = \left(\frac{\partial V}{\partial S}\right)_P \tag{18.8}$$

When looking at Maxwell relations, there are few things to notice (and that can help you make sure you did them correctly). First, note that the variables in the denominator and outside the parentheses switch positions on the two sides of the relation. Also, note that the variable in the numerator is the conjugate of the variable outside the parentheses. Any negative signs in the governing relation, such as Eqs. 18.1 or 18.4, carry through to the Maxwell relation.

## 18.1.4 Gibbs and Helmholtz Energies

We have now seen how to switch between $V$ and $P$, depending on what is most convenient. However, $U$ and $H$ are still natural functions of $S$, which is a difficult variable to control. We can use a similar Legendre transform between $S$ and $T$—its conjugate variable—to define two new quantities. The Helmholtz energy is defined as

$$A = U - TS \tag{18.9}$$

The Gibbs energy is defined as

$$G = H - TS \tag{18.10}$$

We'll look at the Helmholtz energy first. We can write the differential of $A$ as

$$dA = dU - T\,dS - S\,dT = T\,dS - P\,dV - T\,dS - S\,dT$$

$$dA = -S\,dT - P\,dV \tag{18.11}$$

$A$ is a natural function of $T$ and $V$, which is very nice for certain applications. Mathematically, $A(T,V)$. We also readily see that

$$\left(\frac{\partial A}{\partial T}\right)_V = -S \qquad \left(\frac{\partial A}{\partial V}\right)_T = -P \qquad (18.12)$$

and we can derive the third Maxwell relation

$$\left(\frac{\partial P}{\partial T}\right)_V = \left(\frac{\partial S}{\partial V}\right)_T \qquad (18.13)$$

We can do the same thing for the Gibbs energy

$$dG = dH - TdS - SdT = TdS + VdP - TdS - SdT$$

$$dG = -SdT + VdP \qquad (18.14)$$

The natural variables of the Gibbs energy are temperature and pressure, which is very convenient for chemistry applications. Mathematically, $G(T,P)$. We can define entropy and volume as

$$S = -\left(\frac{\partial G}{\partial T}\right)_P \qquad V = \left(\frac{\partial G}{\partial P}\right)_T \qquad (18.15)$$

We can also determine the last of the four Maxwell relations from Eq. 18.14.

$$\left(\frac{\partial V}{\partial T}\right)_P = -\left(\frac{\partial S}{\partial P}\right)_T \qquad (18.16)$$

The quantities $U$, $H$, $A$, and $G$ are all known as **thermodynamic potentials**. They are not equivalent, and the one we chose to use will depend on the situation at hand. In fact, the only one the universe tells us about is the internal energy. The other quantities are in some sense "accounting tricks" that we have devised for our convenience for solving problems under certain conditions. For example, the enthalpy is equivalent to the heat at constant pressure. For many chemistry applications, we have control over temperature and pressure, making the Gibbs energy a good choice to use.

In this section, we have developed a lot of equations, so you may be wondering what is really important and what you need to memorize. It's all important, but don't try to memorize it all. In particular, don't try to memorize the Maxwell relations. They are very easy to mess up if you try. Instead, know how to derive them. With a little practice, you can recreate all the Maxwell relations in a matter of seconds without making any mistakes. In fact, this is a general pattern for mastering thermodynamics: Reduce the number of things you try to memorize. There are certain key relations you need to know, but almost everything else can be derived fairly quickly. You should know the definitions of the thermodynamic potentials and their differential expressions in terms of the thermodynamic variables. These four equations (Eqs. 18.1, 18.4, 18.11, and 18.14) are known collectively as the **Gibbs equations**. Everything else can be derived from them.

### 18.1.5 Thermodynamic Equation of State

Let's use what we have learned to develop a particularly useful thermodynamic relation. We have shown here that the natural variables of the internal energy are entropy and volume. Entropy, however, is a hard variable to work with. In Chapter 16, we considered the internal energy to be a function of temperature and volume. So which way is correct? They both are, as long as we're careful. Remember that nature doesn't do math, so it doesn't care how we describe things. Let's again write the differential of the internal energy as a function of temperature and volume.

$$dU = \left(\frac{\partial U}{\partial T}\right)_V dT + \left(\frac{\partial U}{\partial V}\right)_T dV$$

The partial derivative in the first term is simply the constant volume heat capacity. What about the other partial derivative that tells us how internal energy changes with volume at constant temperature? What does that tell us? (If you did Problem 16.4, you have already seen this last partial derivative.)

What we are going to do next is another good example of how to derive new thermodynamic relations from the fundamentals. We start with the Gibbs equation for the internal energy

$$dU = TdS - PdV$$

We will now do something that mathematicians hate, but that thermodynamicists do all the time; we will divide this expression by the differential of volume at constant temperature. By the rules we learned back in Chapter 15, we can write such a ratio of differentials as a partial differential.

$$\frac{dU}{dV_T} = \left(\frac{\partial U}{\partial V}\right)_T = T\left(\frac{\partial S}{\partial V}\right)_T - P\left(\frac{\partial V}{\partial V}\right)_T = T\left(\frac{\partial S}{\partial V}\right)_T - P$$

where we used the fact that $\left(\frac{\partial V}{\partial V}\right)_T = 1$. We can now look back to our Maxwell relations to replace the entropy derivative with something more convenient; entropy is hard to measure so we would like to remove it from our expression. Specifically, we use Eq. 18.13. This gives us a relation that is just in terms of $T$, $P$, and $V$—variables that are easy to measure and control.

$$\left(\frac{\partial U}{\partial V}\right)_T = T\left(\frac{\partial P}{\partial T}\right)_V - P \tag{18.17}$$

Eq. 18.13 is known as the **thermodynamic equation of state**. Let's evaluate this quantity for an ideal gas. To do so, we simply take the temperature derivative of the ideal gas law and plug it in. You can do this yourself fairly quickly, so we won't do it here. (See Problem 16.4a.) What you find is that this quantity is identically equal to zero for an ideal gas. This matches what we said earlier—that the internal energy of an ideal gas only depends on the temperature. If the temperature is held constant, the energy of an ideal gas can't change—even though the volume may.

For a different equation of state, this quantity can be either positive or negative. (See Problems 16.4b and c.) This quantity, which is also called the **internal pressure**, can actually be very useful in understanding molecular interactions. If it is positive, that tells us attractive interactions dominate the molecular behavior. If molecules are attracted to each other and we want to increase the distance between them while keeping the temperature fixed, we have to put in extra energy to overcome those attractive interactions. Likewise, if the internal pressure is negative, then repulsions dominate the interactions, and the energy decreases to keep the temperature fixed as the molecules are forced apart. If that energy was not removed, the repulsive energy would convert into kinetic energy, and the temperature would increase.

Other relations between thermodynamic potentials and state variables can be derived. A full compilation of such relations is at the end of the chapter in Table 18.1.

## 18.1.6 Relationship Between $C_P$ and $C_V$

In this section, we will derive a general relationship between the constant pressure and constant volume heat capacities. This will also serve as another example of the power of the Gibbs equations and the properties of partial derivatives to generate useful thermodynamic relationships.

We start with the definition of enthalpy

$$H = U + PV$$

then take the temperature derivative at constant pressure, similar to what we did in the last section. This gives us

$$C_P = \left( \frac{\partial H}{\partial T} \right)_P = \left( \frac{\partial U}{\partial T} \right)_P + P \left( \frac{\partial V}{\partial T} \right)_P$$

where we have included the definition of the constant pressure heat capacity. We need to be careful and recognize that the first term on the right is different from the definition of $C_V$; a different variable is being kept constant. We therefore need to determine an expression for $\left( \frac{\partial U}{\partial T} \right)_P$. To do this, we take $U(T,V)$ and write the total differential

$$dU = C_V dT + \left( \frac{\partial U}{\partial V} \right)_T dV$$

where we included the definition of $C_V$. We divide this expression by $dT$ at constant $P$ to get

$$\left( \frac{\partial U}{\partial T} \right)_P = C_V \left( \frac{\partial T}{\partial T} \right)_P + \left( \frac{\partial U}{\partial V} \right)_T \left( \frac{\partial V}{\partial T} \right)_P$$

In the last term, we have the thermodynamic equation of state, so we can substitute in Eq. 18.17

$$\left( \frac{\partial U}{\partial V} \right)_T = T \left( \frac{\partial P}{\partial T} \right)_V - P$$

Now we have the full energy derivative we need.

$$\left( \frac{\partial U}{\partial T} \right)_P = C_V + \left( \frac{\partial V}{\partial T} \right)_P \left[ T \left( \frac{\partial P}{\partial T} \right)_V - P \right]$$

This expression looks complicated because $T$ and $P$ are not the natural variables of the internal energy. Substituting this into the $C_P$ expression above gives us

$$C_P = C_V + \left(\frac{\partial V}{\partial T}\right)_P \left[T\left(\frac{\partial P}{\partial T}\right)_V - P\right] + P\left(\frac{\partial V}{\partial T}\right)_P$$

Simplifying and rearranging gives us

$$C_P - C_V = T\left(\frac{\partial V}{\partial T}\right)_P \left(\frac{\partial P}{\partial T}\right)_V$$

using $\left(\dfrac{\partial V}{\partial T}\right)_P = V\alpha$ and $\left(\dfrac{\partial P}{\partial T}\right)_V = \dfrac{\alpha}{\kappa}$ we now have

$$\boxed{C_P - C_V = \frac{TV\alpha^2}{\kappa}}$$

(18.18)

The parameters $\alpha$ and $\kappa$ are the thermal expansion coefficient and isothermal compressibility, respectively, that we encountered back in Chapter 15. (See Eqs. 15.12, 15.13, and Problem 15.1).

Eq. 18.18 is a general relationship; we have made no assumptions up to this point. It is often desirable to convert this to molar quantities, which only involves using molar heat capacities and the molar volume in Eq. 18.18. In Problem 18.5, you will explore this relation a bit more.

# 18.2 The Gibbs Energy

## 18.2.1 Helmholtz and Gibbs Energies in Terms of the Canonical Partition Function

In Chapter 14, we developed expressions for various thermodynamic variables in terms of the canonical partition function. We will now develop such expressions for the Helmholtz and Gibbs energies. To begin, we first recall the thermodynamic definition of the Helmholtz energy

$$A = U - TS$$

as well as how internal energy and entropy depend on the canonical partition function (see Table 14.1).

$$U = k_B T^2 \left(\frac{\partial \ln Q}{\partial T}\right)_{N,V} \qquad \text{and} \qquad S = k_B T \left(\frac{\partial \ln Q}{\partial T}\right)_{N,V} + k_B \ln Q$$

Direct substitution gives us the expression

$$A = -k_B T \ln Q$$

(18.19)

(This expression is actually offset by the zero-point energy, which we have left out for clarity.) Notice there are no derivatives involved here. This is about the simplest relation we could have between a thermodynamic variable and the canonical partition function.

In fact, it looks very similar to Boltzmann's original relation between entropy and statistical weight, $S = k_B \ln W$. Recall that the variables we control in the canonical ensemble are number, temperature, and volume ($N$, $T$, and $V$). These are the same as the natural variables of the Helmholtz energy, which again suggests a strong connection.

Using the definition of the Gibbs energy, we can construct a similar expression.

$$G = H - TS = U + PV - TS = A + PV$$

$$G = -k_B T \ln Q + k_B TV \left( \frac{\partial \ln Q}{\partial V} \right)_{N,T} \tag{18.20}$$

This expression is not as simple as the one for the Helmholtz energy, which reflects the fact that there is a difference in the natural variables of the two thermodynamic potentials. In the isothermal isobaric ensemble, where we control $N$, $T$, and $P$, the Gibbs energy has a very simple relation to the corresponding partition function. For that reason, Eq. 18.20 is not widely used (and was not included in Table 14.1).

## 18.2.2 Spontaneity Revisited

As we discussed in the last chapter, a spontaneous process is one for which the entropy of the universe increases. To determine spontaneity, we had to do separate calculations for the system and the surroundings to determine the total entropy change for the universe. This can become quite cumbersome. It would be nice if we could just focus on the system and not have to do the second set of calculations all the time. Fortunately, there is a way, and it involves the thermodynamic potentials we have just introduced.

Let's consider the case of heating at a constant volume, with no other work being done. In this case

$$dU_V = \delta q_V$$

According to the Clausius inequality, we can write

$$dS \geq \frac{\delta q}{T} \qquad \text{or} \qquad dS_V \geq \frac{dU_V}{T}$$

or, more conveniently

$$TdS_V \geq dU_V \tag{18.21}$$

(The subscript $V$ tells us volume is held constant.) If we now require that the total energy or the entropy be kept constant, we can write

$$dS_{U,V} \geq 0 \qquad\qquad dU_{S,V} \leq 0 \tag{18.22}$$

Because we are using the Clausius inequality, we are talking now in terms only of the system. What we have here are two more definitions of spontaneity. If the energy and volume of the system are constant, a spontaneous process will increase the entropy of the system. Likewise, a process at constant volume and constant entropy is spontaneous only if the internal energy of the system decreases. This does not simply mean the system is tending to a state of lower internal energy. It means that if the entropy and volume of the system are constant, the entropy of the universe is increasing because of a loss of heat from the system. If the internal energy also does not change under conditions of constant entropy and volume, the system is at equilibrium with the surroundings.

If we go through a similar analysis for the enthalpy at constant pressure, with no other form of work taking place, we can write

$$T\,dS_P \geq dH_P \tag{18.23}$$

$$dS_{H,P} \geq 0 \qquad\qquad dH_{S,P} \leq 0 \tag{18.24}$$

So for a system at constant pressure with no change in entropy, the enthalpy must decrease if the process is spontaneous; again, this tells us that heat is flowing to the surroundings, increasing the entropy of the surroundings. Or if the enthalpy and pressure are held constant, the entropy of the system must increase in order for the process to be spontaneous.

As we have said before, keeping the entropy constant is not always easy; we usually have more control over the temperature. So, let's now look at the criteria for spontaneity for the Helmholtz and Gibbs energies. We start with the definitions of the Helmholtz and Gibbs energies, and their differential forms.

$$A = U - TS \qquad\qquad dA = dU - TdS - SdT$$

$$G = H - TS \qquad\qquad dG = dH - TdS - SdT$$

From Eq. 18.21 we have, at constant $V$, $dU_V - TdS \leq 0$, which at constant $T$ gives us

$$dA_{T,V} \leq 0 \tag{18.25}$$

At constant volume and temperature, the Helmholtz energy will decrease for a spontaneous process. If we look back at Eq. 18.19, which relates the Helmholtz energy to the partition function, we see that a decrease in the Helmholtz energy corresponds to an increase in the canonical partition function, which relates to the number of ways to arrange the system at a particular temperature and volume. A spontaneous process is one that causes energy to be distributed among more possible states than before, which goes back to Boltzmann's conception of entropy and ties back to the Second Law.

From Eq. 18.23, we have at constant $P$, $dH_P - TdS_P \leq 0$, which at constant $T$ gives us

$$dG_{T,P} \leq 0 \tag{18.26}$$

So, for a process at constant temperature and pressure, it is spontaneous if $dG_{T,P} < 0$, and at equilibrium if $dG_{T,P} = 0$. This relation will become our workhorse for the next three chapters. Note that we are only talking about $dG$ of the system.

The question is often asked how $dU$ or $dG$ can be less than zero if we are keeping our natural variables constant. To understand this, we need to look back at the Clausius inequality. This inequality is defined in terms of the entropy of the system. The equality only holds for a reversible process. Since the Gibbs energy is the potential of most use to chemists, let's consider it. We know that the total entropy must not decrease for a process, or expressed mathematically,

$$\Delta S_{tot} = \Delta S_{sys} + \Delta S_{sur} \geq 0$$

At constant $T$, we can relate the entropy of the surroundings to the heat, which at constant $P$ is the enthalpy, and write

$$\Delta S_{sur} = \frac{q_{sur}}{T} = \frac{-q_{sys}}{T} = \frac{-\Delta H_{sys}}{T}$$

$$\Delta S_{sys} + \Delta S_{sur} = \Delta S_{sys} - \frac{\Delta H_{sys}}{T} \geq 0$$

Since at constant $T$, $\Delta G = \Delta H - T\Delta S$, this lets us write

$$\Delta H_{sys} - T\Delta S_{sys} = \Delta G_{sys} \leq 0$$

It all comes back to the Second Law. The second term in the inequality is the entropy change of the system. The first term relates to the heat exchange between the system and the surroundings. Thus the process is only spontaneous if the total entropy of the universe increases, or if the Gibbs energy of the system decreases.

This change in Gibbs energy is most likely because of a physical or chemical change taking place. Let's look back at the freezing of supercooled water. If we take the numbers we used previously for $\Delta_{frz}H° = -5.232$ kJ mol$^{-1}$ and $\Delta_{frz}S° = -19.047$ J mol$^{-1}$ K$^{-1}$ for water freezing at 253.15 K, we have $\Delta_{frz}G° = -410$ J mol$^{-1}$. Because $\Delta G$ is negative, that tells us that the freezing process is spontaneous at that temperature.

Let's also look back at the internal energy. What we are saying is that if we keep the volume and entropy of the system constant, the internal energy of the system must decrease for a spontaneous process. For a reversible process, nothing happens and $dU = 0$. But for an irreversible process, we can consider that there is an energy loss by the system, in the form of heat, that increases the entropy of the universe even though the entropy of the system has not changed. Again, spontaneity is driven by the Second Law.

## 18.2.3 Maximum Work

Let's look at the Helmholtz energy briefly. If we combine the Clausius inequality with the First Law statement of internal energy, we can write

$$dU \leq TdS + \delta w$$

We can rewrite this as

$$\delta w \geq dU - TdS$$

The most negative work (meaning the most work produced by the system) will be when the quantity on the right is a minimum, or

$$\delta w_{max} = dU - TdS$$

If we say the process is at constant temperature, we can write

$$dA = dU - TdS$$

and state our relationship as

$$\delta w_{max} = dA \tag{18.27}$$

The Helmholtz energy gives us the maximum amount of work that can be produced from a given isothermal process. For this reason, the Helmholtz energy is also known as the work function. (The German word for work is *arbeit*, hence the $A$, although some texts use $F$ for the Helmholtz energy.) If we fix the temperature, we can write for a macroscopic change

$$w_{max} = \Delta A = \Delta U - T\Delta S \tag{18.28}$$

Remember, work done by the system is negative, so we want $\Delta A$ to be as negative as possible. This suggests that we want the internal energy of the system to decrease. However, if $\Delta S < 0$ ($T$ is always positive), then the second term is positive and we can't get as much work out as the decrease in internal energy would suggest. Some of the energy is lost as heat to the surroundings to overcome the decrease in entropy of the system; the Second Law is inviolate.

If $\Delta S$ of our process is positive, then we actually get more work out than just our decrease in internal energy, but this comes about from heat flowing into the system from the surroundings and helping increase the work. In this case, the Second Law helps us out. The total entropy change for the universe must always be positive for any irreversible process.

Now, let's look at the Gibbs energy. We can write

$$dG = dH - SdT - TdS = dU + PdV + VdP - SdT - TdS$$

$$dG = \delta q + \delta w + PdV + VdP - SdT - TdS$$

Let's require that our process be reversible, meaning

$$\delta q = \delta q_{rev} = TdS$$

$$\delta w = \delta w_{rev} = -PdV + \delta w_{add}$$

where the last term accounts for nonexpansion work. Putting all this together gives us

$$dG = TdS - PdV + \delta w_{add} + PdV + VdP - SdT - TdS = VdP - SdT + \delta w_{add}$$

If we now require that the process occur at constant temperature and pressure, we have

$$dG_{T,P} = \delta w_{add} \tag{18.29}$$

Because we have said the process is reversible, this is the maximum additional work that can be performed. This is why the Gibbs energy is often referred to as the "free energy"; it is the energy that is available to do nonexpansion work. (Gibbs himself never used the term "free energy.") In particular we are concerned about chemical work. So for a measurable change,

$$w_{max,\,add} = \Delta G = \Delta H - T\Delta S \tag{18.30}$$

Of course, an irreversible process will produce less work than $\Delta G$.

## 18.2.4 Standard Gibbs Energies

As we did for the enthalpy and the entropy, we can determine a standard Gibbs energy of reaction at a particular temperature

$$\Delta_r G^\circ = \Delta_r H^\circ - T\Delta_r S^\circ \tag{18.31}$$

We can also use the standard Gibbs energy of formation to determine $\Delta_r G^\circ$

$$\Delta_r G^\circ = \sum_{products} v\Delta_f G^\circ - \sum_{reactants} v\Delta_f G^\circ \tag{18.32}$$

As with standard enthalpies of formation, the standard Gibbs energy of formation for an element in its standard form is taken to be exactly zero by convention. The sign of this quantity tells us whether a reaction is spontaneous under standard conditions at a given temperature, usually 298 K. We will revisit this for different experimental conditions in Chapter 20.

# 18.3 Properties of the Gibbs Energy

The Gibbs energy is often our thermodynamic potential of choice for chemistry applications because we can generally control the temperature and pressure of a chemical process. However, these parameters are not always held constant. We now discuss how to account for changes in the Gibbs energy with changes in temperature and pressure.

Let's first write the fundamental relation for the Gibbs energy for a one-component system

$$dG = -SdT + VdP$$

If we write the total differential of the Gibbs energy as a function of $T$ and $P$ we have

$$dG = \left(\frac{\partial G}{\partial T}\right)_P dT + \left(\frac{\partial G}{\partial P}\right)_T dP$$

Comparison of terms gives us the temperature derivative of the Gibbs energy

$$\left(\frac{\partial G}{\partial T}\right)_P = -S \tag{18.33}$$

We know that the entropy for all substances is greater than zero; thus as the temperature increases, the Gibbs energy must *decrease*. Also, because $(\partial G/\partial T)_P$ becomes more negative as $S$ increases, $G$ decreases the most with temperature when the entropy of the system is large. Since the entropy of a gas is much greater than that of a liquid, the temperature variation of $G$ with $T$ is greater for a gas than a liquid, which is greater than that of a solid. One thing this tells us is that even though the energy of a system necessarily increases with an increase in temperature, that energy becomes less available to perform useful work because of the increased entropy of the system.

Looking at the pressure derivative, we have

$$\left(\frac{\partial G}{\partial P}\right)_T = V \tag{18.34}$$

Similarly because $V > 0$ for all substances, the Gibbs energy must *increase* with increasing pressure. This increase is greater when the volume of the system is large, as is the case for a gas. Increasing the pressure of the system leads to greater confinement; thus the available energy can't spread out as much and can be more readily harnessed for performing useful work.

## 18.3.1 Changes with Temperature

Let's explore these ideas more quantitatively. First, let's consider the change of $G$ with $T$. We already have $\left(\frac{\partial G}{\partial T}\right)_P = -S$. However, it isn't very convenient to have to measure the entropy. We'll now derive an important thermodynamic expression that makes it more convenient to quantify changes of Gibbs energy with temperature. We start with the definition $G = H - TS$ and substitute Eq. 18.33 for $S$ to get

$$G = H + T\left(\frac{\partial G}{\partial T}\right)_P$$

Now we don't have $S$ in the expression; however, we have a different problem. This equation involves both $G$ and the temperature derivative of $G$, which still complicates things.

If we instead look at changes in $G/T$, we can write the partial derivative as

$$\left(\frac{\partial(G/T)}{\partial T}\right)_P = \frac{-G}{T^2} + \frac{1}{T}\left(\frac{\partial G}{\partial T}\right)_P = \frac{1}{T}\left[\left(\frac{\partial G}{\partial T}\right)_P - \frac{G}{T}\right]$$

From above, we have $\left(\frac{\partial G}{\partial T}\right)_P - \frac{G}{T} = \frac{-H}{T}$ which allows us to write

$$\left(\frac{\partial(G/T)}{\partial T}\right)_P = \frac{-H}{T^2} \tag{18.35}$$

This is known as the Gibbs–Helmholtz equation and is a very important result. Since we are at constant pressure, the enthalpy is simply the heat—which we *can* readily measure, unlike the entropy. If we do this for a physical or chemical change, we can write

$$\left(\frac{\partial(\Delta G/T)}{\partial T}\right)_P = \frac{-\Delta H}{T^2} \tag{18.36}$$

Let's revisit the freezing of supercooled water that we looked at previously.

$$H_2O\,(l)\,[253.15\ \text{K, 1 atm}] \rightarrow H_2O\,(s)\,[253.15\ \text{K, 1 atm}]$$

We want to calculate $\Delta G$ for the system. To do so, we need the following information:

$$\Delta_{fus}H^\circ\,(\text{ice}) = 6.008\ \text{kJ mol}^{-1}\ \text{at } 273.15\ \text{K}$$

(We'll assume $\Delta_{fus}H^\circ$ is constant over this temperature range.) At the normal transition temperature, $\Delta_{fus}G^\circ = 0$, because the two phases are in equilibrium. Let's take the Gibbs–Helmholtz equation and integrate it (assuming constant $\Delta_{fus}H^\circ$) from 273.15 to 253.15 K. This gives us

$$\frac{\Delta G^\circ}{253.15\text{K}} = -\Delta_{fus}H^\circ\left(\frac{1}{253.15\text{K}} - \frac{1}{273.15\text{K}}\right)$$

which leads to $\Delta G^\circ\,(253.15\ \text{K}) = -440\ \text{J mol}^{-1}$, meaning that the freezing process is spontaneous at this temperature. If we take the numbers we used in Section 17.2.4, we have $\Delta G^\circ = -410\ \text{J mol}^{-1}$. The difference in the values comes from our assumption that $\Delta_{fus}H^\circ$ is constant, which we didn't make previously. With better data on the temperature dependence of $\Delta_{fus}H^\circ$, we would get a better answer. Note also that this result only holds true if the pressure is held constant.

## 18.3.2 Changes with Pressure

Let's now look at the change in Gibbs energy with changes in the pressure. From Eq. 18.34 we can write, for constant temperature,

$$dG = VdP \tag{18.37}$$

or, for molar quantities

$$dG_m = V_m dP \tag{18.38}$$

Let's consider the case of a solid or a liquid where the volume doesn't change much with the pressure. We can integrate this expression to write

$$G_m(P_f) = G_m(P_i) + V_m \int_{P_i}^{P_f} dP = G_m(P_i) + V_m \Delta P \qquad (18.39)$$

Under laboratory conditions, we don't often change the pressure by very much, so we can generally consider $G$ to be a constant for condensed phases.

We have to do more with gases, however, because their volumes do change considerably with pressure. If we assume the gas is ideal, we can write

$$G_m(P_f) = G_m(P_i) + \int_{P_i}^{P_f} V_m \, dP = G_m(P_i) + RT \int_{P_i}^{P_f} \frac{1}{P} dP = G_m(P_i) + RT \, \ln \frac{P_f}{P_i}$$

If we take the initial condition to be our standard-state pressure, then we can write

$$\boxed{G_m(P) = G_m^\circ + RT \, \ln \frac{P}{P^\circ}} \qquad (18.40)$$

The $^\circ$ sign indicates the standard-state pressure. Since the standard state is typically 1 bar, some authors will drop the denominator. This is somewhat sloppy notation, however, because the argument of a ln must be unitless. It's important to remember that $G$ is always considered relative to our standard state.

## 18.3.3 Fugacity

The relationship we derived above, Eq. 18.40, only holds true for an ideal gas. The world, of course, is not always ideal. However, it would be nice to use the same type of relationship for real gases. To achieve this, Lewis defined a quantity known as the **fugacity**, $f$, defined as

$$\lim_{P \to 0} \frac{f}{P} = 1 \qquad (18.41)$$

With this definition, we can then write

$$G_m(P) = G_m^\circ + RT \, \ln \frac{f}{P^\circ} \qquad (18.42)$$

We can also define a **fugacity coefficient** as

$$\phi = \frac{f}{P} \qquad (18.43)$$

(The ratio of the $f/P^\circ$ will later be called *activity*, a very important quantity that we will work with quite a bit. Activity tells us how the system behaves relative to the standard state—in this case ideal gas at 1 bar.)

Note that fugacity has units of pressure. You can think of the fugacity as an "effective pressure" that accounts for the nonideal behavior of real gases. It differs from the mechanical pressure and can be greater than or less than this pressure. Table 18.1 shows the pressures and corresponding fugacities for nitrogen gas at 273 K.

**TABLE 18.1. Fugacity of Nitrogen Gas at 273 K.**

| P/atm | f/atm |
|-------|---------|
| 1 | 0.99955 |
| 10 | 9.9560 |
| 100 | 97.03 |
| 1000 | 1839 |

The term fugacity comes from the Latin *fugare*, meaning "to flee," and is also described as the "fleeing tendency" of the gas. This means how likely it is to leave the container if given the chance. At low pressure, attractive interactions between the molecules make the gas less likely to flee the container than the pressure would suggest; the fugacity is less than the pressure. At high pressures, however, repulsive interactions dominate, and the molecules want to move apart from each other; therefore the gas flees more readily than the mechanical pressure alone would suggest.

### 18.3.4 Relation Between Fugacity Coefficient and Equation of State

What follows is the formal derivation of the fugacity coefficient in terms of the equation of state. Let's start with the dependence of the Gibbs energy on pressure (Eq. 18.34).

$$\left(\frac{\partial G_m}{\partial P}\right)_T = V_m \quad \text{or} \quad dG_m = V_m dP$$

For an ideal gas, we would write

$$dG_m^{id} = V_m^{id} dP$$

Let's write the difference between the real and ideal Gibbs energy changes

$$dG_m - dG_m^{id} = \left(V_m - V_m^{id}\right) dP$$

Let's integrate this expression from some low-pressure $P'$ to $P$

$$\int_{G_m' - G_m'^{id}}^{G_m - G_m^{id}} d\left(G_m - G_m^{id}\right) = \int_{P'}^{P} \left(V_m - V_m^{id}\right) dP$$

$$\left(G_m - G_m^{id}\right)_P - \left(G_m' - G_m'^{id}\right)_{P'} = \int_{P'}^{P} \left(V_m - V_m^{id}\right) dP$$

Now, we let $P'$ go to zero, thus $G_m' \to G_m'^{id}$. Remember, the ideal gas law holds in the limit of zero pressure. This causes the second term on the left to vanish, leaving us

$$\left(G_m - G_m^{id}\right)_P = \int_0^P \left(V_m - V_m^{id}\right) dP$$

Now, we use our general expression for the Gibbs energy for a real gas, Eq. 18.42:

$$G_m(P) = G_m^\circ + RT \ln\frac{f}{P^\circ}$$

Likewise, for an ideal gas

$$G_m^{id}(P) = G_m^\circ + RT \ln\frac{P}{P^\circ}$$

(The standard state is an ideal gas for both cases.) Substituting these into our expression gives us

$$RT \ln \frac{f}{P^\circ} - RT \ln \frac{P}{P^\circ} = RT \ln \frac{f}{P} = \int_0^P \left( V_m - V_m^{id} \right) dP$$

Notice that the standard pressure has dropped out of the expression, so it really doesn't matter what we choose as the standard state.

From the definition of the compression factor, $Z$, we have (Eq. 15.16)

$$V_m = \frac{ZRT}{P}$$

and from the ideal gas law

$$V_m^{id} = \frac{RT}{P}$$

We can then write

$$RT \ln \frac{f}{P} = \int_0^P \left( \frac{ZRT}{P} - \frac{RT}{P} \right) dP = RT \int_0^P \frac{Z-1}{P} dP$$

The fugacity coefficient is defined as

$$\phi = \frac{f}{P}$$

which lets us write

$$\ln \phi = \int_0^P \frac{Z-1}{P} dP$$

or

$$\phi = \exp \left( \int_0^P \frac{Z-1}{P} dP \right) \qquad (18.44)$$

All the nonideal behavior has been collected into the fugacity coefficient, which is tabulated for many real gases. If $\phi < 1$, then the gas molecules are less likely to leave the container compared to an ideal gas. This means that attractions dominate the behavior. Note that this also agrees with a compression factor of $Z < 1$. If $\phi > 1$, then the intermolecular repulsions try to drive the gas molecules apart. Again, this corresponds to $Z > 1$. For an ideal gas, $Z = 1$, so $\phi = 1$. Note that $\phi$ is an integral, so it includes the behavior all the way up to the pressure of interest. In molecular terms, it effectively averages over all the intermolecular distances.

## 18.4 Summary, and Where We Go Next

In this chapter, we have developed the Gibbs energy, one of the most useful concepts in chemical thermodynamics. We have also learned how the Gibbs energy changes with conditions of temperature and pressure. We should note, however, that everything we have done to this point is for systems of only one component. In the next chapter, we will allow for multiple components to be in our system as we discuss phase and solution equilibria. We will also introduce another powerful concept, the chemical potential.

**18.1** Let's further consider the differentials we encountered in Sample Problem 18.1.

$$1) \quad df = 2xy \, dx + x^2 dy \qquad\qquad 2) \quad df = \frac{ax}{y} dx + b \, y \, dy$$

a) Check the path independence of each differential by integrating from the point (1, 1) to the point (2, 3) along two right-angle paths—for example, change the value of $x$ followed by $y$, then change the value of $y$ followed by $x$, then repeat in the other order.

b) Knowing that differential 1) is an exact differential, reconstruct the original function $f$ to within an arbitrary constant.

**18.2** This problem will further explore the idea of an exact differential in the context of thermodynamics.

a) Consider the molar volume to be a function of pressure and temperature. Write the total differential for molar volume and evaluate this expression for an ideal gas.

b) Show that the total differential for the molar volume of an ideal gas is exact.

c) Show that for a reversible process involving an ideal gas we can write

$$\delta q_{rev} = \frac{RT}{V_m} dV_m + C_{V,m} dT$$

d) Show that this differential is inexact.

e) Convert the differential in part c) to $dS$ and show that this function is an exact differential.

**18.3** Consider the entropy as a function of temperature and pressure. Derive an expression for the total change in entropy in terms of parameters such as $C_p$, $\alpha$, $\kappa$, $T$, and $V$.

**18.4** We have derived a general expression for the quantity $\left(\dfrac{\partial U}{\partial V}\right)_T$.

a) Derive a general expression for $\left(\dfrac{\partial H}{\partial V}\right)_T$

b) Evaluate the expression from part a) for both an ideal gas and a van der Waals gas.

c) What do the results in part b) tell us about the interactions in each case?

**18.5** This expression will further explore the relation between the constant volume and constant pressure heat capacities given in Eq. 18.18.

a) Derive an expression for the difference between $C_{P,m}$ and $C_{V,m}$ for an ideal gas.

b) The molar volume of copper at 298.15 K and 1 atm is 7.09 cm$^3$ mol$^{-1}$. The coefficient of thermal expansion at room temperature is $0.501 \times 10^{-4}$ K$^{-1}$, and the isothermal compressibility is $7.3 \times 10^{-7}$ bar$^{-1}$. Calculate the difference between $C_{P,m}$ and $C_{V,m}$ for copper.

c) Derive an expression for the difference between $C_{P,m}$ and $C_{V,m}$ for a van der Waals gas.

**18.6** In Section 18.2.1, we derived expressions for the Helmholtz and Gibbs energy in terms of the canonical partition function.

a) Derive a corresponding expression for the enthalpy.

b) Derive a relationship between the constant pressure heat capacity and constant volume heat capacity for a system of independent, noninteracting, indistinguishable particles.

c) Derive an expression for the Helmholtz energy for a system composed of independent, noninteracting, indistinguishable particles. Compare your answer to the entry in Table 13.4.

d) As the temperature of the system described in part c) increases, does the numerical value of the Helmholtz energy increase or decrease? Briefly discuss the meaning of this result.

**18.7** 2.00 moles of ideal gas at 3.50 bar and 330 K are expanded isothermally. The entropy of the system is found to increase by 25.0 J K$^{-1}$.

a) Calculate the final pressure and volume of the system.

b) Calculate $\Delta G$ for this process.

**18.8** In Problem 16.11, we considered the combustion of propane. Let's now consider this process in connection with the Gibbs energy. The standard Gibbs energy of formation of propane, $CO_2$, and $H_2O$ ($l$) are −23.49, −384.36, and −237.13 kJ mol$^{-1}$, respectively, all at 298 K. ($\Delta_f G^\circ = 0$ for $O_2$, by convention.) The standard enthalpy of combustion of propane is −2220 kJ mol$^{-1}$ at 298 K.

a) Calculate $\Delta G^\circ$ for the combustion of propane at 298 K.

b) Assuming the enthalpy of combustion is constant with temperature, calculate $\Delta G^\circ$ for the combustion of propane at 1500°C.

c) Using heat capacity data you can find online, calculate $\Delta G^\circ$ for the combustion of propane where you do not assume the enthalpy of combustion is constant with temperature. Comment on the difference between your results in parts b) and c).

**18.9** In Section 18.3.2, we derived the following expression for the change in Gibbs energy with pressure for a condensed phase.

$$G_m(P_f) = G_m(P_i) + V_m \Delta P$$

In deriving this expression, we assumed that the volume did not change.

a) Derive a more general expression, involving the isothermal compressibility $\kappa$, where you do not make this assumption.

b) Show that you recover the first expression in the limit that the product of $\kappa$ and the pressure change is small.

**18.10** Methanol vapor, at its normal boiling point of 64.7°C, is reversibly condensed at constant pressure of 1.00 atm. A total of 1.00 kg of liquid is collected, the density of which is 0.792 g cm$^{-3}$. The enthalpy of vaporization of methanol is 35.2 kJ mol$^{-1}$.

a) Calculate the heat of the process.

b) Treating the vapor as an ideal gas, calculate the work of the process.

c) Calculate $\Delta U$, $\Delta H$, $\Delta S$, and $\Delta G$ for this process.

**18.11** The pressure on a 70.0 g sample of liquid is increased from 1.0 to 30.0 bar isothermally. The Gibbs energy is found to increase by 0.24 kJ.

a) Calculate the density of the liquid.

b) If the liquid is replaced by an equivalent mass of ideal gas, with a molecular weight of 40.0 g mol$^{-1}$, calculate the change in Gibbs energy for the same compression process.

**18.12** Given the following data for the compression factor of oxygen at 200.0 K:

| P/atm | 1.0000 | 4.0000 | 7.0000 | 10.000 | 40.00 | 70.00 | 100.0 |
|-------|--------|--------|--------|--------|-------|-------|-------|
| Z | 0.9971 | 0.98796 | 0.97880 | 0.96956 | 0.8734 | 0.7764 | 0.6871 |

a) Evaluate the fugacity and fugacity coefficient at each pressure.

b) Determine the Gibbs energy change associated with an isothermal pressure change at 200.0 K from 10.0 atm to 100.0 atm and compare to the Gibbs energy change for an ideal gas undergoing the same pressure increase.

c) The Berthelot equation of state is given by

$$V_m = \frac{RT}{P} + \frac{9RT_c}{128P_c} - \frac{54RT_c^3}{128P_cT^2}$$

Derive an expression for the fugacity coefficient of a Berthelot gas. (Note the difference between the critical and absolute temperatures and pressures in the EOS.)

d) The critical temperature and pressure of oxygen are 154.8 K and 50.14 atm, respectively. Calculate the fugacity coefficient for each pressure in part a) and plot the calculated and experimental values. Comment on how well, and over what pressure range, the Berthelot equation accurately describes the behavior of oxygen gas.

# Chemical Potential, Phase Equilibrium, and Solution Thermodynamics

## 19.1 Chemical Potential

To this point, our systems have consisted of only one chemical species in only one phase (solid, liquid, or gas). What if we have two phases, such as a slurry of ice and water—or two materials, such as a mixture of gases that can chemically react? Clearly, we need to be able to deal with more complicated systems. This chapter will start building the tools needed to do so.

### 19.1.1 Fundamental Equation of Chemical Thermodynamics

With more than one component, the thermodynamic potentials will depend on the composition of the system. Let's consider the Gibbs energy of a two-component system. In addition to temperature and pressure, the total Gibbs energy will now depend on the amount of components A and B. Mathematically, we would write

$$G(T, P, n_A, n_B)$$

The total differential of the Gibbs energy is now written as

$$dG = \left(\frac{\partial G}{\partial T}\right)_{P, n_A, n_B} dT + \left(\frac{\partial G}{\partial P}\right)_{T, n_A, n_B} dP + \left(\frac{\partial G}{\partial n_A}\right)_{T, P, n_B} dn_A + \left(\frac{\partial G}{\partial n_B}\right)_{T, P, n_A} dn_B \quad (19.1)$$

From what we did before, we know that for the entire system

$$\left(\frac{\partial G}{\partial T}\right)_{P, n_A, n_B} = -S \qquad \left(\frac{\partial G}{\partial P}\right)_{T, n_A, n_B} = V$$

What do we do with the partial derivatives with respect to amounts? These are given a new name, **chemical potential**, symbolized as $\mu$. Chemical potential is defined as

$$\mu_i = \left(\frac{\partial G}{\partial n_i}\right)_{T,P,n_{j \neq i}} \qquad (19.2)$$

In words, the chemical potential tells us how the total Gibbs energy of the system changes when we fix the temperature, pressure, and all the amounts but one and allow the other amount to change. We need to include the chemical potential for each component in the system. Going back to our two-component system, we now write

$$dG = -SdT + VdP + \mu_A dn_A + \mu_B dn_B$$

We can generalize this result to a multicomponent, multiphase system quite easily

$$dG = -SdT + VdP + \sum_i \mu_i dn_i \qquad (19.3)$$

This expression is known as the **fundamental equation of chemical thermodynamics**.

Chemical potential is an intensive quantity and it is the conjugate variable to amount. In addition to $T$–$S$ and $P$–$V$, we have the conjugate pair of $\mu$–$n$. Just as differences in temperature lead to changes in entropy (heat flow) and differences in pressure lead to changes in volume, differences in chemical potential will lead to changes in amount until the chemical potentials of all the species and phases are the same. This final condition is called **chemical equilibrium**.

When we have a system at a constant temperature and pressure, the total change in Gibbs energy can be written as

$$dG_{T,P} = \sum_i \mu_i dn_i \qquad (19.4)$$

We can write the total Gibbs energy of a multicomponent system at a given temperature and pressure by integrating this expression, where each amount goes from zero to the final amount. However, because the chemical potential depends on the conditions of the system in ways that we'll explore throughout this chapter and the next, this integration must be done in a somewhat peculiar way. We need to keep the relative amounts of the various components the same to ensure that the chemical potential of each component doesn't change. Doing so lets us write

$$G_{T,P} = \sum_i \int_0^{n_i} \mu_i \, dn_i = \sum_i \mu_i \int_0^{n_i} dn_i$$

$$G_{T,P} = \sum_i \mu_i n_i \qquad (19.5)$$

Note how the units work out; chemical potential has units of energy per mole, and the Gibbs energy has units of energy. For a given multicomponent system of fixed composition and at a given temperature and pressure, Eq. 19.5 gives the total Gibbs energy of that system. If anything about the system changes, the chemical potentials will change, so we need to pay attention to those changes.

We can actually use Eq. 19.5 to derive another important relation for chemical thermodynamics. Let's take the derivative of this equation.

$$dG_{T,P} = \sum_i \mu_i dn_i + \sum_i n_i d\mu_i$$

Comparing this result to Eq. 19.3 (remember $T$ and $P$ are fixed) shows that we have extra terms. Therefore, these extra terms need to add up to zero.

$$\sum_i n_i d\mu_i = 0 \tag{19.6}$$

Eq. 19.6 is known as the Gibbs–Duhem equation and tells us how the chemical potentials of the various components are related to each other. In particular, for a two-component system, if the chemical potential of one component is increasing, it follows from the Gibbs–Duhem equation that the chemical potential of the other must be decreasing. When they become the same, the system has come to equilibrium.

As we will see in the following sections and the next chapter, the chemical potential is probably the single most powerful quantity we will use in our discussion of chemical thermodynamics. We will use the chemical potential to describe such things as:

Single-component phase transitions

Simple mixtures and binary phase diagrams

Chemical reactions

It is also worth noting that chemical potential itself is rarely calculated or measured.

## 19.1.2 Chemical Potential of a Single Component System

Before moving on to multicomponent systems, let's consider a single-component system for a little longer. We can write the following relation for the total Gibbs energy in terms of the molar Gibbs energy at some particular $T$ and $P$:

$$G = nG_m$$

If we take the derivative of this expression, (keeping $T$ and $P$ constant) we can write

$$dG = G_m dn \quad \text{or} \quad \frac{dG}{dn} = G_m$$

(The molar Gibbs energy is a ratio of Gibbs energy to amount, so it doesn't change as the other two quantities change; the ratio stays the same.) If we look at the chemical potential for a one-component system, we can see that

$$\mu = \left(\frac{\partial G}{\partial n}\right)_{T,P} = G_m \tag{19.7}$$

For a pure material, the chemical potential is equivalent to the molar Gibbs energy. We arrive at the same conclusion by considering Eq. 19.5 for a single-component system. If the system is an ideal gas, we can look back to Eq. 18.40 and readily write the chemical potential as

$$\mu = \mu^\circ + RT \ln\frac{P}{P^\circ} \tag{19.8}$$

For a real gas, we replace $P$ with the fugacity, $f$. We'll deal with other phases as we go along.

Continuing with a pure material, we can write the change in chemical potential as

$$d\mu = dG_m = -S_m dT + V_m dP \tag{19.9}$$

We also conclude that

$$\left(\frac{\partial \mu}{\partial T}\right)_P = -S_m \qquad\qquad \left(\frac{\partial \mu}{\partial P}\right)_T = V_m \qquad\qquad (19.10)$$

Because we have criteria for spontaneity in terms of the Gibbs energy (Eq. 18.26), we can write that a spontaneous process is one that reduces the chemical potential.

$$dG_{T,P,m} = d\mu < 0 \qquad\qquad (19.11)$$

With these relations, we are prepared to discuss the phase equilibrium of a pure substance.

## 19.2 Phase Equilibrium

### 19.2.1 Phase Transitions of a Pure Component

You are familiar with phase equilibrium. You have seen ice melt and water boil. You should also be familiar with phase diagrams that indicate the temperature and pressure conditions under which different phases are stable. As an example, the phase diagram for $CO_2$ is shown in Figure 19.1. The different regions on the diagram show where the labeled phase is thermodynamically stable. Along the boundaries between regions, the two phases exist in equilibrium with each other. If conditions change such that we move from one region to another, the material will undergo a phase transition. For example, if we start in the liquid region and increase the temperature until we cross into the gas region, the liquid will boil. Note that for $CO_2$ at 1 atm, the solid will transition directly to gas; this type of transition is called sublimation.

These types of diagrams are generally based on empirical data. We will now develop the underlying thermodynamics that cause these phase transitions to take place. Let's take a closed system of one component at constant $T$ and $P$, but allow for two different phases, which we'll call $\alpha$ and $\beta$. We would then write the differential of the total Gibbs energy as

$$dG_{T,P} = \mu_\alpha dn_\alpha + \mu_\beta dn_\beta \qquad\qquad (19.12)$$

Now, because this is a closed system, any increase in the moles of phase $\alpha$ must have an accompanying decrease in the moles of phase $\beta$. Thus, we can write

$$dn_\beta = -dn_\alpha \qquad \text{and} \qquad dG_{T,P} = (\mu_\alpha - \mu_\beta)dn_\alpha$$

Recall our criterion for a spontaneous process, that $dG_{T,P,m} < 0$. This means that if $dn_\alpha > 0$ then

$$\mu_\alpha - \mu_\beta < 0 \qquad \text{or} \qquad \mu_\alpha < \mu_\beta$$

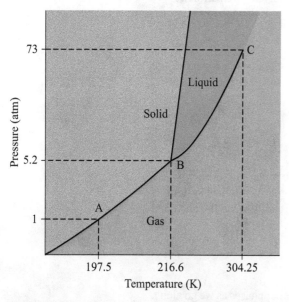

**FIGURE 19.1.** Phase diagram of $CO_2$. Point A is the normal sublimation point, Point B is the triple point, and Point C is the critical point.

This tells us that we will have spontaneous conversion from phase $\beta$ to phase $\alpha$ if the inequality holds. Thus the thermodynamically stable phase is the one with the lower chemical potential. If the chemical potentials are equal, then

$dG_{T,P,m} = 0$ and the two phases are in equilibrium, so no amounts need to change. This is what happens along a boundary in the phase diagram.

## 19.2.2 Changes of Phase Boundaries With Temperature

The result we just derived is general; at any given temperature and pressure, the stable phase is the one with the lower chemical potential. If the chemical potentials of the two phases are equal, the two phases exist in equilibrium. When we look at a phase diagram, we see a boundary between the two phases to indicate where two phases can coexist. How does that boundary depend on changes in conditions? We will first look at how the equilibrium boundary depends on temperature.

We already have the general result

$$\left(\frac{\partial \mu}{\partial T}\right)_P = -S_m \qquad (19.13)$$

Since entropy is always a positive quantity, the chemical potential must decrease as the temperature increases. Let's consider the chemical potential of the solid, liquid, and gas phases of a pure substance. We know that the entropy of a condensed phase is less than that for the gaseous phase, and the entropy of a solid is less than a liquid. Or, mathematically

$$S_{gas} > S_{liq} > S_{solid}$$

Therefore, the chemical potential of a gas will drop more rapidly than that of a liquid, which drops faster than the chemical potential of a solid. Assuming that the entropy of the individual phases is constant with respect to $T$, we would plot the temperature dependence of the chemical potential (or the Gibbs energy) as seen in Figure 19.2.

The temperature at which the transition occurs from solid to liquid is known at the **melting point**, and this is seen as the crossing point of the *solid* and *liquid* lines in the plot. If the pressure is our standard pressure, then this is the standard melting point. Likewise, the temperature at which a liquid transitions to a gas at the standard pressure (the point where those two lines cross) is the standard **boiling point**. It is possible, depending on the chemical potentials of the different species, to go directly from solid to vapor; and if that happens, the temperature at which that occurs is the **sublimation point**. (Look back at the phase diagram of $CO_2$ to see a sublimation transition at 1 atm pressure.)

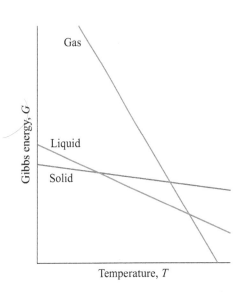

**FIGURE 19.2.** Variation of Gibbs energy with temperature for solid, liquid, and gas phases. Chemical potential follows the same trends.

## 19.2.3 Response of Melting and Boiling Points to Applied Pressure

Let's consider what happens to our melting point as we change the pressure. We know that at a given temperature, the change in chemical potential with changes in pressure is given by

$$\left(\frac{\partial \mu}{\partial P}\right)_T = V_m \qquad (19.14)$$

Since the molar volume is always a positive quantity, the chemical potential will increase with increasing pressure. If we do this at each temperature, we will see our line of $\mu$ (or $G$) vs. $T$ in Figure 19.2 move to higher $\mu$ (or $G$). To a first approximation, $S_m$ won't change much with these changes in pressure, so the slope doesn't change. But, we also have to consider the fact that the molar volume of the different phases can be different. If the molar volume of the liquid is greater than that of the solid, or the density of the liquid is less than the solid, the *liquid* line will move up more than the *solid* line. This means the temperature at which they intersect, the melting point, will increase with increasing pressure. For water we have the reverse case. The density of the solid is less than the density of the liquid, meaning the molar volume of the solid is greater than that of the liquid, so the *solid* curve will move up more than the *liquid* curve. This means that the melting point will decrease as the pressure increases.

The change in boiling point with a change in pressure is a little easier to understand. The molar volume of a gas is always significantly greater than the molar volume of a liquid. Thus, with an increase in pressure, the *gas* line in Figure 19.2 will shift upwards much more than the *liquid* line. This means the boiling point will increase with an increase in ambient pressure. The reverse is also true; the boiling point will decrease if the ambient pressure drops. This is one reason for high-altitude directions on cake mixes.

## 19.2.4 Quantitative Treatment of Phase Boundaries

Now that we have qualitatively discussed how phase transitions depend on the temperature and pressure, we can develop a more quantitative treatment. Let's again consider the case of two phases, $\alpha$ and $\beta$, present in equilibrium at some particular $T$ and $P$. In order to be at equilibrium, the chemical potential of the two phases must be equal.

$$\mu_\alpha(T,P) = \mu_\beta(T,P) \tag{19.15}$$

It is also necessary that $dT$, $dP$, and $d\mu$ be the same for both phases if we are staying on the phase boundary as conditions change. Mathematically,

$$d\mu_\alpha = d\mu_\beta \tag{19.16}$$

We can write for each phase

$$d\mu_i = -S_i dT + V_i dP \tag{19.17}$$

Since we require that $d\mu_\alpha = d\mu_\beta$, we can write

$$-S_\alpha dT + V_\alpha dP = -S_\beta dT + V_\beta dP$$

We can collect the pressure and temperature terms and write

$$(V_\beta - V_\alpha)dP = (S_\beta - S_\alpha)dT$$

We now define the entropy and volume changes of the phase transition as

$$\Delta_{trs}S = S_\beta - S_\alpha \quad \Delta_{trs}V = V_\beta - V_\alpha \tag{19.18}$$

Putting all this together lets us write

$$\boxed{\frac{dP}{dT} = \frac{\Delta_{trs}S}{\Delta_{trs}V}} \tag{19.19}$$

This is known as the Clapeyron equation. This expression is exact and applies to any phase boundary of a pure substance, and we have not made any assumptions in deriving this relation. Keep in mind that we are allowing temperature and pressure to vary; in principle, the volume and the entropy of the transition will also vary with those conditions. Assuming we know these quantities—and how they change with temperature and pressure—this expression gives us the slope of the phase boundary at any point.

*Solid–Liquid Phase Boundary* – A melting (fusion) process is accompanied by an enthalpy change $\Delta_{fus}H$ at a particular temperature. If we know this quantity per mole of material, we know the heat at the pressure of the phase transition. Thus we can write for the entropy (see Eq. 17.10):

$$\Delta_{trs}S = \frac{q_{trs}}{T} = \frac{\Delta_{trs}H}{T}$$

We can put this into Eq. 19.19 to write

$$\frac{dP}{dT} = \frac{\Delta_{trs}H}{T\Delta_{trs}V} \tag{19.20}$$

This form of the Clapeyron equation is often more convenient, because it is in terms of heat—which we can measure—rather than entropy, which is difficult to measure. If we have data for the enthalpy and the volume of the transition as a function of temperature, we can determine a formula for the phase boundary, which will be a curve on our $P$–$T$ plot.

What can we say about the slope of this curve? $\Delta_{fus}H > 0$ is always true; it always takes heat to make a solid melt. However, $\Delta_{fus}V$ can be positive or negative, depending on the relative density of the liquid and solid. For most materials, the solid is denser than the liquid, so the volume increases upon melting. Thus the $P$–$T$ line will have a positive slope. With water, however, the liquid density is greater than that of the solid, so this line has a negative slope. For many materials, however, the solid and liquid densities are fairly similar, meaning $\Delta_{fus}V$ is approximately 0, thus solid–liquid phase boundaries tend to be quite steep.

*Liquid–Vapor Boundary* – Let's go back to our restatement of the Clapeyron equation (Eq. 19.20), but now write it for a liquid–vapor phase boundary.

$$\frac{dP}{dT} = \frac{\Delta_{vap}H}{T\Delta_{vap}V}$$

Because the molar volume of a gas is much larger than that of the liquid, we can treat the volume change as the gas volume; $\Delta_{vap}V \approx V_{m,g}$. If we treat the gas as ideal, we can write

$$\frac{dP}{dT} = \frac{\Delta_{vap}H}{T(RT/P)}$$

$$\frac{1}{P}\frac{dP}{dT} = \frac{d\ln P}{dT} = \frac{\Delta_{vap}H}{RT^2} \tag{19.21}$$

This is known as the Clausius–Clapeyron equation and is an approximation for the liquid–vapor phase boundary. Note that we have assumed ideal gas behavior in deriving this expression. It should be noted that $\Delta_{vap}H$ approaches 0 as $T$ approaches the critical temperature. Thus, there is no phase boundary above $T_c$, where we have a supercritical fluid.

*Solid–Vapor Phase Boundary* – The Clausius–Clapeyron equation also applies to the boundary between the solid and vapor phases, again because the volume of the vapor is much greater than the molar volume of the solid. Also, recall that $\Delta_{sub}H = \Delta_{fus}H + \Delta_{vap}H$, so the solid–vapor line should be steeper than the liquid–vapor line at similar temperatures. You can see this in the phase diagram of $CO_2$ in Figure 19.1.

### 19.2.5 Note on Standard States

It should be noted that all pressures should be defined relative to our standard pressure. This makes sense from a consideration of the units of our expressions. In deriving the Clausius–Clapeyron equation, we switched from $P$ to $\ln P$, but you may be concerned about the units when we do this; you can't take the logarithm of a unit. Because we are writing a differential equation, we can always add a constant factor and not change the derivative. Thus, in the step when we used $\frac{1}{P} dP = d \ln P$, we should technically write

$$\frac{1}{P} dP + \frac{1}{P^\circ} dP^\circ = d \ln P - d \ln P^\circ = d \ln \frac{P}{P^\circ}$$

where $P^\circ$ is our standard pressure. Because $P^\circ$ is a fixed point, its derivative is zero; so we can add it, or the derivative of its ln, without changing our equation. Writing the expression in this way keeps our units constant. Because $P^\circ$ is usually taken to be 1 bar, it is often dropped in the expression of the Clausius–Clapeyron equation. When we integrate the equation, the standard state is removed from the expression, and only the initial and final pressures remain. So, the way we wrote it works and is a simpler notation, but you need to keep in mind that all pressures are with respect to the standard-state pressure.

### 19.2.6 Vapor Pressure and Liquid–Gas Coexistence

We know from observations that when we have a sample of liquid there exists some amount of vapor of that material. For example, if we have a closed container of a particular liquid and we remove all other gas from it, there will be some pressure still in the container from the vapor of the substance. This amount of pressure is known as the **vapor pressure**. We can use the chemical potential to determine the vapor pressure of a pure material at conditions other than the equilibrium phase boundary. We define the standard boiling point as the temperature at which a liquid boils at 1 bar pressure. (The normal boiling point is when the pressure is 1 atm.) With this, we can approximately determine the vapor pressure at any other temperature by integrating the Clausius–Clapeyron equation from the standard boiling point, or any other temperature where the vapor pressure is known, to the temperature of interest.

An alternate form of the Clausius–Clapeyron equation is

$$\frac{d \ln P}{d(1/T)} = \frac{-\Delta_{vap}H}{R}$$

(19.22)

This equation tells us that the ln of the vapor pressure should decrease linearly with the reciprocal temperature. This is what is observed sufficiently far from the critical point; at $T_c$, $\Delta_{vap}H$ goes to zero and this expression breaks down. As with many properties, vapor pressures for many liquids are tabulated at a variety of temperatures.

## Sample Problem 19.1

The vapor pressure of dichloromethane (methylene chloride) is 53.3 kPa at 24.1°C. Estimate the vapor pressure at 30°C. The enthalpy of vaporization is 28.7 kJ mol⁻¹.

## Solution

Assuming we can treat the enthalpy of vaporization as constant, we can simply integrate Eq. 19.22 to obtain

$$\ln\frac{P_2}{P_1} = \frac{-\Delta_{vap}H}{R}\int_{1/T_1}^{1/T_2} d(1/T) = \frac{-\Delta_{vap}H}{R}\left(\frac{1}{T_2} - \frac{1}{T_1}\right)$$

$$P_2 = P_1 e^{\Delta_{vap}H(1/T_1 - 1/T_2)/R}$$

$$P_2 = (53.3 \text{ kPa})e^{(28.7 \cdot 10^3 \text{ J mol}^{-1})[1/(297.25 \text{ K}) - 1/(303.15 \text{ K})]/(8.3145 \text{ J mol}^{-1}\text{K}^{-1})}$$

$$P_2 = 66.8 \text{ kPa}$$

The vapor pressure has increased to 66.8 kPa. Keep in mind that the boiling point will be reached when the vapor pressure is 1 bar = 100 kPa, so we're getting close to that.

---

Solids also have a vapor pressure—although generally much lower than a liquid—and this expression can be used to estimate those vapor pressures as well. We simply use the heat of sublimation instead of the heat of vaporization in the Clausius–Clapeyron equation.

## 19.2.7  Degrees of Freedom and the Triple Point

For a pure material, we have three variables, or degrees of freedom, that we can in principle change: $T$, $P$, and $V_m$. However, because of the equation of state, we can only independently vary two of them. If we require that we keep two phases in equilibrium with each other, that adds an additional constraint. Now we can only vary one parameter, such as the pressure. The temperature is fixed by the Clapeyron equation and the molar volume is fixed by the equation of state. Each constraint removes a degree of freedom. If we want to have three phases in equilibrium with each other, that adds another constraint, meaning we can't change any of the state variables. This is why phase diagrams have **triple points**, which are invariant. Triple points thus make very useful reference points. This is also why you can't have a point in a single-component phase diagram where more than three phases are in equilibrium; that would require negative degrees of freedom, which doesn't make physical sense.

Mathematically, this can be written as

$$F = C - P + 2 \tag{19.23}$$

where $F$ is the number of variables ($T$, $P$, and $V_m$) that are free to change, $C$ is the number of components (chemically independent constituents) of the system, and $P$ is the number of phases. For a solid–liquid slurry of water, we have one component and two phases, so there is only one variable that can be changed. If we, for example, want to change the temperature and maintain both phases in equilibrium, we have no choice on the pressure. The volume is constrained by the relevant equations of state for each phase. Eq. 19.23 is known as the Gibbs phase rule. Extension of these ideas to multicomponent systems is beyond the scope of this book, but it is possible to make multicomponent phase diagrams. These can be very important in some areas of materials science.

### 19.2.8 Other Types of Phase Transitions

The types of phase transitions we have discussed so far are known as **first-order phase transitions**. They receive this name because there is a discontinuity in the volume, enthalpy, and entropy across the phase transition. There are other phase transitions where this is not the case. Consider solid ice, which is less dense than water because of the structure of the hydrogen bonding network between water molecules. As the pressure on ice (also known as ice I) is increased, the molecules need to rearrange in a way to decrease the space between them. This new phase of ice is known as ice II. Eleven different solid forms of ice have been observed, each stable within a certain range of temperature and pressure. This phenomenon of multiple solid phases is called **polymorphism**, and each form is called a **polymorph**. Another material that exhibits polymorphism is alumina ($Al_2O_3$), an important substrate for heterogenous catalysts. Each of the different polymorphs, labeled by Greek letters, exhibits different properties, making some polymorphs better catalytic supports than others.

The transitions between polymorphs generally do not exhibit changes in volume, enthalpy, and entropy, but they do show a change in the derivatives of these variables. They also show a discontinuity in the heat capacity. These transitions are known as **second-order phase transitions**. (This classification system was developed by Paul Ehrenfest in 1933.) These transitions can be very subtle and difficult to measure, requiring carefully designed experiments. Other phase transitions exhibit changes in electronic or magnetic properties of materials, such as the onset of superconductivity in certain metals and ceramics at low temperatures. Helium-4 even exhibits a liquid–liquid phase transition below about 2 K that is due to quantum-mechanical effects. We will not consider these other types of transitions further in this text, but you should be aware that they are out there and still being studied.

# 19.3 Thermodynamics of an Ideal Mixture

## 19.3.1 Thermodynamics of Mixing of Ideal Gases

Let's begin our discussion of mixtures with the simplest possible case, a mixture of ideal gases. We start with two containers of gas with $n_A$ moles of gas A at $T$ and $P$ and $n_B$ moles of gas B at the same $T$ and $P$. We then allow the two to mix by removing the barrier between them. The temperature stays the same and, using Dalton's law of partial pressures, we write the total pressure of the mixture as $P = P_{A + PB}$. Note that the initial pressures are each the same and the same as the final total pressure. Let's do this in a more quantitative fashion. For each component,

$$ G_m = G_m^\circ + RT \ln\frac{P}{P^\circ} \quad \text{or} \quad \mu = \mu^\circ + RT \ln\frac{P}{P^\circ} \tag{19.24} $$

where $\mu^\circ$ is the standard chemical potential at our standard state of $P^\circ$, taken to be 1 bar.

Using Eq. 19.5, we write the total Gibbs energy prior to mixing (the initial state) as

$$ G_i = n_A\mu_A + n_B\mu_B = n_A\left(\mu_A^\circ + RT \ln\frac{P}{P^\circ}\right) + n_B\left(\mu_B^\circ + RT \ln\frac{P}{P^\circ}\right) $$

After mixing, the total pressure is $P = P_A + P_B$, the sum of the partial pressures. We then write the Gibbs energy of the mixture (the final state) as the sum of the Gibbs energies of each component, or

$$G_f = n_A \left( \mu_A^\circ + RT \ln \frac{P_A}{P^\circ} \right) + n_B \left( \mu_B^\circ + RT \ln \frac{P_B}{P^\circ} \right)$$

We can then write the Gibbs energy of mixing as $\Delta_{mix} G = G_f - G_i$, which gives us

$$\Delta_{mix} G = n_A RT \ln \frac{P_A}{P} + n_B RT \ln \frac{P_B}{P}$$

Note that the standard state has dropped out of the expression. Let's recall the definition of the **mole fraction**

$$x_i = \frac{n_i}{n} \tag{19.25}$$

where $n$ is the total number of moles. The mathematical form of Dalton's law lets us write the partial pressure as

$$P_i = x_i P \tag{19.26}$$

where $P$ is the total pressure. This lets us write for the $\Delta_{mix} G$

$$\Delta_{mix} G = nRT(x_A \ln x_A + x_B \ln x_B)$$

Because mole fractions are always less than or equal to 1, the ln terms are always negative or zero. Thus $\Delta_{mix} G$ is guaranteed to be less than 0; ideal gases will spontaneously mix in all proportions, just as you probably knew they would.

Let's look back at the expression of the chemical potential briefly. Instead of using the 1 bar standard state, we could use the total pressure of the mixture, which we'll designate as $P_{tot}$, and then write

$$\mu_i = \mu_i^* + RT \ln \frac{P_i}{P_{tot}}$$

$$\mu_i = \mu_i^* + RT \ln x_i \tag{19.27}$$

In these expressions we write $\mu^*$ instead of $\mu^\circ$ to signify the change in standard state from 1 bar pressure to the pure gas, where the mole fraction equals 1. Eq. 19.27 can actually be used to define an **ideal mixture**. If the chemical potential of a component in a mixture can be related to the chemical potential of the single component at the total pressure of the mixture through this expression, then the mixture is behaving ideally. As you might expect, an ideal mixture of gases is one in which the different components do not interact, which is the basis for Dalton's law. The Gibbs energy of mixing for an ideal mixture of multiple components can then be written as

$$\Delta_{mix} G = nRT \sum_i x_i \ln x_i \tag{19.28}$$

where $n$ is the total number of moles in the mixture.

## 19.3.2 Other Thermodynamic Quantities of Mixing

At constant temperature we can write

$$\Delta_{mix}G = \Delta_{mix}H - T\Delta_{mix}S$$

We have simply added the subscript "mix" to the general expression, which still holds true; it doesn't matter what the process is, these are still state variables. So we can identify two factors that contribute to the Gibbs energy of mixing; changes in the enthalpy of the system, which relate to heat exchange between system and surroundings, and changes in the entropy of the system. Let's explore each of these quantities, starting with the entropy of mixing.

We start with Eq. 19.28 and simply take $\left(\dfrac{\partial \Delta_{mix}G}{\partial T}\right)_{P,n_i} = -\Delta_{mix}S$ (see Eq. 18.33) to write

$$\Delta_{mix}S = -nR\sum_i x_i \ln x_i \tag{19.29}$$

Again, because the ln terms are all negative, the entropy of mixing is positive, and the mixing process is spontaneous. Ideal gases will mix in all proportions.

Now let's look at the enthalpy. We can write the enthalpy of mixing as

$$\Delta_{mix}H = \Delta_{mix}G + T\Delta_{mix}S = nRT\sum_i x_i \ln x_i - TnR\sum_i x_i \ln x_i$$

Combining Eqs. 19.28 and 19.29 gives us

$$\Delta_{mix}H = 0 \tag{19.30}$$

Thus, the enthalpy of the mixture is the same as that of the separate components and there is no heat flow into or out of the system for an ideal mixture. For a mixture of ideal gases, this is clearly due to the fact that there are no interactions between the gas molecules. For an ideal mixture of any other type, such as a solution, this means the interactions between the various molecules are all the same.

Lastly, we can write for the volume change upon mixing (see Eq. 18.34)

$$\Delta_{mix}V = \left(\frac{\partial \Delta_{mix}G}{\partial P}\right)_{T,n_i} = nRT\sum_i \frac{d}{dP}(x_i \ln x_i)$$

The composition does not change with the pressure, so

$$\frac{d}{dP}(x_i \ln x_i) = 0$$

therefore

$$\Delta_{mix}V = 0 \tag{19.31}$$

for an ideal mixture. Thus, the volume of the mixture is just the sum of the volumes of the components before mixing.

For an ideal mixture, all the driving force for mixing comes from the entropy of mixing. For real mixtures, interactions can lead to a heat of mixing and a change in the volume of the final mixture relative to the two initial volumes. Particularly for liquids, the volume of the mixture may be significantly different from the total volume of the separate components.

A container has a removable wall placed one quarter of the way along its length. The smaller side contains 1 mol of Ar gas at 25°C. The larger side contains 3 mol of Ne gas, also at 25°C. When the wall is removed, calculate $\Delta_{mix}G$ and $\Delta_{mix}S$.

Solution

Before we begin, we need to consider the initial and final pressures of the two gases. For the Ar gas, we initially have a pressure of $P_{Ar,\,init} = \dfrac{1RT}{1/4V} = 4\dfrac{RT}{V}$, where $V$ is the total volume of the container. Likewise, for the Ne gas, we have an initial pressure of $P_{Ne,init} = \dfrac{3RT}{3/4V} = 4\dfrac{RT}{V}$. The final pressure will be due to the 4 mol total gas in the full volume, or $P_{tot,\,final} = 4\dfrac{RT}{V}$. This is the same as the two initial pressures, so we have the same situation we just discussed. Lastly, we need the final partial pressures of the two gases. These are $P_{Ar,\,final} = \dfrac{RT}{V}$ and $P_{Ne,final} = \dfrac{3RT}{V}$. The final mole fractions are $x_{Ar} = \dfrac{1}{4}$ and $x_{Ne} = \dfrac{3}{4}$. Using Eq. 19.28, we can calculate

$$\Delta_{mix}G = (4\text{ mol})R(298\text{ K})\left[\frac{1}{4}\ln\frac{1}{4} + \frac{3}{4}\ln\frac{3}{4}\right]$$

$$\Delta_{mix}G = -5.57\text{ kJ}$$

The entropy of mixing is readily calculated from Eq. 19.29, or by dividing $\Delta_{mix}G$ by $-T$,

$$\Delta_{mix}S = 18.7\ J\ K^{-1}$$

The sign of both quantities shows that the mixing is spontaneous.

# 19.4 Solution Thermodynamics

## 19.4.1 Ideal Solutions

In order to discuss mixtures with liquid phases, we first recognize that a liquid is always at equilibrium with some vapor that is present at the vapor pressure. The chemical potentials of the liquid and vapor are always equivalent (otherwise they wouldn't be in equilibrium). Mathematically,

$$\mu(l) = \mu(g)$$

and for an ideal gas

$$\mu(P) = \mu^\circ + RT\ \ln\frac{P}{P^\circ}$$

This equilibrium means we can discuss what is happening in the liquid phase in terms of the vapor phase. For a pure material, we write the chemical potential as

$$\mu_A^*(l) = \mu_A^\circ + RT \ln \frac{P_A^*}{P^\circ} \tag{19.32}$$

where the $^*$ denotes the pure material and the pressure $P_A^*$ is the vapor pressure over the pure liquid A. Note that the left-hand side of Eq. 19.32 represents the pure liquid and the right-hand side the pure vapor that exists above that liquid.

If we have a mixture instead of a pure liquid, the vapor phase will also be a mixture. We can therefore write the chemical potential of component A in the liquid in terms of the vapor pressure of A above the mixture

$$\mu_A(l) = \mu_A^\circ + RT \ln \frac{P_A}{P^\circ} \tag{19.33}$$

Here, we have dropped the $^*$ because the material is no longer pure. Again, the left-hand side of Eq. 19.33 corresponds to the liquid and the right-hand side to the vapor. We can subtract Eq. 19.32 from Eq. 19.33 to write

$$\mu_A - \mu_A^* = RT \ln \frac{P_A}{P^\circ} - RT \ln \frac{P_A^*}{P^\circ}$$

or

$$\mu_A = \mu_A^* + RT \ln \frac{P_A}{P_A^*} \tag{19.34}$$

Note that the standard pressure and standard chemical potential both disappear when we do this. In fact, the way this expression is written, we are effectively using the vapor pressure of the pure liquid as our standard state rather than the conventional standard state of 1 bar. Ultimately, we use the standard state that is the most convenient for us.

Above, we derived an expression for an ideal mixture (Eq. 19.27),

$$\mu_i = \mu_i^* + RT \ln x_i$$

The French chemist François Raoult observed that for certain mixtures, such as benzene and toluene, the ratio of the partial pressure of each component to its vapor pressure for the pure materials was approximately equal to the mole fraction in the liquid solution. We see this naturally from our above expressions. If we equate the two expressions (Eqs. 19.34 and 19.27), we naturally see that

$$\frac{P_A}{P_A^*} = x_A \quad \text{or} \quad P_A = x_A P_A^* \tag{19.35}$$

This is known as **Raoult's law** and serves as the definition of an **ideal solution**. Historically, it was observed before Gibbs developed the idea of chemical potential, but it is a natural conclusion of our treatment of the chemical potential. Note that the pressures we are talking about are in the vapor phase, but the mole fraction is that of the liquid mixture. The vapor phase composition (mole fraction) will be different than the liquid phase composition, with the vapor being more concentrated in the more volatile component.

The vapor pressure of propan-1-ol at 340 K is 27.98 kPa. The vapor pressure of propan-2-ol at 340 K is 52.83 kPa. You are given a mixture of the two alcohols. The total vapor pressure above the mixture is measured to be 38.4 kPa. Assuming this is an ideal mixture, what is the composition (mole fraction) of the liquid and vapor phases?

Solution

The total pressure above the mixture is the sum of the two partial pressures, each of which is given by Raoult's law. We can write this as

$$P_{tot} = P_1 + P_2 = x_1 P_1^* + x_2 P_2^*$$

Doing a bit of algebra, and recalling that the two mole fractions have to add up to 1, gives us

$$x_1 = \frac{P_{tot} - P_2^*}{P_1^* - P_2^*}$$

Solving this expression with the data we were given, we find the mixture is 58% propan-1-ol and 42% propan-2-ol.

To determine the vapor-phase composition, we use Raoult's law to determine the partial pressure of each component.

$$P_1 = 0.58 \times (27.98 \text{ kPa}) = 16.23 \text{ kPa}$$

$$P_2 = 0.42 \times (52.83 \text{ kPa}) = 22.19 \text{ kPa}$$

The total pressure is the sum of these two, 38.4 kPa. The compositions can be found using Dalton's law. (Note, that when we have both liquid and vapor mixtures, we typically use $x$ for the mole fraction in the liquid phase and $y$ for the mole fraction in the vapor phase.)

$$y_1 = \frac{P_1}{P_{tot}} = \frac{16.23}{38.4} = 0.42$$

The vapor phase is 42% propan-1-ol and 58% propan-2-ol. Notice that the vapor is richer in the more volatile component.

---

Raoult's law behavior tends to be seen when the components of a mixture are chemically similar, such as benzene and toluene, as shown in Figure 19.3a. Note that the total vapor pressure above the mixture follows a straight line between the vapor pressures of the pure components. As you might expect, many solutions do not strictly follow Raoult's law. Significant deviations are often observed, such as in the mixture of chloroform/acetone and carbon disulfide/acetone, shown in Figures 19.3b and 19.3c. These deviations tell us something about the interactions in the mixture. If the vapor pressure is greater than Raoult's law predicts (known as positive deviations), this means that the molecules prefer to be in the vapor phase rather than in the liquid mixture. In other words, the interactions between the two types of molecules are less favorable than the interactions between themselves. These unfavorable interactions force molecules into the vapor phase where they will interact less. Negative deviations from Raoult's law are also observed—as seen in the plot for acetone and chloroform, which indicate that the molecules have favorable interactions with each other; they want to be close together, so they prefer to be in the liquid phase, which lowers the pressure in the vapor phase.

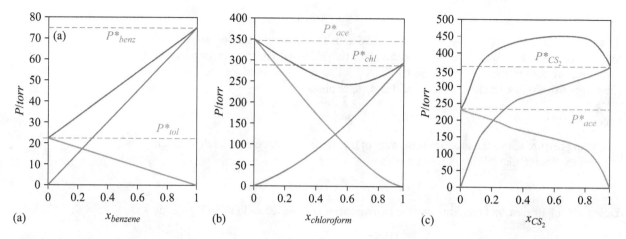

**FIGURE 19.3.** Pressure-composition diagrams for mixtures of a) benzene and toluene at 20°C, b) chloroform and acetone at 25°C, c) $CS_2$ and acetone at 0°C.

## 19.4.2 Ideal-Dilute Solutions

In the last section, we discussed Raoult's law and the ideal solution. We also saw that many mixtures will deviate, sometimes significantly, from Raoult's law behavior. However, in the limit that the solution is dilute, we again observe behavior that we can easily model. Let's look at the vapor pressure of one of the components of a mixture as the concentration is changed, shown in Figure 19.4. In the region of pure component B, we see that the *real* curve approaches the line given by Raoult's law. Look also at the dilute limit, where $x_B$ approaches zero. Here we also observe the *real* curve approaching a straight line.

William Henry, an English chemist, found that for real solutions at low solute concentrations, the vapor pressure of the solute was proportional to the mole fraction. However, the constant of proportionality was not the vapor pressure of the pure material but a different value. He wrote this observation as

$$P_B = x_B K_B \tag{19.36}$$

where $K_B$ is an empirical constant with units of pressure. This is known as **Henry's law** and describes the behavior of the solute in the limit of a dilute solution. The Henry's law constant is often written in terms of the molality $b$ (moles of solute per kg of solvent) of the solute

$$P_B = b_B K_B' \tag{19.37}$$

We won't do it here, but it can be shown that if the solute obeys Henry's law, then the solvent must obey Raoult's law. Such a system is called an **ideal-dilute solution**. It should be noted that Henry's law constants must be determined for a given solute in each individual solvent.

Henry's law perhaps finds is most useful application in the solubility of gases in a liquid solution. As you might expect, most gases would rather be in the gas phase than tied up in a liquid, so the amount of gas in solution tends to be fairly low and we can treat the solution

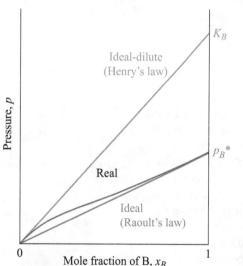

**FIGURE 19.4.** Model of an ideal-dilute solution with a Henry's law constant greater than the pure vapor pressure.

as ideal dilute. Measurement of the partial pressure above a liquid can tell us important things about the solution. This is why anesthesiologists use blood gas monitors during an operation; measurements of the partial pressures of $O_2$ and $CO_2$ provide vital information to keep a patient alive during surgery.

### Sample Problem 19.4

The Henry's law constant for $CO_2$ in water is $3.01 \times 10^3$ kPa kg mol$^{-1}$ at 298 K. If a sealed container has 2 bar of $CO_2$ pumped into the head space, what is the concentration of $CO_2$ in the solution? Report the concentration in molality, molarity, and mole fraction.

Solution

We can use the molality form of Henry's law (Eq. 19.37) to calculate the molal concentration of $CO_2$ when the pressure is 2 bar (200 kPa); $b_{CO_2} = 6.64 \times 10^{-2}$ mol kg$^{-1}$. We can convert to molarity with the density of water (1 g mL$^{-1}$). This gives us $6.64 \times 10^{-2}$ mol L$^{-1}$. 1 L of water is about 55.5 mol, so the mole fraction of $CO_2$ is $1.20 \times 10^{-3}$. (Note: We have neglected the equilibrium between $CO_2$ and carbonic acid in this treatment. The Henry's law constant accounts for that, so what we have here is the total concentration of $CO_2$, $H_2CO_3$ and $HCO_3^-$ in the solution. We would need to know the pH of the solution to determine each individual concentration.)

## 19.4.3 Molecular Description of Ideal and Ideal-Dilute Solutions

We started talking about mixing in the context of ideal gases. Clearly, there are no interactions between the gas molecules (that's what makes them ideal), even if they are different types of molecules. How does this work for liquid systems? If there were no interactions at all, we couldn't have a liquid. Thus, for an ideal solution it is more correct to say that the interactions in the mixture are the same as in the pure liquids. This is most commonly seen with mixtures of chemically similar compounds, such as hexane and heptane or benzene and toluene. If the interactions in liquid A are similar to the interactions in liquid B, then the A–B interactions will be similar to the A–A and B–B interactions, and the solution will behave close to ideally.

If the solution is ideal dilute, then the solvent is behaving practically the same as the pure material. This makes sense from a molecular standpoint, because most of the solvent molecules only see other solvent molecules. The solute molecules, however, only see solvent molecules and rarely see other solute molecules. Thus, the solute molecules are in a very different environment from the pure solute. The Henry's law constant is an extrapolation of what the vapor pressure of the pure solute would be if the pure material behaved like the solute behaves in dilute solution where solute molecules only interact with solvent molecules. The Henry's law constant reflects a hypothetical situation that does not actually exist in the physical world.

## 19.4.4 Colligative Properties

Now that we have discussed how the chemical potential varies with composition, let's go back to phase transitions and see what effect composition has on them. We call these effects

**colligative properties**, because they depend on the collection of the system. These properties depend on changes in the chemical potential of the liquid phase. As we have seen, we can write the chemical potential of the liquid phase of an ideal mixture as (see Eq. 19.27)

$$\mu_A = \mu_A^* + RT \ln x_A$$

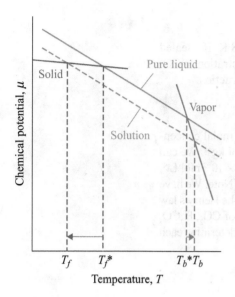

The $^*$ denotes the pure liquid. Because the mole fraction is always between 0 and 1, the ln term is always negative if the liquid is not pure. Thus, the addition of any solute lowers the chemical potential of the solvent relative to the pure liquid. For a nonvolatile solute, the chemical potential of the pure solid and pure gas do not change, so we can graphically represent the changes as shown in Figure 19.5. We can readily see from this plot that a lowering of the chemical potential of the liquid results in a lowering of the melting point and an increase of the boiling point. Let's look at these effects more quantitatively.

*Boiling Point Elevation* – We know from experience that adding salt to water raises the boiling point. Here's why: Boiling occurs when the chemical potential of the solvent equals that of the pure gas, assuming the solute is nonvolatile. This also means the vapor pressure of the solvent equals the ambient pressure. If the solvent obeys Raoult's law, we have

$$\mu_A^*(g) = \mu_A(l) = \mu_A^*(l) + RT \ln x_A$$

**FIGURE 19.5.** With addition of a solute, the chemical potential of the liquid decreases.

The change of Gibbs energy for vaporization for the pure liquid can be written as

$$\Delta_{vap} G = \mu_A^*(g) - \mu_A^*(l) = RT \ln x_A$$

or

$$\ln x_A = \frac{\Delta_{vap} G}{RT}$$

Note, for a pure liquid at its boiling point, $\Delta_{vap} G = 0$; the two phases are in equilibrium with each other. Now, we want to know how this changes with temperature and composition, so we differentiate this expression with respect to $T$ and use the Gibbs–Helmholtz equation (Eq. 18.36):

$$\frac{d \ln x_A}{dT} = \frac{1}{R} \frac{d(\Delta_{vap} G/T)}{dT} = \frac{-\Delta_{vap} H}{RT^2}$$

To determine the boiling point at a given composition, we need to integrate this expression. To do so, we will assume that $\Delta_{vap} H$ is constant over a narrow temperature range

$$\int_0^{\ln x_A} d \ln x_A = \frac{-\Delta_{vap} H}{R} \int_{T^*}^{T} \frac{1}{T^2} dT$$

Our lower limit on the left is the pure solvent, so $x_A = 1$ and $\ln x_A = 0$. The upper limit is the composition of the mixture. The lower limit of temperature is $T^*$, the normal boiling point. The upper limit is the boiling point of the mixture, $T$. After evaluation, the integral can be written as

$$\ln x_A = \ln(1 - x_B) = \frac{\Delta_{vap} H}{R} \left( \frac{1}{T} - \frac{1}{T^*} \right)$$

Now, we will make some assumptions. If $x_B \ll 1$, we can write $\ln(1 - x_B) \approx -x_B$. For the temperature, we can write

$$\left( \frac{1}{T} - \frac{1}{T^*} \right) = \frac{T^* - T}{TT^*} \approx \frac{-\Delta T}{T^{*2}}$$

which only holds if $T \approx T^*$. If we plug these approximations into our expression, we have

$$x_B = \frac{\Delta_{vap} H \Delta T}{RT^{*2}}$$

or

$$\Delta T = K x_B \quad \text{with} \quad K = \frac{RT^{*2}}{\Delta_{vap} H} \qquad (19.38)$$

All the constants in $K$ are properties of the solvent, so it shouldn't matter what the solute is. Often, we write this expression in terms of the molality of the solute

$$\Delta T = K_b b \qquad (19.39)$$

where $K_b$ is the boiling-point elevation constant of the solvent.

*Freezing Point Depression* – We can go through a similar analysis for the freezing point and obtain an expression similar to Eq. 19.39.

$$\Delta T = K_f b \qquad (19.40)$$

Note that $\Delta T$ is the difference in melting point, a positive quantity, which must be subtracted from the melting point of the pure liquid. The freezing-point depression constant, $K_f$, is again a property of the solvent, and depends on the heat of fusion. The freezing-point depression of a solution can actually be used to determine the molar mass of the solute; however, we have better ways now.

*Osmosis* – Let's consider the following situation, shown in Figure 19.6. We have two sides to our system, separated by a semipermeable membrane. The membrane lets solvent through but not solute. What will happen? The chemical potential on the solution side is lower than that of the pure solvent. (See Eq. 19.27.) Because of this difference in chemical potentials, this system is not in equilibrium. One way to equilibrate would be to lower the chemical potential of the pure solvent by the movement of solute, but the membrane prevents that. Instead, pure solvent will flow from the solvent side to the solution side, which makes the solution more dilute and raises its chemical potential. The flow of solvent to the solution side will actually cause the column of liquid to rise. This process is known as **osmosis**. The pressure difference due to the height of the column is called the **osmotic pressure**.

Applying additional external pressure to the solution also raises the chemical potential. If we apply enough pressure, we can bring the chemical potential of the solution up to that of the pure liquid and stop

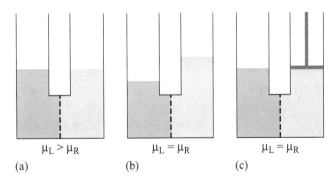

$\mu_L > \mu_R$      $\mu_L = \mu_R$      $\mu_L = \mu_R$

(a)                (b)               (c)

**FIGURE 19.6.** a) A pure solvent (left), separated from a solution (right) by a semipermeable membrane. Initially, the chemical potential of the solvent is greater than that of the solution. b) Flow of solvent to the solution side equalizes the chemical potentials. c) Application of an external pressure equal to $\Pi$ also equalizes the chemical potentials.

the flow of solvent across the membrane. With extra pressure, we can actually reverse the flow of solvent across the membrane; this is reverse osmosis. Let's explore all of this more quantitatively.

We will designate the chemical potential of the pure liquid on the left side as $\mu_L^*$. The * reminds us that this is the pure solvent side. We will designate the chemical potential of the solvent in the solution on the right side as $\mu_R$. In order to be in equilibrium, we need to have

$$\mu_L^* = \mu_R$$

Keep in mind the chemical potential depends both on composition and applied pressure. We represent the additional pressure on the solution side as $\Pi$, and we write the equilibrium condition as

$$\mu_L^*(P) = \mu_R(x_R, P + \Pi)$$

where $P$ is the ambient external pressure and $x_R$ is the mole fraction of the solvent on the right side. Let's look at the right side of the equation and take the effect of composition into account with a modified form of Eq. 19.27.

$$\mu_R(x_R, P + \Pi) = \mu_R^*(P + \Pi) + RT \ln x_R$$

Now we can take the pressure increase into account as follows (see Eq. 19.14)

$$\mu_R^*(P + \Pi) = \mu_R^*(P) + \int_P^{P+\Pi} V_m \, dP$$

When we combine these expressions, we have

$$\mu_L^*(P) = \mu_R^*(P) + \int_P^{P+\Pi} V_m \, dP + RT \ln x_A$$

Because $\mu_L^*$ and $\mu_R^*$ both describe the chemical potential of the pure solvent at ambient pressure $P$, we can say that $\mu_L^* = \mu_R^*$. This leaves us with

$$-RT \ln x_A = \int_P^{P+\Pi} V_m \, dP$$

Recall that $x_A = 1 - x_B$, and $\ln(1 - x_B) \approx -x_B$ for $x_B \ll 1$. Using this, and assuming the solution is relatively incompressible, we can write

$$RTx_B = V_m(P + \Pi - P) = V_m \Pi$$

If the solution is dilute, then $n_A \gg n_B$, and $x_B$ is about equal to $n_B/n_A$. Likewise, the volume of the solution is basically the volume of the solvent, or $V_m \approx \dfrac{V}{n_A}$. This lets us write

$$RTn_B = \Pi V \quad \text{or} \quad \Pi = RT[B] \tag{19.41}$$

where [B] is the molar concentration of the solute, $n_B/V$. This is known as the **van 't Hoff equation**. (The general form of it should look familiar.)

The van 't Hoff equation really only works in very dilute solutions. To account for the nonideality of a solution, we can do a virial-like expansion on the van 't Hoff equation and write

$$\Pi = [J]RT(1 + B[J] + C[J]^2 + ...) \tag{19.42}$$

Here we are using [J] for the concentration of solute, rather than [B]. $B$ in the above expression is the second osmotic virial coefficient. $C$ is the third osmotic virial coefficient. Higher order terms can be used if needed.

*Summary of Colligative Properties* – A final note on what we have done here is in order. In treating each situation, we have made certain assumptions: the solvent behaves ideally, the enthalpies of transition don't change with $T$, and so on. To the extent that these assumptions are valid, the expressions we derived can be applied to real situations. For other systems, such as the solubility of ionic solids or mixtures of water and volatile liquids, these assumptions may not hold, and we have to derive more complicated expressions. (Ionic solutes will be treated in Chapter 21.) The expressions we have developed here are the limiting-case expressions.

As we have seen throughout this text, the general approach in science is to start with some assumptions and see where that leads us and what we can do with it. If the assumptions are good, then why do something more complicated? Once the assumptions don't hold, then we have to do more work. We can either develop a more sophisticated molecular model or tabulate the data of real systems and attempt to fit that data to an empirical model.

Sample Problem 19.5

For water, the freezing-point depression and boiling-point elevation constants are 1.86 and 0.513 K kg mol$^{-1}$, respectively. If 0.050 mol of a nonvolatile solute, such as a sugar, is dissolved in 1.00 kg of water, what is the effect on the freezing and boiling points? Also, calculate the osmotic pressure of such a solution at 300 K.

Solution

We can use Eqs. 19.39 and 19.40, with the appropriate constants, to find that the boiling point is raised by 0.093 K and the freezing point is lowered by 0.026 K. These are rather small temperature differences. For the osmotic pressure, recall that 1 kg of water has a volume of 1 L. Making this conversion, using Eq. 19.41 we find an osmotic pressure of 1.2 atm. This is a very large pressure and should be very easy to measure. (It's also probably an overestimate, because the solution is not ideal dilute.)

# 19.5 Summary, and Where We Go Next

In this chapter, we have developed the concept of chemical potential and seen how it can help us understand phase equilibrium, mixing, and solutions. We will build on these concepts in the next chapter to fully develop the tools we need to discuss chemical equilibrium, the main goal of chemical thermodynamics.

# PROBLEMS

**19.1** The standard molar entropy of liquid water is 69.91 J mol⁻¹ K⁻¹ at 298 K. The density is 0.997 g mL⁻¹ at this temperature. For each part, justify any approximations.

   a) What is the effect on the chemical potential if liquid water is heated by 5°C?

   b) What is the effect on the chemical potential if the pressure on the liquid water is increased from 1 bar to 200 bar?

**19.2** A mixture of two liquids is prepared. The minor component has a mole fraction of 0.35. If a small change in the composition results in the chemical potential of the major component increasing by 0.15 J mol⁻¹, what is the effect on the chemical potential of the minor component?

**19.3** In Figures 19.2 and 19.5, we drew the curves as straight lines. This is an approximation, assuming the entropy of each phase does not change with temperature. Derive an expression for the curvature of these curves. Will they be curved up or curved down? Comment on the degree of curvature for the different phases.

**19.4** For supercooled liquid water at −5°C, the vapor pressure is 4.108 mbar. The vapor pressure of ice at the same temperature is 3.912 mbar. Based on this information, calculate $\Delta G_m$ for the conversion of supercooled water to ice at −5°C.

**19.5** Gallium metal has a normal melting point of 302.92 K. The standard molar entropies of the liquid and solid are 59.25 and 40.83 J mol⁻¹ K⁻¹, respectively, at 298 K. The densities of the liquid and solid are 6.095 g mL⁻¹ and 5.91 g mL⁻¹, respectively.

   a) Estimate the slope of the solid–liquid boundary on the phase diagram in the vicinity of the melting point. Justify any approximations.

   b) Estimate the standard enthalpy of fusion for gallium metal. Justify any approximations.

   c) What other compound exhibits a similar solid–liquid phase boundary?

**19.6** A liquid is allowed to vaporize reversibly.

   a) Starting with Eq. 19.21, derive Eq. 19.22.

   b) Calculate the vapor pressures for liquid water at 50°C. For water, $\Delta_{vap}H° = 44.01$ kJ mol⁻¹.

   c) Using the data available in Sample Problem 19.1, estimate the boiling point of dichloromethane and compare to a published value.

**19.7** When forming a binary ideal mixture, what composition will lead to the largest entropy of mixing? Provide both a mathematical and nonmathematical justification for your answer.

**19.8** In Section 19.3.1, we derived an expression for the mixing of ideal gases when the initial pressures are the same as the final total pressure. Derive a more general expression where the initial pressures are not necessarily the same as each other, nor the same as the final total pressure of the gas mixture.

**19.9** At 241.95 K, the vapor pressures of liquid propane and *n*-butane are 160.0 kPa and 26.7 kPa, respectively.

    a) Calculate the total pressure above a solution that contains 0.2 moles of propane and 0.6 moles of *n*-butane. Assume that the two components form an ideal solution.

    b) What is the composition of the vapor phase in equilibrium with the liquid phase?

    c) Calculate $\Delta_{mix}G$ and $\Delta_{mix}S$ for the formation of this mixture.

**19.10** A mixture is observed to exhibit negative deviations from Raoult's law.

    a) Will the enthalpy of mixing be positive, negative, or zero? Justify your answer.

    b) Will the volume of mixing be positive, negative, or zero? Justify your answer.

    c) Will the boiling point of the mixture be higher or lower than the lowest boiling point of the two components of the mixture? Justify your answer.

    d) Will the Henry's law constants for this mixture be greater than, less than, or equal to the pure vapor pressures of the components? Justify your answer.

**19.11** The following data were obtained for the mixture of carbon tetrachloride and benzene at 40°C (*J. Am. Chem. Soc.*, **1940**, *62*, 712). *x* refers to the liquid phase mole fraction, and *y* is the vapor phase mole fraction.

| $x$ ($CCl_4$) | 0.1398 | 0.2378 | 0.3735 | 0.4919 | 0.4986 | 0.6201 | 0.7585 | 0.8718 |
|---|---|---|---|---|---|---|---|---|
| $y$ ($CCl_4$) | 0.1703 | 0.2774 | 0.4159 | 0.5295 | 0.5359 | 0.6475 | 0.7739 | 0.8783 |
| P/torr | 190.18 | 194.70 | 200.07 | 204.02 | 204.20 | 207.44 | 210.37 | 211.97 |

The vapor pressure of pure benzene is 182.70 torr at 40°C; the vapor pressure of pure carbon tetrachloride is 213.34 torr at 40°C.

    a) From these data, calculate the partial pressure of carbon tetrachloride and benzene at each liquid-phase composition. Do this by treating the vapor phase as a mixture of ideal gases.

    b) Calculate the Henry's law constants for each component. You can do this by fitting the partial pressure data you generated in part a) to a polynomial and considering the slope of the tangent line in the dilute limit for each component.

    c) Would you describe the interactions between carbon tetrachloride and benzene as favorable or unfavorable? Is the degree of favorability or unfavorability strong or weak? Justify your answers.

**19.12** Reverse osmosis is a very effective way to purify water. If you have a water source where the osmolarity (total concentration of all ions and other dissolved solids) is 0.125 M, what is the minimum pressure that needs to be applied to the water to purify it?

**19.13** 3.5 mg of a water-soluble macromolecule is dissolved in 10 mL of water. The osmotic pressure of this solution is measured to be $2.30 \times 10^{-3}$ atm at 25°C. Determine the molar mass of the macromolecule.

# Activity and Chemical Equilibrium

## 20.1 Activity

We saw in the last chapter that most real solutions do not behave ideally. However, we derived some nice mathematical expressions for ideal mixtures that we would like to use for real systems. We had a similar problem with the Gibbs energy of a real gas. In order to use the same expression we had derived for an ideal gas, we defined a new quantity called the fugacity. We will now do something similar for solutions. The new quantity we will use is called **activity**. Along with the definition of activity, we have to carefully define a **standard state**.

## 20.1.1 Solvent Activity

We generally consider the solvent to be the component of the solution that is present in the greatest concentration. For an ideal mixture, the solvent obeys Raoult's law (Eq. 19.35)

$$\frac{P_A}{P_A^*} = x_A$$

and the chemical potential can be written as (Eq. 19.27)

$$\mu_A = \mu_A^* + RT \ln x_A$$

We took this expression as our definition of an ideal mixture. Let's back up a step and write a more general expression, where we are not necessarily assuming ideal-solution behavior.

$$\mu_A = \mu_A^* + RT \ln \frac{P_A}{P_A^*} \tag{20.1}$$

Any volatile liquid has a vapor pressure, so we can write Eq. 20.1 without making any assumptions. To deal with real gases, we need to use fugacity, and we write (see Eq. 18.42)

$$\mu = \mu^\circ + RT \ln \frac{f}{P^\circ} \tag{20.2}$$

In Eq. 20.2, our standard state is 1 bar of the pure ideal gas. We can instead define a new standard state for the solvent, which is the pure solvent with its vapor. In this case we write

$$\mu_A = \mu_A^* + RT \ln \frac{f_A}{f_A^*} \tag{20.3}$$

where the * denotes the pure solvent and $f^*$ is the fugacity of the vapor over the pure solvent. We now define the activity of the solvent as

$$a_A = \frac{f_A}{f_A^*} \approx \frac{P_A}{P_A^*} \tag{20.4}$$

(if the pressures are low, they are close to the fugacities) which lets us write an equation similar to Eq. 19.27, but for a real solution.

$$\mu_A = \mu_A^* + RT \ln a_A \tag{20.5}$$

Just like fugacity is an "effective pressure," activity can be thought of as an "effective concentration," given in terms of mole fraction. Note that the activity is a unitless parameter and the mole fraction is in the liquid phase. As with the fugacity, the activity should approach the mole fraction as the solvent becomes purer, or

$$\lim_{x_A \to 1} \frac{a_A}{x_A} = 1 \tag{20.6}$$

As we did for the fugacity coefficient (see Eq. 18.43), we define an **activity coefficient** as

$$\gamma_A = \frac{a_A}{x_A} \tag{20.7}$$

Note that, according to Eq. 20.6, $\gamma_A$ approaches 1 as $x_A$ approaches 1.

We can alternatively write our expression for the chemical potential as

$$\mu_A = \mu_A^* + RT \ln a_A = \mu_A^* + RT \ln x_A + RT \ln \gamma_A$$

If the activity coefficient is close to 1, the last term will drop out and we go back to the description of an ideal mixture. The standard state is pure solvent, where $x_A = 1$, with its vapor; this is known as the **Raoult's law standard state**. In this standard state, both ln terms drop out, therefore under standard conditions of the pure solvent, $\mu_A = \mu_A^*$.

## 20.1.2 Solute Activity

Now, let's look at the activity of the solute in an ideal-dilute mixture. If the solute satisfies Henry's law, then

$$P_B = K_B x_B$$

(See Eq. 19.36.) We can use this relation in our general expression for the chemical potential, in a Raoult's law standard state (Eq. 20.5) and with a Raoult's law activity (Eq. 20.4).

$$\mu_B = \mu_B^* + RT \ln \frac{P_B}{P_B^*} = \mu_B^* + RT \ln \frac{K_B}{P_B^*} + RT \ln x_B$$

(Note that we have split the ln term into two.) As written, our standard state is the pure solute with its vapor. Note that only the last term depends on composition; $K_B$ and $P_B^*$ are both constants. We can combine the first two terms to define a new standard state

$$\mu_B^\circ = \mu_B^* + RT \ln \frac{K_B}{P_B^*} \tag{20.8}$$

If Henry's law is being followed, this lets us write

$$\mu_B = \mu_B^\circ + RT \ln x_B$$

where our standard state is a hypothetical pure solute with a vapor pressure equal to $K_B$. This is the **Henry's law standard state**.

As we did for the solvent of a real solution, we need to introduce a solute activity, $a_B$, into this expression in place of the mole fraction of the solute

$$\mu_B = \mu_B^\circ + RT \ln a_B \tag{20.9}$$

The activity in a Henry's law standard state is defined as

$$a_B = \frac{f_B}{K_B} \approx \frac{P_B}{K_B} \tag{20.10}$$

(again, assuming the pressures are low and the fugacities and pressures are roughly equal). We write the activity coefficient as

$$\lim_{x_B \to 0} \gamma_B = 1 \quad \text{with} \quad \gamma_B = \frac{a_B}{x_B} \tag{20.11}$$

where $\gamma_B$ approaches 1 as $x_B$ approaches 0. Remember that this standard state is for a hypothetical pure solute that obeys Henry's law. So if we are dealing with pure B, we probably don't want to use this standard state; it would be better to use a Raoult's law standard state. But in the dilute limit, the Henry's law standard state makes the most sense, because the activity coefficient will approach 1.

We have considerable flexibility in defining our standard state. Another way to express concentration is as molality, which is moles of solute per kg of solvent. We can then write a slightly different expression for the chemical potential

$$\mu_B = \mu_B^\circ + RT \ln \gamma_B \frac{b_B}{b_B^\circ} \tag{20.12}$$

The $\mu^\circ$ used here is different from that in Eq. 20.9. This standard state is typically taken to be an ideal solution of 1 molal concentration, or $b^\circ = 1$ mol kg$^{-1}$. We can incorporate nonideal behavior by defining the activity as

$$a_B = \gamma_B \frac{b_B}{b_B^\circ} \tag{20.13}$$

where $\gamma_B$ approaches 1 as $b_B$ approaches 0. As before, use of the activity lets us write

$$\mu_B = \mu_B^\circ + RT \ln a_B$$

(This expression is probably starting to look familiar.) Note, that it is important when we write such an expression that we also define our standard state. An alternative approach uses molarity instead of molality, symbolized as $c$, and the standard state would be a concentration of $c° = 1$ mol/L.

You may be wondering how we deal with a solution that is neither ideal nor ideal dilute. In this case, we can use either standard state for the solvent or the solute. Our choice of standard state is purely up to us; nature doesn't care what we choose. We typically choose whichever standard state is closest to the prevailing conditions. For example, if we have a solution that is fairly dilute, but not dilute enough to exhibit ideal-dilute behavior, it would make sense for us the Raoult's law standard state for the solvent and the Henry's law standard state for the solute. For a solution that is roughly 50:50 in composition, we could choose either standard state for either component. As long as we are consistent and don't change standard states when working with a given process, the choice is up to us.

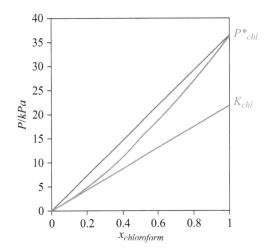

FIGURE 20.1. Partial pressure of chloroform in acetone compared to Raoult's (black) and Henry's (orange) laws.

## Sample Problem 20.1

The vapor pressure of chloroform is 36.4 kPa at 25°C. For a solution of chloroform and acetone with $x_{chloroform} = 0.40$, the vapor pressure of chloroform is found to be 11.0 kPa. The Henry's law constant for chloroform in acetone is 22.0 kPa. Calculate the activity and activity coefficients for chloroform in both a Raoult's law and Henry's law standard state. (See Figure 20.1.)

## Solution

The Raoult's law activity is found by using Eq. 20.4 (we are using the pressures rather than fugacities because the pressures are low)

$$a_{RL} = \frac{P}{P^*} = \frac{11.0}{36.4} = 0.30$$

The activity coefficient is found from Eq. 20.5

$$\gamma_{RL} = \frac{a_{RL}}{x} = \frac{0.30}{0.40} = 0.75$$

In a Henry's law standard state, we use Eqs. 20.10 and 20.11

$$a_{HL} = \frac{P}{K} = \frac{11.0}{22.0} = 0.5$$

$$\gamma_{HL} = \frac{a_{HL}}{x} = \frac{0.50}{0.40} = 1.25$$

Note that the Raoult's law activity coefficient is less than 1, but the Henry's law activity coefficient is greater than 1. This is consistent with the fact that the Henry's law constant is lower than the pure vapor pressure. All these observations indicate favorable interactions between chloroform and acetone.

### 20.1.3 Comparison of Raoult's and Henry's Law Activities

Since we have now introduced two different ways to determine activities, it is worth spending a little time to compare them. Figure 20.1 contains more data on the behavior of chloroform in acetone, the system we worked with in Sample Problem 20.1. Note that the true partial pressure of chloroform always falls between the top line, representing Raoult's law, and the bottom line, representing Henry's law. This will always be the case, since Raoult's law and Henry's law are limiting cases. The magnitude of the activity coefficient tells us how far the real situation is from either of those limiting cases. For the chloroform–acetone mixture, the vapor pressure is generally lower than Raoult's law would predict, so the Raoult's law activity coefficient is less than one. On the other hand, the vapor pressure is greater than Henry's law would predict, so the Henry's law activity coefficient is greater than one.

We can also get a sense of the meaning of activity as effective concentration. If we look at the $x = 0.4$ point on the graph, and extend a horizontal line from the true vapor pressure to the Raoult's law line, we find that they intersect at about $x = 0.3$. This is what we calculated in the sample problem for the activity. The real system behaves as if there were less chloroform than there would be if the mixture were ideal. Likewise, if we extend to the right to the Henry's law line, we find they would intersect at about $x = 0.5$; the real system behaves as if there were more chloroform than there would be if it were following Henry's law.

The chloroform–acetone system exhibits negative deviations from Raoult's law, suggesting favorable interactions between the two molecules. The Raoult's law activity coefficients in a system with favorable interactions will always be less than 1, and the Henry's law activity coefficients will be greater than 1. The situation is reversed for a system with unfavorable interactions; Raoult's law activity coefficients will be greater than 1 and Henry's law activity coefficients will be less than 1. The real vapor pressure will still lie between the Raoult's law– and Henry's law–limiting behavior. The extent to which the activity coefficients differ from a value of 1 gives us a sense of the nonideality of the solution.

### 20.1.4 Activity for Additional Systems

While we are on the subject of activities, let's formally define them for some additional systems, staring with pure materials.

*Ideal Gas* – This one is the easiest. We just use the ratio of the partial pressure to the standard pressure, typically 1 bar

$$a_i(ideal\ gas) = \frac{P_i}{P^\circ} \tag{20.14}$$

*Real Gas* – In order to account for real gas behavior, we use fugacity instead of pressure

$$a_i(real\ gas) = \frac{f_i}{P^\circ} \tag{20.15}$$

The standard state is still taken as an ideal gas at 1 bar pressure.

*Pure Liquids and Solids* – We need to do a little work to properly define the activity for a pure liquid or solid. For gases and for liquid mixtures, we have a common expression to determine the chemical potential relative to the standard state. That is $\mu_i = \mu_i^\circ + RT \ln a_i$ where the standard state is properly defined. It would be nice to keep this general formula in defining the activity of pure condensed phases. We can start with our Raoult's law standard state, which is the vapor pressure of the pure component at a given temperature. If we take the equilibrium condition as our standard state, then we would write the chemical potential at some other ambient pressure as

$$\mu_i = \mu_i^{eq} + RT \ln \frac{f_i}{f_i^{eq}}$$

where the superscript *eq* denotes the equilibrium between the condensed phase and the vapor. We would probably rather take as our standard state whatever the vapor pressure is at 1 bar ambient pressure, to be more consistent with our other standard states. (The vapor pressure of a pure liquid or solid does change with the ambient pressure. An increase in ambient pressure leads to an increase in vapor pressure.) We can change the standard state by writing a Hess's law cycle:

condensed phase $[T, P_{amb} = 1 \text{ bar}] \rightarrow$ condensed phase $[T, P^{eq}]$

$$\mu^{eq} - \mu^\circ = RT \ln \frac{f^{eq}}{f^\circ}$$

condensed phase $[T, P^{eq}] \rightarrow$ condensed phase $[T, P]$

$$\mu_P - \mu^{eq} = RT \ln \frac{f_P}{f^{eq}}$$

Adding the two expressions and canceling common terms gives

$$\mu_P = \mu^\circ + RT \ln \frac{f_P}{f^\circ}$$

where $f_P$ is the fugacity at some ambient pressure $P$ and $f^\circ$ is the fugacity at the standard ambient pressure of 1 bar. The fugacity is not itself 1 bar, but is instead given by the actual vapor pressure at an ambient pressure of 1 bar; this is an important distinction from the treatment of a gas. So, to adopt our earlier notation, we define the activity for a pure condensed phase material as

$$a_i (pure\ liquid/solid) = \frac{f_P}{f^\circ} \tag{20.16}$$

and use the same general expression for the chemical potential, $\mu_i = \mu_i^\circ + RT \ln a_i$.

You may have heard in the past that we treat the activity of a condensed phase as 1, but let's prove that more fully. We start with the variation of the chemical potential with pressure.

$$\left( \frac{\partial \mu}{\partial P} \right)_T = V_m \qquad \text{or} \qquad d\mu = V_m dP$$

(See Eq. 19.14.) We integrate this expression from our standard state to the pressure of interest.

$$\mu = \mu^\circ + \int_{P^\circ}^{P} V_m dP$$

By using our general relation for chemical potential, $\mu_i = \mu_i^\circ + RT \ln a_i$, we can also write

$$RT \ln a = \int_{P^\circ}^{P} V_m dP \tag{20.17}$$

The ln of the activity depends on this integral. What we need is some feel for how the volume changes with pressure. As you know, liquids and solids are relatively incompressible, so the volume doesn't change much with increases in pressure. We can model this behavior with a function of the form $V = cP + d$. Usually $c$ has a value of around $10^{-4}$ mL/bar. Only over very large pressure changes will the volume change appreciably. Note that it is the ln of the activity that changes, so it changes even less than the volume itself. Taking ice as an example, at 1.0 bar, $a = 1.0000$ (by definition). At 10 bar, $a = 1.007$. At 218 bar, $a = 1.177$. So, for all practical purposes, if the pressures are moderate, we can take the activity of a pure condensed phase to be identically 1.

*Ionic Solutions* – For ionic solutions, we can't really define the activity in terms of the vapor pressure, since we don't typically have ions in the vapor phase. In general, the standard state is taken to be a solution of 1 molal (or molar) concentration of the ion. (Since 1 L water is equivalent to 1 kg and 55.5 mol at 298 K, the values of molarity and molality for dilute solutions are very similar.) Because of the charges, ionic solutions behave non-ideally even at very low concentrations. With Debye–Hückel theory, we can calculate the activity coefficients for ionic solutions, which is something we can't do in most cases. We will formally treat the activity of ionic solutions in the next chapter.

*The Biological Standard State* – The final standard state we will consider at this point is the one used in describing biological systems. For most ionic systems, we take the standard state to be a concentration of 1 molar (or 1 molal). For hydrogen ions, this would be a pH of 0, but that doesn't work so well for most of biology. For biological systems, we use a new standard state, defined as a solution with pH = 7. In our conventional standard state, this would be an activity of $10^{-7}$. In the biological standard state, however, pH 7 now corresponds to an activity of 1 for $H^+$. All other ions still use a 1 molar (or molal) standard state. Thermodynamic functions are often labeled $G^+$, $H^+$, $S^+$, and so on when the biological standard state is being used.

## 20.1.5 Why Activities?

You may wonder why we have to make all this fuss with activities. The answer is that it doesn't matter how much of something there is, but what it can do. This is actually a big deal in food science. It doesn't matter how much water is in a food, but how "available" that water is for microbial growth and other spoilage mechanisms. Consider honey, which has a water content of about 17% by weight. Have you ever seen spoiled honey? Honey cannot grow mold. Many breads and baked goods have similar water content as honey but will grow mold or the bread will otherwise spoil. So what is the difference? It's not water content, but water activity. Honey has a water activity of about 0.6, whereas bread can have a water activity between 0.8 and 0.95. This is because of all the hydrogen bonding between water and sugar molecules in honey. If a food has high water activity, that water is available for mold or other microbes to use, leading to spoiling of the food. It is also easier for that food to dry out and become stale. If the food has low water activity, that water is not available for microbial growth, regardless of the water content, and hence the food is more resistant to spoilage. Foods with low water activity behave as if they have less water than they really do.

Table 20.1 summarizes how we define activity and the corresponding standard states for various systems. In all cases, the chemical potential changes according to the relation

$$\mu_i = \mu_i^\circ + RT \ln a_i$$

In the limit of the standard state, $\gamma_i = 1$ and $\mu_i = \mu_i^\circ$.

# 20.2 Chemical Equilibrium

Now that we have introduced the idea of activity, we are prepared to treat chemical reactions from the perspective of thermodynamics.

## 20.2.1 Simple Description of Chemical Equilibrium

Let's consider a case where A and B are ideal gases involved in the following chemical reaction.

$$A (g) \rightarrow B (g)$$

The chemical potential of each species is given by the relation (Eq. 19.8)

$$\mu_i = \mu_i^\circ + RT \ln \frac{P_i}{P^\circ}$$

We can write the change in chemical potential for this chemical reaction as

$$\mu_B - \mu_A = \mu_B^\circ + RT \ln \frac{P_B}{P^\circ} - \mu_A^\circ - RT \ln \frac{P_A}{P^\circ} = \left(\mu_B^\circ - \mu_A^\circ\right) + RT \ln \frac{P_B}{P_A}$$

We will denote the ratio of partial pressures as $Q$, which we call the **reaction quotient**. We will also call the difference in chemical potentials the **reaction Gibbs energy**, written here as

$$\Delta_r G = \mu_B - \mu_A$$

The difference of standard chemical potentials, called the **standard reaction Gibbs energy**, is

$$\Delta_r G^\circ = \mu_B^\circ - \mu_A^\circ$$

We can calculate the standard reaction Gibbs energy in terms of the Gibbs energies of formation, because a formation reaction is done at standard conditions.

$$\Delta_r G^\circ = \Delta_f G_B^\circ - \Delta_f G_A^\circ$$

Putting all this together lets us write

$$\Delta_r G = \Delta_r G^\circ + RT \ln Q \qquad (20.18)$$

Let's return briefly to the reaction quotient for this example reaction. We defined $Q$ as the ratio of partial pressure of B and A. Mathematically,

$$Q = \frac{P_B}{P_A}$$

This quantity ranges from 0—when we have pure A—to infinity, when we have complete reaction to B. Let's instead look at the condition of equilibrium. If the reacting system is at equilibrium, the chemical potential of the two species is the same and $\Delta_r G = 0$. In this case we can write

$$\Delta_r G = 0 = \Delta_r G^\circ + RT \ln \left(\frac{P_B}{P_A}\right)_{equilibrium} = \Delta_r G^\circ + RT \ln Q_{equilibrium}$$

or

$$\Delta_r G^\circ = -RT \ln Q_{equilibrium}$$

Let's denote the reaction quotient under these conditions as $K$, which we call the **equilibrium constant**. We can then determine the ratio of pressures at equilibrium.

$$K = \left( \frac{P_B}{P_A} \right)_{equilibrium}$$

This gives us what is one of the most useful relations from chemical thermodynamics,

$$\Delta_r G^\circ = -RT \ln K \tag{20.19}$$

So if we know the standard Gibbs energy change of the reaction, which can be determined from thermodynamic tables, we can determine the equilibrium composition of the reaction mixture. No matter what the initial composition is, we know where it goes. Many of these ideas should be familiar from your general chemistry courses.

## 20.2.2 Reaction Gibbs Energy

We introduced the idea of the reaction Gibbs energy and the equilibrium constant with a simple reaction and in a way that may have been familiar from your general chemistry courses. Let's now develop a more general description of the reaction Gibbs energy that is more rigorous. We again start with the chemical reaction

$$A\,(g) \rightarrow B\,(g)$$

Now, for this detailed treatment, we have to consider the fact that the chemical potential of each species may depend on the composition of the reaction mixture. The system still wants to lower its total Gibbs energy, however. Let's say we start with some amount of each gas, $n_A$ moles of gas A and $n_B$ moles of gas B. We previously (see Eq. 5.1) defined the **extent of reaction** as:

$$\xi = \frac{n_i - n_{i,0}}{\nu_i} \tag{20.20}$$

where $\nu_i$ is the stoichiometric coefficient for species $i$. As before, we use the following convention: $\nu_i$ is positive for products and negative for reactants. Using this convention, extent of reaction is always positive.

Let's suppose that an infinitesimal amount of A reacts to form B. We will denote this amount as $dn_A$. Because we are reacting A and forming B, we can readily see that

$$dn_A = -d\xi \qquad \text{and} \qquad dn_B = d\xi$$

Now, let's suppose that we are at constant $T$ and $P$. Under these conditions, the total differential of the Gibbs energy is expressed as

$$dG = \mu_A dn_A + \mu_B dn_B$$

We can replace the $dn$ terms with $\pm d\xi$, each with the proper sign.

$$dG = -\mu_A d\xi + \mu_B d\xi = (\mu_B - \mu_A)d\xi$$

If we divide by $d\xi$, we can write

$$\frac{dG}{d\xi} = \left(\frac{\partial G}{\partial \xi}\right)_{T,P} = \mu_B - \mu_A$$

This difference in chemical potentials is what we used before to define the reaction Gibbs energy. However, the partial derivative with respect to extent of reaction provides a more general definition of the reaction Gibbs energy.

$$\Delta_r G \equiv \left(\frac{\partial G}{\partial \xi}\right)_{T,P} \qquad (20.21)$$

Note that Eq. 20.21 is somewhat different from the standard reaction Gibbs energies we used before. Because chemical potentials change with composition, the reaction Gibbs energy changes as the composition of the reaction mixture changes. We can use the reaction Gibbs energy to determine if a particular reacting system will either move forward or backward, or it is at equilibrium. Recall that the system will try to minimize the Gibbs energy. If we plot Gibbs energy vs. extent of reaction, as in Figure 20.2, the reaction Gibbs energy is the slope of this curve. The reaction proceeds in the direction that lowers the total Gibbs energy of the system. We see that in some regions the reaction will go forward; in other regions it will go backward; and at a particular point, the slope will be zero. That point is when the reacting system is at equilibrium.

If $\Delta_r G < 0$, the forward reaction is spontaneous and is called **exergonic**.

If $\Delta_r G > 0$, the forward reaction is not spontaneous and is called **endergonic**.

If $\Delta_r G = 0$, the reaction is at equilibrium.

This plot of $G$ vs. extent of reaction in Figure 20.2 can be viewed as a potential energy surface. A system at some initial composition will move towards the equilibrium position, just as a marble placed at some point will move towards the bottom of the well. Note that the standard state is also located somewhere on this curve and could be on either side of the equilibrium point. This is why $\Delta G°$ can be positive for some reactions and negative for others. The value of $\Delta G°$ tells us how far the standard state is from the equilibrium condition.

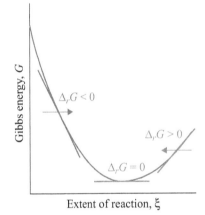

FIGURE 20.2. Variation of the Gibbs energy of a reacting system with extent of reaction.

## 20.2.3 Molecular Considerations

Let's look at our simple gas-phase reaction in molecular terms, where B is a more stable molecule than A. If we only had to consider the chemical change from A to B, we would predict that the reaction would move to completion and form the compound with the lower Gibbs energy. However, as the reaction progresses, the reactant and the product mix. This mixing process provides additional entropy to the system, which also lowers the total Gibbs energy of the system. So long as the Gibbs energy of mixing lowers the total Gibbs energy of the system below the Gibbs energy of the pure product, the reaction will not go to completion; entropy shows up again. The reaction Gibbs energy accounts for all these effects: enthalpy to form stronger bonds, which releases heat to the surroundings and increases the entropy of the surroundings; the change of entropy between reactants and products; and entropy to mix reactants and products. Hopefully now you have an even better sense of why the Gibbs energy is such a powerful concept.

### 20.2.4 General Equilibrium Constant

Let's generalize our discussion to any reaction, in any phase. Let's take as our test reaction

$$2A + B \rightarrow 3C + D.$$

We can rewrite this as $0 = 3C + D - 2A - B$. In general, we write

$$\sum_J \nu_J J = 0 \tag{20.22}$$

where $J$ denotes the species and $\nu_J$ is the stoichiometric coefficient. For a product, these coefficients are positive, but they are negative for reactants. When the reaction proceeds by an amount $d\xi$, the number of moles of each species changes by

$$dn_J = \nu_J d\xi \tag{20.23}$$

We then write the total differential of the Gibbs energy, at constant $T$ and $P$, as

$$dG = \sum_J \mu_J dn_J = \sum_J \mu_J \nu_J d\xi = d\xi \left( \sum_J \nu_J \mu_J \right)$$

Dividing by $d\xi$ gives our general definition of $\Delta_r G$, which we can write in terms of the chemical potentials as

$$\Delta_r G = \left( \frac{\partial G}{\partial \xi} \right)_{T,P} = \sum_J \nu_J \mu_J \tag{20.24}$$

We can expand the chemical potentials for each component using the expression

$$\mu_J = \mu_J^\circ + RT \ln a_J$$

where the activity and standard states are properly defined for each species. This gives us

$$\Delta_r G = \sum_J \nu_J \mu_J^\circ + RT \sum_J \nu_J \ln a_J = \Delta_r G^\circ + RT \sum_J \ln a_J^{\nu_J}$$

Using our rules of logarithms, we can write the sum of lns as a ln of the product, or

$$\Delta_r G = \Delta_r G^\circ + RT \ln \prod_J a_J^{\nu_J} \tag{20.25}$$

(Recall that the $\Pi$ symbol denotes a product, similar to how $\Sigma$ denotes a sum.) We now define our general reaction quotient as

$$Q = \prod_J a_J^{\nu_J} \tag{20.26}$$

which again gives us

$$\Delta_r G = \Delta_r G^\circ + RT \ln Q \tag{20.27}$$

For the reaction we had earlier, $2A + B \rightarrow 3C + D$, we would write the reaction quotient as

$$Q = a_A^{-2} a_B^{-1} a_C^{3} a_D = \frac{a_C^{3} a_D}{a_A^{2} a_B^{1}}$$

Again, when the reaction is at equilibrium, we have $\Delta_r G = 0$, so $\Delta_r G^\circ = -RT \ln K$ and we can write the equilibrium constant as

$$K = \left( \prod_J a_J^{v_J} \right)_{equilibrium} \tag{20.28}$$

The quantity $K$ is the **thermodynamic equilibrium constant**. From now on, if we write $K$ we mean at equilibrium. If we write $Q$, we are at some condition other than equilibrium.

Note that the equilibrium constant must be unitless. Activities already are, so that is not a problem. In many cases, if the system is behaving near ideally, we can use the numerical values of the pressures or concentrations in the proper units. For liquid-phase reactions, our standard state becomes either 1 molal or 1 molar, depending on the units of concentration we are using. For gases, we properly use the fugacity divided by the standard pressure of 1 atm or 1 bar. If we are treating the gas as ideal, we use the value of the pressure. Note that for heterogeneous reactions, we use the definition of activity that is appropriate for each chemical species.

### Sample Problem 20.2

Determine the general equilibrium constant for the following reaction:

$$N_2\,(g) + 3\,H_2\,(g) \rightarrow 2\,NH_3\,(g)$$

Is the reaction spontaneous under standard conditions? Also, estimate the pressure of $NH_3$ at equilibrium if there is 0.1 bar each of $N_2$ and $H_2$ present.

Solution

We write the equilibrium constant as
$$K = \frac{a_{NH_3}^2}{a_{N_2}\,a_{H_2}^3}$$

For a gas, we use $a = f/P^\circ$.

$$K = \frac{f_{NH_3}^2\,P^{\circ 2}}{f_{N_2}\,f_{H_2}^3} \quad \text{or} \quad K = \frac{P_{NH_3}^2\,P^{\circ 2}}{P_{N_2}\,P_{H_2}^3}$$

if the pressures are low.

Now, we ask if this reaction is spontaneous. We can look up the Gibbs energy of formation for $NH_3$ (the values for $N_2$ and $H_2$ are both zero, by definition.)

$$\Delta_f G^\circ\,(NH_3\,(g),\,298\,K) = -16.45\,\text{kJ mol}^{-1}$$

For the reaction as written, we need to double this amount to obtain $\Delta_r G^\circ = -32.9\,\text{kJ mol}^{-1}$. Because $\Delta_r G^\circ$ is negative, this reaction is spontaneous under standard conditions, and, using Eq. 20.19, gives a value for the equilibrium constant of $K = 5.84 \times 10^5$.

If at equilibrium we have 0.1 bar pressure each of $N_2$ and $H_2$, we should have 7.64 bar of $NH_3$.

---

Sample Problem 20.2 showed us how we can use thermodynamic data to evaluate the conditions of a reaction at equilibrium. We can also evaluate the spontaneity of a reaction under standard conditions. If the initial conditions are not standard, we can use Eq. 20.27 and evaluate $Q$ for the actual conditions. If $\Delta G$ is less than zero under those conditions, then the reaction is spontaneous. If $\Delta G$ is positive, the reverse reaction will be spontaneous under those conditions. Note that this analysis says nothing about how quickly the ammonia will form. For ammonia synthesis, a catalyst is needed to make this process feasible. This process, known as the Haber process, is also typically done at high pressures and temperatures to speed up the conversion process.

## 20.2.5 Thermodynamics of Chemical Bonding

Let's now discuss some of the molecular details of chemical bonding and chemical equilibrium. When a chemical bond forms, this leads to stabilization (lowering of the energy) of the bonding partners. If the bond didn't lower the energy, then why would the bond form? So you might argue that bonds should always form, if that lowers the energy (enthalpy). However, we need to look at some other considerations to understand the full story.

Let's consider two atoms coming together to form a stable bond. We know that bond formation lowers the enthalpy, so $\Delta H$ for the bond formation process is negative.

$$A + A \rightarrow A_2 \qquad \Delta H < 0$$

Bond formation is *always* exothermic. So, from an enthalpic perspective, all atoms should form the strongest bonds possible. However, we have gone from having two atoms to having a single molecule. What does this do to the entropy? For this process $\Delta S < 0$; the entropy has gone down. The universe likes to maximize entropy, so the tendency of the two atoms from an entropic perspective is to not form the bond. So, which process wins? We have competing effects, and the Gibbs energy lets us describe them both.

At constant temperature,

$$\Delta G = \Delta H - T\Delta S$$

So, when we form a bond with two atoms, we have $\Delta H < 0$, but $\Delta S$ of the system is also negative. Whether or not the bond forms will depend on the relative magnitude of $\Delta H$ and $T\Delta S$. If the energy released from forming the bond is greater in magnitude than $T\Delta S$, then the bond can form. The energy released from forming the bond goes into the surroundings as heat and increases the entropy of the surroundings by more than the loss of entropy of the system. However, if the bond is very weak, then the energy stabilization doesn't overcome the entropy cost, and the bond won't form.

Let's consider a couple of other cases. First, take a dimer of noble gas. The "bond" between two noble gas atoms will be very weak—much less than the entropy cost of forming the bond—so a bond generally doesn't form. You only get dimers and clusters of noble gas atoms at low temperatures, where the strength of the van der Waals interactions is greater than $T\Delta S$. Now, consider the case of fluorine atoms. Fluorine is very strongly electronegative and it wants to form a bond. Any bond will stabilize it, much more than the entropy cost of forming the bond.

For a complete chemical reaction, we can look at all the bonds that are formed and broken. If the bonds in the products are stronger than the bonds in the reactants, then the total $\Delta_r H$ will be negative. If the reverse is true, then $\Delta_r H$ will be positive. In general, the entropy will decrease if the number of moles decreases as product is formed; you have fewer molecules, so the system is "more ordered." If a single large molecule breaks down to form many small molecules, then $\Delta_r S$ will generally be positive. To fully understand the process, we have to consider $\Delta_r G$. One of the great things about $\Delta_r G$ is that it captures this compromise between the energy stabilization and the entropy cost of forming and breaking bonds.

## 20.3 Response of Equilibrium to Changes in Conditions

Now we will look at how equilibria change with experimental conditions—notably pressure, temperature, and composition.

### 20.3.1 Changes With Pressure

The equilibrium constant depends on the value of $\Delta_r G°$, which is defined at the standard pressure. Thus, the equilibrium constant does not change with $P$. Expressed mathematically,

$$\left(\frac{\partial K}{\partial P}\right)_T = 0 \tag{20.29}$$

However, the fact that the equilibrium constant doesn't change does not mean that the equilibrium conditions don't change with changes in pressure. There are two ways to increase the pressure in a reacting vessel. First, inert gas can be added. So long as the gases are treated as ideal, this does not change the partial pressures of the reacting gases; thus the equilibrium composition doesn't change. The second approach is to change the volume of the container.

For the activity of real gases, we have to use the fugacities, and those do change with changes in total pressure. This can lead to changes in composition for real gases with addition of inert gas. In general, we write the equilibrium constant for a mixture of real gases as

$$K = \prod_J a_J^{v_J} = \prod_J \left(\frac{f_J}{P°}\right)^{v_J}$$

Let's recall the fugacity coefficient (see Eq. 18.43):

$$\phi_J = \frac{f_J}{P_J} \qquad \text{or} \qquad f_J = \phi_J P_J$$

This lets us write

$$K = \prod_J \phi_J^{v_J} \cdot \prod_J \left(\frac{P_J}{P°}\right)^{v_J} = \prod_J \phi_J^{v_J} \cdot K_P \tag{20.30}$$

Where $K_P$ is the ratio of the partial pressures, not the activities. Now, if $\left(\frac{\partial K}{\partial P}\right)_T = 0$, then we can also say $\left(\frac{\partial \ln K}{\partial P}\right)_T = 0$. Substituting in Eq. 20.30 gives us

$$\left(\frac{\partial \ln K}{\partial P}\right)_T = 0 = \sum_J v_J \left(\frac{\partial \ln \phi_J}{\partial P}\right)_T + \left(\frac{\partial \ln K_P}{\partial P}\right)_T$$

$$\left(\frac{\partial \ln K_P}{\partial P}\right)_T = -\sum_J v_J \left(\frac{\partial \ln \phi_J}{\partial P}\right)_T \tag{20.31}$$

So, to the extent that the fugacity coefficients are affected by the added pressure of the inert gas, the partial pressures of the reacting gases will change. Note that the changes in the partial pressures will be opposite to the changes in the fugacity coefficients. If the gases are all behaving ideally, the fugacity coefficients will all be 1 and will not change, so the entire right-hand side of Eq. 20.31 will equal 0.

The other way to increase the pressure is to compress the reaction vessel. Now, even for ideal gases, the partial pressures can change, but the equilibrium constant still does not change. For example, let's take a dissociation reaction of the form

$$A\ (g) \rightarrow 2\ B\ (g)$$

Treating the gases as ideal, we write

$$K = \frac{(P_B/P^\circ)^2}{(P_A/P^\circ)} = \frac{P_B^2}{P_A P^\circ}$$

The total pressure is always written as

$$P_{tot} = P_A + P_B$$

Let's say that $K = 1.25$, and we start at total pressure of 1 bar. This means that

$$P_A + P_B = 1 \text{ bar} \qquad \text{and} \qquad \frac{P_B^2}{P_A P^\circ} = 1.25$$

Solving this system of equations gives us $P_A = 0.344$ bar and $P_B = 0.656$ bar. Now, let's compress the container so that the total pressure becomes 10 bar. Solving the new system of equations gives $P_A = 7.03$ bar and $P_B = 2.97$ bar. At 1 bar, we had 65.6% B; but at 10 bar, we have 70.3% A.

As the pressure increases, the composition will shift to favor more A. This is one example of Le Châtelier's principle that if a system is disturbed, it will respond in a way that tends to minimize the effects of the disturbance. For our test reaction, as the pressure increases, the system can minimize the effects of that compression by reducing the number of molecules in the system and reversing the reaction.

## 20.3.2 Changes With Temperature

Le Châtelier's principle also tells us that if we raise the temperature, the reaction will shift in the endothermic direction. Likewise, if we lower the temperature, the exothermic reaction is favored.

Let's look at this in more detail. We start with the relation (Eq. 20.19)

$$\Delta_r G^\circ = -RT \ln K \qquad \text{or} \qquad \ln K = \frac{-\Delta_r G^\circ}{RT}$$

We take the derivative of this expression with respect to $T$ and write

$$\frac{d \ln K}{dT} = \frac{-1}{R} \frac{d(\Delta_r G^\circ / T)}{dT}$$

We then recall the Gibbs–Helmholtz equation (Eq. 18.36),

$$\frac{d(\Delta_r G^\circ / T)}{dT} = \frac{-\Delta_r H^\circ}{T^2}$$

Substitution of the last two expressions into each other gives

$$\boxed{\frac{d \ln K}{dT} = \frac{\Delta_r H^\circ}{RT^2}}$$

(20.32)

This is known as the **van 't Hoff equation**. Let's look at it briefly. If the reaction is exothermic, $\Delta_r H^\circ < 0$, so ln $K$ will decrease with increasing temperature, meaning the reaction will shift to favor the reactant side. Likewise, if the reaction is endothermic, meaning $\Delta_r H^\circ > 0$, then ln $K$ will increase as the temperature increases, leading to more product formation.

There is another way to write the van 't Hoff equation that is often more useful. We start with the equation

$$\frac{d(1/T)}{dT} = \frac{-1}{T^2} \qquad \text{or} \qquad dT = -T^2 d(1/T)$$

We can substitute this in to Eq. 20.32 and write

$$\frac{d \ln K}{dT} = \frac{-d \ln K}{T^2 d(1/T)} = \frac{\Delta_r H^\circ}{RT^2}$$

$$\frac{d \ln K}{d(1/T)} = \frac{-\Delta_r H^\circ}{R}$$

(20.33)

This last form is convenient, because if we plot ln $K$ vs. $1/T$, the slope at any point is $-\Delta_r H^\circ/R$. If the enthalpy doesn't change with temperature, such a plot will give a straight line. (This is similar to how we can analyze kinetic data to determine the activation energy; see Section 4.1.3.)

To find the value of the equilibrium constant at a different temperature, we integrate Eq. 20.33 to get

$$\ln K_2 - \ln K_1 = \frac{-1}{R} \int_{1/T_1}^{1/T_2} \Delta_r H^\circ d(1/T)$$

(20.34)

If we assume $\Delta_r H^\circ$ is constant, which is not always a good assumption but works fairly well for small temperature differences, we have

$$\ln \frac{K_2}{K_1} = \frac{-\Delta_r H^\circ}{R} \left( \frac{1}{T_2} - \frac{1}{T_1} \right)$$

If we increase the temperature, then $T_2 > T_1$. This gives us $\frac{1}{T_2} < \frac{1}{T_1}$ or $\frac{1}{T_2} - \frac{1}{T_1} < 0$. If the reaction is endothermic, $\Delta_r H^\circ > 0$ and the right-hand side is positive. This means the value of $K$ will increase, favoring the product side. If the reaction is exothermic, then $\Delta_r H^\circ < 0$ and the right-hand side will be negative. The reaction will shift to favor the reactant side as temperature is increased. These results agree with the qualitative ideas of Le Châtelier's principle.

## 20.3.3 Initial Conditions

Another way to change the equilibrium is to change the composition of the initial mixture. If the reaction quotient is different from the equilibrium constant, then the reaction will proceed in the direction given by $\Delta_r G$. For example, a dissociation reaction of the form

$$A \rightarrow B + C$$

initially has only A present. As dissociation occurs, each mole of A that decomposes produces a mole of B and a mole of C. At equilibrium, the ratio of the activities must equal the equilibrium constant. Often, it is helpful to construct a chart of the initial number of moles, the change in number of moles, and the final number of moles of each species. If the reaction is gas phase at moderate pressure, then partial pressures will be used in constructing the equilibrium constant. For aqueous reactions, activities in terms of concentrations will be used. Let's treat this as a gas phase reaction of ideal gases for demonstration purposes.

|  | A | B | C |
|---|---|---|---|
| initial | $n$ | 0 | 0 |
| change | $-x$ | $+x$ | $+x$ |
| final | $n - x$ | $x$ | $x$ |
| mole fraction | $n - x/n + x$ | $x/n + x$ | $x/n + x$ |
| partial press. | $P(n - x)/n + x$ | $Px/n + x$ | $Px/n + x$ where $P$ is the total pressure. |

We write the equilibrium constant as

$$K = \frac{\left(\dfrac{x}{n+x}\right)\dfrac{P}{P^\circ}\left(\dfrac{x}{n+x}\right)\dfrac{P}{P^\circ}}{\left(\dfrac{n-x}{n+x}\right)\dfrac{P}{P^\circ}} = \frac{x^2 P}{(n-x)(n+x)P^\circ} = \frac{x^2}{n^2 - x^2}\frac{P}{P^\circ}$$

If we know the total pressure and the value of $K$, we can solve for $x$ and determine the equilibrium composition. Note that the solution to a quadratic expression will yield two possible answers; however, only one of them will be physically valid.

Let's look at this process in terms of the Gibbs energy of reaction. We can always write

$$\Delta_r G = \Delta_r G^\circ + RT \ln Q$$

If we start with only A, then the value of $Q$ is zero. The $\ln Q$ term is then negative infinity, and the reaction will proceed in the forward direction, regardless of the value of $\Delta_r G^\circ$. However, if the value of $K$ for this reaction is very small, the reaction won't go very far forward before equilibrium is reached. On the other hand, if we start with all the reactants and products in their standard states, the value of $Q$ is then 1, so $\ln Q = 0$ and $\Delta_r G = \Delta_r G^\circ$. If $\Delta_r G^\circ$ is negative, the reaction will go forward to produce more product, but if it is positive, the reaction will go in reverse. If we have excess B such that $Q > K$, $\Delta_r G$ is again positive, and the reaction will go in reverse until equilibrium is reached. Keep in mind, though, that the value of $\Delta_r G$ only tells us the direction of reaction; it tells us nothing about how fast the reaction will proceed. Thermodynamic results tell us very little about kinetics.

### Sample Problem 20.3

Is the reaction to form ammonia spontaneous at 298 K under the conditions where the pressures of each reactant and product is 5 bar? What about if all pressures are 1 mbar? (See Sample Problem 20.2 for the reaction and value of $K$.)

## Solution

We can judge spontaneity by calculating $\Delta_r G$ under the specified conditions. $\Delta_r G° = -32.9$ kJ mol$^{-1}$.

$$\Delta_r G = \Delta_r G° + RT \ln Q = \Delta_r G° + RT \ln \frac{P_{NH_3}^2 \, P^{°2}}{P_{N_2} P_{H_2}^3}$$

$$\Delta_r G = -40.9 \text{ kJ mol}^{-1}$$

The Gibbs energy of reaction is negative, so the forward reaction is spontaneous under the conditions where all pressures are 5 bar.

Another way to judge spontaneity is to compare the value of $Q$ to that of $K$. If $Q < K$, then the forward reaction is spontaneous. For these conditions, we calculate

$$Q = \frac{5^2}{5(5)^3} = 0.04 < K = 5.84 \times 10^5$$

Again, the forward reaction is spontaneous.

For the conditions where all pressures are 1 mbar, we find that

$$Q = \frac{0.001^2}{0.001(0.001)^3} = 1 \times 10^6 > K = 5.84 \times 10^5$$

and the forward reaction is not spontaneous. (Calculating $\Delta_r G$ gives a value of 1.33 kJ mol$^{-1}$, which is positive, telling us the forward reaction is not spontaneous under these conditions.)

## 20.3.4 Biological Equilibria

We are all alive because of complicated biological processes. Many of these processes are not spontaneous under physiological conditions. So why do they happen? Many biological reactions are coupled. This means that one reaction with a negative $\Delta_r G$ can be used to drive a reaction that has a positive $\Delta_r G$. Think of it as weights coupled by a pulley. If I want to raise a weight, I can connect it to a heavier weight that will fall under the force of gravity, pulling up the lighter weight. By coupling them, processes that would otherwise not be spontaneous can be driven forward. This is shown in Figure 20.3. Biological processes can also generally be considered to be isothermal, so they don't suffer the same type of inefficiency as heat-driven processes.

ATP is very useful biologically because the phosphate group does not bind too tightly. You may have heard the phrase *high-energy phosphate bond*, but this is really bad usage of terms. The bond enthalpy is actually quite low; it is a weak bond. Hydrolysis of ATP releases energy not because we break the phosphate bond, but because of the formation and solvation of the products and the increase in entropy by going from one thing to two smaller things. Remember, it always takes energy to break a bond and energy is released when bonds are formed. The fact that the ATP bond is rather weak makes it easy for the cell to use it as an energy-transport mechanism; the phosphate group can be taken off and put back on with relative ease. Another reason to do energy conversions in small steps is that this more closely resembles a reversible process, which increases the overall efficiency of the energy conversion.

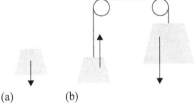

(a)          (b)

**FIGURE 20.3.** a) If a weight is released, it will fall. b) If that weight is coupled to another heavier weight, then it will rise as the heavier weight falls.

Many biological processes operate very close to equilibrium, and slight changes in conditions can cause a reaction to reverse direction. In fact, many diseases are caused because these equilibria are disrupted. An important biochemical reaction is

$$\text{NADH}\,(aq) + \text{H}^+\,(aq) \rightarrow \text{NAD}^+\,(aq) + \text{H}_2\,(g) \qquad 37°C$$

Under standard ionic conditions, $\Delta_r G° = -21.8$ kJ mol$^{-1}$, so this reaction is spontaneous. However, under standard biological conditions (pH = 7), $\Delta_r G^+ = +19.7$ kJ mol$^{-1}$. Now the forward reaction is not spontaneous, but the reverse reaction is. Slight changes in conditions affect the direction it goes. Conditions can be different in different tissues; thus one reaction can be spontaneous in one part of the body while the reverse is spontaneous somewhere else.

# 20.4 Statistical Mechanical Treatment of Chemical Equilibrium

We now have a good sense of chemical equilibrium from a macroscopic, thermodynamic perspective. As has been our pattern, however, we want to also explore these ideas at the molecular level. We also want to apply the tools of statistical mechanics to chemical potential and chemical equilibrium.

## 20.4.1 Chemical Potential From Partition Functions

To develop an expression for the chemical potential in terms of the canonical partition function, we first need to go back to the fundamental equation of chemical thermodynamics (Eq. 19.3).

$$dG = -SdT + VdP + \sum_i \mu_i dn_i$$

Recall that the natural variables of the Gibbs energy are $T$, $P$, and $n$, but the variables we control in the canonical ensemble are $T$, $V$, and $N$ (or $n$). This suggests we should switch our attention back to the Helmholtz energy, which has natural variables of $T$, $V$, and $n$. Mathematically, we have $A(T, V, n_1, n_2, ...)$, and we write the total differential of $A$ as

$$dA = \left(\frac{\partial A}{\partial T}\right)_{n,V} dT + \left(\frac{\partial A}{\partial V}\right)_{n,T} dV + \sum_i \left(\frac{\partial A}{\partial n_i}\right)_{T,V,n_{j \neq i}} dn_i \qquad (20.35)$$

Extending Eq. 18.11 to account for variable amounts, we write the total differential of the Helmholtz energy as

$$dA = -SdT - PdV + \sum_i \mu_i dn_i \qquad (20.36)$$

We can thus see a new way to express the chemical potential, in terms of the Helmholtz energy.

$$\mu_i = \left(\frac{\partial A}{\partial n_i}\right)_{T,V,n_{j \neq i}} \qquad (20.37)$$

We can further show the equivalence of these expressions for the chemical potential by going back to thermodynamic definitions.

$$G = H - TS = U + PV - TS = A + PV$$

$$dG = dA + PdV + VdP = -SdT - PdV + \sum_i \mu_i dn_i + PdV + VdP$$

We can substitute Eq. 20.37 in here and cancel terms to give us

$$dG = -SdT + VdP + \sum_i \left( \frac{\partial A}{\partial n_i} \right)_{T,V,n_{j\neq i}} dn_i$$

Comparison with the fundamental equation of chemical thermodynamics, and inclusion of the definition of chemical potential in terms of the Gibbs energy, gives us

$$\mu_i = \left( \frac{\partial A}{\partial n_i} \right)_{T,V,n_{j\neq i}} = \left( \frac{\partial G}{\partial n_i} \right)_{T,P,n_{j\neq i}} \tag{20.38}$$

Similar expressions for the chemical potential can also be written in terms of the internal energy and the enthalpy, where the respective natural variables are kept constant. These other forms, however, have limited use, so we just mention them here for completeness.

Now that we have shown we can use the Helmholtz energy to express the chemical potential, let's return to the expressions we already have for internal energy and entropy in terms of the canonical partition function. (See Table 14.1.)

$$U = k_B T^2 \left( \frac{\partial \ln Q}{\partial T} \right)_{N,V} \quad \text{and} \quad S = k_B T \left( \frac{\partial \ln Q}{\partial T} \right)_{N,V} + k_B \ln Q$$

Using the thermodynamic definition of the Helmholtz energy, $A = U - TS$, we can write (Eq. 18.19):

$$A = -k_B T \ln Q$$

There is actually a fair amount of meaning contained in this simple expression. Recall our picture of the canonical ensemble as consisting of microsystems—all with the same temperature, volume, and number of molecules. Also recall our condition for spontaneity in terms of the Helmholtz energy for a process at constant volume and constant temperature (Eq. 18.25)

$$dA_{T,V} \leq 0$$

Thus, we can see that a spontaneous process for a closed system under conditions of constant temperature and volume is one that leads to an increase in the value of the canonical partition function. If we also recall that the partition function tells us something about the number of available states, we can see that this number must increase for a spontaneous process under the conditions we have imposed. It all comes back to probabilities.

We can now use the Helmholtz energy to develop an expression for the chemical potential in terms of the canonical partition function. Simply combining Eq. 20.37 and Eq. 18.19 gives us

$$\mu_i = -RT \left( \frac{\partial \ln Q}{\partial N_i} \right)_{T,V,N_{j \neq i}} \tag{20.39}$$

so long as we recognize that $dn$ and $dN$ are related, since $n$ and $N$ are directly proportional by Avogadro's number. This completes the types of derivatives we can take of $\ln Q$. Internal energy and entropy both depend on the temperature derivative of $\ln Q$. Pressure depends on the volume derivative. Now we have the number derivative, which relates to chemical potential.

As we have done before, we need to make sure that we recover the ideal gas law, or something we derived from it, for the case of noninteracting molecules. Recall that for a collection of particles with no interactions, the canonical partition function can be written in terms of the molecular partition function (Eq. 14.12)

$$Q = \frac{q^N}{N!}$$

Putting this in to Eq. 20.39, and doing a bit of algebra, gives us

$$\mu_i = -RT \ln \frac{q_i}{N_i} \tag{20.40}$$

We're now going to do some more quick algebra. For simplicity, we'll consider a system with only one type of molecule, so we can drop the subscripts. Remember, in algebra, we can always multiply something by 1. One way to do this is to multiply the numerator and denominator by the same thing. We'll do this with a factor of $P°V$ inside the $\ln$ of Eq. 20.40.

$$\mu = -RT \ln \frac{qP°V}{NP°V}$$

We can replace the factor of $V/N$ with the ideal gas law, which lets us write

$$\mu = -RT \ln \left( \frac{qk_BT}{P°V} \frac{P°}{P} \right)$$

We can rewrite this slightly by pulling $\ln P/P°$ into a separate term. (Remember that the argument of a logarithm can't have units.) Doing so lets us write

$$\mu = -RT \ln \left( \frac{qk_BT}{P°V} \right) + RT \ln \frac{P}{P°}$$

Because the first term represents a gas under standard conditions, we can rewrite things slightly

$$\mu = -RT \ln \frac{q°}{N} + RT \ln \frac{P}{P°}$$

where we are using the ° sign to indicate the partition function under standard conditions. We can now identify the entire first term with the standard chemical potential and write

$$\mu = \mu° + RT \ln\frac{P}{P°}$$

Comparison to Eq. 19.8 shows the same result as we had previously for an ideal gas. Thus, for a system of noninteracting particles, we can use Eq. 20.40 to describe the chemical potential in terms of the molecular partition function. (You should now also be able to see where the last entry in Table 13.4 comes from.)

## 20.4.2 Equilibrium Constant From the Molecular Partition Function

The Gibbs energy for a single-component system can be written in terms of the chemical potential as (see Eq. 19.7)

$$G = n\mu$$

In molecular terms, we would write the Gibbs energy for ideal gas molecules as

$$G - G_0 = -Nk_B T \ln\frac{q}{N} \tag{20.41}$$

As we discussed back in Chapter 13, our reference of the zero of energy can't have any impact on our calculations. When dealing with only one type of molecule, it didn't really matter what we chose as the reference. Now that we want to have chemical reactions take place, we need to be a bit more careful. We will pick $G_0 = E_0$, the zero-point energy of the molecule. We also tend to like to work in molar units, so we can write the standard molar Gibbs energy as

$$G_m° = E_0 - RT \ln\frac{q°}{N} \tag{20.42}$$

We now use the general relation from classical thermodynamics, Eq. 20.19, to write

$$\Delta_r G° = \sum_J v_J G_J° = \sum_J v_J E_{0,J} - RT \sum_J v_J \ln\frac{q_J°}{N} = -RT \ln K$$

We can collect the zero-point energies and write

$$\sum_J v_J E_{0,J} = \Delta E_0 \tag{20.43}$$

This is necessary to bring all the molecular energy states onto the same scale and with the same reference. This common reference is effectively the fully dissociated molecules for all reactants and products. Solving for $K$ gives us the general expression

$$K = \prod_J \left(\frac{q_J°}{N}\right)^{v_J} e^{-\Delta E_0/RT} \tag{20.44}$$

Thus, if we can calculate molecular partition functions for all the reactants and products, and we know their relative zero-point energies, we can calculate the equilibrium constant for a reaction between them, assuming they individually behave as ideal gases.

One distinct advantage of this approach is that it allows us to calculate equilibrium constants based on partition functions—which are in turn based on spectroscopic measurements or quantum chemistry calculations—for reactions that are difficult to perform in the lab, or for reactions that haven't been done yet and for which thermodynamic data is unavailable.

### Sample Problem 20.4

Using statistical mechanics, determine the fractional dissociation of $H_2$ at a temperature of 2500 K and a pressure of 0.5 bar.

Solution

The first thing we need to do is write the chemical reaction we are considering.

$$H_2 \rightleftarrows 2\,H$$

Next, we need an expression for the equilibrium constant in terms of the respective partition functions.

$$K = \frac{q_H^{\circ\,2}}{N q_{H_2}^{\circ}} e^{-\Delta E_0 / RT}$$

Let's now write the two partition functions.

$$q_H^{\circ} = \left( \frac{2\pi m_H k_B T}{h^2} \right)^{3/2} V g_{el,H}$$

$$q_{H_2}^{\circ} = \left( \frac{2\pi m_{H_2} k_B T}{h^2} \right)^{3/2} V \frac{T}{2\Theta_{rot}} \frac{1}{1 - e^{-\Theta_{vib}/T}} g_{el,H_2}$$

All the molecular and atomic constants are available in Tables 13.1 and 13.2. Putting things together gives us

$$K = \left( \frac{2\pi k_B T}{h^2} \right)^{3/2} \frac{m_H^3 g_{el,H}}{m_{H_2}^{3/2} \dfrac{T}{2\Theta_{rot}} \dfrac{1}{1 - e^{-\Theta_{vib}/T}} g_{el,H_2}} \frac{k_B T}{P^{\circ}} e^{-\Delta E_0 / RT}$$

where we have replaced the factor of $V/N$ with $k_B T/P^{\circ}$. (We have already assumed ideal behavior by using molecular partition functions, so using the ideal gas law again is really nothing new.)

Now, we can insert the various atomic and molecular parameters from Tables 13.1 and 13.2 to determine the value of $K$ at a temperature of 2500 K. When doing this, we need to be careful with the change in zero-point energies in the exponential term. Because this is a dissociation reaction, the value of $\Delta E_0$ must be positive, meaning the argument of the exponential is negative, which will decrease the value of $K$. Plugging it all in gives us $K = 3.42 \times 10^{-3}$.

Assuming ideal gas behavior, the partial pressures are related to the mole fraction through Dalton's law. We can draw up a table of the changes

| | H₂ | H |
|---|---|---|
| initial | $n_0$ | 0 |
| change | $-x$ | $+2x$ |
| final | $n_0 - x$ | $2x$ |

The final mole fractions are

$$y(H_2) = (n_0 - x)/(n_0 + x) \qquad y(H) = 2x/(n_0 + x)$$

and the final partial pressures are

$$P(H_2) = (n_0 - x) P_{tot}/(n_0 + x) \qquad P(H) = 2x P_{tot}/(n_0 + x)$$

The equilibrium constant is written in terms of pressure as

$$K = \frac{P_H^2}{P_{H_2} P^\circ} = \frac{P}{P^\circ} \frac{4x^2}{(n_0 - x)(n_0 + x)} = \frac{P}{P^\circ} \frac{4x^2}{n_0^2 - x^2}$$

The percent dissociation is written as

$$\% \text{ dissociated} = 100 \frac{n_0 - n(H_2)}{n_0} = 100 \frac{x}{n_0}$$

Let's take $n_0$ to be 1 mol. We can then write

$$x = \left( \frac{KP^\circ}{4P + KP^\circ} \right)^{1/2}$$

Solving for the extent of reaction, which we can readily write as a percentage, we have 1.3% dissociation of $H_2$ at 2500 K and 0.5 bar.

(Note: When working these kinds of problems, you need to be very careful with units. Everything needs to be in SI units. Pressure must be in Pa, not bar. The masses are per atom/molecule, not molar masses.)

### 20.4.3 Molecular Interpretation of Equilibrium Constants

Let's consider a simple reaction of the form

$$R \rightleftharpoons P$$

Each type of molecule will have a distribution of molecular states, all of which are populated according to a Boltzmann distribution. Now let's put all the states of R and P together on the same energy scale. We have $N$ total molecules: $N = N_R + N_P$. The total of each type of molecule is given by

$$N_R = \sum_r n_r = \frac{N}{q} \sum_r e^{-\epsilon_r/kT} \qquad N_P = \sum_p n_p = \frac{N}{q} \sum_p e^{-\epsilon_p'/kT}$$

where $n_R$ is the number of R molecules in a particular energy state, $n_P$ is the same for P molecules, and $q$ is the partition function of the composite system. The ′ in the energies for the P states is to indicate that R and P molecules are not yet referenced to the same zero of energy. The individual sums are effectively partition functions for each type of molecule. However, we need to note that the ground state for the two molecules is not the same. Let's assume that $\epsilon'_{p,0} > \epsilon_{r,0}$; the ground state of P is greater than R. This difference we call $\Delta_r E_0$. This amount then needs to be added to every energy term for P. In other words, we are taking the ground-state energy of R as the lowest possible energy for this system. Now, we can properly define partition functions for R and P

$$q_R = \sum_r e^{-\epsilon_r/kT} \qquad \sum_p e^{-(\epsilon_p + \Delta\epsilon_0)/kT} = \left(\sum_p e^{-\epsilon_p/kT}\right) e^{-\Delta\epsilon_0/kT} = q_p e^{-\Delta_r E_0/RT}$$

This gives us

$$N_R = \frac{Nq_R}{q} \qquad \text{and} \qquad N_P = \frac{Nq_p}{q} e^{-\Delta_r E_0/RT}$$

We can identify the ratio of $N_P$ to $N_R$ as the equilibrium constant, or

$$\frac{N_P}{N_R} = K = \frac{q_p}{q_r} e^{-\Delta_r E_0/RT} \tag{20.45}$$

This general expression works whether P or R has the lower energy ground state; we just change the sign of $\Delta_r E_0$.

Let's consider Eq. 20.45 in certain limits. If the molecules are very similar, with similar partition functions and a small $\Delta E_0$, we can clearly see that the value of $K$ will be close to 1. Now, what if we have two molecules with similar partition functions separated by a fairly large $\Delta E_0$? The equilibrium will favor the one at the lower energy. What if we have a reactant with only one accessible state ($q_R = 1$) and a product at higher energy but with lots of states? Equilibrium will favor the product because there are more ways to arrange things. If we extend this to reactions with more than two species, we get the general result in Eq. 20.44.

We can also look at this another way. We always have $\Delta_r G° = -RT \ln K$, or

$$K = e^{-\Delta_r G°/RT} = e^{-\Delta_r H°/RT} e^{\Delta_r S°/R} \tag{20.46}$$

Let's compare this to Eq. 20.44. We can readily identify $\Delta_r H°$ with $\Delta E_0$; equilibrium favors the molecule(s) with the lower ground-state energy or the strongest bonds. What about the entropy? Recall that for noninteracting, indistinguishable particles (Eq. 13.38),

$$S = Nk_B T \left(\frac{\partial \ln q}{\partial T}\right)_V + Nk_B \ln \frac{q}{N} + Nk_B$$

For a reaction, assuming that the rate of change of $q_R$ and $q_p$ with temperature are similar:

$$\Delta_r S = Nk_B \ln \frac{q_P}{q_R} = n\, R\, \ln \frac{q_P}{q_R}$$

$$e^{\Delta_r S/R} = \frac{q_P}{q_R} \tag{20.47}$$

(Entropies of reaction are typically molar quantities, so we drop the $n$ in the second expression.) We can now identify the entropy of reaction with the ratio of partition functions. If there are more states available in the product, the entropy increases, making the reaction more likely and increasing the value of $K$.

# 20.5 Summary, and Where We Go Next

In this chapter, we have developed and explored the concept of chemical equilibrium, which is at the heart of chemistry and chemical engineering. We have seen how to approach problems from both a macroscopic, thermodynamic perspective and from a microscopic, statistical-mechanical perspective. The ideas we have discussed are very powerful, and hopefully you have a much better grasp of them than you did after completing your general chemistry courses. The next chapter presents some additional applications of these ideas—specifically to ionic solutions, electrochemistry, and other types of equilibrium.

TABLE 20.1.  Summary of Definitions of Activity and Standard States.

| System | Standard state | Activity | Limits |
|---|---|---|---|
| Ideal Gas | $P° = 1$ bar | $a_i = \dfrac{P_i}{P°}$ | Ideal gas behavior |
| Real Gas | Ideal Gas at $P° = 1$ bar | $a_i = \dfrac{f_i}{P°}$ | At low pressure, $f_i \rightarrow P_i$ |
| Pure Liquid or Solid | $f°$, fugacity of pure component at 1 bar ambient pressure | $a_i = \dfrac{f_P}{f°}$ | At moderate pressure, $a_i \approx 1$ |
| Solvent | pure solvent (Raoult's law standard state) | $a_A = \gamma_A x_A = \dfrac{f_A}{f_A^*} \approx \dfrac{P_A}{P_A^*}$ | $\gamma_A \rightarrow 1$ as $x_A \rightarrow 1$ |
| Solute, volatile | hypothetical state of pure solute (Henry's law standard state) | $a_B = \gamma_B x_B = \dfrac{f_B}{K_B} \approx \dfrac{P_B}{K_B}$ | $\gamma_B \rightarrow 1$ as $x_B \rightarrow 0$ |
| Solute, nonvolatile | hypothetical state of the solute at 1 molal (molar) concentration | $a_B = \gamma_B \dfrac{b_B}{b_B°} = \gamma_B \dfrac{c_B}{c_B°}$ | $\gamma_B \rightarrow 1$ as $c_B \rightarrow 0$ |

# PROBLEMS

**20.1** A binary mixture is prepared of two volatile liquids at 45°C. The pure vapor pressures of A and B are 64 and 83 kPa, respectively. The mixture is prepared with $x_A = 0.35$. The vapor phase mole fraction of A is found to be 0.31 when the total pressure of A and B is 1 atm. Determine the Raoult's law activities and activity coefficients for both components of the mixture.

**20.2** a) Derive an expression for the Gibbs energy of mixing for a real solution that exhibits positive deviations from Raoult's law. Use a Raoult's law standard state for both components.

b) What would happen if the activity coefficients were sufficiently large such that $\Delta_{mix}G$ were positive?

**20.3** One model of real solutions that is particularly useful is known as a regular solution. In a regular solution, the entropy of mixing is the same as for an ideal solution, but the Gibbs energy of mixing is not.

a) Derive an expression for the enthalpy of mixing for a regular solution. (The results of Problem 20.2a) will be helpful here.)

b) If the regular solution exhibits negative deviations from Raoult's law, what is the sign of the enthalpy of mixing? What does this tell you about the interactions in the solution?

**20.4** This problem will use the data in Problem 19.11 for the mixture of carbon tetrachloride and benzene.

a) For each composition, calculate the Raoult's law and Henry's law activities and activity coefficients for carbon tetrachloride and benzene. Use 238 and 206 torr as the Henry's law constants for carbon tetrachloride and benzene, respectively.

b) Calculate the Gibbs energy for mixing to prepare a mixture of carbon tetrachloride and benzene at 40°C where the mole fraction of carbon tetrachloride is 0.3735 in the liquid phase. Do this calculation using a Raoult's law standard state for both components.

c) Repeat the calculation from part b), but use a Raoult's law standard state for benzene and a Henry's law standard state for carbon tetrachloride.

d) Were the results of parts b) and c) the same or different? Should they be the same or different? Justify your answers.

**20.5** For each of the following chemical reactions, write two expressions for the equilibrium constant. The first should be the most correct with no assumptions. For the second, make reasonable assumptions and state them.

a) $2 NO (g) + O_2 (g) \rightleftarrows 2 NO_2 (g)$

b) $CO (g) + H_2O (g) \rightleftarrows CO_2 (g) + H_2 (g)$      (This is known as the water–gas shift reaction.)

c) $H_2O (g) + C (s, graphite) \rightleftarrows H_2 (g) + CO (g)$

d) $Hg_2Cl_2 (s) + H_2 (g) \rightleftarrows 2 HCl (aq) + 2 Hg (l)$

**20.6** For the decomposition of ethane at 900 K, $\Delta G° = 22.38$ kJ mol$^{-1}$.

$$C_2H_6 (g) \rightleftarrows C_2H_4 (g) + H_2 (g)$$

Calculate the mole percent of $C_2H_4 (g)$ when the reaction system has reached equilibrium if the total pressure in the reactor is 1 bar at equilibrium.

**20.7** The standard Gibbs energies of formation of NO and $NO_2$ are 86.55 and 51.31 kJ mol$^{-1}$, respectively, at 298 K. Calculate the equilibrium constant for the oxidation of NO to $NO_2$ at 298 K. (Recall that formation reactions produce 1 mole of the desired compound.)

**20.8** Consider the reaction

$$3 C (graphite) + 2 H_2O (g) \rightleftarrows CH_4 (g) + 2 CO (g)$$

The following data are needed (all are at 298 K):

| Compound | $\Delta_f H°$ (kJ mol⁻¹) | $S°$ (J mol⁻¹ K⁻¹) | $\Delta_f G°$ (kJ mol⁻¹) |
|---|---|---|---|
| C, graphite | 0 | 5.740 | 0 |
| $H_2O$ (g) | −241.82 | 188.83 | −228.57 |
| $CH_4$ (g) | −74.81 | 186.26 | −50.72 |
| CO (g) | −110.53 | 197.67 | −137.17 |

a) Determine $\Delta_r G°$ and $K$ for this reaction at 298 K and comment on the spontaneity of this process under standard conditions.

b) If you find that this process is spontaneous, estimate the temperature below which it is no longer spontaneous; or if you find that it is not spontaneous, estimate the temperature above which it is. Clearly state any assumptions made.

**20.9** If you were to carry out the reaction described in Problem 20.8 at 298 K, what is the maximum total pressure of CO and $CH_4$ you could permit in the reaction vessel and still have the reaction be spontaneous? The vapor pressure of $H_2O$ at 298 K is 3.17 kPa.

**20.10** A reaction is carried out, and the equilibrium constant is measured over the temperature range from 400 to 600 K.

| T/K | 400 | 425 | 450 | 475 | 500 | 525 | 550 | 575 | 600 |
|---|---|---|---|---|---|---|---|---|---|
| K | 2.43 | 1.96 | 1.65 | 1.44 | 1.28 | 1.17 | 1.09 | 1.03 | 0.98 |

a) With these data, determine the enthalpy and entropy of reaction at 500 K.

b) Extrapolate back to determine $\Delta_r H°$, $\Delta_r S°$, and $\Delta_r G°$ at 298 K. State any assumptions that are needed for this calculation.

**20.11** This problem will compare aerobic respiration and the efficiency of a diesel engine. You will need the following data:

$\Delta_c G°$ (glucose) = −2880 kJ mol⁻¹

ATP $(aq)$ + $H_2O$ $(l)$ → ADP $(aq)$ + $P_i^-$ $(aq)$ + $H_3O^+$ $(aq)$    $\Delta_r G^+$ = −31 kJ mol⁻¹ at 37°C

(The difference in the superscripts reflects the different standard states.) Complete oxidation of 1 mol of glucose produces 38 moles of ATP.

a) Calculate the efficiency of aerobic respiration under standard biochemical conditions.

b) The following conditions are more typical of a biological system: $P$ ($CO_2$) = 5.3 × 10⁻² atm, $P$ ($O_2$) = 0.132 atm, [glucose] = 5.6 × 10⁻² mol L⁻¹, [ATP] = [ADP] = [$P_i$] = 1.0 × 10⁻⁴ mol L⁻¹, pH = 7.4, $T$ = 310 K. Assuming that we can use concentrations and partial pressures for the activities, calculate the efficiency of aerobic respiration under these physiological conditions.

c) A typical diesel engine operates between $T_{lo}$ = 873 K and $T_{hi}$ = 1923 K with an efficiency about 75% that of an ideal (Carnot) engine. Compare the efficiency of a diesel engine to aerobic respiration from part b).

d) Compare the efficiency of biological energy conversion and a diesel engine. Provide reasoning that explains your observations.

**20.12** Using statistical mechanics, solve the following:

a) Calculate the fractional dissociation of $N_2$ at 5000 K as a function of pressure from 1 to 100 bar. (The electronic degeneracy of N atom is 4.)

b) Calculate the temperature required for 1% dissociation at 10 bar.

# Ionic Solutions, Electrochemistry, and Other Applications of Equilibrium

## 21.1 Activity of Electrolyte Solutions

In Chapter 20, we introduced the concept of activity as an effective concentration. We were not, however, able to calculate activity coefficients, because they depend on complicated interactions within a solution. For electrolyte solutions, which contain ionic species, theoretical models have been developed that allow us to calculate activity coefficients. This approach is known as Debye–Hückel theory, which we will now begin to develop.

### 21.1.1 Henry's Law Revisited

Henry's law was developed to describe the behavior of a solute in a dilute solution. We originally dealt with volatile solutes that had a measurable vapor pressure above the liquid mixture, so let's briefly review some of those ideas. An ideal solution will follow Raoult's law over its entire composition range, and the vapor pressure of a component in a liquid mixture will smoothly go from 0, when there is none of that species present, to the vapor phase of the pure liquid, $P^*$, when it is a pure liquid. This is shown as the black line in Figure 21.1. For a real solution, however, the vapor pressure can deviate from Raoult's law. The blue curve in Figure 21.1 shows a negative deviation from Raoult's law, because the vapor pressure is always below what would be predicted by Raoult's law. The Henry's

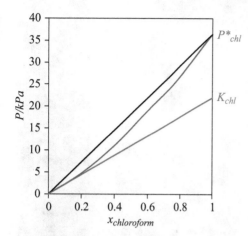

**FIGURE 21.1.** Partial pressure of chloroform in acetone compared to Raoult's (black) and Henry's (orange) laws. The value of the Henry's law constant is found by extrapolating the behavior of the dilute solution to $x = 1$.

law behavior is shown by the red line in Figure 21.1 The value of the Henry's law constant is found by extrapolating the vapor pressure curve at low concentration to a mole fraction of 1. The limiting law was written in terms of concentration as (Eq. 19.37)

$$P_B = b_B K_B'$$

where $K_B'$ is the extrapolation to a concentration of 1 mol/kg.

Ionic species, however, don't readily enter the vapor phase, so we will start with the alternate form of the Henry's law activity for nonvolatile species (Eq. 20.13):

$$a_B = \gamma_B \frac{b_B}{b_B°}$$

where $b_B$ is the molality of species B and $\gamma_B$ is the Henry's law activity coefficient. Recall that $\gamma_B$ approaches 1 as $b_B$ approaches 0. The standard state is an ideal solution with a 1 molal (1 mol kg$^{-1}$) concentration. Recall that the Henry's law standard state is a hypothetical situation. As we will see, the actual solution will probably not behave ideally at a 1 molal concentration, thus the value of the activity coefficient will be quite different from 1. For ionic solutions, significant deviations from ideality will be observed even at millimolal concentrations ($10^{-3}$ mol kg$^{-1}$).

### 21.1.2 Activities of Ions in Solutions

For all solutes, as the concentration approaches zero, the activity also approaches zero. The Henry's law constant for a volatile solute is found by looking at the slope of the pressure curve in the limit that concentration approaches zero, as shown in Figure 21.1. Let's consider a solution of HCl, which is a stable gas-phase molecule, and so does have a vapor pressure. HCl is also a strong electrolyte, so it completely dissociates in solution. If we were to make a plot similar to Figure 21.1, the slope of the pressure curve is actually equal to zero in the dilute limit, which would give us a Henry's law constant of zero. Clearly, we need to do something different.

Based on experimental observations, the limiting law for a 1:1 electrolyte is of the form

$$P_B = K_B' b_B^2$$

Therefore, a better way to treat the activity of HCl is to define the activity (in the dilute limit) as

$$a_{electrolyte} = \gamma_{electrolyte} \left( \frac{b_{electrolyte}}{b°} \right)^2 \tag{21.1}$$

Note that we use the square of the concentration, not the concentration itself. As with the conventional Henry's law standard state, the activity coefficient will approach 1 as the concentration approaches 0.

Let's use the dissociation of NaCl (which will not have a vapor pressure) as our example to develop a general model for the activity of an ionic solution. We first write the dissociation reaction as

$$NaCl\ (aq) \rightleftarrows Na^+\ (aq) + Cl^-\ (aq)$$

(Note that we have written the left-hand side as NaCl $(aq)$, not NaCl $(s)$. This will be important later on.) As we have done before, we can write $\Delta_r G$ for the process as

$$\Delta_r G = \mu_+ + \mu_- - \mu_{salt} \tag{21.2}$$

Here, we are indicating the chemical potential of the +1 ion as $\mu_+$, that of the −1 ion as $\mu_-$, and that of the aqueous salt as $\mu_{salt}$. Similar subscripts are used for the activities. We can also write expressions for the chemical potential of each species as follows:

$$\mu_+ = \mu_+^\circ + RT\ \ln a_+ \tag{21.3}$$

$$\mu_- = \mu_-^\circ + RT\ \ln a_- \tag{21.4}$$

$$\mu_{salt} = \mu_{salt}^\circ + RT\ \ln a_{salt} \tag{21.5}$$

We have not yet defined the standard states, but we will shortly. That does not prevent us from moving forward in our derivation.

If we combine Eqs. 21.3–21.5 with Eq. 21.2, we can write

$$\Delta_r G = (\mu_+^\circ + \mu_-^\circ) - \mu_{salt}^\circ + RT\ \ln\frac{a_+ a_-}{a_{salt}} \tag{21.6}$$

This is where the distinction between NaCl $(s)$ and NaCl $(aq)$ becomes important. What does it mean to say aqueous NaCl? Because NaCl is a strong electrolyte, it means complete dissociation of NaCl into $Na^+$ and $Cl^-$ ions. Thus, the two sides of our chemical reaction are really just two ways of saying the same thing. In other words, our chemical reaction is always at equilibrium. For a reaction at equilibrium, we know that $\Delta_r G = 0$, which lets us write Eq. 21.6 as

$$\Delta_r G^\circ = -RT\ \ln\frac{a_+ a_-}{a_{salt}} \tag{21.7}$$

where we have called the difference of standard chemical potentials $\Delta_r G^\circ$.

$$\Delta_r G^\circ = (\mu_+^\circ + \mu_-^\circ) - \mu_{salt}^\circ \tag{21.8}$$

We are going to push our thinking about a strong electrolyte even further. For a strong electrolyte behaving ideally under standard conditions, there is no distinction between dissolved salt and separate, dissolved ions. Thus it is appropriate to say that $\Delta_r G^\circ = 0$. If this is true, then by Eq. 21.7, we can say that

$$\frac{a_+ a_-}{a_{salt}} = 1$$

or, alternatively,

$$a_{salt} = a_+ a_- \tag{21.9}$$

This, at long last, is the formal definition of the **strong-electrolyte standard state**. A strong electrolyte is one where the activity of the dissolved salt is the same as the product of the activities of the individual ions.

The activity of each ion can be written as

$$a_+ = \gamma_+ \frac{b_+}{b^\circ} \tag{21.10}$$

$$a_- = \gamma_- \frac{b_-}{b^\circ} \tag{21.11}$$

Putting these together gives us

$$a_{salt} = \left( \gamma_+ \frac{b_+}{b^\circ} \right) \left( \gamma_- \frac{b_-}{b^\circ} \right)$$

We know from charge and mass balance that for a salt like NaCl, $b_+ = b_- = b$ must always be true. This lets us write

$$a_{salt} = \gamma_+ \gamma_- \frac{b^2}{b^{\circ 2}} \tag{21.12}$$

which resembles the form of Eq. 21.1. Because we always have both cations and anions together in solution (the solution cannot have a net charge), it doesn't make much sense to talk about their activities independently. We therefore define a **mean ionic activity coefficient** as

$$\gamma_\pm = (\gamma_+ \gamma_-)^{1/2} \tag{21.13}$$

(Mathematically, this is a geometric mean.) This lets us write

$$a_{salt} = a_\pm^2 = \gamma_\pm^2 \frac{b^2}{b^{\circ 2}} \tag{21.14}$$

where $a_\pm$ is the **mean ionic activity**. The form of Eq. 21.14 exactly matches Eq. 21.1, which was based on experimental observations. Note that the standard concentration is still 1 molal, and the concentration we are considering is the concentration of dissolved salt. In the dilute limit, $\gamma_\pm$ approaches 1.

Not all salts have a 1:1 ratio of cations to anions, like NaCl does. For example, $MgCl_2$ will dissolve to produce one equivalent of $Mg^{2+}$ ions and two equivalents of $Cl^-$ ions. For a salt of the form $M_p X_q$, we find the limiting behavior has the form

$$a_{salt} \propto \left( \frac{b}{b^\circ} \right)^s \qquad \text{where } s = p + q \tag{21.15}$$

Going through a similar analysis to what we did for NaCl gives us

$$a_{salt} = a_+^p a_-^q = \left( \gamma_+ \frac{b_+}{b^\circ} \right)^p \left( \gamma_- \frac{b_-}{b^\circ} \right)^q \tag{21.16}$$

When one equivalent of salt dissolves, we have $p$ equivalents of cations and $q$ equivalents of anions. The mean ionic activity coefficient is now written as

$$\gamma_\pm = (\gamma_+^p \gamma_-^q)^{1/s} \tag{21.17}$$

(Again, this is a geometric mean.) The **mean ionic molality** is written as

$$b_\pm = (b_+^p b_-^q)^{1/s} = (p^p b_{salt}^p q^q b_{salt}^q)^{1/s}$$

$$b_\pm = b_{salt}(p^p q^q)^{1/s} \tag{21.18}$$

The mean ionic activity can be generally written as

$$a_\pm = \gamma_\pm \frac{b_\pm}{b^\circ} \tag{21.19}$$

Putting all this together gives us

$$a_{salt} = a_\pm^s = \left( \gamma_\pm \frac{b_\pm}{b^\circ} \right)^s = p^p q^q \gamma_\pm^s \left( \frac{b_{salt}}{b^\circ} \right)^s \tag{21.20}$$

where, again, $b$ is the molality of dissolved salt in solution.

### 21.1.3 Calculating Mean Ionic Activity Coefficients

We now have an effective activity and activity coefficient to describe an ionic solution, but our goal now is to determine their values. Peter Debye and Erich Hückel went through a lengthy derivation based on physical arguments to calculate the mean ionic activity coefficient. We won't go through the whole thing here because it requires some rather detailed electrostatics. We will, however, discuss the basic ideas and the final conclusions.

Ions in a solution interact with each other through Coulombic interactions, which can be quite long range. However, because the ions can move around in the solution, an ion of a given charge is likely to be surrounded by counter ions of the opposite charge. Overall, the solution is electrically neutral, but the local density of ions will fluctuate, with negative ions grouping around a single positive ion, and vice versa. A diagram of this is shown in Figure 21.2. (Note that the distances in the figure are much closer than the simple model can actually describe.) Because of this, an ion is effectively

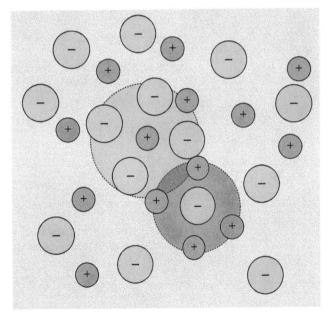

FIGURE 21.2. Schematic of ion positions in solution. Note that the number of ions is the same, but they position such that opposite charges surround each other.

screened from other ions of the same charge by a cloud of counter ions, sometimes called the **ionic atmosphere**. This stabilizes the ion in solution, lowering its chemical potential. The distance over which this shielding takes place is known as the **Debye length**. (The Debye length is not just used in ionic solutions, but also in plasma physics and other applications of electrostatics where you have species of opposite charge.) Water is a polar solvent, so it also interacts with the ions—although the simple model neglects that detail.

After working through some very involved electrostatics and statistical mechanics, Debye and Hückel were able to show that the mean ionic activity coefficient for a dilute electrolyte solution can be written as

$$\log \gamma_{\pm} = -|z_+ z_-| A I^{1/2} \tag{21.21}$$

This expression is known as the **Debye–Hückel limiting law**. Some of the components of Eq. 21.21 need a little more explanation. First, this is a base 10 log, not the natural logarithm. The $z$'s in this expression represent the charge number of each ion. $A$ is a constant; it equals 0.509 for an aqueous solution at 25°C and concentrations given in molality. $I$ is the **ionic strength** of the solution, calculated as

$$I = \frac{1}{2} \sum_i z_i^2 \left( \frac{b_i}{b^\circ} \right) \tag{21.22}$$

For a given salt, the ionic strength is readily related back to the concentration of the dissolved salt, as illustrated in Sample Problem 21.1.

## Sample Problem 21.1

Determine the ionic strengths, mean ionic activity coefficients, mean ionic molalities, and mean ionic activities of two solutions, one of NaCl and the other of $CaCl_2$, each with a concentration of 5.0 mmolal.

Solution

NaCl will dissociate into $Na^+$ and $Cl^-$ ions. The charge numbers are $z_{Na^+} = 1$, $z_{Cl^-} = -1$. The ionic strength is calculated to be

$$I = \frac{1}{2} \left( (1)^2 \times \frac{b}{b^\circ} + (-1)^2 \times \frac{b}{b^\circ} \right)$$

$$I = \frac{1}{2} \left( 2 \frac{b}{b^\circ} \right) = \frac{b}{b^\circ}$$

The ionic strength will just have the numerical value of the concentration; $I = 0.0050$. The mean ionic activity coefficient is calculated by Eq. 21.21 to be

$$\log \gamma_{\pm} = -|(+1)(-1)|(0.509)(0.005)^{1/2}$$

$$\log \gamma_{\pm} = -0.036$$

$$\gamma_{\pm} = 0.92$$

The mean ionic molality for a 1:1 electrolyte is just the concentration of dissolved salt.

$$b_{\pm} = b_{salt}(1^{1}1^{1})^{1/2} = b = 0.005 \text{ mol/kg}$$

The mean ionic activity is now the product of the mean ionic activity coefficient and the mean ionic molality.

$$a_{\pm} = \gamma_{\pm} \frac{b_{\pm}}{b^{\circ}} = \frac{0.92 \times 0.005}{1}$$

$$a_{\pm} = 0.0046$$

Again, activity is an effective concentration. This mean ionic activity is less than the value of the concentration of dissolved NaCl, 0.0050 mol/kg, reflecting both ion–ion and ion–solvent interactions.

Repeating this analysis for 5.0 mmol $CaCl_2$ solution, we have

$$I = \frac{1}{2}\left((+2)^{2} \times \frac{b}{b^{\circ}} + (-1)^{2} \times \frac{2b}{b^{\circ}}\right)$$

$$I = \frac{1}{2}\left(6\frac{b}{b^{\circ}}\right) = \frac{3b}{b^{\circ}}$$

The charge numbers are $z_{Ca^{+}} = 2$, $z_{Cl^{-}} = -1$. The ionic strength is now 3 times the numerical value of the concentration; $I = 0.015$. The mean ionic activity coefficient is calculated by Eq. 21.21 to be

$$\log \gamma_{\pm} = -|(+2)(-1)|(0.509)(0.015)^{1/2}$$

$$\log \gamma_{\pm} = -0.125$$

$$\gamma_{\pm} = 0.75$$

The mean ionic molality is no longer the concentration of dissolved salt; it has to account for the 2:1 ratio of anions to cations. Instead, we have

$$b_{\pm} = b_{salt}(1^{1}2^{2})^{1/3} = 2^{2/3}b = 0.0079 \text{ mol/kg}$$

The mean ionic activity is now calculated as

$$a_{\pm} = \gamma_{\pm}\frac{b_{\pm}}{b^{\circ}} = \frac{0.75 \times 0.0079}{1}$$

$$a_{\pm} = 0.0059$$

Note that the mean ionic activity is higher for $CaCl_2$ than for NaCl, because there are more total ions in a $CaCl_2$ solution, and some of them carry a +2 charge. (In fact, at this concentration, the limiting law is beginning to break down.)

Several important assumptions were made in developing the Debye–Hückel limiting law. In particular, it was assumed that the charge distribution around any particular ion is spherically symmetric. The size of the individual ions was also ignored, as were any aspects of their shape. Solvent properties, such as polarizability, were also ignored. (The value of $A = 0.509$ includes the dielectric constant of water at 25.0°C.) Because of these assumptions, which are only valid at low ion concentrations, the limiting law breaks down at fairly moderate concentrations.

### 21.1.4 Activity Coefficients at Higher Electrolyte Concentrations

The Debye–Hückel limiting law only works at very low concentrations and actually shows significant deviation from experimental results at concentrations of even a few mmol/kg. (See Sample Problem 21.1.) To remedy this problem, Debye and Hückel went back to their electrostatic models and made less stringent assumptions, particularly relating to the effective size of the ions. The result is the extended Debye–Hückel law.

$$\log \gamma_{\pm} = \frac{-A \, | \, z_+ z_- \, | \, I^{1/2}}{1 + BI^{1/2}}$$ (21.23)

where $A$ is the same constant as before and $B$ is a new dimensionless constant that depends on the effective ionic diameter. (In reality, $B$ is an empirical parameter, similar to higher order coefficients in the virial equation of state.) Note that in the limit of very low ionic strength, or if $B$ is zero, this expression returns to the limiting law. Further extension was made by C. W. Davies in 1938, based on empirical results, leading to the Davies equation

$$\log \gamma_{\pm} = \frac{-0.51 \, | \, z_+ z_- \, | \, I^{1/2}}{1 + I^{1/2}} - 0.30I$$ (21.24)

At high-electrolyte concentrations, other nonideal effects begin to manifest. One of the assumptions of the Debye–Hückel model is that all the ions act more or less independently of each other. While this is true at low concentrations, at higher concentrations effects such as **ion pairing** can be observed. This effect is typically negligible for 1:1 electrolytes but can be quite pronounced with different stoichiometric ratios. If ion pairing is taking place, the total number of dissolved ions is reduced, meaning colligative properties such as boiling-point elevation and osmotic pressure will be less than predicted. The electrical conductivity of such a solution will also be less than predicted based on the concentration of dissolved salt. This effect is sometimes represented by an empirical factor known as the van 't Hoff factor, often symbolized as $i$. When dealing with ionic solutions, Eqs. 19.39, 19.40, and 19.41 are often written with the van 't Hoff factor included to account for the nonideal behavior of dissolved ions.

## 21.2 Electrochemistry

We will now explore a particular type of reaction that involves ions: an electrochemical reaction. Such reactions are particularly useful because we can use them to produce electrical work, either to use in an appliance or as occurs in biological systems. This is also a good application of many of the ideas we have already developed. First, we need to establish some ground work.

## 21.2.1 Redox Reactions and Half Reactions

In your general chemistry class, you should have learned about the concept of **oxidation numbers**. This is a formalism to keep track of how the electrons around an atom are affected by the chemical state of that atom. For a monatomic ion, the oxidation number is simply the charge number of the ion. The oxidation number of $Na^+$ is +1, and that of $Cl^-$ is −1. For polyatomic compounds and ions, oxidation numbers can be more complicated. For example, in $NH_3$, the oxidation number of the nitrogen atom is −3, but in $NO_3^-$, the oxidation number of the nitrogen is +5. Keep in mind that this is an accounting system that we have developed and is not intended to be an accurate depiction of nature; the N atom in $NO_3^-$ is not a +5 ion. (In fact, fractional oxidation numbers are seen in many geological minerals, such as magnetite, $Fe_3O_4$.)

In many chemical reactions, the oxidation number (or oxidation state) of an atom can change. When the oxidation number increases, we say the atom has been **oxidized**; when the oxidation number decreases, the atom has been **reduced**. A chemical reaction that results in changes in oxidation states is known as a **redox** (short for reduction–oxidation) reaction. Note that in order for one species to be oxidized, something else must be reduced. An example of this is the reaction of copper metal in a solution of $AgNO_3$. Over time, metallic silver is seen to decorate the copper surface, so clearly the $Ag^+$ ions have been reduced to Ag metal. But where did those electrons come from? They come from the oxidation of the Cu metal to $Cu^+$ ions.

The overall reaction for the process we just described is written as

$$Cu\ (s) + Ag^+\ (aq) \rightarrow Cu^+\ (aq) + Ag\ (s)$$

Notice that the electrons are absent in this balanced reaction. We can see them more explicitly by writing a **half reaction** for each process—oxidation and reduction. The oxidation half reaction is written as

$$Cu\ (s) \rightarrow Cu^+\ (aq) + e^-$$

The reduction half reaction is written as

$$Ag^+\ (aq) + e^- \rightarrow Ag\ (s)$$

When these two reactions are written together, the electrons cancel out and we obtain the full reaction. All redox reactions can be written in terms of half reactions.


### Sample Problem 21.2

Solid AgCl can form from the reaction of silver metal and chlorine gas. Identify the oxidation and reduction reactions, write the separate half reactions, and write the full reaction.

Solution

First, we want to assign the oxidation states of our reactants and products. For Ag metal, the oxidation state is 0. The same is true for $Cl_2$ gas. In AgCl, the Ag has a +1 oxidation state, and Cl has a −1 oxidation state. Because the oxidation number of Ag increased, it was oxidized. The oxidation number of Cl decreased, so Cl was reduced.
We can now write the oxidation half reaction as

$$Ag\ (s) \rightarrow Ag^+ + e^-$$

(We are not indicating the state of the ion here, because it is going to become part of the solid AgCl; this reaction is not taking place in aqueous solution.) The reduction half reaction can be written as

$$Cl_2 (g) + 2 \; e^- \rightarrow 2 \; Cl^-$$

Each Cl atom is reduced, so we need two electrons in this half-reaction. In order to combine these two reactions, we will need to multiply the first reaction by 2; this is to ensure that the electrons cancel out in the final reaction. Doing this gives the overall reaction as

$$2 \; Ag \; (s) + Cl_2 \; (g) \rightarrow 2 \; AgCl \; (s)$$

(We have implicitly combined the two ions, $Ag^+$ and $Cl^-$, into the solid AgCl.)

---

In our earlier example of the reduction of silver ions in the presence of copper, we described a spontaneous redox reaction; this reaction proceeds on its own. If we were, however, to immerse a piece of silver metal in a solution of copper nitrate, nothing would happen. We would not observe copper metal forming on the surface of the silver, nor would we find silver ions in solution. This reaction is not spontaneous. Copper ions will be reduced on the surface of zinc metal, however. Clearly there is a preference for some metals to oxidize more easily than others, likewise there is a preference for some metal cations to reduce more easily than others. We'll begin to explore how we can understand that idea in the next section.

## 21.2.2 The Nernst Equation

Recall from Section 18.2.3 that one interpretation of the Gibbs energy change for a process is as the maximum nonexpansion work. Electrochemical processes fall into that category. Going further back to Section 16.2.4, we had an expression for electrical work as

$$\delta w_{elec} = \phi dQ \tag{21.25}$$

where $\phi$ is the electrical potential and $Q$ is charge. Let's explore this a bit more. If we have a reaction that produces or consumes electrons, then there is a change in charge. The change in the amount of charge will be given by

$$dQ = -\nu e N_A d\xi \tag{21.26}$$

where $\nu$ is the stoichiometric coefficient of the electrons, $e$ is the elementary charge, $N_A$ is Avogadro's number, and $d\xi$ is the change in extent of reaction (which has units of moles). The negative sign reflects the fact the electrons carry a negative charge. This expression can be simplified somewhat by the use of Faraday's constant, $F = e \, N_A = 96485 \; C \; mol^{-1}$. We will also make a notational switch for the electrical potential from $\phi$ to $E$. This potential has units of volts, or energy per charge. (1 V = 1 J/C.) Putting all this together lets us write

$$dw_e = -\nu F E d\xi \tag{21.27}$$

for the electrical work.

We also need to bring back our definition of the reaction Gibbs energy (Eq. 20.21).

$$\Delta_r G \equiv \left( \frac{\partial G}{\partial \xi} \right)_{T,P}$$

This can be rearranged to give us, at constant temperature and pressure,

$$dG = \Delta_r G d\xi \qquad (21.28)$$

Recall that the extent of reaction, and its change, has units of moles and $\Delta_r G$ has units of energy/mole. Equating the change in Gibbs energy (Eq. 21.28) with the electrical work (Eq. 21.27) and cancelling $d\xi$ from both sides lets us write

$$\boxed{\Delta_r G = -\nu FE} \qquad (21.29)$$

This expression shows us how we can understand the change in Gibbs energy, which is often hard to measure, in terms of an electric potential, or voltage, which can be quite easy to measure. Notice that there is a negative sign here. We have already established that a process is spontaneous if $\Delta_r G$ is negative under the prevailing conditions. Eq. 21.29 tells us that the potential $E$ needs to be positive for an electrochemical process to be spontaneous.

If an electrochemical process is taking place under standard conditions (ideal solutions with a 1 molar or 1 molal concentration), we can write Eq. 21.29 as

$$\Delta_r G° = -\nu FE° \qquad (21.30)$$

where $E°$ is now the standard potential. Recall that we could determine $\Delta_r G$ for a reaction under nonstandard conditions by the relation (Eq. 20.18)

$$\Delta_r G = \Delta_r G° + RT \ln Q$$

Inserting Eqs. 21.29 and 21.30 into this relation gives us what is known as the Nernst equation

$$\boxed{E = E° - \frac{RT}{\nu F} \ln Q} \qquad (21.31)$$

Note that if we are operating under standard conditions, the reaction quotient $Q$ goes to 1 and $E$ goes to $E°$. Under nonstandard conditions, the potential must be positive for the reaction to proceed spontaneously. Qualitatively, we can see that if a reaction has not proceeded very far, $Q$ will be less than zero, so the potential will be greater than under standard conditions. In other words, the reaction is more likely to proceed if there is not enough product present. On the other hand, if there is too much product, $Q$ will be greater than 1 and $E$ could be negative. The reverse reaction would now be spontaneous.

Now that we have the Nernst equation, we can also see how we can determine equilibrium constants for electrochemical processes. First, we recall Eq. 20.19.

$$\Delta_r G° = -RT \ln K$$

Setting this equal to Eq. 21.30 gives us

$$\ln K = \frac{\nu FE°}{RT} \qquad (21.32)$$

Again, qualitatively, a reaction with a large standard potential will have a long way to go to reach equilibrium; thus the value of the equilibrium constant will be large. We'll start to get more quantitative with these ideas in the next section.

## 21.2.3 Electrochemical Cells and Reduction Potentials

We can now see that the transfer of electrons involves a change in Gibbs energy, which suggests that we should be able to harness that energy in some way. Going back to our

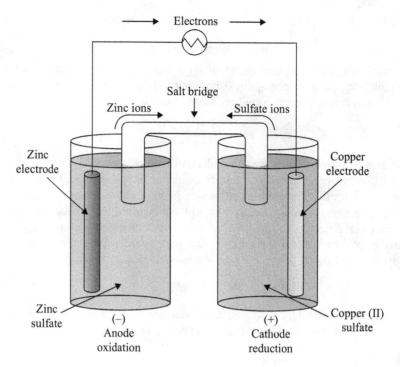

Electrons

Salt bridge

Zinc ions

Sulfate ions

Zinc electrode

Copper electrode

Zinc sulfate

(−)
Anode
oxidation

(+)
Cathode
reduction

Copper (II) sulfate

**FIGURE 21.3.** Schematic of an electrochemical cell with a Zn anode and a Cu cathode. If Ag were used instead of Zn, then Ag would be the cathode and Cu the anode.

example of copper metal in the silver nitrate solution, however, there's not much we can do in that situation to extract energy. What we need to do is separate the two metals so that the electrons have to travel through a wire. This is the idea behind an **electrochemical cell** (also called a **voltaic** or **galvanic cell**). The schematic of an electrochemical cell is shown in Figure 21.3. The two metal plates are known as **electrodes**. The site of oxidation is called the **anode**, and the site of reduction is called the **cathode**. The flow of electrons through a wire connecting anode to cathode can be used to perform work. Note that in order to complete the electrochemical circuit, the two solutions need to be connected in some way, often by a **salt bridge**. The reason for this is quite simple. Oxidation will produce cations in the solution surrounding the anode, which would lead to a charge imbalance in that solution unless cations can move to the solution surrounding the cathode, or anions can move from the cathodic solution to balance the new cations formed at the anode. Reduction in the cathodic solution would also lead to a charge imbalance if not for the salt bridge.

Let's construct an electrochemical cell with a piece of copper metal in a 1.0 mol/kg solution of $CuNO_3$ and a piece of silver metal in a 1.0 mol/kg solution of $AgNO_3$, where the two solutions are connected by a salt bridge. Upon connecting the anode to the cathode with a wire, we would start to see more silver metal forming on the cathode and the copper anode losing mass and starting to look pitted. We could even connect a light bulb, buzzer, or some other device between the anode and cathode. If we were to use a voltmeter, we would measure a voltage of 0.279 V. Because both solutions have the standard 1.0 molal concentration, this is the **standard cell potential** for this Cu|Ag electrochemical cell. If we were to build a similar cell with zinc instead of silver, we would measure a voltage of 1.104 V. We would also see the zinc electrode becoming pitted and the copper electrode gaining mass; zinc is serving as the anode and copper as the cathode.

Just as we have standard states for various phases of matter, it was quickly realized that we need a standard state for electrochemical reactions. The choice was made to adopt the **standard hydrogen electrode** (SHE) as the reference point. This electrode consists of a platinum electrode immersed in an ideal solution with $[H^+] = 1.0$ mol/kg and a partial pressure of $H_2$ gas of 1.0 bar. The reduction reaction that can take place at this electrode is written as

$$2\,H^+\,(aq) + 2\,e^- \rightarrow H_2\,(g) \qquad E° = 0.000\text{ V}$$

All other possible electrodes can now be connected to a SHE, and measurements taken of the voltage. If we connect a copper electrode, immersed in 1.0 mol/kg $CuNO_3$, we will measure a voltage of 0.521 V. Over time, the copper electrode will gain mass, showing us that the copper is acting as the cathode and $Cu^+$ ions are being reduced to Cu metal. We write the half reaction, with its **standard reduction potential** as

$$Cu^+\,(aq) + e^- \rightarrow Cu\,(s) \qquad E° = 0.521\text{ V}$$

If we repeat this process with a zinc electrode, we will measure a voltage of 0.762 V. We will find, however, that the zinc electrode is becoming pitted over time and losing mass, showing us that the zinc is acting as the anode and being oxidized. (We will also see bubbles of $H_2$ gas forming at the SHE as a result of the reduction of $H^+$ taking place there.) Because the electrons are flowing in the opposite direction for this situation, we write the reduction half reaction for $Zn^{2+}$ and its standard reduction potential as

$$Zn^{2+}\,(aq) + 2\,e^- \rightarrow Zn\,(s) \qquad E° = -0.762\text{ V}$$

The negative sign tells us that, when connected to a SHE, a zinc electrode will act as the anode and be oxidized.

Measurements of this type lead to the **electrochemical series**, which can be used to rank metals by their propensity to be reduced from cation to solid metal. A metal with a high standard reduction potential, such as gold or silver, has a greater preference to be reduced from cation to metal than does a metal with a lower reduction potential, such as sodium or lithium. Thus, if each metal is immersed in a solution of its cations and connected in an electrochemical cell, the metal with the higher reduction potential will be the site of reduction—that is, it will be the cathode—and the metal with the lower reduction potential will be the site of oxidation—the anode. We can determine the standard cell potential by taking the difference of the standard reduction potentials.

$$E°_{cell} = E°_{cathode} - E°_{anode} \qquad (21.33)$$

From our example of the Zn|Cu cell, with a standard voltage of 1.104 V, and our knowledge that the reduction potential for $Zn^{2+}$ is −0.762 V, we can calculate $E°\,(Cu^{2+}) = 0.342$ V. Note that the reduction potentials for $Cu^{2+}$ and $Cu^+$ to Cu metal are different. This is generally the case for cations with different oxidation states.

## Sample Problem 21.3

A standard electrochemical cell is constructed with Sn and Fe electrodes, each in 1.0 mol/kg solutions of $Sn^{2+}$ and $Fe^{2+}$, respectively. The standard reduction potentials of $Sn^{2+}$ and $Fe^{2+}$ to their metals are −0.136 and −0.447 V, respectively. Identify the function of each electrode, write the relevant half reactions, write the full reaction, and determine the standard cell potential.

Solution

The standard reduction potential of both cations is negative, however, the value of $E°$ for $Sn^{2+}$ is greater than that for $Fe^{2+}$. This means that $Sn^{2+}$ has a greater tendency to be reduced, so the Sn electrode will serve as the cathode. The Fe electrode will serve as the anode. The reduction half reaction is written as

$$Sn^{2+}(aq) + 2\,e^- \rightarrow Sn\,(s)$$

The oxidation half reaction is written as

$$Fe\,(s) \rightarrow Fe^{2+}(aq) + 2e^-$$

The overall reaction is

$$Sn^{2+}(aq) + Fe\,(s) \rightarrow Sn\,(s) + Fe^{2+}(aq)$$

The standard cell potential is readily found by Eq. 21.33 to be 0.311 V.
(Note: Remember that for a spontaneous process, the potential needs to be positive.)

---

It should be fairly obvious that the SHE is not a standard piece of laboratory equipment. It involves working both with a solution that has a pH of 0 and with high pressure (1 bar) of $H_2$ gas, which is flammable. The beauty of reduction potentials, however, is that so long as we know the value for one electrode, we can determine the reduction potential for another electrode by setting up a standard cell and measuring the voltage. A common choice for a reference electrode these days is known as the silver–silver chloride electrode, which contains both silver metal and the chloride salt of silver. The relevant reduction half reaction for this cell is written as

$$AgCl\,(s) + e^- \rightarrow Ag\,(s) + Cl^-(aq)$$

This electrode has a standard voltage vs. SHE of 0.22249 V for the reaction where AgCl is reduced to Ag.

It should be noted that when balancing a full redox reaction, we need to ensure that the number of electrons balances, since no electrons appear in the overall reaction. We do not, however, scale the standard reduction potential by the number of electrons. Reduction potentials are intensive quantities; they only depend on the chemical identity of the various species, not their amounts. The number of electrons comes into play if you want to determine the amount of energy involved in the electrochemical process. See Eqs. 21.29 and 21.30. Note also that we have generally considered standard electrochemical cells. If the concentrations of relevant ions are not 1.0 mol/kg, then the full Nernst equation (Eq. 21.31) needs to be used to determine the potential of the electrochemical cell.

### Sample Problem 21.4

You want to determine the concentration of $Zn^{2+}$ in a solution of $Zn(NO_3)_2$. You have a Ag/AgCl electrode and a zinc electrode. You prepare a 0.015 mol/kg solution of NaCl in which to immerse the Ag/AgCl electrode and assemble an electrochemical cell. A voltmeter in the circuit gives a reading of 1.17 V at 25°C. What is the concentration of $Zn^{2+}$ in the solution? Also, what is the change in Gibbs energy for the electrochemical process taking place at these concentrations?

Solution

The standard reduction potentials of the Ag/AgCl and Zn electrodes are, respectively, 0.22249 and −0.762 V. Because the reduction potential higher for Ag/AgCl, that electrode will be the site of reduction, and the zinc electrode will be oxidized. The standard cell potential is found from Eq. 21.33 to be 0.984 V.

This is not a standard cell, however, because the concentrations are not 1.0 mol/kg. In order to write the Nernst equation for this situation, we first need to write the complete chemical reaction. Let's first write the relevant half reactions.

$$AgCl\,(s) + e^- \rightarrow Ag\,(s) + Cl^-\,(aq)$$

$$Zn\,(s) \rightarrow Zn^{2+}\,(aq) + 2e^-$$

In order to combine these reactions (and cancel out the electrons), we need to multiply the first reaction by 2. Combining the reactions then gives us

$$2\,AgCl\,(s) + Zn\,(s) \rightarrow 2\,Ag\,(s) + 2\,Cl^-\,(aq) + Zn^{2+}\,(aq)$$

We can now write the Nernst equation as

$$E = E^\circ - \frac{RT}{2F} \ln a_{Zn^{2+}} a_{Cl^-}^2$$

For a first calculation, let's assume the concentrations are low enough that we can treat the activity coefficients as being 1. Thus, the activities are equal to the molal concentrations. We have $E = 1.17$ V, $E^\circ = 0.984$ V, $b\,(Cl^-) = 0.015$ mol kg$^{-1}$. Using the values of $R$, $T$, and $F$, and doing some algebra, we calculate a $b\,(Zn^{2+})$ of 2.3 mmol kg$^{-1}$.

This was an approximate calculation that neglected the effect of activity coefficients. To check the validity of our assumption, we could use the techniques of Section 21.1.3 to calculate the mean ionic activity coefficients at these concentrations. We would find $\gamma_\pm = 0.87$ for the NaCl solution, and $\gamma_\pm = 0.82$ for the Zn(NO$_3$)$_2$ solution. These are different enough from unity that we should probably take them into account. This can be done in a spreadsheet by varying the concentration (starting from 2.3 mmol kg$^{-1}$) until we calculate the observed cell potential of 1.17 V. Doing so will give us a $b\,(Zn^{2+})$ of 4.0 mmol kg$^{-1}$. For ionic solutions, even at moderate concentrations, activity can differ significantly from concentration, so if we don't take it into account, we can easily be off by a factor of 2 in our determination of a concentration.

For the change in Gibbs energy, we simply use Eq. 21.29 with the cell potential and $v = 2$. This gives us $\Delta G = -224$ kJ mol$^{-1}$ for this process.

### 21.2.4 Applications of Principles of Electrochemistry

There are numerous applications of the concepts and principles of electrochemistry, so this discussion will in no way be exhaustive. One obvious application of these ideas is with batteries. A battery is basically a portable electrochemical cell that provides a source of energy with which to perform work, such as powering an appliance or starting a car. Most portable batteries are of the "alkaline dry cell" variety, meaning they do not contain solutions of ions like the cells we discussed in the last section. Instead, they involve suspensions of metal oxides and hydroxides, such as MnO$_2$, MnO(OH) and Zn(OH)$_2$, in an electrolyte paste that contains OH$^-$ ions as the charge carriers. (Alkaline batteries do not leak battery acid.) Lithium-ion batteries are another type of portable electrochemical cell; however, these can be recharged—which isn't the case with an alkaline battery.

One advantage of these types of cells is that the overall reaction only involves these solid species, so the activities are all close to 1. For a "wet cell," as the concentrations change, the cell potential also changes. That could be a significant problem in some applications.

On the other hand, a dry cell cannot provide as much current as a wet cell, which is why car batteries are very different from laptop and cell phone batteries. There are, of course, many other considerations in designing batteries that we will not go into here. Factors such as internal resistance, charge mobility, and others will affect the design and performance of actual batteries.

Another source of electrical power is a **fuel cell**. As with a battery, the redox reaction in a fuel cell takes place in such a way that the electrons have to travel from the anode to the cathode through an external load. One prominent fuel cell design uses oxygen and hydrogen as the inputs. The relevant half reactions are

$$H_2 (g) \rightarrow 2 H^+ (aq) + 2 e^- \quad E° = 0.000 \text{ V}$$

$$O_2 (g) + 4 H^+ (aq) + 4 e^- \rightarrow 2 H_2O (l) \quad E° = 1.229 \text{ V}$$

The "exhaust" of a $H_2/O_2$ fuel cell is water. This same reaction takes place when hydrogen gas is combusted, however the fuel-cell process is significantly more efficient than the combustion process. Fuel cells have been used on space stations, where the production of clean water is an added benefit to the electrical power, but they have not yet found wide usage in automobiles. Some of the technological hurdles of this fuel cell are hydrogen storage and design of good proton-exchange membranes. Another fuel-cell option that is being explored is the methanol fuel cell, which uses methanol instead of hydrogen gas as its fuel.

A voltaic cell operates in the direction that spontaneously gives a positive cell potential. An external power supply, however, can be used to force the reaction to go in reverse. This is the idea behind **electrolysis**. We began our discussion of electrochemistry with a Cu|Ag electrochemical cell. In that arrangement, the Cu electrode acted as the anode and the Ag electrode as the cathode. If we apply an external voltage, however, we could force the Ag electrode to be oxidized and the Cu electrode to be the site of reduction. We still call the site of oxidation the anode and the site of reduction the cathode. Water splitting is an electrolytic process. Hydrogen and oxygen gas will spontaneously react to form water, so reversing this reaction requires energy to come from somewhere else. We can do it with electricity; plants can do it with sunlight.

Most metals occur in nature not as the pure element, but rather in minerals, typically as oxides, hydroxides, and sulfides. (The ones that do occur as pure metals have rather high reduction potentials.) Extracting pure metals from minerals is called **refining**. Many metals can be refined in the presence of suitable reducing agents (which themselves are oxidized), such as CO. Some metals (such as Na), however, have such low reduction potentials that they can only be recovered electrolytically.

The propensity for metals to form compounds such as oxides and hydroxides also leads to the problem of **corrosion**. Modern societies spend billions of dollars a year trying to prevent and/or mitigate the effects of corrosion. One approach that can be used is known as **cathodic protection**. A metal that we want to protect from oxidation is kept in electrical contact with another metal with a lower reduction potential. In a corrosive environment, this second metal serves as a sacrificial anode; it is oxidized, but the metal we want to protect is not. Deep-sea oil rigs and even buried pipes can be protected in this fashion.

These ideas also find applications in biology. Typically, there is a difference in concentration of certain ions, such as $Na^+$, $K^+$ and $Cl^-$, across a cell membrane. This difference in concentration sets up a **membrane potential**. The "firing" of neurons involves changes in this membrane potential. To reestablish the potential (so the neuron can fire again), ions need to be actively transported across the membrane. Because this transport is happening against a concentration gradient, in the nonspontaneous direction, energy must be expended. These membrane potentials are typically a few tens of mV, but that is enough for the biological systems to function properly.

# 21.3 Other Applications of Concepts of Equilibrium

This section will briefly discuss a few more applications of the concepts of equilibrium. There are, of course, others that you may encounter in your career. By applying the fundamental ideas we have discussed, you will hopefully better understand those processes.

## 21.3.1 Solubility Equilibria

Water is known as the universal solvent, meaning that everything dissolves to some extent in water. We know that some things dissolve quite well, other things not so much. We can describe the solubility of a solid by an equilibrium expression of the form

$$\text{solid} + \text{water} \rightleftharpoons \text{solid } (aq)$$

Let's write the equilibrium constant for this process. In general, we write

$$K = \frac{a_{solid(aq)}}{a_{solid}\, a_{water}} \tag{21.34}$$

Under moderate pressure, the activity of the solid and the pure water are both unity. This lets us write the equilibrium constant as

$$K = a_{solid(aq)} \tag{21.35}$$

If the mixing is ideal, we can approximate the activity of the solute in the solution as the concentration divided by the standard concentration.

*Nonionic solids* – Let's consider sucrose, or table sugar, which is a nonionic solid. If we approximate the activity of dissolved sucrose in terms of its concentration, we would write

$$K \approx \frac{[\text{sucrose}(aq)]}{c^{\circ}}$$

where $c^{\circ}$ is the standard concentration. In this case, $K = 1.971$ at 25°C. In other words, the saturated concentration is 1.971 mol sucrose per L of solution. If we have less sucrose than this amount, it will all fully go into solution. If we try to put in more than this amount, then some will not dissolve and instead form a solid at the bottom of the container. Increasing the temperature generally leads to an increase in solubility of most nonionic materials. This is why candy makers need to heat their syrup solutions; increasing the temperature allows for the inclusion of more sugar in the solution.

*Ionic solids* – As we have already seen in this chapter, the situation is more complicated with ionic solutions because of the charges. Ionic solutions become nonideal at fairly low concentrations. Let's consider an ideal ionic solution, where we can use the concentration as the activity. Let's take the example of the mineral cinnabar, which chemically is HgS.

$$HgS \text{ (s)} \rightleftarrows Hg^{2+} + S^{2-} \qquad K_{sp} = [Hg^{2+}][S^{2-}] = 5 \times 10^{-54}$$

(The subscript $sp$ refers to "solubility product".) We would expect that the equilibrium concentration of $Hg^{2+}$ would be $2.2 \times 10^{-27}$ mol/L, since the concentration of the two ions needs to be the same. However, there are often other processes that need to be considered. For example, $S^{2-}$ can react with water to form $HS^-$. This process is represented by

$$S^{2-} + H_2O \rightleftarrows HS^- + OH^- \qquad K_{b1} = [HS^-][OH^-]/[S^{2-}] = 0.80$$

(The subscript $b1$ refers to the first base-dissociation reaction. For a review of acid–base chemistry and associated equilibrium constants, consult any general chemistry textbook.) This process will consume $S^{2-}$ and lead to more dissociation of HgS. A full treatment of this situation requires consideration of several other processes, including

$$HS^- + H_2O \rightleftarrows H_2S \text{ (aq)} + OH^- \qquad K_{b2} = 1.1 \times 10^{-7}$$
$$H_2O \rightleftarrows H^+ + OH^- \qquad K_w = 1.0 \times 10^{-14}$$

One more process is often ignored for this problem; that is

$$H_2S \text{ (aq)} \rightleftarrows H_2S \text{ (g)}$$

In order to determine the equilibrium concentration of $Hg^{2+}$, we need to solve this system of equations. If we fix the pH at 7, the value of $[Hg^{2+}]$ is about $10^{-23}$ M, 4 orders of magnitude greater than our simple treatment would indicate. For higher concentrations of ions, we would need to take the activity coefficients into account.

You might be wondering how equilibrium constants as small at $10^{-54}$ can possibly be measured. Even taking into account the factors that increase the solubility of HgS, we still have about one $Hg^{2+}$ ion per liter of water. How can that possibly be measured? One way to determine these equilibrium constants is electrochemically, as shown in Sample Problem 21.5.

### Sample Problem 21.5

The standard reduction potential of $Pb^{2+}$ is −0.126 V. The standard reduction potential of PbS to form Pb and $S^{2-}$ is −0.928 V. (Both values at 298.15 K.) From these standard potentials, determine the value of $K_{sp}$ for PbS.

Solution

Let's begin by writing the half reactions that correspond to these reduction potentials.

$$Pb^{2+} \text{ (aq)} + 2\,e^- \rightarrow Pb \text{ (s)} \qquad E° = -0.126 \text{ V}$$
$$PbS \text{ (s)} + 2e^- \rightarrow Pb \text{ (s)} + S^{2-} \text{ (aq)} \qquad E° = -0.928 \text{ V}$$

If we were to construct a standard electrochemical cell with Pb and PbS electrodes, we would have reduction at the Pb electrode and oxidation at the PbS electrode. The overall reaction would be

$$Pb^{2+} \text{ (aq)} + S^{2-} \text{ (aq)} \rightarrow PbS \text{ (s)} \qquad E° = 0.802 \text{ V}$$

This is the reverse reaction for the dissociation of PbS, so we can write that reaction as

$$PbS \text{ (s)} \rightarrow Pb^{2+} \text{ (aq)} + S^{2-} \text{ (aq)} \qquad E° = -0.802 \text{ V}$$

From this value of $E°$, we can calculate an equilibrium constant with Eq. 21.32 ( $v = 2$ )

$$\ln K = \frac{vFE°}{RT} = \frac{2(96475 \text{ C/mol})(-0.802 \text{ V})}{(8.3145 \text{ J/mol K})(298.15 \text{ K})} = -62.43$$

$$K_{sp} = 7.7 \times 10^{-28}$$

This value would be extremely difficult to determine if we had to measure the concentrations of dissolved ions directly.

---

*Common ion effect* – Consider a saturated solution of a particular salt. It should be apparent that adding more of one of the constituent ions, by adding in a different salt, will affect the solubility of the compound of interest. If we have one compound that is very soluble, and another that is less soluble, but they share a common ion, we would expect less of the compound with the lower solubility to be in solution. For example, AgCl will be less soluble in a solution of NaCl than in pure water. This is one more example of Le Châtelier's principle; presence of a product causes the reaction to shift to the reactant side. Another thing to keep in mind is that the ionic strength is affected by all the ions in a given solution, not just those due to the salt we are interested in, so the activity coefficients of a particular salt will be different if there are other ions present.

*Salt effect* – As was just mentioned, the ionic strength depends on all the ions in solution. Thus the addition of other ions can affect solubility of a given salt. This is known as the salt effect, and it can be quite pronounced for salts with low solubility in the presence of lots of other ions. This can also affect the properties of biomolecules, such as proteins that may have charged residues in solutions of a particular pH.

## 21.3.2 Partitioning

Back in Section 19.3, we discussed the thermodynamics of mixing. For an ideal mixture, mixing is always spontaneous and is driven by entropy. The interactions between the components of an ideal mixture are the same as for the individual components. The enthalpy of mixing in an ideal mixture is zero, reflecting the sameness of these interactions. In a nonideal mixture, however, there may be either favorable or unfavorable interactions between the components. If the interactions are favorable, that tends to facilitate mixing, but if the interactions are so unfavorable that the positive $\Delta H$ is greater than the magnitude of $T\Delta S$, then $\Delta_{mix}G$ may be positive. A positive $\Delta_{mix}G$ would mean the mixing would not be spontaneous, therefore the two components will not mix. When a mixture will not form between two components due to unfavorable interactions, those two components are said to be **immiscible**. Oil and water are a classic example of immiscible fluids; without an emulsifying agent, oil and water will phase separate into two distinct layers.

Let's consider a situation where we have two immiscible liquids in the same beaker. Because they are immiscible, they will form two separate liquid phases, with the more dense phase being on the bottom of the beaker. Now, we have a solute that is somewhat soluble in both liquids. What will the equilibrium situation look like? We write the expression as

$$\text{S (in phase 1)} \rightleftarrows \text{S (in phase 2)} \qquad K = \frac{a_{S_2}}{a_{S_1}} \approx \frac{[S]_2}{[S]_1}$$

In this context, $K$ is often called the **partition coefficient**. Let's say we have $n$ moles of solute in volume $V_1$ of phase 1, and we add $V_2$ of solvent 2 to the beaker. If we denote the fraction of moles left in phase 1 by the symbol $q$, then we can write

$$K \approx \frac{(1-q)n / V_2}{qn / V_1}$$

Solving for $q$ gives us

$$q = \frac{V_1}{V_1 + KV_2} \tag{21.36}$$

Let's say that we have a solute that has a $K = 3$ for two particular solvents. We have 100 mL of initial solution and add 500 mL of the second solvent. If we combine the two and allow the solute to partition, what fraction will be left in solvent 1?

$$q = \frac{100}{100 + (3 \times 500)} = \frac{100}{1600} \approx 6\%$$

What if instead of doing this all at once, we do five extractions of 100 mL each? For each extraction we have

$$q = \frac{100}{100 + (3 \times 100)} = \frac{100}{400} = 25\%$$

This doesn't look as good for a single extraction, but the final fraction left is going to be $q^n$, with $n = 5$, or 0.1%. This is about 60 times better than the single extraction. It is better to do several small extractions than a single large extraction. Notice that to get the fraction left in solvent 1 down to a very small number we have to do many small extractions; it takes a lot of work to get things really pure. All chemical separation techniques are based on similar ideas to these.

## 21.4 Summary, and Where We Go Next

In this chapter, we have discussed activity of ionic solutions, including a method that can be used to calculate their activity coefficients. We also extended those ideas to a discussion of electrochemistry. Lastly, we briefly touched on some other aspects of equilibrium. This concludes our coverage of chemical thermodynamics. In the next chapter, the last to contain highly technical material, we will bring together ideas of thermodynamics, quantum mechanics, and statistical mechanics to predict the actual values of kinetic rate constants. This approach is known as transition state theory, and it is one of the triumphs of physical chemistry.

**21.1** Determine the ionic strength, mean ionic activity coefficients, mean ionic molalities, and mean ionic activities for each of the following solutions using both the Debye–Hückel limiting law and the Davies equation. Comment on any differences in the results. Assume complete dissociation.

   a) 4.5 mmol kg$^{-1}$ NaBr

   b) 4.5 mmol kg$^{-1}$ BaCl$_2$

   c) 4.5 mmol kg$^{-1}$ MgSO$_4$

**21.2** As was seen in Sample Problem 21.1, the ionic strength can be written in terms of an integer multiple of the concentration of dissolved salt. Determine the value of that integer multiplier for a general salt of the form M$_p$X$_q$, where $p$ and $q$ can each take the value of 1, 2, 3, or 4. Consider all possible combinations of $p$ and $q$ and present the results in a table.

**21.3** The following data were reported for the vapor pressure of HCl ($g$) above mixtures of HCl and water at 20°C. (*Chem. Eng. Data Ser.*, **1956**, *1*, 10)

| $b$ (mol kg$^{-1}$) | 0.01 | 0.05 | 0.10 | 0.20 |
|---|---|---|---|---|
| $P$ (torr) | $5.01 \times 10^{-8}$ | $3.88 \times 10^{-7}$ | $1.43 \times 10^{-6}$ | $5.28 \times 10^{-6}$ |
| $b$ (mol kg$^{-1}$) | 0.50 | 1.0 | 2.0 | 4.0 |
| $P$ (torr) | $3.26 \times 10^{-5}$ | $1.49 \times 10^{-4}$ | $9.44 \times 10^{-4}$ | 0.0114 |

(Note: These low pressures were not measured directly but were determined from electrochemical measurements.)

   a) Plot the data up to a concentration of 0.10 mol kg$^{-1}$ as $P$ vs. $b^2$ and perform a linear fit. The slope of this fit is the constant that could be used in a Henry's law–style limiting law for the 1:1 electrolyte in dilute solution. Report this constant and write the form of the limiting law.

   b) Using the limiting law and the value of the constant determined in part a), propose a definition for the activity of HCl and calculate the value of the mean ionic activity coefficient at each concentration.

   c) Calculate mean ionic activity coefficients for each concentration using both the Debye–Hückel limiting law and the Davies equation. Compare your results to those of part b. Comment on your results.

**21.4** Acetic acid has a dissociation constant ($K_a$) of $1.76 \times 10^{-5}$ at 25°C.

   a) Assuming you can treat the solution as ideal, calculate the percent ionization for a solution of 0.085 mol kg$^{-1}$ acetic acid.

   b) Redo the calculation in part a), taking the effects of the ions into account and remembering that equilibrium constants depend on activity, not concentration. Use the Debye–Hückel limiting law to determine the activity coefficients. (You may want to solve this problem iteratively.)

c) Will the percent ionization of acetic acid be affected by the presence of other ions? If so, how?

d) Consider a 0.085 mol kg$^{-1}$ solution of acetic acid that is also 0.150 mol kg$^{-1}$ in NaCl. Using the limiting law, determine the percent ionization of acetic acid. (Recall that the ionic strength depends on the concentration of all ions in solution. You will probably need to solve this problem iteratively.)

**21.5** Using online resources, for each electrochemical cell described below determine the value of $E°$ and $\Delta G°$. Also, write out the fully balanced redox reaction corresponding to the cell and identify which electrode is serving as the anode and which is the cathode.

a) Zn (s) in 1.0 mol kg$^{-1}$ Zn(NO$_3$)$_2$ and Fe (s) in 1.0 mol kg$^{-1}$ Fe(NO$_3$)$_2$, connected by a salt bridge.

b) PbO$_2$ (s) and PbSO$_4$ (s) in a common sulfuric acid solution. (Recall that H$_2$SO$_4$ dissociates to form H$^+$ and HSO$_4^-$.)

c) AgCl (s) on Ag (s) and Pt (s) in a common solution of HCl that is open to the atmosphere. (Recall that water itself can participate in redox reactions.)

**21.6** In your general chemistry classes, you probably learned to express equilibrium constants such as $K_a$ and $K_{sp}$ is terms of molarity, not molality. For each situation below, perform the stated conversion(s) and report the percent difference between the molar and molal concentrations.

a) A saline solution with 0.0050 mol kg$^{-1}$ of NaCl. Covert this to molarity.

b) A sugar syrup is prepared from 800.0 g sucrose dissolved in 1.13 L of water. The density of the resulting solution is 1.15 g cm$^{-3}$. Determine the concentration in both molarity and molality.

c) Concentrated HCl solutions are rated at 6.0 M, with a density of 1.098 kg L$^{-1}$. Convert this to a molal concentration.

d) Concentrated sulfuric acid is 96% H$_2$SO$_4$ by mass. Convert this to both molar and molal concentrations. The density of this solution is 1.84 g cm$^{-3}$.

**21.7** Standard reduction potentials are tabulated because they allow for ease of use. This does not mean, however, that they are easy to measure directly. Consider an electrochemical cell where the cathode is AgCl on Ag, and the anode involves the oxidation of Mn$_2$O$_3$ to MnO$_2$. We want to determine the standard reduction potential for MnO$_2$ to Mn$_2$O$_3$.

a) Write the relevant half reactions for both the anode and cathode. The anode reaction takes place in basic solution, so include OH$^-$ ion in the balanced half reaction.

b) Write the full reaction for the entire electrochemical cell.

c) A standard cell would involve working with a concentration of OH$^-$ that is 1 mol kg$^{-1}$, or a pH of 14. Instead, this cell will use a solution that is buffered at a pH of 10.5. Write an expression for the Nernst equation for this cell where the OH$^-$ concentration is fixed, but the Cl$^-$ concentration is variable. Be sure to include a mean ionic activity coefficient for the Cl$^-$ ion. You can just use the concentration for the OH$^-$ ions, since that concentration will be much lower than for Cl$^-$.

d) Given the following data for cell potential as a function of Cl$^-$ concentration, determine the value of $E°$ for the cell and, knowing that $E°$ for the Ag|AgCl electrode is 0.2249 V, determine $E°$ for the MnO$_2$|Mn$_2$O$_3$ electrode. (Hint: You'll need to do some algebra and manipulate the Nernst equation to make use of these data. Use the rules of logarithms to manipulate the expression so that the left side includes the cell potential, the Cl$^-$ concentration, and the OH$^-$ concentration. The right side will contain $E°$ and the mean ionic activity coefficient. Because the ln of $\gamma_\pm$

depends on $b^{1/2}$, this side of the equation can be written in the form of a line where $x = b^{1/2}$. For this line, $y$ will be the function on the left side.)

| $b/b°$(mmol kg$^{-1}$) | 2.35 | 3.42 | 5.15 | 6.04 |
|---|---|---|---|---|
| $E_{cell}$ (mV) | 29.85 | 20.45 | 10.38 | 6.62 |

**21.8** In biology, there is often a difference in concentration for certain ions, such as $Na^+$, $Ca^{2+}$, and $Cl^-$ across the cell membrane. This concentration difference sets up what is known as a membrane potential. Maintaining a proper membrane potential is particularly important for heart and nerve cells.

a) What is the proper value of $E°$ to use in this situation? Provide justification.

b) Determine the membrane potential if the concentration of $K^+$ ions is 38 mM in the cell and 4 mM in the extracellular fluid. Use a temperature of 37°C. (By convention, a membrane potential is taken to be negative.)

c) How much biochemical energy (probably coming from ATP hydrolysis) must be expended per mol of $K^+$ for ion pumping proteins to maintain this potential by bringing $K^+$ from the extracellular fluid into the cell at a temperature of 37°C?

**21.9** Permanganate ion ($MnO_4^-$) is a very strong oxidizing agent. In a solution of neutral to slightly basic pH, $MnO_4^-$ will be reduced to $MnO_2$ (s). The standard reduction potential for this process is +0.59 V. For a standard electrochemical cell made with a Zn anode in $ZnCl_2$ solution and a $MnO_2$ cathode in $KMnO_4$ solution, calculate $E°$, $\Delta G°$, and $K$ for the overall reaction.

**21.10** The solubility product for $Ag_2S$ (s) has the very small value of $K_{sp} = 6.3 \times 10^{-50}$.

a) For a saturated solution of $Ag_2S$, what are the equilibrium concentrations of $Ag^+$ and $S^{2-}$ ions? (Treat the solutions as ideal.)

b) $Ag^+$ can react with cyanide ions, $CN^-$, to form the complex ion $Ag(CN)_2^-$. The equilibrium constant for this process is $K_f = 1.0 \times 10^{21}$. What would be the concentration of $S^{2-}$ if $Ag_2S$ (s) were placed in a solution that was 0.025 mol kg$^{-1}$ $CN^-$?

**21.11** The table below has $\Delta_f H°$ and $\Delta_f G°$ values for the solid and aqueous forms of two salts, $AgNO_3$ and $MgSO_4$. All data are at 298.15 K.

| Substance | $\Delta_f H°$ (kJ mol$^{-1}$) | $\Delta_f G°$ (kJ mol$^{-1}$) |
|---|---|---|
| $AgNO_3$ (s) | −124.4 | −33.4 |
| $AgNO_3$ (aq) | −101.7 | −34.2 |
| $MgSO_4$ (s) | −1283.7 | −1169.6 |
| $MgSO_4$ (aq) | −1374.8 | −1198.4 |

a) For each salt, determine $\Delta H°$ of solution.

b) What do the values in part a) tell you about the strengths and types of interactions that are taking place in both the solid and aqueous forms of the salts? Also, make predictions about the solubilities of each salt based on the $\Delta°_{solH}$ values.

c) For each salt, calculate $\Delta S°$ of solution. Comment on the meaning of the numerical values and provide a molecular interpretation of them.

d) Based on your results in part c), do your predictions about the solubilities of the two salts need to change? Why or why not?

e) Find values for the solubility of each salt and determine the molar solubility of each salt. Compare to your predictions in part d).

**21.12** A solute has a partition coefficient of 4.5 across two solvents. You have 25 mL of solution in solvent 1.

a) What volume of solvent 2 would be needed to extract 99% of the solute in a single extraction?

b) What total volume of solvent 2 would be needed to extract 99% of the solute in a series of four extractions?

# BRINGING IT ALL TOGETHER

# Transition State Theory and Reaction Dynamics

## 22.1 What Happens During a Reaction

Throughout this text, we have discussed various processes, including chemical reactions where one or more compounds change to one or more other compounds. We can understand this in some sense by looking at how the bonding between the various atoms has changed, in particular what bonds have been broken and what new bonds have formed; this is the molecular basis for the reaction enthalpies we talked about in Chapter 16. We also know, from our work in Chapters 4 and 5, that collisions need to happen for these rearrangements to occur. Even though we were able to develop a fairly strong molecular understanding of the reaction process, we were not able to calculate the exact values of the rate constants a priori. Within the structure of the Arrhenius equation, we could estimate the preexponential factor by considering the frequency of collisions, but determining the steric factor was a significant problem and the best we could do was estimate it or resort to measuring the rate constants experimentally.

We have a pretty good sense of what a reaction looks like before and after it occurs. But only focusing on the states before and after a reaction doesn't tell us *how* the chemical reaction takes place. Can we learn more about the detailed changes that take place *during* the chemical reaction? We can, and it requires that we bring to bear all the tools we've already put in place. In this chapter, we'll explore one of the crowning achievements of physical chemistry, **transition state theory**. By the use of this theoretical framework, we can predict the values of rate constants from quantum and statistical mechanics and gain a deeper understanding of how chemical reactions actually occur on the molecular level.

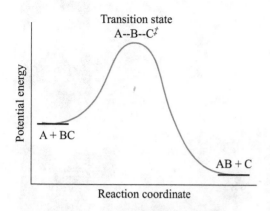

**FIGURE 22.1.** Plot of potential energy with reaction coordinate for the reaction A + BC → AB + C.

## 22.1.1 The Transition State

To begin the discussion, we need to go back to the kinds of energy plots we encountered back in Chapter 5. An example is shown in Figure 22.1. On the left, we have the reactant(s) and on the right, we have the product(s). The reactant and product sides are at different energies, which we now understand better as chemical potentials. To get from one side to the other requires traversal over an activation barrier, represented by the energy "hill" between the reactant and product sides. As the system moves towards the top of the hill, it is often described as an **activated complex**. The position right at the top of the hill is known specifically as the **transition state**, because at this point the system is in transition from the reactant side to the product side.

We are particularly concerned with the molecular structure of the transition state. Simply put, in a transition state, chemical bonds are simultaneously being broken and formed; the molecules are in transition. This provides an important way to distinguish a transition state from an intermediate. An intermediate is a stable chemical species that can, in principle, be isolated and studied. Intermediates do not appear in overall reactions, as we saw back in Chapter 5, but they are distinct chemical species. The fact that many of them are highly reactive and short lived doesn't change that. Transition states, on the other hand, are not stable species; thus we cannot "freeze" them and observe them at our leisure. Transition states typically only exist for times as short as a few fs ($10^{-15}$ s), making them very difficult to observe directly. The desire to observe transition states was, in fact, one of the drives for the development of ultrafast lasers.

## 22.1.2 Formal Development of Transition State Theory

We now move to the formal development of transition state theory. The principle developer of this theoretical framework was Henry Eyring (1901–1981). Meredith Gwynne Evans (1904–1952) and Michael Polanyi (1891–1976) also made significant contributions to developing this theory. We begin by considering a reaction of the form

$$A + BC \rightarrow AB + C$$

Treating this reaction as an elementary reaction, we can write the rate law as

$$\frac{d[AB]}{dt} = k_2[A][BC] \tag{22.1}$$

The subscript 2 reminds us this is for a bimolecular, elementary reaction. We can clearly see that one bond (the B–C bond) has broken, and a new bond (the A–B bond) has been formed. What happens in between? If this is a single elementary step, then at the transition state, the A–B bond is forming while the B–C bond is breaking. This transition state structure is symbolized as A–B–C$^\ddagger$, where the "double dagger" symbol denotes the transition state. See Figure 22.1.

The first step in developing transition state theory is to write the reaction as a sequential process

$$A + BC \rightleftarrows A-B-C^\ddagger \rightarrow AB + C \tag{22.2}$$

The first part of this mechanism looks very similar to a sequential reaction with a preequilibrium step, similar to what we saw in Section 5.2.5. Let's write an effective equilibrium constant just for this activation step, where the transition state is formed.

$$K^{\ddagger} = \frac{P_{ABC^{\ddagger}} P^{\circ}}{P_A P_{BC}} \qquad (22.3)$$

We are considering a gas-phase reaction here, so it makes sense to write the equilibrium constant in terms of pressure. Much of the formalism of reaction kinetics, however, is done in terms of concentrations. Assuming we can treat the gases as ideal, we can make the conversion to write

$$K^{\ddagger} = \frac{[ABC^{\ddagger}]}{[A][BC]} \frac{P^{\circ}}{RT} \qquad (22.4)$$

We can then solve for the concentration of the transition state as

$$[ABC^{\ddagger}] = \frac{RT}{P^{\circ}} K^{\ddagger} [A][BC] \qquad (22.5)$$

We now use some of the same tools we developed in the kinetics of sequential reactions to better understand the rate constant for this overall reaction. We can write the rate of formation of product from the transition state as

$$\frac{d[AB]}{dt} = k^{\ddagger} [ABC^{\ddagger}] \qquad (22.6)$$

where $k^{\ddagger}$ is the rate constant for passage through the transition state. Substitution of Eq. 22.5 into Eq. 22.6, and comparison with Eq. 22.1 lets us write an expression for the second-order rate constant in terms of $K^{\ddagger}$ and $k^{\ddagger}$.

$$k_2 = \frac{RT}{P^{\circ}} k^{\ddagger} K^{\ddagger} \qquad (22.7)$$

So, if we can say something about the equilibrium between the reactants and the transition state, as well as the rate of passage through the transition state, we can calculate the value of the second-order rate constant. Let's tackle the rate constant $k^{\ddagger}$ first.

To discuss the rate of passage through the transition state, we need to think of the kind of motion involved. There are two general approaches to this problem. The first considers the passage through the transition state as a kind of translational motion. The other approach, which we will show here, assumes the possibility of the transition state having a characteristic vibrational degree of freedom that helps it move to the product side of the reaction. For our test reaction, this would look something like an antisymmetric stretch where the A–B bond is contracting (getting stronger) while the B–C bond is extending (getting weaker). We can thus, to a first approximation, write the rate of passage through the transition state in terms of the frequency of this characteristic vibration.

$$k^{\ddagger} = \kappa \nu^{\ddagger} \qquad (22.8)$$

The letter $\kappa$ here is a transmission coefficient, and basically reflects the probability that one cycle of this vibration will lead to the formation of product. (The letter k and its variants are rather abused in most treatments of transition state theory.)

Using what we learned in Section 20.4.2, we can write the equilibrium constant for activation in terms of the relevant partition functions.

$$K^{\ddagger} = \frac{Nq^{\circ}_{ABC^{\ddagger}}}{q^{\circ}_A q^{\circ}_{BC}} e^{-\Delta E^{\ddagger}/RT} \tag{22.9}$$

where

$$\Delta E^{\ddagger} = E_0(ABC^{\ddagger}) - E_0(A) - E_0(BC) \tag{22.10}$$

Eq. 22.9 is fairly complicated, so it merits some discussion. The partition functions in the denominator are of the individual reactants, and those are calculated in the normal way. The partition function in the numerator is of the particular arrangement that corresponds to the transition state, which is not something we have readily calculated. Determination of this partition function typically requires detailed quantum-mechanical calculations, or at least some assumptions about the geometry of the transition state. The quantity $\Delta E^{\ddagger}$ is the energy difference between the transition state and the reactants. This may make you think of the activation energy from Arrhenius kinetics, and there is a connection that we'll formally make later on.

Now that we know we need the partition function of the transition state, let's think about what goes into that partition function. We clearly have the normal translational component, as well as rotational, vibrational, and electronic parts. One of those vibrational partition functions corresponds to the motion that will carry the transition state over to the product side of the reaction. We write the partition function for that particular vibration as

$$q_{vib^{\ddagger}} = \frac{1}{1 - e^{-h\nu^{\ddagger}/k_B T}} \tag{22.11}$$

The vibration we are talking about is the vibration that allows the transition state to fall apart and form the eventual products. As such, this is an inherently weak vibration, and we expect the frequency to be low, compared to $k_B T$. Thus, we can write the high-temperature version of the vibrational partition function as

$$q_{vib^{\ddagger}} \approx \frac{k_B T}{h\nu^{\ddagger}} \tag{22.12}$$

Because this particular vibration is so important, we will split it out from the rest of the partition function and write the total partition function of the transition state as

$$q_{ABC^{\ddagger}} = \frac{k_B T}{h\nu^{\ddagger}} \overline{q}_{ABC^{\ddagger}} \tag{22.13}$$

where $\overline{q}_{ABC^{\ddagger}}$ represents the rest of the partition function except for the specific vibrational motion we have been talking about. This modified partition function will only have $3N - 7$ vibrational partition functions if the transition state is nonlinear, and $3N - 6$ if linear. The equilibrium constant for activation is now written as

$$K^{\ddagger} = \frac{k_B T}{h\nu^{\ddagger}} \frac{N\overline{q}^{\circ}_{ABC^{\ddagger}}}{q^{\circ}_A q^{\circ}_{BC}} e^{-\Delta E^{\ddagger}/RT} = \frac{k_B T}{h\nu^{\ddagger}} \overline{K}^{\ddagger} \tag{22.14}$$

where again the bar means we have taken out the partition function of the critical vibration.

We can now put all of this (Eqs. 22.7, 22.8, and 22.14) together to write

$$k_2 = \kappa \frac{k_B T}{h} \frac{RT}{P^\circ} \overline{K}^\ddagger$$ (22.15)

This result is known as the Eyring equation. Notice that the low frequency of the vibrational motion that carries the transition state over to the product side has cancelled out, so we don't actually have to know what that frequency is. (We will return to this frequency later on, though.) Very often, the transmission coefficient, $\kappa$ will be taken to be 1, so it drops out of the equation. (Other treatments take it to be 1/2.) One of the key results of this expression is the factor of $k_B T/h$. The hard part of using this equation is determining the partition function of the transition state.

It needs to be noted that the form of the Eyring equation in Eq. 22.15 applies specifically to a gas-phase bimolecular elementary reaction. A unimolecular reaction can be written as

$$AB \rightleftarrows AB^\ddagger \rightarrow A + B$$

The Eyring equation for such a reaction is written as

$$k_1 = \kappa \frac{k_B T}{h} \overline{K}^\ddagger$$ (22.16)

where the equilibrium constant will be similar to what we have in Eq. 22.14, except there is only one partition function in the denominator. Notice also that the factor of $RT/P^\circ$ has also dropped out, because we don't need it t convert pressures to concentrations.

For reactions in solution, we have to be a bit more careful, because writing the partition functions gets more complicated. However, the general form of the Eyring equation will resemble that of Eq. 22.16, because the equilibrium constant is properly written in terms of concentrations from the outset; there are no gas-phase reactants present in a solution phase reaction. For other than very dilute reactions, and particularly reactions with ions, activity coefficients will also need to be included.

Despite its deceptively simple appearance, the Eyring equation is very powerful. Eyring himself published hundreds of papers based on this framework, and it has been applied in contexts ranging from simple gas-phase reactions to complex biochemical processes. It does have limitations, some of which we will discuss, but transition state theory provides a very strong foundation for discussing the inner workings of chemical reactions. The challenge in fully utilizing this approach is often the lack of information about the structure of the transition state.

## 22.1.3 Thermodynamic Aspects of Transition State Theory

Another helpful way to think about the ideas of transition state theory is in terms of thermodynamics. We can begin by turning our equilibrium constant for activation into a Gibbs energy of activation

$$\Delta^\ddagger G = -RT \ln \overline{K}^\ddagger = \Delta^\ddagger H - T\Delta^\ddagger S$$ (22.17)

Putting this into Eq. 22.15 gives us

$$k_2 = \frac{k_B T}{h} \frac{RT}{P^\circ} e^{\Delta^\ddagger S/R} e^{-\Delta^\ddagger H/RT}$$ (22.18)

Again, this is the correct form for a bimolecular elementary reaction. For a unimolecular reaction, or reactions in solution, the factor of $RT/P°$ will drop out.

This way of writing things gives us valuable insight into molecular aspects of the rate constant. The last exponential term includes $\Delta^{\ddagger}H$, the enthalpy of activation, which will always be a positive quantity; the transition state is, by definition, going to be of higher energy than the reactant(s) alone. Because this term is a negative exponential, the more energy required to reach the transition state, the slower the reaction will go. The first exponential term includes $\Delta^{\ddagger}S$, the entropy of activation, which will (except in very special circumstances) be a negative quantity. The entropy of activation is typically negative because the transition state is a particular arrangement of the atoms in the reactant(s) that is generally more constrained than the free reactant(s). This is particularly true for a bimolecular reaction; two separate molecules have to come together in just the right way to form the transition state, meaning the number of possible configurations has been dramatically reduced, and the entropy has decreased. The more constrained the arrangement, often referred to as a "tight" transition state, the greater the magnitude of $\Delta^{\ddagger}S$, and the smaller the rate constant. For reactions with a "loose" transition state, where the transition state is not as tightly constrained, the exponential term won't be quite as small (because $\Delta^{\ddagger}S$ is less negative), and the reaction will proceed more quickly.

Even if we can't directly calculate the rate constant with the Eyring equation, because we lack detailed information about the structure of the transition state, we can still learn about details of the process. If we have measured the rate constant, this analysis can help us learn about the enthalpy and entropy of activation, from which we can infer details of the structure of the transition state. As we have seen in other areas of physical chemistry, we often need to go back and forth between experiment and theory to come to a more complete understanding.

### 22.1.4 Comparison of Transition State Theory to Collisional Theory

Not surprisingly, we can compare the results of transition state theory to what we saw back in Chapter 4. There, we used kinetic molecular theory to derive the experimentally observed Arrhenius equation. To review, the Arrhenius equation (Eq. 4.10) is written as

$$k = Ae^{-E_a/RT}$$

In terms of collisional theory, we wrote this as (Eq. 4.11)

$$k = PN_A\sigma\bar{v}_{rel}e^{-E_a/RT}$$

where $P$ was an empirical steric factor. We won't do it here, but it can be shown that when two atoms collide to form a diatomic molecule, the results of transition state theory agree exactly with the simple collisional theory.

In order to make comparisons to more complicated reactions, we need to first establish a link between the activation energy of Arrhenius and the enthalpy of activation of transition state theory. In our formulation of kinetics in terms of collisions, we treated the activation energy as a constant parameter. A more rigorous way to define the activation energy is as

$$E_a = RT^2\frac{d\ln k}{dT} \tag{22.19}$$

If we assume the activation energy is temperature independent and integrate this expression, the result is simply the Arrhenius equation. If we substitute Eq. 22.18 into this expression, we have

$$E_a = \Delta^{\ddagger} H + 2RT \qquad (22.20)$$

For a unimolecular reaction, or a reaction in solution, the correct expression is

$$E_a = \Delta^{\ddagger} H + RT \qquad (22.21)$$

If we solve for the enthalpy of activation, and substitute back into Eq. 22.18, we can write the following two equations—the first for a bimolecular gas-phase reaction, and the second for a unimolecular gas-phase reaction or reaction in solution

$$k_2 = e^2 \frac{k_B T}{h} \frac{RT}{P^{\circ}} e^{\Delta^{\ddagger} S/R} e^{-E_a/RT} \qquad (22.22)$$

$$k_2 = e \frac{k_B T}{h} e^{\Delta^{\ddagger} S/R} e^{-E_a/RT} \qquad (22.23)$$

For the bimolecular reaction, we can now expression the Arrhenius prefactor as

$$A = e^2 \frac{k_B T}{h} \frac{RT}{P^{\circ}} e^{\Delta^{\ddagger} S/R} \qquad (22.24)$$

(For unimolecular reactions, or reactions in solution, the first exponential in Eq. 22.24 will be to the first power and we again drop the factor of $RT/P^{\circ}$.)

We won't go through all the details here, but we can imagine that the entropy of activation has two parts. The first part has to do with the fact that the reactants need to be in relatively close proximity in order to form the transition state. Thus, there should be some dependence on the collisional cross section. There will also be some dependence on the relative motion of the reactants. This first part could be termed $\Delta^{\ddagger} S_{position}$. The second part has to do with the orientation of the two reactants. Even if the two reactants are sufficiently close to each other, if they don't collide with the correct orientation, the reaction won't happen. Therefore, the second part of the entropy of activation relates to the steric hindrance for the collision being of the proper orientation. We can call this $\Delta^{\ddagger} S_{steric}$. The steric factor can now be represented as

$$P = e^{\Delta^{\ddagger} S_{steric}/R} \qquad (22.25)$$

Calculating $\Delta^{\ddagger} S_{steric}$ is far from easy, but we have a richer understanding of what the steric factor means by thinking of it explicitly in terms of entropy.

## 22.1.5 Summary of Transition State Theory

Transition state theory is one of the most successful theories about chemical reactions ever developed. It has been applied to everything from simple gas-phase reactions to enzyme catalysis and everything in between. Hopefully now you can understand why we have put this important theory last in our treatment of physical chemistry; transition state theory involves concepts and aspects of quantum mechanics, statistical mechanics, and thermodynamics all in an effort to predict the absolute values of kinetic rate constants. Although the foundational ideas of transition state theory are relatively straightforward, its application is anything but. Despite the complexity, however, it can greatly improve our understanding of chemical reactions and how they really take place at the molecular level.

Transition state theory does have one significant complication: How do we know the structure of the transition state? As we've already discussed, the transition state isn't something we can isolate and study. The transition state is inherently unstable and only exists for maybe a few fs. Some modern lasers have pulse durations on the order of a few fs, so it is possible to do spectroscopy on the transition state, but these are far from routine experiments. Computational chemistry can certainly help, but it requires a deeper understanding of the atomic and molecular motion during a chemical reaction. We need to think of a reaction as a dynamic process.

## 22.2 Reaction Dynamics

Chemical reactions are dynamic events, meaning they involve the motion of one or more atoms and/or molecules. As you learned in your physics classes, and as we've seen throughout this text, these motions are influenced and affected by surrounding forces and interactions. In this section, we explore some of these fundamental aspects of chemical reactions.

### 22.2.1 Potential Energy Surfaces

We often draw two-dimensional depictions of the potential energy during a reaction, similar to Figure 22.1. The horizontal axis is typically labeled as the *reaction coordinate*, meaning the motion that allows the reaction to happen. This does not tell the whole story, however. For example, in our test reaction of A + BC → AB + C, the BC molecule could be rotating and/or vibrating in ways that either make it easier or harder to reach the particular arrangement corresponding to the transition state. Accounting for all these other types of motion makes it hard to plot the energy, but computers can easily keep track of what's going on in these multidimensional spaces. The dependence of the energy on all the positional coordinates can be thought of as a surface in this multidimensional parameter space, and we call this a **potential energy surface**.

To understand this a little better, let's consider one of the simplest possible gas-phase reactions

$$H + H_2 \rightarrow H_2 + H$$

Now, you might be saying that this isn't a very interesting reaction, because nothing has changed chemically; we still have a H atom and a $H_2$ molecule after the reaction has taken place. On a macroscopic scale, you are correct that nothing has happened. However, on a molecular scale, a collision results in an exchange of bonding partners, and we want to understand that process.

To help us interpret things better, let's assign labels A, B, and C to the H atom and the two atoms in the $H_2$ molecule, respectively. This would let us rewrite the reaction as

$$H_A + H_B H_C \rightarrow H_A H_B + H_C$$

Let's begin by considering the potential energy when the lone H atom ($H_A$) is a long distance away from the $H_2$ molecule. The potential energy should simply be that of the $H_2$ molecule, which we have seen before (see Figures 12.2 and 12.7), and which is reproduced in Figure 22.2. The horizontal axis is the distance

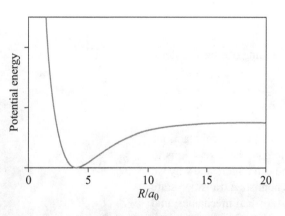

**FIGURE 22.2.** Potential energy curve for the $H_2$ molecule, where $R$ is the bond length. $R$ is in units of the Bohr radius, $a_0$.

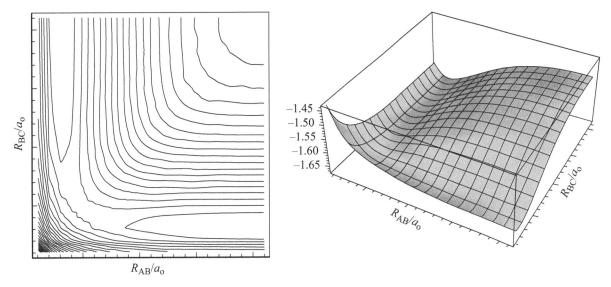

**FIGURE 22.3.** Contour plot (left) and surface plot (right) for the potential energy surface of the linear collision of $H_2$ with a H atom.

between any two atoms. If we are looking at things before the reaction, then $R_{BC}$ is in the vicinity of the well, and $R_{AB}$ is very large. After the reaction, $R_{AB}$ is in the vicinity of the well and $R_{BC}$ is large. What about when the two distances are similar to each other? As we approach the transition state, these two distances will be fairly small and the energy will have to be larger than the minimum in the well when only two atoms are close to each other. If all three atoms are very far apart from each other, then it is as if we have no molecule and the potential energy will be significantly higher than the minimum of the well for the stable molecule.

We can better appreciate this if we make a contour or surface plot of the energy, which allows us to plot the energy as a function of both distances. We do this in Figure 22.3. Now we can consider what happens as we change both distances at the same time. Let's have hydrogen atom A approach the $H_B H_C$ molecule along the molecular axis, starting $R_{BC}$ at the equilibrium bond length. When $H_A$ is far away from the molecule, the potential energy is just that of the molecule; the lone atom doesn't really contribute anything. As the atom comes in closer, however, it starts to interact with the molecule, which weakens the bond and raises the energy. As $H_A$ approaches, let's allow the distance between $H_B$ and $H_C$ to change to keep the energy as low as possible. The result of this is that $R_{BC}$ will increase as $H_A$ gets closer, which keeps us in the lower part of the potential energy surface, sometimes called the **reaction channel**. Eventually, we reach the point where $R_{AB} = R_{BC}$. If we keep going, then $H_C$ moves away from the new $H_A H_B$ molecule, and we can keep $R_{AB}$ at the equilibrium bond length. We have just simulated a **trajectory** on the potential energy surface that leads to reaction, shown in Figure 22.4a.

Note that there are many possible trajectories we could take. If $H_A$ is approaching very quickly, the molecule may not have time to respond. As $R_{AB}$ decreases, the repulsive interactions between $H_A$ and $H_B$ will take over, and the energy increases significantly. This will slow down the approach of $H_A$ and cause it to "bounce back" along the initial trajectory, and the reaction won't happen, as shown in Figure 22.4b. This can also happen if $H_A$ approaches with insufficient energy. Something else we need to keep in mind is that the molecule is not sitting at a fixed distance but is in fact vibrating. That vibrational motion

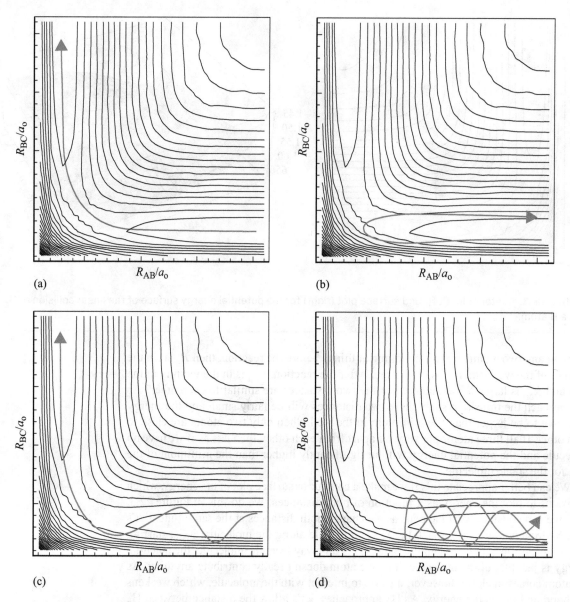

**FIGURE 22.4.** Trajectories on the potential energy surface for $H + H_2$. a) Successful trajectory through the transition state. b) Unsuccessful trajectory. c) Successful trajectory with vibrational motion in $H_2$. d) Unsuccessful trajectory with too much vibrational motion in $H_2$.

could also help or hinder passage to the product side of the potential energy surface, as shown in Figure 22.4c and d.

Let's consider once more the trajectory that takes us along the minimum energy path from the reactant to the product sides of the potential energy surface. This is depicted in Figure 22.4a. In particular, let's consider the curvature of the potential energy surface along this path. When one atom is very far from the molecule, either on the product side or the reactant side, we can see that the curvature is positive in both directions. At the transition state, however, we have something different. Along the direction where $R_{AB} = R_{BC}$, the curvature is positive. Along the orthogonal direction, however, we have negative curvature.

The transition state thus represents the maximum energy point along the minimum energy path. Note that the direction with the negative curvature is the direction in which $R_{AB}$ is decreasing while $R_{BC}$ is increasing, which makes sense since that's what happens during the reaction; this motion corresponds to the reaction coordinate. Note that all of this would change if we altered the angle of attack of the $H_A$ atom relative to the molecular axis.

Mathematically, the transition state is described as a **saddle point** on the potential energy surface. Saddle points happen when all curvatures except one are positive. Locating the saddle point on a potential energy surface is actually how computational chemists identify transition states. Recall that in Section 10.4.2 we identified the vibrational force constant $k$ with the second derivative, or curvature, of the intermolecular potential. Eq. 10.42 gives us the relationship between this curvature and the vibrational frequency.

$$\nu = \frac{1}{2\pi}\left(\frac{k}{\mu}\right)^{1/2}$$

If the curvature, represented by $k$, is negative, then what happens to the vibrational frequency? It becomes imaginary. Computational chemists thus use a vibrational analysis of the potential energy surface to find the location with a single imaginary frequency, which must be the transition state. This also lets them identify the motion associated with passage through the transition state, which we have previously called the reaction coordinate.

More complicated reactions will, of course, have more complicated potential energy surfaces. Recall from your study of organic chemistry that many reactions have multiple sets of products, and the distribution of these different products is described by a product-branching ratio. The reason this is possible is because of details in the reaction mechanism and with the associated potential energy surfaces. In cases such as these, transition state theory can break down, because there are sequential transition states and/or transition states that can lead to multiple products, known as **bifurcated transition states**. One of the assumptions of transition state theory, as we developed it, is that an equilibrium is established between the reactants and the transition state. For these complicated potential energy surfaces, the actual trajectories along the surface dominate the reaction and such an equilibrium is never reached. The actual motion of the atoms, known as the **dynamics**, as they near the transition state may cause them to come out of one product channel or the other, thus the progress of the reaction depends on the detailed molecular motion and not just the energy differences between various stable reactants/intermediates and transition states. Quantum-mechanical effects, such as tunneling and the presence of additional electronic states, can further influence the reaction dynamics. Computational chemistry tools can be used to model these potential energy surfaces, but this is by no means a trivial undertaking. Understanding these surfaces, however, could enable us to manipulate reaction conditions to achieve more of a desired product by channeling the dynamics in a particular direction on the surface.

## 22.2.2 Experimental Methods for Investigating Potential Energy Surfaces

In addition to computational methods, there are also well-established experimental approaches for investigating potential energy surfaces, which we will briefly discuss here. One of the key elements of such experiments is maintaining very tight control over the energy states of the relevant molecules. Only by imposing experimental constraints on the specific quantum states of the reactant molecules can we have any hope of making sense of the multidimensional potential energy surface.

One of the key experimental tools for investigating chemical reaction dynamics was the development of **molecular beams**. In their simplest form, a high-pressure source of molecules expands into a vacuum chamber. As this expansion takes place, the gas molecules rapidly cool and occupy only a few rotational and vibrational states. They are also translationally cold, even though the beam of molecules is traveling at high speed. Remember, temperature has to do with the distribution of molecules among available energy states; if all the molecules are mostly in the same state, that corresponds to a low temperature. Through proper design of the nozzles and other aspects of the experiment, particular rotational and vibrational states can be selected.

One of the big breakthroughs in this type of experiment was the development of crossed molecular beams, for which Dudley Herschbach and Yuan Lee received the Nobel Prize in 1986. In this apparatus, two molecular beam sources are crossed in a vacuum chamber. It is at the crossing of these beams that reactive collisions take place. The product molecules are scattered away from the reaction volume and can be detected by mass spectrometry or other means. By measuring the angular distribution of products, as well as determining the vibrational and rotational energy states of the products, the details of the reaction process can be determined. The use of lasers to preferentially excite vibrational and/or rotational motion in the reactants is now very standard in this type of experiment.

Initial experiments focused mainly on simple reactions between single atoms and diatomic molecules. However, with advancements in experimental equipment and data-analysis techniques, much more complicated reactions are being investigated at their most fundamental level. When combined with high-level quantum chemistry calculations, highly detailed pictures of chemical reactions and the relevant potential energy surfaces can be constructed.

## 22.3 Summary, and Where We Go Next

In this chapter, we have explored one of the crowning achievements of physical chemistry—transition state theory. This powerful theoretical framework brings aspects of quantum mechanics, statistical mechanics, and thermodynamics to bear on the problem of calculating rate constants for chemical reactions. Full use of this approach also requires sophisticated experimental and computational methods. We have also explored some of the ideas of chemical reaction dynamics.

This chapter concludes the technical material in this text. In the next and final chapter, we will explore and discuss some of the philosophical ideas that have arisen from physical chemistry. Science does not happen in isolation, but rather is a significant element in our society. It should come as no surprise, therefore, that scientific ideas would have an influence on the way we think about the world around us.

**22.1** The second-order gas phase reaction of NO and $O_3$ to produce $NO_2$ and $O_2$ has a preexponential factor of $7.9 \times 10^8$ L mol$^{-1}$ s$^{-1}$ at 300 K. The activation energy is 10.5 kJ mol$^{-1}$.

a) Calculate the enthalpy of activation.

b) Calculate the entropy of activation.

**22.2** Consider the collision of two atoms to form a diatomic molecule. Show that transition state theory predicts the exact same result as collision theory for this case. The transition state in this situation is a diatomic system. Since a diatomic molecule only has one vibrational degree of freedom, and we remove one vibration from the partition function of the transition state, the partition function we need to consider only has rotational and translational components. You can also assume that the cross section is given by $\pi r^2$, where $r$ is the "bond length" of the transition state.

**22.3** For the second-order reaction

$$OH + H_2 \rightarrow H_2O + H$$

the following kinetic data were measured:

| $T$ (°C) | $k$ (L mol$^{-1}$ s$^{-1}$) |
|---|---|
| 12.50 | 1.66 |
| 25.00 | 3.49 |
| 37.50 | 6.95 |

a) Calculate the activation energy for this reaction.

b) Calculate the enthalpy of activation for this reaction.

c) Calculate the entropy of activation for this reaction.

d) Using thermodynamic data available online, draw a potential energy diagram for this reaction with reasonable scaling on the energy axis.

**22.4** a) Calculate the value of the rate constant at 75.00°C for the reaction in Problem 22.3.

b) If the initial concentration of each reactant is 0.050 M, how long will the reaction have to run for half of the reactants to disappear at 75.00°C.

**22.5** The reaction of ethyl bromide and hydroxide ion to form ethanol and bromide ion proceeds in a single bimolecular step.

a) Sketch the structure of the transition state for this reaction.

b) Describe the vibrational motion that corresponds to the reaction coordinate.

c) How many vibrational degrees of freedom of the transition state will be included in a calculation of the rate constant?

**22.6** In Chapter 5, we considered multistep mechanisms for chemical reactions. If a reaction mechanism has $n$ intermediates, how many transition states need to be considered?

**22.7** a) For a chemical reaction with a certain standard molar enthalpy of activation, determine the fractional change in the rate constant if the standard molar entropy of activation increases by $4 \text{ J mol}^{-1} \text{ K}^{-1}$.

b) Provide a physical rationale for the results of part a).

**22.8** In this problem, we will attempt to calculate a rate constant from transition state theory. The reaction we are considering is

$$H + D_2 \rightarrow HD + D$$

Let's assume that the direction of attack of the H atom is along the bond axis. We will assume the following about the bond lengths:

The D–D bond distance is 89 pm

The H–D distance is 96 pm

We will also assume that all vibrations are at $1000 \text{ cm}^{-1}$. The activation energy for this reaction has been determined to be $35 \text{ kJ mol}^{-1}$. Take $T$ to be 400 K.

a) Calculate the rate constant for this reaction based on the information given.

b) The experimental value for this rate constant is $4 \times 10^5 \text{ L mol}^{-1} \text{ s}^{-1}$. Discuss differences between this value and your result and what can be done to your model to make the results agree better.

# Philosophy of Physical Chemistry

## 23.1 Philosophy and Science, From Ancient to Early Modern Times

Science is a very human endeavor. Thus, it should come as no surprise that the ideas of science should have an impact on other aspects of human activity, including philosophy. In this chapter, we will explore how the ideas we have encountered throughout this text have impacted philosophy, society, and our deeper understanding of the universe. Unlike the main narrative of the text, where we took a carefully chosen path through the various topics, this chapter will proceed historically.

### 23.1.1 Ancient Science

Since the dawn of history, mankind has tried to make sense of the natural world. In the earliest societies, this understanding involved unseen powers and forces, often regarded as supernatural or divine, that caused things to happen. It didn't take long, however, for people to observe patterns in the natural world, such as the cycle of the seasons and the movements of the stars. As civilizations developed and advanced, so did the level of sophistication of their explanations of natural phenomena.

It is clear from ancient records that civilizations such as ancient Egypt, Babylon, and others had fairly advanced mathematics. These techniques were mostly developed to solve practical problems related to undertakings such as agriculture, architecture, and taxation. How do you measure the area of an irregular field? How do you determine the amount of material needed to build a pyramid? Practical mathematics became quite advanced in these societies. In fact, many of the surviving cuneiform tablets we have from the Babylonian and Assyrian periods involve mathematical exercises—ancient homework, if you will.

It was really the ancient Greeks that began exploring mathematics on its own merits. Much of the mathematics you have learned throughout your education, particularly geometry and the development of proofs, is based on Greek mathematics. Pythagoras (~500 BCE), Euclid (~300 BCE), and Archimedes (~250 BCE) are still known to modern students because their work was so fundamentally important. The logical system developed by Euclid, which is based on a small set of axioms (postulates), should be very familiar to you by now.

The Greeks also started formulating the field of **natural philosophy**, which takes the logical systems developed in other areas of thought, particularly mathematics, and applies them to the natural world. One of the greatest natural philosophers was Aristotle (384–322 BCE), whose writings formed the foundation of Western thought for the better part of the next 2,000 years. Even though much of Aristotle's work was more qualitative than quantitative, it represented a generally successful application of reason and logic to understanding the world around us.

## 23.1.2 The Ascension of Mathematics

Throughout the Dark and Middle Ages in Europe, Aristotle reigned supreme. To a large extent, learning in a formal sense stagnated, and universities were dominated by scholars who were experts on recognized authorities, not necessarily practitioners of science in the way we would describe a professor today. Advancements were made in the Islamic world, but Europe was largely stuck. Not until the Renaissance—when many of the classical works of antiquity were rediscovered and people were willing to challenge the established authorities—did significant progress resume.

One of the main differences in this rebirth of scientific thought was the use of mathematics to more fully describe the natural world. One of the first to perform quantitative (rather than qualitative) experiments was Galileo Galilei (1564–1642). He was able to refute the Aristotelian notion that heavy bodies fall more quickly than light bodies by carefully designed experiments. Rather than simply applying reasoning and logic to a situation, he recognized that we have to let Nature speak for itself. Many natural philosophers were trying their best to describe how the world should be; science would now be the attempt to describe Nature as it actually is. Speaking of Galileo's contribution to science, Albert Einstein said in 1954:

> Propositions arrived at by purely logical means are completely empty as regards reality. Because Galileo realized this, and particularly because he drummed it into the scientific world, he is the father of modern physics – indeed, of modern science altogether.

A contemporary of Galileo, Johannes Kepler (1571–1630), was also successfully applying mathematics to astronomy. For centuries, the motion of the planets was believed to follow circular orbits, because the circle was thought to be the perfect shape; the Ptolemaic geocentric system was based on this assumption. After centuries of use, however, predictions based on the geocentric model did not match the actual observations of planetary motion. In order to fix things, astronomers added circular corrections—known as epicycles—to the orbits. Not surprisingly, this system became very complicated. It was a partly a desire to simplify the mathematical description of planetary motion that led Copernicus (1473–1543) to propose the heliocentric model. Kepler took things one step further, proposing a heliocentric system where the planetary orbits were elliptical, not circular. Kepler's three laws of planetary motion, which fit the data much better, are elegant in their simplicity and represent one more step forward in the mathematical description of the universe. Once Galileo observed moons orbiting Jupiter, he also became convinced that the heliocentric model was more correct.

The use of mathematics to describe nature achieved supremacy with Isaac Newton (1642–1727). In his *Philosphiae Naturalis Prinicipia Mathematica* (Mathematical Principles of Natural Philosophy), published in 1687, Newton used mathematics to describe all motion, on earth as well as in the heavens. He even developed new mathematics—calculus—to better describe the physical world. In fact, Newton's mathematics could be used to derive Kepler's laws. Writer Daniel Boorstin, in his work *The Discoverers*, stated "The grand unifying force in Newton's system, even before gravitation, was mathematics." To a large extent, once Newton established his mathematical principles, if a phenomenon in the physical world could not be described mathematically, it was not fully understood.

## 23.1.3 Classical Determinism

Once Newton enshrined mathematics as the primary tool of physics, it didn't take long before we had the picture of a mechanical, clockwork universe. Knowledge of current conditions can allow us to determine what will happen in the future. This idea of **determinism** was perhaps best summarized by the French mathematician Pierre-Simon Laplace (1749–1827):

> We may regard the present state of the universe as the effect of its past and the cause of its future. An intellect which at a certain moment would know all forces that set nature in motion, and all positions of all items of which nature is composed, if this intellect were also vast enough to submit these data to analysis, it would embrace in a single formula the movements of the greatest bodies of the universe and those of the tiniest atom; for such an intellect, nothing would be uncertain and the future just like the past would be present before its eyes.

The "intellect" referred to here has often been called "Laplace's Demon," although he himself never used that term. The basic idea is that if we could, at any instant in time, know the positions, momenta, and interactions of all the components of the universe, we could run time either forward or in reverse using Newton's laws of motion and know the state of the universe at any point in time, future or past. Thus, the only limit to our ability to describe the universe is the finite amount of information we have, not the laws of physics.

What effect does a deterministic, mathematical representation of the universe have on our society and our philosophy? As it turns out, a very significant one. One major impact was in the area of religion. In early societies, the gods were often depicted as fairly intemperate and fickle, hence the need to constantly appease them. With the rise of Christianity in the Western world, religion became more predictable, and there was even a sense in some traditions that everything was predestined and predetermined. The mechanical view of the universe also fits into this deterministic way of thinking. Rather than needing to make sacrifices to appease a capricious deity, Western religion was much more systematized, predictable, and deterministic.

It should be noted that Newton was by no means an atheist; he referenced the Divine throughout his writings, which was common in science until the 19th century. There is some debate, however, over Laplace's views on religion. An account exists of a discussion between Laplace and Napoleon, where the emperor asked him why he made no reference to God in his scholarly writing. Laplace is reported to have said that he "had no need of that hypothesis." Whether he was referring to the existence of God, or the need for God to intervene to keep the universe running (as Newton had suggested) is unclear. However, an atheistic sentiment has certainly been adopted by many scientists who have been much more hostile to the religious viewpoint than their predecessors were.

The idea of determinism also found its way into the social sciences. Georg Wilhelm Friedrich Hegel (1770–1831) developed the idea of the *dialectic*, opposite ideas that work together to advance society. A key assumption of his work was that rational thought could be applied to society, and that the underlying rules could be understood, just as they were in the physical sciences. A deterministic history of society was also a key idea explored by Karl Marx (1818–1883) in developing dialectical materialism. Just as Laplace argued that an understanding of the laws of physics can allow us to predict the future of the universe, Hegel and Marx were confident that an understanding of the laws of history would allow us to predict the future of society.

The idea of a deterministic universe—and possibly of deterministic history—raises important philosophical questions. Do we have free will, or are we just cogs in a universal machine? Are the outcomes of personal lives or nations based on the choices of individuals, or merely the natural results of fundamental laws? Should the goal of a society be to maximize the perceived happiness of the individual, or the collective happiness of a society? The rise of social science in the 19th century was certainly influenced by developments in the physical sciences.

### 21.1.4 Thermodynamics and the Fate of the Universe

Physical chemistry also plays a role in our understanding of the universe, including its ultimate fate. Let's begin by stating the first two laws of thermodynamics in nonmathematical terms. The First Law tells us that the amount of energy in the universe is fixed; energy can change forms, but it is neither created nor destroyed. The Second Law states that the entropy of the universe will never decrease. Entropy relates in many ways to the amount of energy that cannot be harnessed in a useful way. So let's take these two ideas to their logical extreme. If the amount of energy in the universe is fixed, and the usability of that energy decreases over time, then eventually we reach a point where there is no usable energy left. (The Gibbs and Helmholtz "free" energies both go to zero.) This scenario is known as the **heat death** of the universe.

The heat-death scenario was recognized fairly early on in the development of thermodynamics. In fact, the basic ideas were in place as early as 1852. The reactions to this idea, however, were varied. William Thomson, Lord Kelvin, wrote in 1865:

> The result would inevitably be a state of universal rest and death, if the universe were finite and left to obey existing laws. But it is impossible to conceive a limit to the extent of matter in the universe; and therefore science points rather to an endless progress, through an endless space, of action involving the transformation of potential energy into palpable motion and hence into heat, than to a single finite mechanism, running down like a clock, and stopping forever.

Thomson recognized that a finite, clockwork universe will eventually wind down and come to an end. He seems, therefore, to question the assumption of the universe as finite to avoid the problem. Other reactions have been less sanguine. In 1946, Léon Brillouin stated

> How is it possible to understand life, when the whole world is ruled by the second law of thermodynamics, which points towards death and annihilation?

The validity of the heat-death scenario is still being discussed in connection to the fate of the universe. The modern conception of these ideas involves aspects of cosmology and other topics beyond the scope of this book. Simply put, if the universe continues to expand, then the universe will eventually reach a state of equilibrium, which is a state of maximum entropy. Some counter these ideas, however, by arguing that we cannot adequately define the entropy of the entire universe. Certainly any isolated system will eventually reach a state of maximum entropy, but does this assumption apply to the entire universe?

Fairly early on, ideas were put forward as to how we could reverse the increase of entropy in the universe. An important thought experiment, put forth by James Clerk Maxwell in 1871, consists of a chamber with two compartments with a door-covered hole between them.

> If we conceive of a being whose faculties are so sharpened that he can follow every molecule in its course, such a being, whose attributes are as essentially finite as our own, would be able to do what is impossible to us. For we have seen that molecules in a vessel full of air at uniform temperature are moving with velocities by no means uniform, though the mean velocity of any great number of them, arbitrarily selected, is almost exactly uniform. Now let us suppose that such a vessel is divided into two portions, A and B, by a division in which there is a small hole, and that a being, who can see the individual molecules, opens and closes this hole, so as to allow only the swifter molecules to pass from A to B, and only the slower molecules to pass from B to A. He will thus, without expenditure of work, raise the temperature of B and lower that of A, in contradiction to the second law of thermodynamics.

In other words, by selectively opening and closing the door when a molecule gets close to the hole, all the fast or "hot" molecules could be separated to the B side, and all the slow or "cold" molecules could be separated to the A side. We would then have a difference in temperature in a system that initially started at a uniform temperature, which would seem to reverse the Second Law. The being that can make these determinations was referred to as a "demon" by Thomson, although not it a malevolent sense, and this scenario has come to be known as "Maxwell's Demon."

The scenario of Maxwell's Demon suggests there is a way to reverse the spontaneous change of entropy if we can make sufficiently precise observations and quickly react to them. Criticism of this scenario was made by Leó Szilard and Léon Brillouin, arguing that the act of making the measurements and opening the door involves an expenditure of energy, and therefore leads to an entropy increase. This increase in entropy will be greater than the decrease resulting from the separation of fast and slow molecules. The Second Law does appear to be inviolable.

These ideas have also had some impact on society and philosophy. We can certainly see some aspects of existentialism and even nihilism in Brillouin's statement above. How can life make sense in a universe that is going to come to a cold, dark end? What is the point of it all if it doesn't end well? It is probably not a coincidence that these philosophical ideas started to take hold around the same time that the thermodynamic universe was being explored and explained.

## 23.2 Philosophy and Science in the Modern Age

### 23.2.1 The Rise of Quantum Mechanics and the End of Determinism

At the end of the 19th century, physics was a very powerful enterprise. Between Newton's equations of motion, and associated refinements by Lagrange, Hamilton, and others, along with Maxwell's equations (which described electric and magnetic fields), it was generally accepted that the important phenomena of the universe were well understood. Thermodynamics only added to the richness of this understanding. As we discussed back in Chapter 7, however, the world of science was about to change. With the advent of quantum mechanics, as well as Einstein's theory of relativity, our view of the universe had to radically change in the early 20th century.

As we discussed earlier, one of the hallmarks of classical physics was the idea of determinism; if we know the position and momentum of a particle, and the forces acting upon it, we can calculate its trajectory with absolute certainty. "Laplace's Demon" merely extends this idea to its logical conclusion. Quantum mechanics, however, tells us that there are limits to what we can know. According to the uncertainty principle, developed by Heisenberg, we cannot simultaneously know both the position and momentum of a quantum mechanical object to arbitrary precision. This is not because of a limitation in our experimental capabilities but in fact reflects the underlying nature of matter at the atomic level. The world of an electron is very different from a classical world of particles, waves, and fields.

This change in our perception of the atomic and subatomic world was actually very helpful in understanding phenomena that were previously difficult to explain. Along the way, however, we had to give up some things we thought we understood, particularly a deterministic universe. For example, classical models could not explain the decay of radioactive nuclei. Why does a radioactive atom spontaneously emit a particle? It turns out this is because of quantum-mechanical fluctuations, and any single decay event is inherently random. Use of statistical mechanics allows us to make predictions about collections of things that behave quantum mechanically, although we cannot predict individual events with absolute certainty. At its roots, the universe appears to be probabilistic, not deterministic.

These were the aspects of quantum mechanics that bothered Einstein and led to his statement about God not playing dice with the universe. In classical physics, everything that happens has a proximate cause; an event happens because something made it happen. In quantum mechanics, however, no such proximate cause can be identified in many cases. Einstein and others, notably David Bohm, argued that there must be "hidden variables"—which may be nonlocal—that actually control things and provide the needed causality. All attempts at formulating a hidden-variable theory, however, have failed. In order to make sense of the atomic world, we have to give up determinism and allow for inherent randomness.

### 23.2.2 The Double-Slit Experiment

One of the advantages of classical physics was that it didn't require much in the way of interpretation. A macroscopic object has a well-specified position, and we can also readily quantify its motion. The same rules that work for billiard balls work for pretty much all the things we can observe and experience with the naked eye. Even moons and planets can be treated with Newtonian mechanics (although once the masses get sufficiently large, relativity needs to be taken into account). John Dalton (1766–1844) formulated his understanding of chemical reactions in terms of Newtonian forces, arguing that the same physical laws that govern the motion of the planets should also govern the motion of the smallest particles of matter. As we have already seen, however, things are very different on the atomic and subatomic scales.

The atomic world is very different from our everyday experience, and so we often have a hard time describing how things work there. In our coverage of quantum mechanics, we learned that it is not correct to think of an electron as just a particle; it also has wavelike properties. But it's not just a wave either. The best thing we can say is that an electron is an electron, which can be unsatisfying to many students. Similar issues arose with our treatment of light. Is light an electromagnetic wave, or is it made of photons? Both descriptions seem to capture important aspects of how light behaves. Again, the best answer is that light is light.

Unlike Newtonian mechanics, where we can understand the world in terms of position, velocity, mass, and forces (things we can readily grasp conceptually), quantum mechanics involves wavefunctions, operators, and expectation values. But what is the meaning behind these mathematical tools? Is the wavefunction a reflection of an underlying reality, or is it purely a convenient mathematical abstraction that captures the correct behavior of the system? What does it mean to take a measurement, and what effect does the act of measuring have on the state of the system?

These questions are perhaps best explored in the context of what is known as the **double-slit experiment**. Consider a wall with a single vertical slit in it and a detector screen behind that wall, shown in Figure 23.1a. If you stand on one side of the wall and throw balls through the slit, registering where they hit on the screen, you would expect only to see hits on the screen directly opposite where you are standing; if you don't throw the ball through the slit, you can't hit the wall. Now, do this with a wall with two slits, shown in Figure 23.1b. You would expect to see two bands of hits registered on the screen, again in a straight line from you, passing through either slit and to the screen.

Now, let's look at how waves pass through the slits. Imagine a trough of water where we generate waves at one end. If we put a wall with a slit in this trough, then we get a radial wave pattern emerging from the slit, shown in Figure 23.2a. If we put two slits in the wall, however, we get two radial wave patterns that can interfere with each other, shown in Figure 23.2b. You've probably seen the same thing if you throw two rocks into a pond; where the ripples overlap in phase, you get constructive interference; and where a crest overlaps with a trough, you get cancellation, or destructive interference. If we put a screen behind these two slits and register where the maxima and minima of this interference pattern hit, we will see a series of bands reflective of that

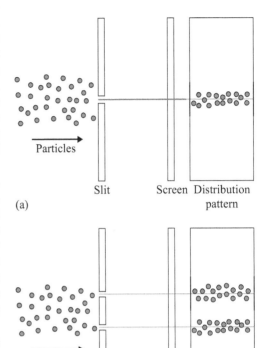

**FIGURE 23.1.** a) Particles traveling through a single slit will make one band of hits on the detector screen. b) With two slits, there will be two bands of hits on the detector.

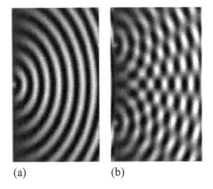

**FIGURE 23.2.** a) Waves from one slit make a radial pattern. b) With two slits, the two radial patterns interfere with each other.

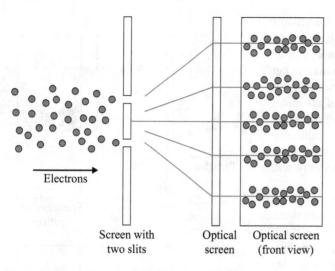

Electrons

Screen with
two slits

Optical
screen

Optical screen
(front view)

**FIGURE 23.3.** Electrons fired through two slits produce multiple bands of hits on the detector screen; an interference pattern is observed.

pattern. To summarize, with balls we see two bands of hits registered on the screen, and with waves passing through two slits, we see an interference pattern.

We can now do this experiment with a stream of electrons. With one slit, we see a single band on the detection screen. However, when we send the electrons through two slits, we do not observe the double band, as we did with the balls; but rather an interference pattern, similar to what we saw with waves, shown in Figure 23.3. Now, one possibility is that the electrons deflect off each other to make the interference pattern. In the experiment we can turn down the intensity of the electron stream so there is only one electron at a time passing through the apparatus. Hits on the screen are registered in only one place at a time, which is what we would expect for particles, but the pattern built up by many hits looks just the same as the interference pattern we saw with the higher intensity electron stream. How can a single electron passing through one of two slits give rise to an interference pattern? It's as if it went through both slits and interfered with itself, but still only hit the screen in a single position.

But this experiment gets stranger. We can imagine adding a measuring device to the apparatus to tell which slit the electron goes through. If we do this, the measured pattern of hits on the screen changes, and it looks more like the double band we would expect for the balls; the interference pattern goes away. Apparently, if we determine which slit the electron goes through, the chance of going through both slits has been eliminated, and it can only go through one slit, giving two bands of registered hits on the screen. But in terms of what we're doing with electrons and slits, we didn't change anything; we just looked to see which slit it went through. So how does knowing which slit the electron goes through affect the outcome of the experiment?

The thing to remember about this situation is that we have to do something to the electron to learn anything about it. In other words, we have to interact with the electron in some way. One way to do this is with light. Using light to tell which slit a ball went through would clearly have no effect on the ball's trajectory. However, as we saw in our discussion of the de Broglie wavelength in Section 8.1.2, this wavelength for an electron is comparable to the wavelength of light. Similarly, the momentum of a photon is comparable to that of an electron. Thus, interaction of the light and the electron can alter the behavior of the electron. In fact, in order to tell which slit the electron went through, the wavelength of the light must be less than the width of the slit. Recall that the shorter the wavelength of the light, the greater the momentum of the photon and the greater the effect on the electron. We could imagine using light of a longer wavelength so as to be less disruptive, but then we wouldn't be able to tell which slit the electron went through, and the interference pattern would again emerge. If the wavelength of the light is somewhere in between, then the interference pattern still appears, but it is fuzzy.

The take-home lesson from the double-slit experiment is that the result of the experiment depends on all parts of it, including whether or not we attempt to determine which slit the electron travels through. Our act of checking one of the slits cannot be thought of as separate from the experiment, because the act of measuring affects what the electron is doing. In other words, there is no such thing as a passive observer; the observer becomes part of the apparatus by making the observation. This is very different from the macroscopic world. For example, whether your favorite sports team wins their game doesn't depend on whether you are watching or not. Likewise, a police officer using a radar gun to check your speed doesn't affect your speed. But this is not the case at the quantum level; your observations do affect the outcome.

### 23.2.3 The Copenhagen Interpretation and the Role of the Observer

These ideas have potentially far-reaching consequences and are definitely open to interpretation. The most commonly accepted interpretation of quantum mechanics is known as the **Copenhagen interpretation**, because it was developed by Bohr and Heisenberg in Copenhagen, Denmark, in the mid-1920s. The Copenhagen interpretation is itself subject to some interpretation, because no definite version of it was ever written down. The key idea, however, has to do with the fact that any observation (measurement) changes the wavefunction of the system. Prior to the observation, the wavefunction must account for all the possibilities open to the system as a superposition. Upon observation, however, the wavefunction collapses to the state corresponding to the result of the observation. Knowledge of the wavefunction will allow us to predict the probability of a given value being measured, but we cannot predict the outcome of a single measurement.

The Copenhagen interpretation, if taken literally, can lead one to the idea that there is no objective reality without some sort of observation. But this raises the questions of what counts as an observation and who counts as an observer? Unfortunately, these issues are not definitively stated by the proponents of the interpretation. A realist would argue that the system has a reality independent of our observations; we just don't have enough information until we do the measurement. A pure Copenhagen description, however, would say that the system is in a superposition state prior to the measurement and it doesn't end up in a particular state until the observation is made.

The best example of these ideas is the thought experiment known as **Schrödinger's cat**. A cat is placed in a box, along with a single radioactive nucleus, a radiation detector, and a bottle of poison. The box is sealed so that we can't see what is happening inside. At some point in time, the atom will decay, which will be registered by the detector, leading to the release of the poison and the death of the cat. Prior to the opening of the box, what is the state of the cat? A realist would say that the cat is either alive or dead; we just don't know which it is. The pure Copenhagen interpretation, however, says that we must consider the cat as being both alive and dead, until we open the box (make the observation), at which time the state of the system collapses to one of the two possibilities, either alive or dead. For experiments with quantum mechanical systems, the superposition analysis better matches the results, giving credence to the Copenhagen interpretation.

Other interpretations of quantum mechanics have been put forward. One, known as the many-worlds interpretation, holds that a new universe is created every time a system is forced to collapse into one of the possible states, and that all the possibilities exist in separate universes. While this makes for interesting science-fiction stories, it does not have much practical use. As discussed earlier, others have attempted to argue for the existence of hidden variables that exist beneath the wavefunction. In this interpretation, everything behaves deterministically, but we don't have access to that information and so things look random to us. No hidden-variable theory, however, has been able to explain all the many experiments that have been performed on quantum mechanical systems. So even though the Copenhagen interpretation seems to lead to some strange conclusions, it appears to be the most consistent with actual experiments.

### 23.2.4 Influence of Quantum Mechanics on Society

The ideas that arise from quantum mechanics and its interpretation have also had influences on our broader society. One of the results of quantum mechanics is that there are limits to our knowledge of a quantum system. Specifically, according to the uncertainty principle, we cannot simultaneously know the position and momentum of a quantum mechanical object. (So much for Laplace's Demon.) Even though we can't say that there is a direct correlation, we can see how modern ideas such as moral and cultural relativism reflect this notion that we can't know all things for certain. A strict Copenhagen interpretation even leads us to question if there is an objective reality, independent of an observer. So what is real? Are we making conscious choices, or do we only have the illusion of free will?

Quantum mechanics, and its ideas, have certainly permeated the popular culture. It's not hard to find references to uncertainty, Schrödinger's cat, and other aspects of quantum theory in movies, television, books, music, and comedy. They may not always be interpreted correctly, but the ideas are there. It is quite impressive how far these ideas have reached beyond the confines of the theoretical physics symposia where they were first developed.

## 23.3 Summary

This concludes our journey through the field of physical chemistry. Hopefully, it has been an enlightening and informative trip. I also hope you have a greater appreciation for how the ideas of quantum mechanics, statistical mechanics, thermodynamics, and kinetics form much of the basis for how we understand the physical world around us. These ideas will find many applications throughout your scientific and professional career, as well as make you a more informed and scientifically literate citizen.

This section does not contain the title portion "Where We Go Next," because that will be up to you. How will you apply what you have learned to your future studies and your future career? Is this the end, or a beginning? I hope you will continue to explore the physical world around you and help us all come to a better understanding of how it operates. Good luck in your continuing journey of discovery.

# Physical Constants and Conversion Factors

| Quantity | Symbol | Value | Units |
|----------|--------|-------|-------|
| Speed of light (vacuum) | $c$ | $2.99792458 \times 10^8$ | m s$^{-1}$ (exact) |
| Elementary charge | $e$ | $1.602176565 \times 10^{-19}$ | C |
| Electron mass | $m_e$ | $9.10938291 \times 10^{-31}$ | kg |
| Proton mass | $m_p$ | $1.672621777 \times 10^{-27}$ | kg |
| Neutron mass | $m_n$ | $1.674927351 \times 10^{-27}$ | kg |
| Planck's constant | $h$ | $6.62606957 \times 10^{-34}$ | J s |
| Planck's constant/$2\pi$ | $\hbar$ | $1.054571726 \times 10^{-34}$ | J s |
| Boltzmann's constant | $k_B$ | $1.3806488 \times 10^{-23}$ | J K$^{-1}$ |
| Avogadro's number | $N_A$ | $6.02214129 \times 10^{23}$ | mol$^{-1}$ |
| Ideal gas constant | $R$ | $8.3144621$ | J mol$^{-1}$ K$^{-1}$ |
| Permittivity of vacuum | $\epsilon_0$ | $8.854187817 \times 10^{-12}$ | C$^2$ J$^{-1}$ m$^{-1}$ |
| Bohr radius | $a_0$ | $5.291772109 \times 10^{-11}$ | m |

| Quantity | | Quantity | Units |
|----------|---|----------|-------|
| 1 Å | = | $1 \times 10^{-10}$ | m (exact) |
| 1 amu | = | $1.660538921 \times 10^{-27}$ | kg |
| 1 eV | = | $1.60217733 \times 10^{-19}$ | J |
| | = | 96.48531 | kJ mol$^{-1}$ |
| 1 cal | = | 4.184 | J (exact) |
| 1 cm$^{-1}$ | = | $1.9864 \times 10^{-23}$ | J |
| 1 bar | = | $1 \times 10^{5}$ | Pa (exact) |
| 1 atm | = | 1.01325 | bar |
| | = | 101.325 | kPa |
| | = | 760 | Torr (exact) |
| 1 L | = | 1000 | mL (exact) |
| | = | 1 | dm$^3$ (exact) |
| | = | $1 \times 10^{-3}$ | m$^3$ (exact) |

# Useful Mathematical Relations

### *Definitions*

Factorial $\qquad x! = x \cdot (x - 1) \cdot (x - 2) \cdots (2) \cdot (1) \qquad 0! = 1$

Summation $\qquad \displaystyle\sum_{i=1}^{n} x_i = x_1 + x_2 + \ldots + x_{n-1} + x_n$

Product $\qquad \displaystyle\prod_{i=1}^{n} x_i = x_1 \cdot x_2 \cdot \ldots \cdot x_{n-1} \cdot x_n$

### *Common Differentials*

$$\frac{d}{dx} \ln f(x) = \frac{1}{f(x)} \frac{d}{dx} f(x) \qquad \frac{d}{dx} e^{f(x)} = e^{f(x)} \frac{d}{dx} f(x)$$

### *Common Integrals*

$$\int \sin^2 bx\,dx = \frac{x}{2} - \frac{1}{4b} \sin 2bx$$

$$\int x \sin^2 bx\,dx = \frac{x^2}{4} - \frac{2}{4b} \sin 2bx - \frac{1}{8b^2} \cos 2bx$$

$$\int xe^{bx}\,dx = \frac{e^{bx}}{b^2} bx - 1 \qquad \int x^2 e^{bx}\,dx = e^{bx} \frac{x^2}{b} - \frac{2x}{b^2} + \frac{2}{b^3}$$

$$\int_0^\infty x^n e^{-qx}\, dx = \frac{n!}{q^{n+1}} \qquad \int_0^\infty e^{-bx^2}\, dx = \frac{1}{2}\frac{\pi}{b}^{1/2}$$

$$\int_0^\infty x^{2n} e^{-bx^2}\, dx = \frac{1\cdot 3\cdots(2n-1)}{2^{n+1}}\frac{\pi}{b^{2n+1}}^{1/2} \qquad \int_0^\infty x^{2n+1} e^{-bx^2}\, dx = \frac{n!}{2b^{n+1}}$$

## Series

$$\frac{1}{1-x} = 1 + x + x^2 + x^3 + \ldots = \sum_{n=0}^\infty x^n \quad \text{if } |x|<1 \qquad \frac{1}{1-x} \approx 1 + x \quad \text{if } |x|<<1$$

$$\frac{1}{1+x} = 1 - x + x^2 - x^3 + \ldots = \sum_{n=0}^\infty (-x)^n \quad \text{if } |x|<1 \qquad \frac{1}{1+x} \approx 1 - x \quad \text{if } |x|<<1$$

$$\frac{1}{1-x^2} = 1 + x^2 + x^4 + x^6 + \ldots = \sum_{n=0}^\infty x^{2n} \quad \text{if } |x|<1 \qquad \frac{1}{1-x^2} \approx 1 + x^2 \quad \text{if } |x|<<1$$

$$\frac{1}{1+x^2} = 1 - x^2 + x^4 - x^6 + \ldots = \sum_{n=0}^\infty (-1)^n x^{2n} \quad \text{if } |x|<1 \qquad \frac{1}{1+x^2} \approx 1 - x^2 \quad \text{if } |x|<<1$$

$$\frac{1}{1-x^2} = 1 + 2x + 3x^2 + \ldots = \sum_{n=0}^\infty nx^{n-1} \quad \text{if } |x|<1 \qquad \frac{1}{1-x^2} \approx 1 + 2x \quad \text{if } |x|<<1$$

$$\frac{x}{1-x^2} = x + 2x^2 + 3x^3 + \ldots = \sum_{n=0}^\infty nx^n \quad \text{if } |x|<1 \qquad \frac{x}{1-x^2} \approx x + 2x^2 \quad \text{if } |x|<<1$$

$$e^x = 1 + x + \frac{x^2}{2!} + \ldots = \sum_{n=0}^\infty \frac{x^n}{n!} \qquad e^x \approx 1 + x \quad \text{if } |x|<<1$$

$$\ln(1+x) = x - \frac{x^2}{2} + \frac{x^3}{3} + \ldots = \sum_{n=1}^\infty (-1)^{n-1}\frac{x^n}{n} \quad \text{if } x < 1 \qquad \ln(1+x) \approx x \quad \text{if } |x|<<1$$

## Rules of Logarithms

In all cases, $a$ and $b$ are positive.

Product $\qquad \ln(a \cdot b) = \ln a + \ln b$

Quotient $\qquad \ln\frac{a}{b} = \ln a - \ln b$

Power $\qquad \ln a^b = b \ln a$

Note: $\qquad \ln(a + b) \neq \ln a + \ln b \qquad \ln(a - b) \neq \ln a - \ln b$

Be careful with these. However, with some algebra you can use the series above to expand the natural log of a sum or difference.

# INDEX

center of mass, 24, 47, 121, 178, 186

central limit theorem, 24, 26, 28, 32, 120, 275, 292

centrifugal distortion, 190–191, 197

chain rule, 295–296

Charles' law, 14

chemical equilibrium, 89, 374, 393, 396, 403, 408, 414, 421

chemical kinetics, 7, 58, 63, 65, 71, 74, 77, 99, 112

chemical potential, 119, 274, 280, 369, 373–375, 414

chemisorption, 105

Clapeyron equation, 379–381

classical equipartition theorem, 56, 119, 122, 247, 253

classically forbidden region, 172, 176, 195

Clausius–Clapeyron equation, 379–381

Clausius inequality, 342–343, 361

closed system, 308, 317, 376, 415

coefficient of isothermal compressibility, 298, 302, 360

coefficient of thermal expansion, 297, 302, 321

colligative properties, 389–390, 393, 432

collisional activation, 96

collisional cross section, 47, 50, 65, 68, 72, 459

collisional deactivation, 96–97

collision density, 51, 65–66

collision energy, 68–69

collision flux, 51–53, 65

collision frequency, 46–48, 65

collision theory, 65, 458

combination bands, 200

combinations, 28–29, 150, 200, 222, 224–225

commutator, 154–155

complex conjugate, 145–146, 149, 167

complex numbers, 145

computational chemistry, 227, 237, 239–240, 264, 460, 463

conduction band, 303

conductivity, thermal, 53, 55–56

configuration, 28, 31, 214, 238

configuration integral, 277

configuration interaction (CI), 238

conjugate variables, 154, 313

consecutive reactions, 90

constant pressure heat capacity, 320, 328, 359

constant pressure process, 319–320

constant volume heat capacity, 258, 272, 311, 318, 320, 324–325, 358

constant volume process, 314, 318, 322

Copenhagen interpretation, 475–476

correspondence principle, 164–165, 173, 195

critical point, 299, 380

critical temperature, 299–300, 379

cross section, 47–50, 67, 69, 71, 73, 128, 300, 459

cyclic rule, 296

## D

Davies equation, 432

De Broglie, Louis, 138

De Broglie wavelength, 138–139, 208, 474

Debye formula, 133–134

Debye frequency, 134

Debye-Hückel limiting law, 430, 432

Debye-Hückel theory, 402, 425

Debye length, 430

degeneracy, 34, 38, 173, 175–176, 184, 189, 211, 248, 251

degrees of freedom, 56, 120–121, 128, 200, 253, 381

density functional theory (DFT), 239

desorption, 106–107, 109–110

Dieterici equation of state, 301

diffraction of electrons, 138, 302

diffusion, 53–54, 98

diffusion coefficient, 54–55

diffusion-controlled limit, 74

dipole moment, 167, 187, 190, 280

dissociation, 410–411, 427, 442

dissociation energy, 204

distribution function, 24, 26, 41, 161, 271, 324, 336

double-slit experiment, 473–474

## E

eigenfunctions, 142–143, 150, 160, 184

eigenvalues, 142–143, 150

Einstein, Albert, 6, 131, 215

Einstein frequency, 132

Einstein model of heat capacity, 132–133, 257, 468

electrochemical cell, 435–439

electrochemical series, 437

electrolysis, 440

electronic partition function, 254

electronic spectroscopy, 234, 240

electronic states, 169, 176, 215, 224, 235, 249, 463

electronic transitions, 234

Eley-Rideal mechanism, 110–111

encounter pair, 98–99

energy levels-anharmonic oscillator, 199

energy levels-harmonic oscillator, 191, 200, 204, 253

energy levels-one-dimensional box, 176, 250

energy levels-rigid rotor, 178, 182, 208, 212, 219, 251

energy levels-three-dimensional box, 173, 250

intramolecular vibrational energy redistribution (IVR), 200
ionic strength, 430–431, 443
isobar, 14, 325, 361
isochore, 15–16
isolated systems, 308, 310, 334–335, 343
isolation method, 79
isotherm, 107–108, 110, 315, 323

## K

kinetic control, 92
kinetic energy, of a gas, 140, 153, 277
kinetic energy operator, 143, 149

## L

Langmuir-Hinshelwood mechanism, 111–112
Langmuir, Irving, 106, 108
Langmuir isotherm, 107–108, 111
Langmuir model, 106, 112
lasers, 215–216, 454
Laws of Thermodynamics, 6, 307, 350
le Châtelier's principle, 93, 105, 410–411, 443
Lennard-Jones potential, 279–280
level of theory, 237–238
light, 7, 108, 127, 234, 468
Lindemann-Hinshelwood mechanism, 96, 98
linear combination, 150–151, 217
linear combination of atomic orbitals (LCAO), 225
linear variational theory, 231, 238
loose transition state, xviii, 89

## M

Maxwell-Boltzmann distribution, 38, 40–41, 43
Maxwell relations, 355–356, 358
mean free path, 49–51
mean ionic activity, 428–429, 431, 439
mean ionic activity coefficient, 428–430
mean square speed, 42, 46
mechanical equilibrium, 13, 313–314, 317
melting point, 377–378, 390
membrane potential, 440–441
microcanonical ensemble, 280
microstate, 31–32
microsystem, 31–32, 268, 270
molar internal energy, 120, 122, 255, 258
molar volume, 13, 16, 279, 291
molecular dynamics (MD), 280
molecularity, 86
molecular modeling, 275
molecular orbitals, 228, 231–232, 240, 303
molecular partition function, 248–249, 256, 259, 416–417
molecular speeds, 41, 119
moment of inertia, 123, 179, 186

momentum, 137–139, 141, 472
momentum operator, 141–142, 148, 150
Monte Carlo (MC) simulations, 280, 283
multilayer adsorption, 106
multinomial distribution, 29
mutual exclusion principle, 202

## N

natural philosophy, 468–469
Nernst equation, 435, 438–439
Newtonian flow, 56
NMR spectroscopy, 36
nodes, 163, 165, 171, 176
nonideal gas, 57, 367, 432
normal (Gaussian) distribution, 23–24, 26
normalization, 22, 147, 170, 224, 228
normalization constant, 147, 149, 181
normal modes, 200
nucleus, 206, 224, 228–229, 475

## O

observable, 44–45, 144, 148, 154, 156
open systems, 308
operator, 141–143, 154, 473
orbitals, 212, 214, 303
orbitals, atomic, 225, 228, 230, 303
orbitals, molecular, 228, 231–232, 234, 303
order of reaction, 79–80
orthogonal, 151, 163, 186, 462
orthonormal, 151–152, 225
oscillator, 128, 191, 193, 198
osmosis, 391–392
overtones, 200
oxidation numbers, 433

## P

pair correlation function, 304
partial derivatives, 143, 293, 295, 356, 359
partial pressure, 382, 385, 400, 410
particle in a box, one dimension, 161
particle in a box, three dimension, 40, 129
particle on a ring, 182, 219
partition coefficient, 444
partition function, 350, 360, 362, 414, 418
partition function, canonical, 414–416, 420
partition function, molecular, 417–418
path functions, 309, 355
Pauli exclusion principle, 214, 232, 303
P branch, 197
permutations, 28–29
perturbation, 105, 167, 185, 220, 224
perturbation theory, 167, 185, 220–221, 224
phase boundary, 378–380
phase equilibrium, 376, 393

phase transition, 6, 119, 328, 339, 349
phosphorescence, 236–237
photoelectric effect, 127, 132, 137
photons, 131, 138, 167, 215, 473
physisorption, 105
Planck, Max, 129
Planck's constant, h, 129, 138, 208
Planck's law, 129, 156
poisoning, 104, 112
polymorph, 382
population, 20–21, 274, 325, 348
population inversion, 215
position operator, 142, 156
potential energy, 140, 143, 161, 171, 192, 405, 460
potential energy barrier, 193, 198, 277, 461
potential energy curve, 199, 235
potential energy surface, 235, 460–461, 463
potential, intermolecular, 340, 463
pre-equilibrium, 313–314
pre-exponential factor, 70–71, 85, 89, 453
probability, 17, 20–21, 26, 284, 455, 475
probability density, 22, 145
probability density function, 22, 145
product of reaction, xix

## Q

Q branch, 197
quantization of energy, 135, 165
quantum mechanical modeling, 176, 282
quantum mechanical tunneling, 6, 172
quantum number, 162, 165, 171, 174, 270
quantum theory, 154, 202, 234, 476

## R

Raman spectroscopy, 201–202
Raoult's law, 386–388, 396–400, 425
rate constant, first-order, 453, 455
rate constants, 67, 89–90, 92, 444
rate constant, second-order, 67, 71, 455
rate constant, zero-order, 85, 220
rate equations, 71, 457
rate law, 67, 79, 454
rate limiting step, 111
Rayleigh scattering, 201–202
R branch, 197
reaction cross section, 68–69
reaction mechanism, 79, 85, 99, 463
real solution, 388, 396–397
reciprocal rule, 294–295
Redlich-Kwong equation, 301
redox reaction, 433–434, 438
reduced mass, 48, 65, 72, 189, 252
relativity, 137–138, 156, 473
residual entropy, 348–349
resonant, 188

reversibility, 74, 315
rigid rotor, classical, 178, 190
rigid rotor, quantum mechanical, 7, 178, 472
rotational constant, 186–187, 252
rotational partition function, 251–252
rotational temperature, 252–253
rovibrational spectrum, 197, 204

## S

Sackur-Tetrode equation, 267
saddle point, 463
Schrödinger equation, 144–145, 147, 156
Schrödinger, Erwin, 144
scientific method, 11–12
Second Law of Thermodynamics, 329, 333, 335, 343, 470
second-order reaction, 83–84, 465
secular determinant, 226
selection rule, 168, 234–235
self-consistent field (SCF), 237
semiempirical methods, 239
space quantization, 184
spectroscopy, atomic, 234
spectroscopy, electronic, 234
spectroscopy, rotational, 185, 190
spectroscopy, vibrational, 196, 200
spectrum, 127, 130, 169
spherical coordinates, 40, 148, 209
spherical harmonics, 183, 209
spin, 182, 214, 236, 254
spin state, 214, 236, 254
spontaneity, 333, 343, 361, 407
spontaneous emission, 215
standard ambient temperature and pressure (SATP), 17, 19
standard cell potential, 436–437, 439
standard enthalpy of reaction, 328
standard entropy of reaction, 350
standard Gibbs energy of reaction, 364
standard hydrogen electrode, 437
standard reduction potential, 437–438, 442
standard state, 16, 326–327, 426, 428
standard temperature and pressure (STP), 17
state functions, 309–310, 326
state variables, 13, 15, 291, 307, 309, 311, 313, 356, 359
stationary states, 166–167
statistical mechanics, xviii, 6–7, 176, 240, 247, 304, 464
statistical thermodynamics, 255
statistical weight, W, 260, 273, 348
steady state, 93, 95
steady state approximation, 93–94, 99
steric factor, 73, 453